REED'S
NAUTICAL COMPANION

THE HANDBOOK TO COMPLEMENT REED'S ALMANACS

Editorial Director: Jean Fowler, M.R.I.N.
Editor: Thomas B. Stableford, Master Mariner, M.R.I.N.

Editorial Team
Lt. Cdr. Harry J. Baker, R.D., R.N.R., M.R.I.N.
Robin Ekblom, F.R.I.C.S.
Arthur Somers, C.ENG., M.I.E.E.

THOMAS REED
PUBLICATIONS LTD
LONDON ● HAMBURG ● BOSTON

NAUTICAL PUBLISHERS SINCE 1782

© Thomas Reed Publications Limited
Hazelbury Manor,
Corsham,
Wiltshire SN14 9HX, U.K.
Tel: 0225 812013
Fax: 0225 812014. Telex: 449816 REED G

First Edition 1993

ISBN 0 947637 67 2
ISSN 0967-0297

Printed in Great Britain by BPCC Wheatons Ltd, Exeter

CONTENTS

ACKNOWLEDGEMENTS

Flag information is provided and authenticated by the Flag Institute, Chester, England.

Inmarsat and GMDSS information compiled by the International Maritime Satellite Organisation, London, England.

'Fast Boat Navigation' and 'Dealing with Water Ingress' written by Kim Hollamby.

State of Sea Photographs:
Force 0, 1, 2, 5, 6, 7, 8, 11, 12 are reproduced with permission of H. M. Stationery Office.
Force 3 (R. Palmer), Force 4, (P. J. Weaver), Force 9 (O. R. Bates), Force 10 (J. Hodkinson).

Cloud photographs are reproduced with permission of R. K. Pilsbury.

International Code Flags and Chart Symbols are reproduced with permission of the Controller, H. M. Stationery Office.

The Story of Reed's Almanac . . .

IT HAS BEEN called the Yachtsman's Bible, the Sailor's Vade Mecum, even the Navigator's ABC. It has done service in countless thousands of ships, yachts and small craft in peace and war. It has saved lives, and brought children into the world. It is *Reed's Nautical Almanac*, known universally as plain *Reed's*, and it owes its existence to the inspired dedication of one man.

In June 1931 a young ex-Merchant Navy officer came to the Sunderland office of Thomas Reed & Co with a proposal for the managing director, Harold Brunton-Reed. Founded in 1782, Reed's were reputed to be the oldest nautical publishers in the world. In 1859, they had produced the first textbook for officers taking the new Masters' and Mates' certificates. Their *Reed's Seamanship*, first published in the 1830s, had sold more than 100,000 copies. How, asked the young man, would they like a chance to publish something even more successful?

At the time Reed's were finding business difficult. The depression had hit publishing hard, if not quite as hard as it had hit the firm's shipyard neighbours on the banks of the River Wear. Their largest regular job was the annual printing of the Christmas catalogue for a local department store. So Brunton-Reed listened to his visitor with interest.

One of the youngest Merchant Navy officers ever to hold a Master's certificate, O. M. Watts had left the sea in 1927. For a time he eked out a precarious living delivering yachts and teaching yachtsmen navigation, supplemented by work editing *Pearson's Nautical Almanac*. While working on the almanac – and using it on his deliveries all around Britain – Watts became convinced that he could improve on the model, with an almanac designed specifically for the yachts, fishing boats and small commercial vessels operating in the treacherous waters around the British Isles.

Watt's idea was that he should compile, and Reed's should publish, a standard reference so comprehensive that it would have a place on every yacht and merchant ship's chart table. In one volume it would assemble all the knowledge a navigator would need to con a vessel in Home Trade Waters. But best of all, as far as Reed's were concerned, was Watts' assertion that its buyers would willingly come back for a replacement every year.

Pearson's was sold in 1931, giving Watts the incentive to take his idea further. First he needed to find a publisher. He had used Reed's before to print his own technical publications, and with their reputation and background felt they would be an ideal choice. Full of confidence, he made the long journey from his home in London to Sunderland.

Brunton-Reed was enthusiastic, even more so when he heard that *Pearson's* would not be published the following year, giving the proposed new title a clear run. Publisher and editor shook hands – as Watts described it, "the only agreement we ever made" – and Watts returned to London to compile the first issue of the new almanac for publication by January 1, 1932.

Often working until two in the morning, Watts spent the next six months compiling his almanac. With his declared intention of comprehensive coverage of Home Trade Waters, he had to draw up a complete list of lights and buoys for British and Continental ports from Brest to the Elbe, including Denmark, the Faeroes and Iceland. He had to prepare the tidal data for countless ports, calculate course and distances from port to port, and write whole sections on maritime law, signalling and pilotage.

The first ediion of *Reed's Home Trade Nautical Almanac and Tide Tables*, as the book was called, was published in the first week of January 1932. A measure of the effort that went into the production is that even the first edition ran to 990 pages.

Sales of the new almanac were everything Watts and Brunton-Reed had hoped for, although Harold's son Kenneth was later to claim that it took twenty years for the almanac to show a profit. Watts immediately began work on the second edition, his enthusiasm bolstered by scores of letters of appreciation from professional seamen and yachtsmen alike.

Many of the letters offered helpful observations and suggestions for other useful sections and tables, which Watts was able to incorporate into the second and subsequent editions. The second edition saw the introduction of a full-colour guide to the International Code of Signals, followed over the next five years by further additions such as tidal stream charts of the Pentland Firth and the Solent, Sun and Star GHA tables, and a section on first-aid at sea. Never too proud to listen to feedback, even when *Reed's* had earned itself the status of navigator's Bible, Watts carefully considered every suggestion for improvement and, if it was practical, adopted it. As a glance through the pages of this edition will show, his policy of continuous improvement is maintained even today.

During the thirties Watts opened a chandlery in Albemarle Street, off London's Piccadilly, where he continued to compile and edit successive editions of *Reed's* from an office in the back of the shop. As the war clouds began to gather over Europe, Albemarle Street was the logical site for his next venture; a sea school where yachtsmen could be taught what they would need to know to serve in the Royal Naval Volunteer Reserve in the coming conflict.

This symbiotic relationship with amateurs who were shortly to become professionals enabled Watts to remain in close touch with the needs of the contemporary navigator and to fine-tune his book to suit the conditions. When war finally broke out, the *Reed's Almanac* that had been a convenience for sailors became a lifeline for the professional, and Watts was acutely aware of the awesome responsi- bility he now bore.

As the bombs fell on London during the Blitz, Watts continued to work on the next year's Almanac. In the preface to the 10th edition, he wrote: "No new features have been introduced into *Reed's Almanac* for 1941 for the main reason that the majority of the pages have been prepared in London during night after night of incessant bombing and gunfire, which has made it a physical impossibility . . . We in London are glad to bear many of the horrors of modern warfare so that some at least may be lifted from the shoulders of our seafarers – Royal and Merchant Navy men both".

Reed's finest hour came in 1944, when the government ordered 3000 extra copies of the almanac for use in vessels involved in the Normandy D-Day landings.

After the war, as yachtsmen began once more to roam the seas, those who had served in the Royal and Merchant Navies naturally continued to use the almanac that had seen them through the hostilities. *Reed's* was now what Watts had promised Harold Brunton-Reed it would be: as essential an item of chartroom equipment as a pair of compasses, and aboard many boats the only reference apart from charts and pilots that any navigator ever used. What was it that made *Reed's* so indispensable? Murray Sayle, reporting to the *Sunday Times* from an OSTAR yacht in mid-Atlantic in 1972, gives a clue:

"Apart from being a quarry of hard-won sea lore, *Reed's* is composed in a unique literary form, half prose, half verse, like some early Norseman's saga. 'Worm and parcel with the lay, turn and serve the other way' is advice which must have comforted many a lonely sailor on a night watch. I turned idly to Section XIX, the most riveting of all Reed's 1240 pages,

'Weather Forecasting by a single observer'. I had just drawn a blanket up to my chin when a couplet leapt from page five: 'At sea with low and falling glass, soundly sleeps a careless ass.' In three seconds I was out of my berth, flashlight in hand, tapping the barometer."

Every year produced new features or improvements, culled from reader's suggestions or dreamt up by Watts' fertile imagination. One of the more extraordinary additions was a section on childbirth at sea, commissioned from a doctor friend. "We never thought it would be used," said Watts. But he had reckoned without pregnant yachtswoman Rosie Swale. As she and her husband set off from Southampton for Italy in their 30ft catamaran, Mrs Swale told a newspaper reporter: "We are putting our faith in good old *Reed's Nautical Almanac* It has loads of information on the subject, including this wonderful advice to keep calm, unhurried and let nature take its course." Six months later, the joke became reality when husband Colin had to deliver Rosie's 12lb baby off Fiumicino, Italy.

O. M. Watts continued to edit *Reed's* until 1981, always from the office in Albemarle Street. On his retirement he was succeeded as Editor by Jean Fowler, who had been working for Thomas Reed Publications for more than twenty years and was able to take over the reins without in any way compromising the accuracy and usability for which *Reed's* was famous.

The change of ownership has made it possible to make significant improvements to *Reed's Almanac* to bring it truly up-to-date. The use of modern desktop publishing technology has enabled the editors to improve the layout and to introduce colour within the main body of the Almanac without affecting publishing lead times. This ensures that the information remains as current as it has always been. And as accurate: Jean Fowler remains at the helm as Editorial Director, supported by a team of long-serving editors – Harry Baker, Robin Ekblom, Arthur Somers and Tom Stableford – to ensure as always that the standard of accuracy is maintained.

Foreign editions and expanded coverage are another part of the story. But the most obvious change, perhaps, is the separation of the almanac into two publications. It might surprise readers to know that this is not the first time that *Reed's* has been a two-volume reference book. In 1942, recognising the value of the Almanac to seamen, the Government was reluctant to put obstacles in the way of publication; but with paper – like everything else imported – then in short supply, the book's customary 1100-plus pages could not be maintained. The company therefore published a slimmed-down version of 250 pages containing only the information that changed annually: Sun, Moon, Stars and the Tide Tables. Readers were asked to keep their 1941 editions as a companion volume to be used in conjunction with the 1942 volumear

More recently, in 1975, 'J.L.D.' wrote in the Journal of the Honourable Company of Master Mariners: "In spite of the Publishers' note 'Less Bulk – More Pages' Reed's still seems to me a bit bulky, and I wonder if thought has ever been given to publishing it in two parts. A yachtsman friend whose opinion I value suggested that all the permanent information such as conversion tables, distance tables, navigation and the like need only be published, say, once in five years and the ephemeris, tide tables, etc, every year. This would reduce the bulk very considerably and the two smaller books would be easier to handle than one large one."

Well, J.L.D., we have done it. We hope you approve.

CONVERSIONS

LINEAR – INTERNATIONAL NAUTICAL MILES, STATUTE MILES AND KILOMETRES

INM	Km	SM	Km	INM	SM	SM	Km	INM
1	1.852	1.15078	1	0.53996	0.62137	1	1.60934	0.86898
2	3.70	2.30	2	1.08	1.24	2	3.22	1.74
3	5.56	3.45	3	1.62	1.86	3	4.83	2.61
4	7.41	4.60	4	2.16	2.49	4	6.44	3.48
5	9.26	5.75	5	2.70	3.11	5	8.05	4.34
6	11.11	6.90	6	3.24	3.73	6	9.66	5.21
7	12.96	8.06	7	3.78	4.35	7	11.27	6.08
8	14.82	9.21	8	4.32	4.97	8	12.87	6.95
9	16.67	10.36	9	4.86	5.59	9	14.48	7.82
10	18.52	11.51	10	5.40	6.21	10	16.09	8.69
11	20.37	12.66	11	5.94	6.84	11	17.70	9.56
12	22.22	13.81	12	6.48	7.46	12	19.31	10.43
13	24.08	14.96	13	7.02	8.08	13	20.92	11.30
14	25.93	16.11	14	7.56	8.70	14	22.53	12.17
15	27.78	17.26	15	8.10	9.32	15	23.14	13.03
16	29.63	18.41	16	8.64	9.94	16	25.75	13.90
17	31.48	19.56	17	9.18	10.56	17	27.36	14.77
18	33.34	20.71	18	9.72	11.18	18	28.97	15.64
19	35.19	21.86	19	10.26	11.81	19	30.58	16.51
20	37.04	23.02	20	10.80	12.43	20	32.19	17.38
21	38.89	24.17	21	11.34	13.05	21	33.80	18.25
22	40.74	25.32	22	11.88	13.67	22	35.41	19.12
23	42.60	26.47	23	12.42	14.29	23	37.01	19.99
24	44.45	27.62	24	12.96	14.91	24	38.62	20.86
25	46.30	28.77	25	13.50	15.53	25	40.23	21.72
26	48.15	29.92	26	14.04	16.16	26	41.84	22.59
27	50.00	31.07	27	14.58	16.78	27	43.45	23.46
28	51.86	32.22	28	15.12	17.40	28	45.06	24.33
29	53.71	33.37	29	15.66	18.02	29	46.67	25.20
30	55.56	34.52	30	16.20	18.64	30	48.28	26.07
31	57.41	35.67	31	16.74	19.26	31	49.89	26.94
32	59.26	36.82	32	17.28	19.88	32	51.50	27.81
33	61.12	37.98	33	17.82	20.51	33	53.11	28.68
34	62.97	39.13	34	18.36	21.13	34	54.72	29.55
35	64.82	40.28	35	18.90	21.75	35	56.33	30.41
36	66.67	41.43	36	19.44	22.37	36	57.94	31.28
37	68.52	42.58	37	19.98	22.99	37	59.55	32.15
38	70.38	43.73	38	20.52	23.61	38	61.15	33.02
39	72.23	44.88	39	21.06	24.23	39	62.76	33.89
40	74.08	46.03	40	21.60	24.85	40	64.37	34.76
45	83.34	51.79	45	24.30	27.96	45	72.42	39.10
50	92.60	57.54	50	27.00	31.07	50	80.47	43.45
55	101.86	63.29	55	29.70	34.18	55	88.51	47.79
60	111.12	69.05	60	32.40	37.28	60	96.56	52.14
65	120.38	74.80	65	35.10	40.39	65	104.61	56.48
70	129.64	80.55	70	37.80	43.50	70	112.65	60.83
75	138.90	86.31	75	40.50	46.60	75	120.70	65.17
80	148.16	92.06	80	43.20	49.71	80	128.75	69.52
85	157.42	97.82	85	45.90	52.82	85	136.79	73.86
90	166.68	103.57	90	48.60	55.92	90	144.84	78.21
95	175.94	109.32	95	51.30	59.03	95	152.89	82.55
100	185.20	115.08	100	54.00	62.14	100	160.93	86.90

FEET TO METRES

Feet	Metres	Feet	Metres
1	0.30	26	7.92
2	0.61	27	8.23
3	0.91	28	8.53
4	1.22	29	8.84
5	1.52	30	9.14
6	1.83	31	9.45
7	2.13	32	9.75
8	2.44	33	10.06
9	2.74	34	10.36
10	3.05	35	10.67
11	3.35	36	10.97
12	3.66	37	11.28
13	3.96	38	11.58
14	4.27	39	11.89
15	4.57	40	12.19
16	4.88	41	12.50
17	5.18	42	12.80
18	5.49	43	13.11
19	5.79	44	13.41
20	6.10	45	13.72
21	6.40	46	14.02
22	6.71	47	14.33
23	7.01	48	14.63
24	7.32	49	14.94
25	7.62	50	15.24

METRES TO FEET

Metres	Feet	Metres	Feet
1	3.28	26	85.30
2	6.56	27	88.58
3	9.84	28	91.86
4	13.12	29	95.14
5	16.40	30	98.43
6	19.69	31	101.71
7	22.97	32	104.99
8	26.25	33	108.27
9	29.53	34	111.55
10	32.81	35	114.83
11	36.09	36	118.11
12	39.37	37	121.39
13	42.65	38	124.67
14	45.93	39	127.95
15	49.21	40	131.23
16	52.49	41	134.51
17	55.77	42	137.80
18	59.06	43	141.08
19	62.34	44	144.36
20	65.62	45	147.64
21	68.90	46	150.92
22	72.18	47	154.20
23	75.46	48	157.48
24	78.74	49	160.76
25	82.02	50	164.04

FATHOMS TO METRES

Fathoms	Metres	Fathoms	Metres
1	1.83	26	47.55
2	3.66	27	49.38
3	5.49	28	51.21
4	7.32	29	53.04
5	9.14	30	54.86
6	10.97	31	56.69
7	12.80	32	58.52
8	14.63	33	60.35
9	16.46	34	62.18
10	18.29	35	64.00
11	20.12	36	65.84
12	21.95	37	67.67
13	23.77	38	69.49
14	25.60	39	71.32
15	27.43	40	73.15
16	29.26	41	74.98
17	31.09	42	76.81
18	32.92	43	78.64
19	34.75	44	80.47
20	36.58	45	82.30
21	38.40	46	84.12
22	40.23	47	85.95
23	42.06	48	87.78
24	43.89	49	89.61
25	45.72	50	91.44

METRES TO FATHOMS

Metres	Fathoms	Metres	Fathoms
1	0.547	26	14.217
2	1.094	27	14.764
3	1.640	28	15.311
4	2.187	29	15.857
5	2.734	30	16.404
6	3.281	31	16.951
7	3.828	32	17.498
8	4.374	33	18.045
9	4.921	34	18.591
10	5.468	35	19.138
11	6.015	36	19.685
12	6.562	37	20.232
13	7.108	38	20.779
14	7.655	39	21.325
15	8.202	40	21.872
16	8.749	41	22.419
17	9.296	42	22.966
18	9.842	43	23.513
19	10.389	44	24.059
20	10.936	45	24.606
21	11.483	46	25.153
22	12.030	47	25.700
23	12.577	48	26.247
24	13.123	49	26.793
25	13.670	50	27.340

Section 1

INCHES TO MILLIMETRES

MILLIMETRES TO INCHES

Inches	mm	Inches	mm	mm	Inches	mm	Inches
1	25.40	15	381.00	1	0.0394	15	0.5906
2	50.80	20	508.00	2	0.0787	20	0.7874
3	76.20	25	635.00	3	0.1181	25	0.9843
4	101.60	30	762.00	4	0.1575	30	1.1811
5	127.00	35	889.00	5	0.1969	35	1.3780
10	254.00	40	1016.00	10	0.3937	40	1.5748

10 MILLIMETRES = 1 CENTIMETRE   100 CENTIMETRES (1000 MM) = 1 METRE = 39.37 INCHES (3.3 FEET)

INCHES TO METRES

METRES TO INCHES

Inches	Metres	Inches	Metres	Metres	Inches	Metres	Inches
1	0.0254	7	0.1778	0.1	3.937	0.7	27.559
2	0.0508	8	0.2032	0.2	7.874	0.8	31.496
3	0.0762	9	0.2286	0.3	11.811	0.9	35.433
4	0.1016	10	0.2540	0.4	15.748	1.0	39.370
5	0.1270	11	0.2794	0.5	19.685	1.1	43.307
6	0.1524	12	0.3048	0.6	23.622	1.2	47.244

To convert metres to centimetres: move decimal point two places to the right

YARDS TO METRES

METRES TO YARDS

Yds	Metres	Yds	Metres	Metres	Yds	Metres	Yds
1	0.91440	6	5.48640	1	1.09361	6	6.56168
2	1.82880	7	6.40080	2	2.18723	7	7.65529
3	2.74320	8	7.31520	3	3.28084	8	8.74891
4	3.65760	9	8.22960	4	4.37445	9	9.84252
5	4.57200	10	9.14400	5	5.46807	10	10.93614

Move decimal point for higher values — eg, 6,000 metres = 6,561.68 yards

POUNDS TO KILOGRAMMES

KILOGRAMMES TO POUNDS

lb	kg	lb	kg	kg	lb	kg	lb
1	0.454	6	2.722	1	2.205	6	13.228
2	0.907	7	3.175	2	4.409	7	15.432
3	1.361	8	3.629	3	6.614	8	17.637
4	1.814	9	4.082	4	8.818	9	19.842
5	2.268	10	4.536	5	11.023	10	22.046

GALLONS TO LITRES

LITRES TO GALLONS

Gallons	Litres	Gallons	Litres	Litres	Gallons	Litres	Gallons
1	4.5461	10	45.4609	1	0.2200	60	13.1982
2	9.0922	20	90.9218	2	0.4399	90	19.7972
3	13.6383	30	136.3826	5	1.0998	120	26.3963
4	18.1844	40	181.8435	10	2.1997	150	32.9954
5	22.7304	50	227.3044	20	4.3994	180	39.5945

PINTS TO LITRES

LITRES TO PINTS

Pints	Litres	Pints	Litres	Litres	Pints	Litres	Pints
1	0.568	6	3.409	1	1.760	6	10.559
2	1.136	7	3.978	2	3.520	7	12.319
3	1.705	8	4.546	3	5.279	8	14.078
4	2.273	9	5.114	4	7.039	9	15.838
5	2.841	10	5.682	5	8.799	10	17.598

SOME USEFUL CONVERSIONS

1 fathom	= 6 feet
1 shackle	= 15 fathoms
1 cable	= 608 ft (approx 100 fathoms)
10 cables	= 1 international nautical mile
1 international nautical mile	= 6076.12 ft = 1.15 statute miles = 1852 m
1 statute mile	= 5280 ft = 1760 yd = 0.87 sea miles

Length

kilometre (km)	= 1093.61yd
metre (m)	= 39.37in
centimetre (cm)	= 0.3937in
millimetre (mm)	= 0.03937in

Weight

tonne	= 2204.6lb
kilogram (kg)	= 2.2046lb
gram (g)	= 0.0353oz

Area

sq metre (m^2)	= 1.196yd^2
sq centimetre (cm^2)	= 0.1550in^2
sq millimetre (mm^2)	= 0.00155in^2

Volume

cubic metre (m)	= 220 gallons = 1000 litres = 1.308yd^3
litre	= 1.7598 pints
centilitre (cl)	= 0.352fl oz
millimetre (ml)	= 0.35fl oz

For **wind speed, temperature and barometer** conversions, see Section 19

OTHER MEASURES

Weight

1 long ton (British) = 2240lb = 1.12 short tons = 1.016 tonne
1 short ton (USA and Canada) = 20 centals of 100lb each = 2000lb = 0.893 long tons = 0.907 tonne
1 tonne = 2204.6lb = 1.1023 short tons = 0.9842 long tons = 1000kg

Nautical

1 ton (displacement) = 35cu ft salt water or 36 cu ft fresh water
1 ton (register) = 100 cu ft   1 ton (measurement) = 40 cu ft

Fresh Water

1 cu ft = 6¼ gallons and weighs 62.5lb
36 cu ft = 224 gallons and weighs 1 ton
1 gallon = 4.546 litres and weighs 10lb
10 British gallons = approx 12 American gallons
1000 litres = 1cu m
1 litre weighs approx 1kg

Salt Water

1 cu ft weighs 64 lb   35 cu ft weighs 1 ton

MISCELLANEOUS

TEMPERATURE

32	40	50	60	70	75	85	95
0	5	10	15	20	25	30	35

SPEEDS

mph	20	30	40	50	60
km/h	32	48	64	80	96

TYRE PRESSURES

lb/sq in	20	22	24	26	28
kg/sq cm	1.41	1.55	1.69	1.83	1.9

CLOTHING SIZES

Men's Suits and Coats

British	36	38	40	42
American	36	38	40	42
Continental	46	48	50	52

Men's Shirts

British	14	14½	15	1!
American	14	14½	15	1!
Continental	36	37	38	39

Men's Shoes

British	7	8	9	1
American	7½	8½	9½	1
Continental	40½	42	43	4

Men's Socks

British	92	10	10½	
American	92	10	10½	
Continental	39	40	41	

Women's Dresses and Suits

British	8	10	12
American	-	8	10
Continental	-	38	40

Women's Shoes

British	4	4½	5
American	5½	6	6½
Continental	37	37½	38

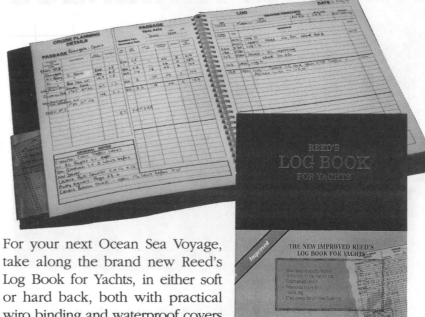

INTERNATIONAL REGULATIONS FOR PREVENTING COLLISIONS AT SEA

2

RECOGNITION OF LIGHTS AND SHAPES
(Complete details in Collision Regulations)
LIGHTS

ASTERN AHEAD

SAILING VESSEL UNDERWAY — NOT USING POWER

Red and green all round mast head lights may be shown in addition to side lights. Under 20m. in length, side lights and sternlight may be combined in tricolour lantern at mast head, e.g. → Ahead

Under 7m. in length, if not practicable to exhibit these lights, shall have a white light ready to display to avoid collision.

**VESSEL SAILING —
AND USING POWER**

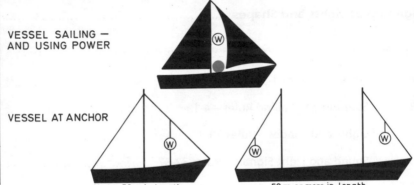

VESSEL AT ANCHOR

Under 50 m. in length   50 m. or more in length

A vessel of 100 m. or more shall also illuminate her decks.
A vessel of less than 7m. in length when at anchor, not in or near a narrow channel, fairway, or anchorage, shall not be required to exhibit these lights.

POWER DRIVEN VESSEL UNDERWAY

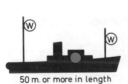   

50 m. or more in length   AHEAD   ASTERN   Under 50 m. in length

Under 12 m. may exhibit all round white light and side lights.

Less than 7m. and maximum speed not exceeding 7 knots an all round white light may be shown, and if practicable side lights.

HOVERCRAFT

Normal lights as for power driven vessels and when in non−displacement mode an all round flashing yellow light.

VESSELS TOWING

←——Length——→

Tow length 200 m. or less, two mast head lights shown; over 200 m. three lights. Yellow towing light shown over stern light. Towed vessels show side and stern lights.

PILOT VESSEL ON DUTY

ANCHORED   UNDERWAY, FROM AHEAD   UNDERWAY, FROM ASTERN

2 all round lights, white over red. When underway shows stern and side lights instead of anchor light.

VESSELS RESTRICTED IN ABILITY TO MANOEUVRE

Shows 3 all round lights, red over white over red.
When making way shows mast head, stern and side lights.
When at anchor shows an anchor light.

VESSEL ENGAGED IN UNDERWATER OPERATIONS

PASS THIS SIDE   OBSTRUCTION THIS SIDE

When making way also shows mast head, stern and side lights.
When at anchor does <u>NOT</u> show anchor light.

VESSEL AGROUND

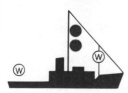

Two all round red lights and anchor light (s).
A vessel of less than 12 m. in length shall not be required to exhibit these lights.

Section 2

3

VESSEL CONSTRAINED BY HER DRAUGHT

Three all round red lights,
with normal navigation lights

VESSEL ENGAGED IN MINESWEEPING

Three all round green lights,
with normal navigation lights

VESSEL TRAWLING

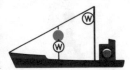

Two all round lights green over white,
with normal navigation lights.
Mast head light optional under 50 m.

VESSEL FISHING, OTHER THAN TRAWLING

Two all round lights red over white with one
all round white light in direction of gear if it
extends more than 150 m. horizontally.
Each vessel engaged in 'pair trawling' may direct
a searchlight forward, and in direction of other
vessel.

VESSEL NOT UNDER COMMAND

Two all round red lights and when making way
stern and side lights.

REMEMBER:

A sailing vessel when using its engine — with or without sails —
is a power driven vessel within the meaning of the Rules
and must act accordingly, showing the appropriate shapes
and lights.
Therefore a tricolour lantern may not be used when under power.

DAYMARKS

VESSEL SAILING AND USING POWER

Black cone, point down.

VESSEL AT ANCHOR

Black ball.

A vessel of less than 7m. in length when at anchor, not in or near a narrow channel, fairway or anchorage, shall not be required to exhibit the ball.

VESSEL TOWING

|← Length →|

If length of tow exceeds 200m. a black diamond shape to be exhibited on each vessel.

VESSEL RESTRICTED IN ABILITY TO MANOEUVRE

Black ball over black diamond over black ball.

VESSEL ENGAGED IN UNDERWATER OPERATIONS

PASS THIS SIDE

OBSTRUCTION THIS SIDE

Two black balls on the side of obstruction.

Two black diamonds on side on which vessels may pass.

If vessel is too small to exhibit above shapes a rigid replica of code flag A shall be flown. White and blue.

Section 2

VESSEL AGROUND

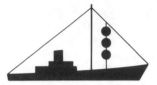

Three black balls to be exhibited.
Not required for vessel under 12 m.

VESSEL CONSTRAINED BY HER DRAUGHT

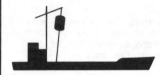

A black cylinder

VESSEL ENGAGED IN MINESWEEPING

Three black balls

VESSEL ENGAGED IN FISHING

Two black cones, points together.
May be replaced by basket if under 20 m.

If outlying gear extends more than 150 m.
horizontally, a black cone point up is shown
in direction of gear, e.g.

VESSEL NOT UNDER COMMAND

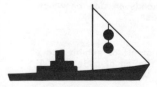

Two black balls

Introduction. Explanatory notes are added to individual rules in the Steering and Sailing Rules Section, whilst general comments only are made in parts C (Lights and Shapes) and part D (Sound and Light Signals). These notes are intended for the less experienced skippers of small craft.

It is important for anyone going to sea to fully understand the rules, and the ability to recognise lights and shapes and understand sound signals is vital. It should never be necessary in an emergency to consult a book to identify a particular group of lights or a signal.

As a matter of interest the newcomer to sailing may consider it odd to refer to arcs of lights in half degrees, when steering to half a degree is impracticable e.g. "the stern light shall be visible 22½° abaft the beam". Originally magnetic compasses were marked in 32 cardinal points thus each point equated to 11½°. Whilst the use of degrees became universal the old arcs of visibility were retained, thus "2 points abaft the beam" became 22½° abaft the beam" in the modern nomenclature.

INTERNATIONAL REGULATIONS FOR PREVENTING COLLISIONS AT SEA.

PART A – GENERAL

Rule 1 *Application*

(a) These Rules shall apply to all vessels upon the high seas and in all waters connected therewith navigable by seagoing vessels.

(b) Nothing in these Rules shall interfere with the operation of special rules made by an appropriate authority for roadsteads, harbours, rivers, lakes or inland waterways connected with the high seas and navigable by seagoing vessels. Such special rules shall conform as closely as possible to these rules.

(c) Nothing in these Rules shall interfere with the operation of special rules made by the Government of any State with respect to additional station or signal lights, shapes or whistle signals for ships of war and vessels proceeding under convoy, or with respect to additional station or signal lights, or shapes for fishing vessels engaged in fishing as a fleet. These additional station or signal lights, shapes or whistle signals shall, so far as possible, be such that they cannot be mistaken for any light, shape or signal authorised elsewhere under these Rules.

(d) Traffic separation schemes may be adopted by the Organisation for the purpose of these Rules.

(e) Whenever the Government concerned shall have determined that a vessel of special construction or purpose cannot comply fully with the provisions of any of these Rules with respect to the number, position, range or arc of visibility of lights or shapes, as well as to the disposition and characteristics of sound-signalling appliances, such vessel shall comply with such other provisions in regard to the number, position, range or arc of visibility of lights or shapes, as well as to the disposition and characteristics of sound-signalling appliances, as her Government shall have determined to be the closest possible compliance with these Rules in respect of that vessel.

Rule 2 *Responsibility*

(a) Nothing in these Rules shall exonerate any vessel, or the owner, master or crew thereof, from the consequences of any neglect to comply with these Rules or of the neglect of any precaution which may be required by the ordinary practice of seamen, or by the special circumstances of the case.

(b) In construing and complying with these Rules due regard shall be had to all dangers of navigation and collision and to any special circumstances, including the limitations of the vessels involved, which may make a departure from these Rules necessary to avoid immediate danger.

NOTE TO RULE 2 It must be remembered that rules do not give absolute right of way to any vessel. Right of way is conferred by one vessel to another by an alteration of course and speed, but both vessels have responsibility to avoid a collision. In certain circumstances the "give way" vessel may be unable to take avoiding action and then the "stand on" vessel is required to take the necessary action.

Rule 3 *General Definitions*

For the purpose of these Rules, except where the context otherwise requires:

(a) The word "vessel" includes every description of water craft including non-displacement craft and seaplanes, used or capable of being used as a means of transportation on water.

(b) The term "power-driven vessel" means any vessel propelled by machinery.

(c) The term "sailing vessel" means any vessel under sail provided that propelling machinery, if fitted, is not being used.

(d) The term "vessel engaged in fishing" means any vessel fishing with nets, lines, trawls or other fishing apparatus which restrict manoeuvrability, but does not include a vessel fishing with trolling lines or other fishing apparatus which do not restrict manoeuvrability.

(e) The word "seaplane" includes any aircraft designed to manoeuvre on the water.

(f) The term "vessel not under command" means a vessel which through some exceptional circumstance is unable to manoeuvre as required by these Rules and is therefore unable to keep out of the way of another vessel.

(g) The term"vessel restricted in her ability to manoeuvre" means a vessel which from the nature of her work is restricted in her ability to manoeuvre as required by these Rules and is therefore unable to keep out of the way of another vessel.

The term "vessels restricted in their ability to manoeuvre" shall include but not be limited to:

(i) a vessel engaged in laying, servicing or picking up a navigation mark, submarine cable or pipeline;

(ii) a vessel engaged in dredging, surveying or underwater operations;

(iii) a vessel engaged in replenishment or transferring persons, provisions or cargo while underway;

(iv) a vessel engaged in the launching or recovery of aircraft;

(v) a vessel engaged in mine clearance operations;

(vi) a vessel engaged in a towing operation such as severely restricts the towing vessel and her tow in their ability to deviate from their course.

(h) The term "vessel constrained by her draught" means a power-driven vessel which because of her draught in relation to the available depth and width of navigable water is severely restricted in her ability to deviate from the course she is following.

(i) The word "underway" means that a vessel is not at anchor, or made fast to the shore, or aground.

(j) The words "length" and "breadth" of a vessel mean her length overall and greatest breadth.

(k) Vessels shall be deemed to be in sight of one another only when one can be observed visually from the other.

(l) The term "restricted visibility" means any condition in which visibility is restricted by fog, mist, falling snow, heavy rainstorms, sandstorms or any other similar causes.

NOTE TO RULE 3 A useful explanation of various terms which occur in the rules and should be known and understood by those in charge of any seagoing vessel.

PART B – STEERING AND SAILING RULES

SECTION 1 – CONDUCT OF VESSELS IN ANY CONDITION OF VISIBILITY.

Rule 4 *Application*

Rules in this Section apply in any condition of visibility.

Rule 5 *Lookout*

Every vessel shall at all times maintain a proper lookout by sight and hearing as well as by all available means appropriate in the prevailing circumstances and conditions so as to make a full appraisal of the situation and of the risk of collision.

NOTE TO RULE 5 Keeping a proper lookout at all times is one of the most important duties of any vessel. It is particularly difficult in a sailing yacht with a long footed headsail especially when heeled but it is vital to keep a good lookout to leeward in these circumstances. Watchkeeping at night also presents problems insofar as the lights on the vessel are concerned. Chart table lights and any internal lights visible to the helmsman should be red which reduces night vision by a relatively small amount. Deck lights for sail changing at night constitute a real difficulty for the lookout both at the time and for a short while afterwards. In conditions of poor visibility a good listening watch is also important – it cannot be kept from inside a closed wheelhouse.

Rule 6 *Safe Speed.*

Every vessel shall at all times proceed at a safe speed so that she can take proper and effective action to avoid collision and be stopped within a distance appropriate to the prevailing circumstances and conditions.

In determining a sage speed the following factors shall be among those taken into account:

(a) By all vessels:

(i) the state of visibility;

(ii) the traffic density including concentrations of fishing vessels or any other vessels;

(iii) the manoeuvrability of the vessel with special reference to stopping distance and turning ability in the prevailing conditions;

(iv) at night the presence of background light such as from shore lights or from back scatter of her own lights;

(v) the draught in relation to the available depth of water.

(b) Additonally, by vessels with operational radar:

(i) the characteristics, efficiency and limitations of the radar equipment;

(ii) any constraints imposed by the radar range scale in use;

(iii) the effect on radar detection of teh sea state, weather and other sources of interference;

(iv) the possibility that small vessels, ice and other floating objects may not be detected by radar at an adequate range.

(v) the number, location and movement of vessels detected by radar.

(vi) the more exact assessment of the visibility that may be possible when radar is used to determine the range of vessels or other objects in the vicinity.

NOTE TO RULE 6 This rule refers to a "safe speed" i.e. not necessarily high speed. High speed in a sailing yacht is rarely a contributory factor in a collision situation but slow speed may be. The essence of the Rule is to have complete control and manoeuvrability at all times. A sailing yacht carrying a spinnaker at night in a congested traffic situation would not be conforming to the spirit of this Rule, she should be sailing more slowly under plain sail but with complete manoeuvrability. For the fast motor yacht high speed in a tight situation may be a danger as it effectively reduces "thinking time".

Rule 7 *Risk of Collision*

(a) Every vessel shall use all available means appropriate to the prevailing circumstances and conditions to determine if risk of collision exists. If there is any doubt such risk shall be deemed to exist.

(b) Proper use shall be made of radar equipment if fitted and operational, including long-range scanning to obtain early warning of risk of collision and radar plotting or equivalent systematic observation of detected objects.

(c) Assumptions shall not be made on the basis of scanty information, especially scanty radar information.

(d) In determining if risk of collision exists the following considerations shall be among those taken into account:

(i) such risk shall be deemed to exist if the compass bearing of an approaching vessel does not appreciably change;

(ii) such risk may sometimes exist even when an appreciable bearing change is evident, particularly when approaching a very large vessel or a tow or when approaching a vessel at close range.

NOTE TO RULE 7 In the situation of an approaching or crossing vessel the first step is to take a compass bearing of the vessel and repeat it at suitable intervals. If the bearing does not change, risk of collision exists. Note that it is the compass bearing, not the relative bearing that is crucial.

Rule 8 *Action to avoid a Collision*

(a) Any action taken to avoid collision shall, if the circumstances of the case admit, be positive, made in ample time and with due regard to the observance of good seamanship.

(b) Any alteration of course and/or speed to avoid collision shall, if the circumstances of the case admit, be large enough to be readily apparent to another vessel observing visually or by radar; a succession of small alterations of course and/or speed should be avoided.

(c) If there is sufficient sea room, alteration of course alone may be the most effective action

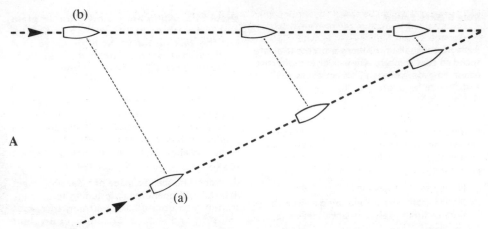

A

In A. the compass bearing of (a) relative to (b) is constant and therefore risk of collision exists. In this particular case the relative bearing of (a) to (b) is also constant.

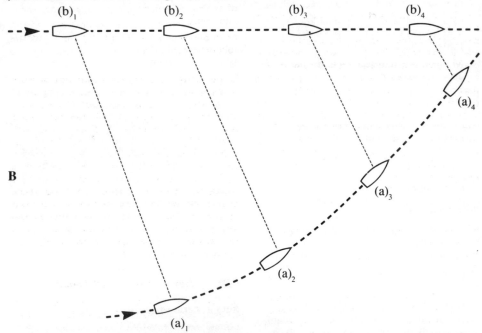

B

In B. the relative bearing of (b)$_1$ from (a)$_1$ is abaft the beam. At (a)$_2$ the bearing is approximately abeam and at (a)$_3$ and (a)$_4$ is moving ahead of the beam. The compass bearing however, remains constant and therefore risk of collision exists.

to avoid a close-quarters situation provided that it is made in good time, is substantial and does not result in another close-quarters situation.

(d) Action taken to avoid collision with another vessel shall be such as to result in passing at a safe distance. The effectiveness of the action shall be carefully checked until the other vessel is finally past and clear.

(e) If necessary to avoid collision or allow more time to assess the situation, a vessel shall slacken her speed to take all way off by stopping or reversing her means of propulsion.

(f) (i) A vessel which, by any of these rules, is required not to impede the passage or safe passage of another vessel shall, when required by the circumstances of the case, take early action to allow sufficient sea room for the safe passage of the other vessel.

(ii) A vessel required not to impede the passage or safe passage of another vessel is not relieved of this obligation if approaching the other vessel so as to involve risk of collision and shall, when taking action, have full regard to the action which may be required by the rules of this part.

(iii) A vessel the passage of which is not to be impeded remains fully obliged to comply with the rules of this part when the two vessels are approaching one another so as to involve risk of collision.

NOTE TO RULE 8 Action to avoid collision must be taken in good time and in such a manner that the "stand on" vessel is left in no doubt that the "give way" vessel is taking avoiding action. In the case of the "give way" vessel being a small yacht any alteration in speed is unlikely to be obvious from any distance. The action therefore must be to alter the profile of the yacht by a marked change of course. Rule 8(f) draws attention to the importance of small vessels navigating in traffic separation schemes not to impede vessels moving in the lane.

Rule 9 *Narrow Channels*

(a) A vessel proceeding along the course of a narrow channel or fairway shall keep as near to the outer limit of the channel or fairway which lies on her starboard side as is safe and practicable.

(b) A vessel of less than 20 metres in length or a sailing vessel shall not impede the passage of a vessel which can safely navigate only within a narrow channel or fairway.

(c) A vessel engaged in fishing shall not impede the passage of any other vessel navigating within a narrow channel or fairway.

(d) A vessel shall not cross a narrow channel or fairway if such crossing impedes the passage of a vessel which can safely navigate only within such channel or fairway. The latter vessel may use the sound signal prescribed in Rule 34(d) if in doubt as to the intention of the crossing vessel.

(e) (i) In a narrow channel or fairway when overtaking can take place only if the vessel to be overtaken has to take action to permit safe passing, the vessel intending to overtake shall indicate her intention by sounding the appropriate signal prescribed in Rule 34(c)(i). The vessel to be overtaken shall, if in agreement, sound the appropriate signal prescribed in Rule 34(c)(ii) and take steps to permit safe passing. If in doubt she may sound the signals prescribed in Rule 34(d).

(ii) This Rule does not relieve the overtaking vessel of her obligation under Rule 13.

(f) A vessel nearing a bend or an area of a narrow channel or fairway where other vessels may be obscured by an intervening obstruction shall navigate with particular alertness and caution and shall sound the appropriate signal prescribed in Rule 34(e).

(g) Any vessel shall, if the circumstances of the case admit, avoid anchoring in a narrow channel.

NOTE TO RULE 9 On occasion doubt may arise whether one is in a "narrow channel" – usually it is obvious, but if not, any channel which has port and starboard hand buoys will be regarded as a narrow channel by ocean-going vessels. Hence all other vessels should have regard to the requirements of this rule when in such a channel. It is important to note that 9(a) refers to "a vessel", hence a sailing yacht is also required to keep as near as possible to the starboard side of the channel and avoid impeding the passage of a vessel which can only navigate with safety in a narrow channel.

Rule 10 *Traffic Separation Schemes*

(a) This Rule applies to traffic separation schemes adopted by the Organisation and does not relieve any vessel of her obligation under any other rule.

(b) A vessel using a traffic separation scheme shall:

(i) proceed in the appropriate traffic lane in the general direction of traffic flow for that lane;

(ii) so far as practicable keep clear of a traffic separation line or separation zone;

(iii) normally join or leave a traffic lane at the termination of the lane, but when

Section 2

11

joining or leaving from either side shall do so at as small an angle to the general direction of traffic flow as practicable.

(c) A vessel shall so far as practicable avoid crossing traffic lanes, but if obliged to do so shall cross on a heading as nearly as practicable at right angles to the general direction of traffic flow.

(d) (i) A vessel shall not use an inshore traffic zone when she can safely use the appropriate traffic lane within the adjacent traffic separation scheme. However, vessels of less than 20 metres in length, sailing vessels and vessels engaged in fishing may use the inshore traffic zone.

(ii) Notwithstanding sub-paragraph (d)(i) a vessel may use an inshore traffic zone when en route to or from a port, offshore installation or structure, pilot station or any other place situated within the inshore traffic zone, or to avoid immediate danger.

(e) A vessel other than a crossing vessel or a vessel joining or leaving a lane, shall not normally enter a separation zone or cross a separation line except:

(i) in cases of emergency to avoid immediate danger;

(ii) to engage in fishing within a separation zone.

(f) A vessel navigating in areas near the terminations of traffic separation schemes shall do so with particular caution.

(g) A vessel shall so far as practicable avoid anchoring in a traffic separation scheme or in areas near its terminations.

(h) A vessel not using a traffic separation scheme shall avoid it by as wide a margin as is practicable.

(i) A vessel engaged in fishing shall not impede the passage of any vessel following a traffic lane.

(j) A vessel of less than 20 metres in length or a sailing vessel shall not impede the safe passage of a power-driven vessel following a traffic lane.

(k) A vessel restricted in her ability to manoeuvre when engaged in an operation for the maintenance of safety of navigation in a traffic separation scheme is exempted from complying with this Rule to the extent necessary to carry out the operation.

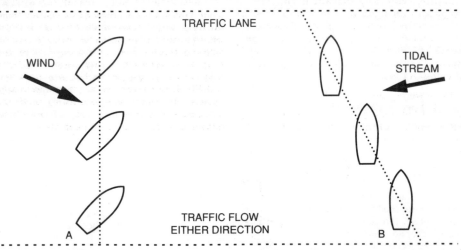

In the sketch, Yacht A is counteracting the effect of the tidal stream to make her track at 90° to the lane, but her profile to vessels in the lane is considerably reduced. This has two results. Firstly, her time in crossing the lane is much increased and secondly, her reduced profile means that she is less visible, both visually and on radar screens, than if she presented a full profile. The action taken by Yacht A is incorrect.

Yacht B is correctly presenting her full profile in the lane and is not attempting to counteract the tidal stream. Although her track is longer than that of Yacht A she will cross in less time. This is the correct procedure.

In the case of having to cross against a head wind and motoring is not practicable, a yacht should sail close hauled on that tack which makes her heading as close as possible to 90° to the lane.

(l) A vessel restricted in her ability to manoeuvre when engaged in an operation for the laying, servicing or picking up of a submarine cable, within a traffic separation scheme, is exempted from complying with this Rule to the extent necessary to carry out the operation.

NOTE TO RULE 10 This is an extremely important rule and there are two aspects of it which are particularly important to sailing vessels

Firstly, all crossing vessels must cross on a heading as nearly as practicable at right angles to the lane, thereby presenting a full profile to vessels using the lane.

Secondly, a sailing vessel is required "not to impede the safe passage of a power-driven vessel following a traffic lane".

This means that the sailing vessel shall achieve maximum speed and hence manoeuvrability. The aim should be to cross as quickly as possible which means using the engine when necessary and not trying to counteract any sideways effect of the tidal stream.

SECTION II – CONDUCT OF VESSELS IN SIGHT OF ONE ANOTHER

Rule 11 *Application*

Rules in this Section apply to vessels in sight of one another.

Rule 12 *Sailing Vessels*

(a) When two sailing vessels are approaching one another, so as to avoid risk of collision, one of them shall keep out of the way of the other as follows:

(i) when each has the wind on a different side, the vessel which has the wind on the port side shall keep out of the way of the other;

(ii) when both have the wind on the same side, the vessel which is to windward shall keep out of the way of the vessel which is to leeward;

(iii) if a vessel with the wind on the port side sees a vessel to windward and cannot determine with certainty whether the other vessel has the wind on the port or on the starboard side, she shall keep out of the way of the other.

(b) For the purposes of this Rule the windward side shall be deemed to be the side opposite to that on which the mainsail is carried or, in the case of a square-rigged vessel, the side opposite to that on which the largest fore-and-aft sail is carried.

NOTE TO RULE 12 (a)(i) and (a)(ii) are quite clear and are well known but (a)(iii) must be fully understood. A yacht close hauled on the port tack approaching a yacht running free and unable to determine her tack must keep clear. The windward boat may be carrying a spinnaker which makes it difficult to determine her tack and in any case at night quite impossible. In these circumstances it is the duty of the close hauled port tack vessel to keep clear.

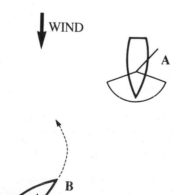

↓WIND

When B is in doubt about
A's tack it is the
responsibility of B to
keep clear.

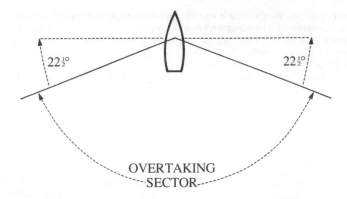

OVERTAKING
SECTOR

Rule 13 *Overtaking*

(a) Notwithstanding anything contained in the Rules of Part B, Sections I and II any vessel overtaking any other shall keep out of the way of the vessel being overtaken.

(b) A vessel shall be deemed to be overtaking when coming up with another vessel from a direction more than 22.5 degrees abaft her beam, that is, in such a position with reference to the vessel she is overtaking, that at night she would be able to see only the sternlight of that vessel but neither of her sidelights.

(c) When a vessel is in any doubt as to whether she is overtaking another, she shall assume that this is the case and act accordingly.

(d) Any subsequent alteration of the bearing between the two vessels shall not make the overtaking vessel a crossing vessel within the meaning of these Rules or relieve her of the duty of keeping clear of the overtaken vessel until she is finally past and clear.

NOTE TO RULE 13 It is important to note the final sentence of this rule, i.e. that the overtaking vessel shall keep clear until she is "past and clear". This applies equally to sailing yachts as well as power-driven craft.

Rule 14 *Head-on Situation*

(a) When two power-driven vessels are meeting on reciprocal or nearly reciprocal courses so as to involve risk of collision each shall alter her course to starboard so that each shall pass on the port side of the other.

(b) Such a situation shall be deemed to exist when a vessel sees the other ahead or nearly ahead and by night she could see the masthead lights of the other in a line or nearly in a line

and/or both sidelights and by day she observes the corresponding aspect of the other vessel.

(c) When a vessel is in any doubt as to whether such a situation exists she shall assume that it does exist and act accordingly.

NOTE TO RULE 14 This very simple rule may cause problems for large vessels on nearly reciprocal courses but from the small vessel's point of view should present no problems as an alteration of course is quickly and easily made.

Rule 15 *Crossing Situation*

When two power-driven vessels are crossing so as to involve risk of collision, the vessel which has the other on her own starboard side shall keep out of the way and shall, if the circumstances of the case admit, avoid crossing ahead of the other vessel.

NOTE TO RULE 15 The normally correct action for A is to alter course to starboard and pass under B's stern.

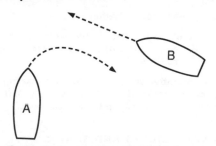

Rule 16 *Action by Give-way Vessel*

Every vessel which is directed to keep out of the way of another vessel shall, so far as possible, take early and substantial action to keep well clear.

Rule 17 *Action by Stand-on Vessel*

(a) (i) Where one of two vessels is to keep out of the way the other shall keep her course and speed.

(ii) The latter vessel may however take action to avoid collision by her manoeuvre alone, as soon as it becomes apparent to her that the vessel required to keep out of the way is not taking appropriate action in compliance with these Rules.

(b) When, from any cause, the vessel required to keep her course and speed finds herself so close that collision cannot be avoided by the action of the give-way vessel alone, she shall take such action as will best aid to avoid collision.

(c) A power-driven vessel which takes action in a crossing situation in accordance with sub-paragraph (a)(ii) of this Rule to avoid collision with another power-driven vessel shall, if the circumstances of the case admit, not alter course to port for a vessel on her own port side.

(d) This Rule does not relieve the give-way vessel of her obligation to keep out of the way.

NOTE TO RULE 17 This is an important rule as it requires the "stand on" vessel to take avoiding action if it appears that the "give way" vessel is not acting in accordance with the rules.

This may pose problems for a small vessel meeting a large ship, particularly at night; the small vessel may well have right of way according to the rules but would be foolish to "stand on" as she may not be visible to the large ship.

The sensible course of action for the small vessel in this situation is to turn completely away from the large ship.

Rule 18 *Responsibilities between Vessels*

Except where Rules 9, 10 and 13 otherwise require:

(a) A power-driven vessel underway shall keep out of the way of:

(i) a vessel not under command;

(ii) a vessel restricted in her ability to manoeuvre;

(iii) a vessel engaged in fishing;

(iv) a sailing vessel.

(b) A sailing vessel underway shall keep out of the way of:

(i) a vessel not under command;

(ii) a vessel restricted in her ability to manoeuvre;

(iii) a vessel engaged in fishing;

(c) A vessel engaged in fishing when underway shall, so far as possible, keep out of the way of:

(i) a vessel not under command;

(ii) a vessel restricted in her ability to manoeuvre.

(d) (i) Any vessel other than a vessel not under command or a vessel restricted in her ability to manoeuvre shall, if the circumstances of the case admit, avoid impeding the safe passage of a vessel constrained by her draught, exhibiting the signals in Rule 28.

(ii) A vessel constrained by her draught shall navigate with particular caution having full regard to her special condition.

(e) A seaplane on the water shall, in general keep well clear of all vessels and avoid impeding their navigation. In circumstances, however, where risk of collision exists, she shall comply with the Rules of this Part.

NOTE TO RULE 18 Basically this rule very sensibly means that the more manoeuvrable vessel shall keep out of the way of the less manoeuvrable one.

Section 2

SECTION III – CONDUCT OF VESSELS IN
RESTRICTED VISIBILITY

Rule 19 *Conduct of Vessels in Restricted Visibility*

(a) This Rule applies to vessels not in sight of
one another when navigating in or near an area
of restricted visibility.

(b) Every vessel shall proceed at a safe speed
adapted to the prevailing circumstances and
conditions of restricted visibility. A power-driven
vessel shall have her engines ready for immediate manoeuvre.

(c) Every vessel shall have due regard to the
prevailing circumstances and conditions of
restricted visibility when complying with the
Rules of Section I of this Part.

(d) A vessel which detects by radar alone the
presence of another vessel shall determine if a
close-quarters situation is developing and/or risk
of collision exists. If so, she shall take avoiding
action in ample time, provided that when such
action consists of an alteration of course, so far
as possible the following shall be avoided:

(i) an alteration of course to port for a
vessel forward of the beam, other than for a
vessel being overtaken;

(ii) an alteration of course towards a vessel
abeam or abaft the beam.

(e) Except where it has been determined that a
risk of collision does not exist, every vessel
which hears apparently forward of her beam
the fog signal of another vessel, or which
cannot avoid a close-quarters situation with
another vessel forward of her beam, shall
reduce her speed to the minimum at which she
can be kept on her course. She shall if necessary
take all her way off and in any event navigate
with extreme caution until danger of collision is
over.

**NOTE TO RULE 19 It is obviously impossible
to lay down a rule where there are so
many imponderables. From the yachtsman's point of view the following points
are vital.**

**(a) Have a radar reflector of proven
efficiency mounted as high as possible.**

**(b) Keep a good lookout, both visual and
aural. If underway with an auxiliary going,
a lookout should be well forward away
from the sound of the engine.**

**(c) Keep clear of shipping lanes and if
possible move into water too shallow for
larger vessels.**

(d) Be ready for immediate action.

**(e) If under sail ensure that sails set and
speed are suitable for complete
manoeuvrability.**

**(f) Remember that Rule 20(c) Navigation
lights in restricted visibility and Rule 35(c)
Sound signals, apply in these situations.**

PART C – LIGHTS AND SHAPES

<u>Note</u> **The rules in this section are clear and
explicit and need no classification.
However, one important rule which is
regrettably not always observed by small
vessels is the use of the correct signals
when anchored (Rule 30). It is not
necessarily obvious to a large vessel
whether a small yacht is anchored if she is
not displaying the correct signals.**

Rule 20 *Application*

(a) Rules in this Part shall be complied with in all
weathers.

(b) The Rules concerning lights shall be complied
with from sunset to sunrise, and during such
times no other lights shall be exhibited, except
such lights as cannot be mistaken for the lights
specified in these Rules or do not impair their
visibility or distinctive character, or interfere
with the keeping of a proper look-out.

(c) The lights prescribed by these Rules shall, if
carried, also be exhibited from sunrise to sunset
in restricted visibility and may be exhibited in all
other circumstances when it is deemed
necessary.

(d) The Rules concerning shapes shall be
complied with by day.

(e) The lights and shapes specified in these Rules
shall comply with the provisions of Annex I to
these Regulations.

Rule 21 *Definitions*

(a) "Masthead light" means a white light placed
over the fore and aft centreline of the vessel
showing an unbroken light over an arc of the
horizon of 225 degrees and so fixed as to show
the light from right ahead to 22.5 degrees abaft
the beam on either side of the vessel.

(b) "Sidelights" means a green light on the starboard side and a red light on the port side each showing an unbroken light over an arc of the horizon of 112.5 degrees and so fixed as to show the light from right ahead to 22.5 degrees abaft the beam on its respective side. In a vessel of less than 20 metres in length the sidelights may be combined in one lantern carried on the fore and aft centreline of the vessel.

(c) "Sternlight" means a white light placed as nearly as practicable at the stern showing an unbroken light over an arc of the horizon of 135 degrees and so fixed as to show the light 67.5 degrees from right aft on each side of the vessel.

(d) "Towing light" means a yellow light having the same characteristics as the "sternlight" defined in paragraph (c) of this Rule.

(e) "All-round light" means a light showing an unbroken light over an arc of the horizon of 360 degrees.

(f) "Flashing light" means a light flashing at regular intervals at a frequency of 120 flashes or more per minute.

Rule 22 *Visibility of Lights*

The lights prescribed in these Rules shall have an intensity as specified in Section 8 of Annex I to these Regulations so as to be visible at the following minimum ranges.

(a) In vessels of 50 metres or more in length:
a masthead light, 6 miles,
a sidelight, 3 miles;
a sternlight, 3 miles;
a towing light, 3 miles;
a white, red, green or yellow all-round light, 3 miles.

(b) In vessels of 12 metres or more in length but less than 50 metres in length:
a masthead light, 5 miles; except that where the length of the vessel is less than 20 metres, 3 miles;
a sidelight, 2 miles;
a sternlight, 2 miles;
a towing light, 2 miles;
a white, red, green or yellow all-round light, 2 miles.

(c) In vessels of less than 12 metres in length:
a masthead light, 2 miles;
a sidelight, 1 mile
a sternlight, 2 miles;
a towing light, 2 miles;
a white, red, green or yellow all-round light, 2 miles.

(d) In inconspicuous, partly submerged vessels or objects being towed:
a white all-round light, 3 miles.

Rule 23 *Power-driven Vessels underway*

(a) A power-driven vessel underway shall exhibit:

(i) a masthead light forward;

(ii) a second masthead light abaft of and higher than the forward one; except that a vessel of less than 50 metres in length shall not be obliged to exhibit such light but may do so;

(iii) sidelights;

(iv) a sternlight.

(b) An air-cushion vessel when operating in the non-displacement mode shall, in addition to the lights prescribed in paragraph (a) of this Rule, exhibit an all-round flashing yellow light.

(c) (i) A power-driven vessel of less than 12 metres in length may, in lieu of the lights prescribed in paragraph (a) of this Rule, exhibit an all-round white light and sidelights;

(ii) a power-driven vessel of less than 7 metres in length whose maximum speed does not exceed 7 knots may in lieu of the lights prescribed in paragraph (a) of this Rule exhibit an all-round white light and shall if practicable, also exhibit sidelights;

(iii) the masthead light or all-round white light on a power-driven vessel of less than 12 metres in length may be displaced from the fore and aft centreline of the vessel if centreline fitting is not practicable, provided that the sidelights are combined in one lantern which shall be carried on the fore and aft centreline of the vessel or located as nearly as practicable in the same fore and aft line as the masthead light or the all-round white light.

Rule 24 *Towing and Pushing*

(a) A power-driven vessel when towing shall exhibit:

(i) instead of the light prescribed in Rule 23 (a)(i) or (a)(ii), two masthead lights in a vertical line. When the length of the tow, measuring from the stern of the towing vessel to the after end of the tow exceeds 200 metres, three such lights in a vertical line;

(ii) sidelights;

(iii) a sternlight;

(iv) a towing light in a vertical line above the sternlight;

(v) when the length of the tow exceeds 200 metres, a diamond shape where it can best be seen.

(b) when a pushing vessel and a vessel being pushed ahead are rigidly connected in a composite unit they shall be regarded as a power-driven vessel and exhibit the lights prescribed in Rule 23.

(c) A power-driven vessel when pushing ahead or towing alongside, except in the case of a composite unit, shall exhibit:

(i) instead of the light prescribed in Rule 23(a)(i) or (a)(ii), two masthead lights in a vertical line;

(ii) sidelights;

(iii) a sternlight.

(d) A power-driven vessel to which paragraphs (a) or (c) of this Rule apply shall also comply with Rule 23(a)(ii).

(e) A vessel or object being towed, other than those mentioned in paragraph (g) of this Rule, shall exhibit:

(i) sidelights;

(ii) a sternlight;

(iii) when the length of the tow exceeds 200 metres, a diamond shape where it can best be seen.

(f) Provided that any number of vessels being towed alongside or pushed in a group shall be lighted as one vessel:

(i) a vessel being pushed ahead, not being part of a composite unit, shall exhibit at the forward end, sidelights;

(ii) a vessel being towed alongside shall exhibit a sternlight and at the forward end, sidelights.

(g) An inconspicuous, partly submerged vessel or object, or combination of such vessels or objects being towed, shall exhibit:

(i) if it is less than 25 metres in breadth, one all-round white light at or near the forward end and one at or near the after end except

that dracones need not exhibit a light at or near the forward end;

(ii) if it is 25 metres or more in breadth, two additional all-round white lights at or near the extremities of its breadth;

(iii) if it exceeds 100 metres in length, additional all-round white lights between the lights prescribed in sub-paragraphs (i) and (ii) so that the distance between the lights shall not exceed 100 metres;

(iv) a diamond shape near the aftermost extremity of the last vessel or object being towed and if the length of the tow exceeds 200 metres an additional diamond shape where it can best be seen and located as far forward as is practicable.

(h) Where from any sufficient cause it is impracticable for a vessel or object being towed to exhibit the lights or shapes prescribed in paragraph (e) or (g) of this Rule, all possible measures shall be taken to light the vessel or object towed or at least to indicate the presence of such vessel or object.

(i) Where from any sufficient cause it is impracticable for a vessel not normally engaged in towing operations to display the lights prescribed in paragraph (a) or (c) of this Rule, such vessel shall not be required to exhibit those lights when engaged in towing another vessel in distress or otherwise in need of assistance. All possible measures shall be taken to indicate the nature of the relationship between the towing vessel and the vessel being towed as authorised by Rule 36, in particular by illuminating the towline.

Rule 25 *Sailing Vessels underway and Vessels under Oars*

(a) A sailing vessel underway shall exhibit:

(i) sidelights;

(ii) a sternlight.

(b) In a sailing vessel of less than 20 metres in length the lights prescribed in paragraph (a) of this Rule may be combined in one lantern carried at or near the top of the mast where it can best be seen.

(c) A sailing vessel underway may, in addition to the lights prescribed in paragraph (a) of this Rule, exhibit at or near the top of the mast, where they can best be seen, two all round lights in a vertical line, the upper being red and the lower green, but these lights shall not be exhibited in conjunction with the combined lantern permitted by paragraph (b) of this Rule.

(d) (i) A sailing vessel of less than 7 metres in length shall, if practicable, exhibit the lights prescribed in paragraph (a) or (b) of this Rule, but if she does not, she shall have ready at hand an electric torch or lighted lantern showing a white light which shall be exhibited in sufficient time to prevent collision.

(ii) A vessel under oars may exhibit the lights prescribed in this Rule for sailing vessels, but if she does not, she shall have ready at hand an electric torch or lighted lantern showing a white light which shall be exhibited in sufficient time to prevent collision.

(e) A vessel proceeding under sail when also being propelled by machinery shall exhibit forward where it can best be seen a conical shape, apex downwards.

Rule 26 *Fishing Vessels*

(a) A vessel engaged in fishing, whether underway or at anchor, shall exhibit only the lights and shapes prescribed in this Rule.

(b) A vessel when engaged in trawling, by which is meant the dragging through the water of a dredge net or other apparatus used as a fishing appliance, shall exhibit:

(i) two all-round lights in a vertical line, the upper being green and the lower white, or a shape consisting of two cones with their apexes together in a vertical line one above the other; a vessel of less than 20 metres in length may instead of this shape exhibit a basket;

(ii) a masthead light abaft of and higher than the all-round green light; a vessel of less than 50 metres in length shall not be obliged to exhibit such a light but may do so;

(iii) when making way through the water, in addition to the lights prescribed in this paragraph, sidelights and a sternlight.

(c) A vessel engaged in fishing, other than trawling, shall exhibit:

(i) two all-round lights in a vertical line, the upper being red and the lower white, or a shape consisting of two cones with their apexes together in a vertical line one above the other; a vessel of less than 20 metres in length may instead of this shape exhibit a basket;

(ii) when there is outlying gear extending more than 150 metres horizontally from the vessel; an all-round white light or a cone apex upwards in the direction of the gear;

(iii) when making way through the water, in addition to the lights prescribed in this paragraph, side lights and a sternlight.

(d) A vessel engaged in fishing in close proximity to other vessels engaged in fishing may exhibit the additional signals described in Annex II to these Regulations.

(e) A vessel when not engaged in fishing shall not exhibit the lights or shapes prescribed in this Rule, but only those prescribed for a vessel of her length.

Rule 27 *Vessels not under command or restricted in their ability to manoeuvre*

(a) A vessel not under command shall exhibit:

(i) two all-round red lights in a vertical line where they can best be seen:

(ii) two balls or similar shapes in a vertical line where they can best be seen;

(iii) when making way through the water, in addition to the lights prescribed in this paragraph, sidelights and a sternlight.

(b) A vessel restricted in her ability to man-oeuvre, except a vessel engaged in mine clear-ance operations, shall exhibit:

(i) three all-round lights in a vertical line where they can best be seen. The highest and lowest of these lights shall be red and the middle light shall be white;

(ii) three shapes in a vertical line where they can best be seen . The highest and lowest of these shapes shall be balls and the middle one a diamond;

(iii) when making way through the water, a masthead light or lights, sidelights and a sternlight, in addition to the lights prescribed in sub-paragraph (i);

(iv) when at anchor, in addition to the lights or shapes prescribed in sub-paragraphs (i) and (ii), the light, lights or shape prescribed in Rule 30.

(c) A power-driven vessel engaged in a towing operation such as severely restricts the towing vessel and her tow in their ability to deviate from their course shall, in addition to the lights or shapes prescribed in Rule 24(a), exhibit the lights or shapes prescribed in sub-paragraphs (b)(i) and (ii) of this Rule.

(d) A vessel engaged in dredging or underwater operations, when restricted in her ability to manoeuvre, shall exhibit the lights and shapes prescribed in sub-paragraphs (b)(i), (ii) and (iii) of this Rule and shall in addition, when an obstruction exists, exhibit:

(i) two all-round red lights or two balls in a vertical line to indicate the side on which the obstruction exists;

(ii) two all-round green lights or two diamonds in a vertical line to indicate the side on which another vessel may pass;

(iii) when at anchor, the lights or shapes prescribed in this paragraph instead of the lights or shape prescribed in Rule 30.

(e) Whenever the size of a vessel engaged in diving operations makes it impracticable to exhibit all lights and shapes prescribed in paragraph (d) of this Rule, the following shall be exhibited:

(i) three all-round lights in a vertical line where they can best be seen. The highest and lowest of these lights shall be red and the middle light shall be white;

(ii) a rigid replica of the International Code flag 'A' not less than 1 metre in height. Measures shall be taken to ensure its all-round visibility.

(f) A vessel engaged in mine clearance operations shall, in addition to the lights prescribed for a power-driven vessel in Rule 23 or to the lights or shape prescribed for a vessel at anchor in Rule 30 as appropriate, exhibit three all-round green lights or three balls. One of these lights or shapes shall be exhibited near the foremast head and one at each end of the fore yard. These lights or shapes indicate that it is dangerous for another vessel to approach within 1,000 metres of the mine clearance vessel.

(g) Vessels of less than 12 metres in length, except those engaged in diving operations, shall not be required to exhibit the lights and shapes prescribed in this Rule.

(h) The signals prescribed in this Rule are not signals of vessels in distress and requiring assistance. Such signals are contained in Annex IV to these Regulations.

Rule 28 *Vessels constrained by their draught*

A vessel constrained by her draught may, in addition to the lights prescribed for power-

driven vessels in Rule 23, exhibit where they can best be seen three all-round red lights in a vertical line, or a cylinder.

Rule 29 *Pilot Vessels*

(a) A vessel engaged on pilotage duty shall exhibit:

(i) at or near the masthead, two all-round lights in a vertical line, the upper being white and the lower red;

(ii) when underway, in addition, sidelights and a sternlight;

(iii) when at anchor, in addition to the lights prescribed in sub-paragraph (i), the light, lights or shape prescribed in Rule 30 for vessels at anchor.

(b) A pilot vessel when not engaged on pilotage duty shall exhibit the lights or shapes prescribed for a similar vessel of her length.

Rule 30 *Anchored Vessels and Vessels aground*

(a) A vessel at anchor shall exhibit where it can best be seen:

(i) in the fore part, an all-round white light or one ball;

(ii) at or near the stern and at a lower level than the light prescribed in sub-paragraph (i), an all-round white light.

(b) A vessel of less than 50 metres in length may exhibit an all-round white light where it can best be seen instead of the lights prescribed in paragraph (a) of this Rule.

(c) A vessel at anchor may, and a vessel of 100 metres and more in length shall, also use the available working or equivalent lights to illuminate her decks.

(d) A vessel aground shall exhibit the lights prescribed in paragraph (a) or (b) of this Rule and in addition, where they can best be seen:

(i) two all-round red lights in a vertical line;

(ii) three balls in a vertical line.

(e) A vessel of less than 7 metres in length, when at anchor, not in or near a narrow channel, fairway or anchorage, or where other vessels normally navigate, shall not be required to exhibit the lights or shape prescribed in paragraphs (a) and (b) of this Rule.

(f) A vessel of less than 12 metres in length, when aground, shall not be required to exhibit the lights or shapes prescribed in sub-paragraphs (d)(i) and (ii) of this Rule.

Rule 31 *Seaplanes*

Where it is impracticable for a seaplane to exhibit lights and shapes of the characteristics or in the positions prescribed in the Rules of this Part she shall exhibit lights and shapes as closely similar in characteristics and position as is possible.

PART D – SOUND AND LIGHT SIGNALS

Note **The rules are clear and explicit and, from the yachtsman's point of view the most important aspects are, firstly to have the most effective fog signal that can be used on board and secondly to carry a supply of white flares or a Very pistol with white cartridges. At night or in fog it is important and reassuring to make one's presence known in a close quarters situation.**

A point to note in sound Signals is Rule 34 – 3 short blasts – "I am operating astern propulsion". In the case of a large vessel she may carry her way for an appreciable time after putting the engines astern. This can appear confusing and should not be overlooked.

Rule 32 *Definitions*

(a) The word "whistle" means any sound signalling appliance capable of producing the prescribed blasts and which complies with the specifications in Annex III to these Regulations.

(b) The term "short blast" means a blast of about one secons's durationn.

(c) The term "prolonged blast" means a blast of from four to six seconds duration.

Rule 33 *Equipment for Sound Signals*

(a) A vessel of 12 metres or more in length shall be provided with a whistle and a bell and a vessel of 100 metres or more in length shall, in addition, be provided with a gong, the tone and sound of which cannot be confused with that of the bell. The whistle, bell and gong shall comply with the specifications in Annex III to these Regulations. The bell or gong or both may be replaced by other equipment having the same respective sound characteristics, provided that manual sounding of the prescribed signals shall always be possible.

(b) a vessel of less than 12 metres in length shall not be obliged to carry the sound signalling appliances prescribed in paragraph (a) of this

Rule but if she does not, she shall be provided with some other means of making an efficient sound signal.

Rule 34 *Manoeuvring and Warning Signals*

(a) when vessels are in sight of one another, a power-driven vessel underway, when manoeuvring as authorised or required by these Rules, shall indicate that manoeuvre by the following signals on her whistle:

> one short blast to mean "I am altering my course to starboard"
>
> two short blasts to mean "I am altering my course to port";
>
> three short blasts to mean "I am operating astern propulsion".

(b) Any vessel may supplement the whistle signals prescribed in paragraph (a) of this Rule by light signals, repeated as appropriate, whilst the manoeuvre is being carried out:

> (i) these light signals shall have the following significance:
>
>> One flash to mean "I am altering my course to starboard"
>>
>> two flashes to mean "I am altering my course to port"
>>
>> three flashes to mean "I am operating astern propulsion";
>
> (ii) the duration of each flash shall be about one second, the interval between flashes shall be about one second, and the interval between successive signals shall be not less than ten seconds;
>
> (iii) the light used for this signal shall if fitted, be an all-round white light, visible at a minimum range of 5 miles and shall comply with the provisions of Annex I to these Regulations.

(c) When in sight of one another in a narrow channel or fairway:

> (i) a vessel intending to overtake another shall in compliance with Rule 9(e)(i) indicate her intention by the following signals on her whistle:
>
>> two prolonged blasts followed by one short blast to mean "I intend to overtake you on your starboard side";
>>
>> two prolonged blasts followed by two short blasts to mean "I intend to overtake you on your port side";

(ii) the vessel about to be overtaken when acting in accordance with Rule 9(e)(i) shall indicate her agreement by the following signal on her whistle:

> One prolonged, one short, one prolonged and one short blast, in that order.

(d) When vessels in sight of one another are approaching each other and from any cause either vessel fails to understand the intentions or actions of the other, or is in doubt whether sufficient action is being taken by the other to avoid collision, the vessel in doubt shall immediately indicate such doubt by giving at least five short and rapid blasts on the whistle. Such signal may be supplemented by a light signal of at least five short and rapid flashes.

(e) A vessel nearing a bend or an area of a channel or fairway where other vessels may be obscured by an intervening obstruction shall sound one prolonged blast. Such signal shall be answered with a prolonged blast by any approaching vessel that may be within hearing around the bend or behind the intervening obstruction.

(f) If whistles are fitted on a vessel at a distance apart of more than 100 metres, one whistle only shall be used for giving manoeuvring and warning signals.

Rule 35 *Sound signals in restricted visibility*

In or near an area of restricted visibility, whether by day or night, the signals prescribed in this Rule shall be used as follows.

(a) A power-driven vessel making way through the water shall sound at intervals of not more than 2 minutes one prolonged blast.

(b) A power-driven vessel underway but stopped and making no way through the water shall sound at intervals of not more than 2 minutes two prolonged blasts in succession with an interval of about 2 seconds between them.

(c) A vessel not under command, a vessel restricted in her ability to manoeuvre, a vessel constrained by her draught, a sailing vessel, a vessel engaged in fishing and a vessel engaged in towing or pushing another vessel shall, instead of the signals prescribed in paragraphs (a) or (b) of this Rule, sound at intervals of not more than 2 minutes three blasts in succession, namely one prolonged followed by two short blasts.

(d) A vessel engaged in fishing, when at anchor, and a vessel restricted in her ability to manoeuvre when carrying out her work at anchor, shall instead of the signals prescribed in paragraph (g) of this Rule sound the signal prescribed in paragraph (c) of this Rule.

(e) A vessel towed or if more than one vessel is towed the last vessel of the tow, if manned, shall at intervals of not more than 2 minutes sound four blasts in succession, namely one prolonged followed by three short blasts. When practicable, this signal shall be made immediately after the signal made by the towing vessel.

(f) When a pushing vessel and a vessel being pushed ahead are rigidly connected in a composite unit they shall be regarded as a power-driven vessel and shall give the signals prescribed in paragraphs (a) or (b) of this Rule.

(g) A vessel at anchor shall at intervals of not more than one minute ring the bell rapidly for about five seconds. In a vessel of 100 metres or more in length the bell shall be sounded in the forepart of the vessel and immediately after the ringing of the bell the gong shall be sounded rapidly for about five seconds in the afterpart of the vessel. A vessel at anchor may in addition sound three blasts in succession, namely one short, one prolonged and one short blast to give warning of her position and of the possibility of collision to an approaching vessel.

(h) A vessel aground shall give the bell signal and if required the gong signal prescribed in paragraph (g) of this Rule and shall, in addition, give three separate and distinct strokes on the bell immediately before and after the rapid ringing of the bell. A vessel aground may in addition sound an appropriate whistle signal.

(i) A vessel of less than 12 metres in length shall not be obliged to give the above mentioned signals but, if she does not, shall make some other efficient sound signal at intervals of not more than 2 minutes.

(j) A pilot vessel when engaged on pilotage duty may in addition to the signals prescribed in paragraphs (a), (b) or (g) of this Rule sound an identity signal consisting of four short blasts.

Rule 36 *Signals to attract attention*

If necessary to attract the attention of another vessel any vessel may make light or sound signals that cannot be mistaken for any signal authorised elsewhere in these Rules, or may direct the beam of her searchlight in the direction of the danger, in such a way as not to embarrass any vessel. Any light to attract the attention of another vessel shall be such that it cannot be mistaken for any aid to navigation. For the purpose of this Rule the use of high intensity intermittent or revolving lights, such as strobe lights, shall be avoided.

Rule 37 *Distress Signals*

When a vessel is in distress and requires assistance she shall use or exhibit the signals described in Annex IV to these Regulations.

PART E – EXEMPTIONS

Rule 38 *Exemptions.*

Any vessel (or class of vessels) provided that she complies with the requirements of the International Regulations for Preventing Collisions at Sea, 1960, the keel of which is laid or which is at a corresponding stage of construction before the entry into force of these Regulations may be exempted from compliance therewith as follows:

(a) The installation of lights with ranges prescribed in Rule 22, until four years after the date of entry into force of these Regulations.

(b) The installation of lights with colour specifications as prescribed in Section 7 of Annex I to these Regulations, until four years after the date of entry into force of these Regulations.

(c) The repositioning of lights as a result of conversion from Imperial to metric units and rounding off measurement figures, permanent exemption.

(d) (i) The repositioning of masthead lights on vessels of less than 150 metres in length, resulting from the prescriptions of Section 3(a) of Annex I to these Regulations, permanent exemption.

(ii) The repositioning of masthead lights on vessels of 150 metres or more in length, resulting from the prescriptions of Section 3(a) of Annex I to these Regulations, until nine years after the date of entry into force of these Regulations.

(e) The repositioning of masthead lights resulting from the prescriptions of Section 2(b) of Annex I to these Regulations, until nine years after the date of entry into force of these Regulations.

(f) The repositioning of sidelights resulting from the prescriptions of Sections 2(g) and 3(b) of Annex I to these Regulations, until nine years after the date of entry into force of these Regulations.

(g) The requirements for sound signal appliances prescribed in Annex III to these Regulations, until nine years after the date of entry into force of these Regulations.

(h) The repositioning of all-round lights resulting from the prescription of Section 9(b) of Annex I to these Regulations, permanent exemption.

ANNEX I

POSITIONING AND TECHNICAL DETAILS OF LIGHTS AND SHAPES

1. Definition

The term"height above the hull" means height above the uppermost continuous deck. This height shall be measured from the position vertically beneath the location of the light.

2. Vertical positioning and spacing of lights

(a) On a power-driven vessel of 20 metres or more in length the masthead lights shall be placed as follows:

(i) the forward masthead light, or if only one masthead light is carried, then that light, at a height above the hull of not less than 6 metres, and, if the breadth of the vessel exceeds 6 metres, then at a height above the hull not less than such breadth, so however that the light need not be placed at a greater height above the hull than 12 metres;

(ii) when two masthead lights are carried the after one shall be at least 4.5 metres vertically higher than the forward one..

(b) The vertical separation of masthead lights of power-driven vessels shall be such that in all normal conditions of trim the after light will be seen over and separate from the forward light at a distance of 1,000 metres from the stem when viewed from sea level.

(c) The masthead light of a power-driven vessel of 12 metres but less than 20 metres in length shall be placed at a height above the gunwale of not less than 2.5 metres.

(d) A power-driven vessel of less than 12 metres in length may carry the uppermost light at a height of less than 2.5 metres above the gunwale. When however a masthead light is carried in addition to sidelights and a sternlight or the all-round light prescribed in Rule 23(c)(i) is carried in addition to sidelights, then such masthead light or all-round light shall be carried at least one metre higher than the sidelights.

(e) One of the two or three masthead lights prescribed for a power-driven vessel when engaged in towing or pushing another vessel shall be placed in the same position as either the forward masthead light or the after masthead light; provided that, if carried on the aftermast, the lowest after masthead light shall be at least 4.5 metres vertically higher than the forward masthead light.

(f) (i) The masthead light or lights prescribed in Rule 23(a) shall be so placed as to be above and clear of all other lights and obstructions except as described in sub-paragraph(ii).

(ii) When it is impracticable to carry the all-round lights prescribed by Rule 27(b)(i) or Rule 28 below the masthead lights, they may be carried above the after masthead light(s), or vertically in between the forward masthead light(s) and after masthead light(s) provided that in the latter case the require-ment of Section 3(c) of this Annex shall be complied with.

(g) The sidelights of a power-driven vessel shall be placed at a height above the hull not greater than three quarters of that of the forward masthead light. They shall not be so low as to be interfered with by deck lights.

(h) The sidelights, if in a combined lantern and carried on a power-driven vessel of less than 20 metres in length, shall be placed not less than one metre below the masthead light.

(i) When the Rules prescribe two or three lights to be carried in a vertical line, they shall be spaced as follows:

(i) on a vessel of 20 metres in length or more such lights shall be spaced not less than 2 metres apart, and the lowest of these lights shall, except where a towing light is required, be placed at a height of not less than 4 metres above the hull;

(ii) on a vessel of less than 20 metres in length such lights shall be spaced not less than 1 metre apart and the lowest of these lights shall, except where a towing light is required, be placed at a height of not less than 2 metres above the gunwale;

(iii) when three lights are carried they shall be equally spaced.

(j) The lower of the two all-round lights prescribed for a vessel when engaged in fishing shall be at a height above the sidelights not less than twice the distance between the two vertical lights.

(k) The forward anchor light prescribed in Rule 30(a)(i), when two are carried, shall not be less than 4.5 metres above the after one. On a vessel of 50 metres or more in length this forward anchor light shall be placed at a height of not less than 6 metres above the hull.

3. Horizontal position and spacing of lights

(a) When two masthead lights are prescribed for a power-driven vessel, the horizontal distance between them shall not be less than one half of the length of the vessel but need not be more than 100 metres. The forward light shall be placed not more than one quarter of the length of the wessel from the stern.

(b) On a power-driven vessel of 20 metres or more in length the sidelights shall not be placed in front of the forward masthead lights. They shall be placed at or near the side of the vessel.

(c) When the lights prescribed in Rule 27(b)(i) or Rule 28 are placed vertically between the forward masthead light(s) and the after masthead light(s) these all-round lights shall be placed at a horizontal distance of not less than 2 metres from the fore and aft centreline of the vessel in the athwartship direction.

4. Details of location of direction – indicating lights for fishing vessels, dredgers and vessels engaged in underwater operations

(a) The light indicating the direction of the outlying gear from a vessel engaged in fishing as prescribed in Rule 26(c)(ii) shall be placed at a horizontal distance of not less than 2 metres and not more than 6 metres away from the two all-round red and white lights. This light shall be placed not higher than the all-round white light prescribed in Rule 26(c)(i) and not lower than the sidelights.

(b) The lights and shapes on a vessel engaged in dredging or underwater operations to indicate the obstructed side and/or the side on which it is safe to pass, as prescribed in Rule 27(d)(i) and (ii), shall be placed at the maximum practical horizontal distance, but in no case less than 2 metres, from the lights or shapes prescribed in Rule 27(b)(i) and (ii). In no case shall the upper of these lights or shapes be at a greater height than the lower of the three lights or shapes prescribed in Rule 27(b)(i) and (ii).

5. Screens for sidelights

The sidelights of vessels of 20 metres or more in length shall be fitted with inboard screens painted matt black, and meeting the requirements of Section 9 of this Annex. On vessels of less than 20 metres in length the sidelights, if necessary to meet the requirements of Section 9 of this Annex, shall be fitted with inboard matt black screens. With a combined lantern, using a single vertical filament and a very narrow division between the green and red sections, external screens need not be fitted.

6. Shapes

(a) Shapes shall be black and of the following sizes:

(i) a ball shall have a diameter of not less than 0.6 metre;

(ii) a cone shall have a base diameter of not less than 0.6 metre and a height equal to its diameter;

(iii) a cylinder shall have a diameter of at least 0.6 metre and a height of twice its diameter;

(iv) a diamond shape shall consist of two cones as defined in (ii) above having a common base.

(b) The vertical distance between shapes shall be at least 1.5 metres.

(c) In a vessel of less than 20 metres in length shapes of lesser dimensions but commensurate with the size of the vessel may be used and the distance apart may be correspondingly reduced.

7. Colour specification of lights

The chromaticity of all navigation lights shall conform to the following standards, which lie within the boundaries of the area of the diagram specified for each colour by the International Commission on Illumination (CIE).

The boundaries of the area for each colour are given by indicating the corner co-ordinates, which are shown at foot of page.

8. Intensity of lights

(a) The minimum luminous intensity of lights shall be calculated by using the formula:

$$1 = 3.43 \times 10^6 \times T \times D^2 \times K^{-D}$$

Where I is luminous intensity in candelas under service conditions,

T is threshold factor 2×10^{-7} lux,

D is range of visibility (luminous range) of the light in nautical miles,

K is atmospheric transmissivity. For prescribed lights the value of K shall be 0.8, corresponding to a meteorological visibility of approximately 13 nautical miles.

(b) A selection of figures derived from the formula is given in the table overleaf

(i)	White						
	x	0.525	0.525	0.452	0.310	0.310	0.443
	y	0.382	0.440	0.440	0.348	0.283	0.382
(ii)	Green						
	x	0.028	0.009	0.300	0.203		
	y	0.385	0.723	0.511	0.356		
(iii)	Red						
	x	0.680	0.660	0.735	0.721		
	y	0.320	0.320	0.265	0.259		
(iv)	Yellow						
	x	0.612	0.618	0.575	0.575		
	y	0.382	0.382	0.425	0.406		

Range of Visibility (luminous range) of light in nautical Miles D	Luminous Intensity of light in candelas for K = 0.8 I
1	0.9
2	4.3
3	12
4	27
5	52
6	94

Note: The maximum luminous intesity of navigation light should be limited to avoid undue glare. This shall not be achieved by a variable control of the luminous intensity.

9. Horizontal sectors

(a) (i) in the forward direction, sidelights as fitted on the vessel shall show the minimum required intensities. The intensities shall decrease to reach practical cut off between 1 degree and 3 degrees outside the prescribed sectors.

(ii) for sternlights and masthead lights and at 22.5 degrees abaft the beam for sidelights, the minimum required intensities shall be maintained over the arc of the horizon up to 5 degrees within the limits of the sectors prescribed in Rule 21. From 5 degrees within the prescribed sectors the intensity may decrease by 50 per cent up to the prescribed limits; it shall decrease steadily to reach practical cut-off at not more than 5 degrees outside the prescribed sectors.

(b) All-round lights shall be so located as not to be obscured by masts, topmasts or structures within angular sectors of more than 6 degrees, except anchor lights prescribed in Rule 30, which need not be placed at an impracticable height above the hull.

10. Vertical sectors

(a) The vertical sectors of electric lights as fitted, with the exception of lights on sailing vessels underway shall ensure that:

(i) at least the required minimum intensity is maintained at all angles from 5 degrees above to 5 degrees below the horizontal;

(ii) at least 60 per cent of the required minimum intensity is maintained from 7.5 degrees above to 7.5 degrees below the horizontal.

(b) In the case of sailing vessels underway the vertical sectors of electric lights as fitted shall ensure that:

(i) at least the required minimum intensity is maintained at all angles from 5 degrees above to 5 degrees below the horizontal;

(ii) at least 50 per cent of the required minimum intensity is maintained from 25 degrees above to 25 degrees below the horizontal.

(c) In the case of lights other than electric these specifications shall be met as closely as possible.

11. Intensity of non-electric lights

Non-electric lights shall so far as practicable comply with the minimum intensities, as specified in the Table given in Section 8 of this Annex.

12. Manoeuvring light

Notwithstanding the provisions of paragraph 2(f) of this Annex the manoeuvring light described in Rule 34(b) shall be placed in the same fore and aft vertical plane as the masthead light or lights and, where practicable, at a minimum height of 2 metres vertically above the forward masthead light, provided that it shall be carried not less than 2 metres vertically above or below the after masthead light. On a vessel where only one masthead light is carried the manoeuvring light, if fitted, shall be carried where it can best be seen, not less than 2 metres vertically apart from the masthead light.

13. Approval

The construction of lights and shapes and the installation of lights on board the vessel shall be to the satisfaction of the appropriate authority of the State whose flag the vessel is entitled to fly.

ANNEX II

ADDITIONAL SIGNALS FOR FISHING VESSELS FISHING IN CLOSE PROXIMITY

1. General

The lights mentioned herein shall, if exhibited in pursuance of Rule 26(d), be placed where they can best be seen. They shall be at least 0.9 metre apart but at a lower level than lights prescribed in Rule 26(b)(i) and (c)(i). The lights shall be visible all round the horizon at a distance of at least 1 mile but at a lesser distance than the lights prescribed by these Rules for fishing vessels.

2. Signals for trawlers

(a) Vessels when engaged in trawling, whether using demersal or pelagic gear, may exhibit:

(i) when shooting their nets: two white lights in a vertical line;

(ii) when hauling their nets: one white light over one red light in a vertical line;

(iii) when the net has come fast upon an obstruction: two red lights in a vertical line.

(b) Each vessel engaged in pair trawling may exhibit:

(i) by night, a searchlight directed forward and in the direction of the other vessel of the pair;

(ii) when shooting or hauling their nets or when their nets have come fast upon an obstruction, the lights prescribed in 2(a) above.

3. Signals for purse seiners

Vessels engaged in fishing with purse seine gear may exhibit two yellow lights in a vertical line. These lights shall flash alternatively every second and with equal light and occultation duration. These lights may be exhibited only when the vessel is hampered by its fishing gear.

ANNEX III

TECHNICAL DETAILS OF SOUND SIGNAL APPLIANCES

1. Whistles

(a) *Frequencies and range of audibility*

The fundamental frequency of the signal shall lie within the range 70-700 Hz.

The range of audibility of the signal from a whistle shall be determined by those frequencies, which may include the fundamental and/or one or more higher frequencies, which lie within the range 180-700 Hz (±1 per cent) and which provide the sound pressure levels specified in paragraph 1(c) below.

(b) *Limits of fundamental frequencies*

To ensure a wide variety of whistle characteristics, the fundamental frequency of a whistle shall be between the following limits:

(i) 70-200 Hz, for a vessel 200 metres or more in length;

(ii) 130-350 Hz, for a vessel 75 metres but less than 200 metres in length;

(iii) 250-700 Hz, for a vessel less than 75 metres in length.

(c) *Sound signal intensity and range of audibility*

A whistle fitted in a vessel shall provide, in the direction of maximum intensity of the whistle and at a distance of 1 metre from it, a sound pressure level in at least one 1/3 octave band within the range of frequencies 180-700 Hz (±1 per cent) of not less than the appropriate figure given in the table overleaf.

The range of audibility in the table is for information and is approximately the range at which a whistle may be heard on its forward axis with 90 per cent probability in conditions of still air on board a vessel having average back-ground noise level at the listening posts (taken to be 68 dB in the octave band centred

Length of vessel in metres	⅓ octave band level at 1 metre in dB referred to 2×10^{-5} N/m^2	Audibility range in nautical miles
200 or more	143	2
75 but less than 200	138	1.5
20 but less than 75	130	1
Less than 20	120	0.5

on 250 Hz and 63 dB in the octave band centred on 500 Hz).

In practice the range at which a whistle may be heard is extremely variable and depends critically on weather conditions; the values given can be regarded as typical but under conditions of strong wind or high ambient noise level at the listening post the range may be reduced.

(d) Directional properties

The sound pressure level of a directional whistle shall be not more than 4 dB below the prescribed sound pressure level on the axis at any direction in the horizontal plane within ± 45 degrees of the axis. The sound pressure level at any other direction in the horizontal plane shall be not more than 10 dB below the prescribed sound pressure level on the axis, so that the range in any direction will be at least half the range on the forward axis. The sound pressure level shall be measured in that 1/3 octave band which determines the audibility range.

(e) Positioning of whistles

When a directional whistle is to be used as the only whistle on a vessel, it shall be installed with its maximum intensity directed straight ahead. A whistle shall be placed as high as practicable on a vessel, in order to reduce interception of the emitted sound by obstructions and also to minimise hearing damage risk to personnel. The sound pressure level of the vessel's own signal at listening posts shall not exceed 110 dB (A) and so far as practicable should not exceed 100 dB(A).

(f) Fitting of more than one whistle

If whistles are fitted at a distance apart of more than 100 metres, it shall be so arranged that they are not sounded simultaneously.

(g) Combined whistle systems

If due to the presence of obstructions the sound field of a single whistle or of one of the whistles referred to in paragraph 1(f) above is likely to have a zone of greatly reduced signal level, it is recommended that a combined whistle system be fitted so as to overcome this reduction. For the purposes of the Rules a combined whistle system is to be regarded as a single whistle. The whistles of a combined system shall be located at a distance apart of not more than 100 metres and arranged to be sounded simultaneously. The frequency of any one whistle shall differ from those of the others by at least 10 Hz.

2. Bell or gong

(a) Intensity of signal

A bell or gong, or other device having similar sound characteristics shall produce a sound pressure level of not less than 110 dB at a distance of 1 metre from it.

(b) Construction

Bells and gongs shall be made of corrosion-resistant material and designed to give a clear tone. The diameter of the mouth of the bell shall be not less than 300 mm for vessels of 20 metres or more in length, and shall be not less than 200 mm for vessels of 12 metres or more but of less than 20 metres in length. Where practicable, a power-driven bell striker is recommended to ensure constant force but manual operation shall be possible. The mass of the striker shall be not less than 3 per cent of the mass of the bell.

3. Approval

The construction of sound signal appliances, their performance and their installation on board the vessel shall be to the satisfaction of the appropriate authority of the State whose flag the vessel is entitled to fly.

ANNEX IV

DISTRESS SIGNALS

1. The following signals, used or exhibited either together or separately, indicate distress and need of assistance:

(a) a gun or other explosive signal fired at intervals of about a minute;

(b) continuous sounding with any fog-signalling apparatus;

(c) rockets or shells, throwing red stars fired one at a time at short intervals;

(d) a signal made by radiotelegraphy or by other signalling method consisting of the group • • • — — — • • • (SOS) in the Morse Code;

(e) a signal sent by radiotelephony consisting of the spoken word "Mayday";

(f) the International Code Signal of distress indicated by N.C.;

(g) a signal consisting of a square flag having above or below it a ball or anything resembling a ball;

(h) flames on the vessel (as from a burning tar barrel, oil barrel, etc.);

(i) a rocket parachute flare or a hand flare showing a red light;

(j) a smoke signal giving off orange-coloured smoke;

(k) slowly and repeatedly raising and lowering arms outstretched to each side;

(l) the radiotelegraph alarm signal;

(m) the radiotelephone alarm signal;

(n) signals transmitted by emergency position-indicating radio beacons;

(o) approved signals transmitted by radio communication systems.

2. The use or exhibition of any of the foregoing signals except for the purpose of indicating distress and need of assistance and the use of other signals which may be confused with any of the above signals is prohibited.

3. Attention is drawn to the relevant sections of the International Code of Signals, the Merchant Ship Search and Rescue Manual and the following signals:

(a) a piece of orange coloured canvas with either a black square and circle or other appropriate symbol (for identification from the air);

(b) a dye marker.

Section 2

Ship & Boat Recognition

SHIP & BOAT RECOGNITION

The following pages are intended only as a simple guide and to stimulate interest in the subject of ship and boat recognition, illustrating some of the wide range of vessels the observer may expect to encounter.

TALL SHIPS

Full Rigged Ship. Sailing vessel with square sails on three or more masts. The few that remain today are used as training vessels.

Barque. Three to five-masted sailing ship, all of them square rigged except the after mast which is fore and aft rigged.

Brig. Two-masted sailing vessel developed from the brigantine and differing from it mainly by being square rigged on both masts.

Brigantine. Two-masted sailing ship, square rigged on the foremast and fore-and-aft rigged the square topsails on the main mast.

Barquentine. Sailing ship with three to five masts, all of them fore-and-aft rigged except the foremast which is square rigged.

Topsail Schooner. Two or more masted vessel, fore-and-aft rigged. The after mast is taller than the foremast which is set with one or more square topsails.

SMALL BOATS

Masthead Cutter. Single masted fore-and-aft rigged sailing vessel with running bowsprit, mainsail, and two or more headsails.

Sloop. Single masted fore-and-aft rigged boat with single headsail set from the forestay.

Gaff Cutter. Single masted fore-and-aft rigged sailing craft with two headsails. A gaff yard supports the top edge of an additional topsail.

Yawl. Two-masted fore-and aft rigged sailing vessel similar to the ketch but with a smaller mizzen mast abaft the rudder.

Ketch. Two-masted fore-and-aft rigged sailing ship with mizzen mast situated aft of the main mast but forward of the rudder.

Staysail Schooner. Two-masted fore-and-aft rigged sailing vessel, with mainsail and staysail set between the masts

WARSHIPS

Frigate. Primarily intended for fast escort duties, the frigate is armed with a mixed array of guns, missiles and torpedoes. It can be difficult to distinguish from the destroyer but has the letter 'F' in front of the pennant number painted on the hull.

Destroyer. A medium-sized fast warship, with an armament of guns, torpedoes, guided missiles and depth charges, noted for its high manoeuvrability. Also used as an escort vessel, providing powerful support in many actions.

Landing Craft. Designed to carry a large number of troops and their vehicles during combined services landing operations. Carries only small arms for defence purposes.

Fleet Service Vessel. An important role is played by these naval support vessels, which carry supplies of oil, fuel, ammunition, spare parts and many other essential items. They are equipped with handling gear and most have a helipad situated aft.

Mine Counter-measure Vessels. The mine-hunter, fitted with sonar equipment, searches for and classifies mines on the seabed, from a distance. The minesweeper is equipped with wires, magnetic cables or acoustic gear to remove and destroy mines from the surface or seabed.

Aircraft Carrier. Easily recognised by its sheer size. Used as a mobile air base at sea, the flat deck extends the length and width of the vessel and serves as a landing strip. Service speed is in excess of 30 knots.

TALL SHIPS

Full Rigged Ship

Three Masted Barque

Brig

Brigantine

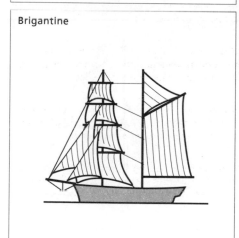

Barquentine

Topsail Schooner

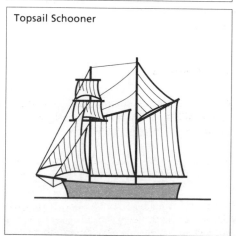

Section 3

SMALL BOATS

Masthead Cutter

Sloop

Gaff Cutter

Yawl

Ketch

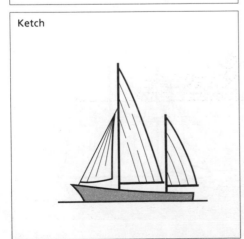

Staysail Schooner

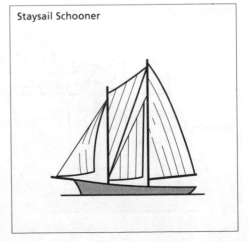

WARSHIPS

Frigate

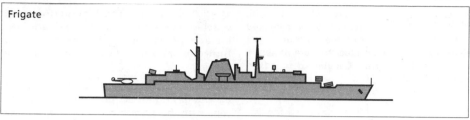

Destroyer

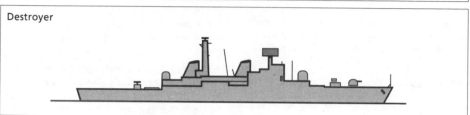

Landing Craft

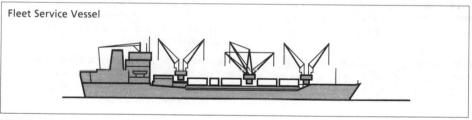

Fleet Service Vessel

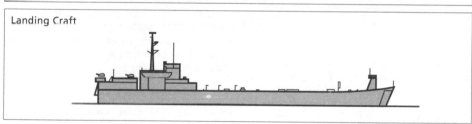

Minesweeper

Aircraft Carrier

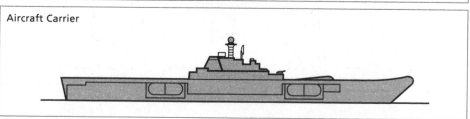

Section 3

MERCHANT SHIPS

Passenger Liner. Mainly used today as a cruise liner, this type of vessel cannot be confused with any other form of sea transport. It's elegant lines and high superstructure present a very individual profile. Capable of speeds in excess of 20 knots.

Car Ferry. Passenger/car ferries are a familiar sight. They are designed so that the motorist can drive on/drive off the unobstructed vehicle decks without delay. Nowadays they are of considerable size and can attain high speeds.

General Cargo Vessel. Designed for the transport of varying types of cargo, the handling gear is an important feature. Cranes and derricks are carried on deck and are used to facilitate the loading or discharging of cargo from the holds.

Container Ship. The function of this vessel is to package cargo in large, standardised containers to facilitate shipping and handling, thereby leading to much quicker turn-arounds. Mainly dry cargo is shipped, but specialised units can handle liquid or refrigerated cargoes. As these are very costly vessels, many are owned by a consortium of companies, some multi-national.

OBO Carrier. The oil/bulk/ore ship is different from a normal bulk carrier because of its wide range of deck fittings, vents and piping, and the steel hatch covers that encompass most of the width of the deck. The hull is sub-divided, so that the holds containing such cargo as grain or ore, are flanked by oil tanks.

WORK BOATS

Multi-Purpose Tug. This high performance vessel is suitable for a wide range of activities, including berthing, anchor handling, fire fighting, salvage, dive support and hose flushing.

Supply and Support Vessel. Used for servicing oil and gas rig installations and designed to cope with the adverse wind, weather and sea conditions often encountered, these vessels can carry a diverse range of cargoes, e.g. fuel oil, fresh water, ballast water, mud, brine and cement.

Fire fighting Tug. Instantly recognisable by the two fire monitors positioned on a platform above the superstructure. Powerful pumps supply the monitors with either foam or water.

Stern Trawler. The vessel is equipped with gantry and net handling gear at the stern. The net with full catch is hauled in through the stern ramp and the catch dropped through a hatch to below deck for processing.

Seiner. These vessels shoot their net and haul in over the stern into a space behind the wheelhouse. The seine net is made to hang vertically in the water by weights on the lower edge and floats at the top. Strings at the lower edge are made taut and the catch scooped up and hauled inboard.

Fish Factory Ship. This ship carries equipment for processing its catch on board including a complete freezing plant, which means that the vessel can remain at sea for much longer periods. Every process is carried out, the fish being cleaned, gutted, filleted etc, before finally being frozen and stored until return to portS

MERCHANT SHIPS

Obo Carrrier

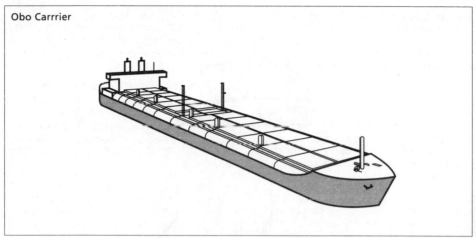

Passenger Liner

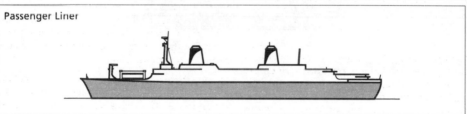

Container Ship

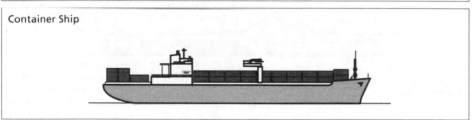

General Cargo Liner

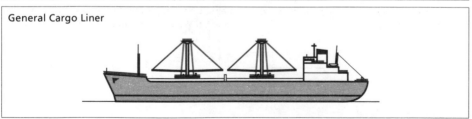

Car Ferry

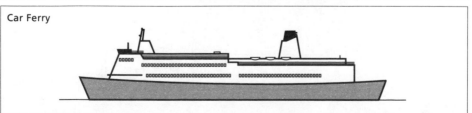

Section 3

WORK BOATS

Scottish Seiner

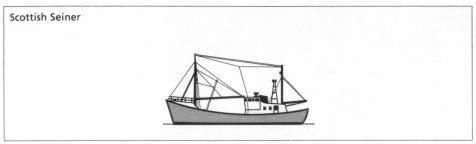

Stern Trawler

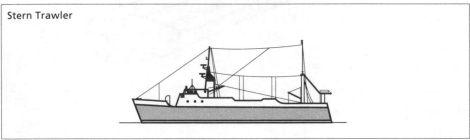

Factory/Freezer Ship

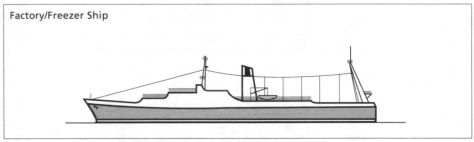

Multi-Purpose Tug

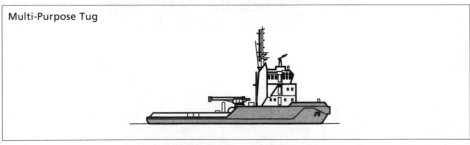

Offshore Supply Vessel

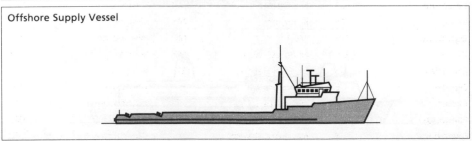

FISHING VESSEL IDENTIFICATION – PORTS OF REGISTRY

Port Name	Ident Letters	Port Name	Ident Letters	Port Name	Ident Letters
UNITED KINGDOM					
Aberdeen	A	Fleetwood	FD	Newry	N
Aberystwyth	AB	Folkestone	FE	Oban	OB
Alloa	AA	Fowey	FY	Padstow	PW
Arbroath	AH	Fraserburgh	FR	Penzance	PZ
Ardrossan	AD	Glasgow	GW	Peterhead	PD
Ayr	AR	Gloucester	GR	Plymouth	PH
Ballantrae	BA	Goole	GE	Poole	PE
Banff	BF	Grangemouth	GH	Portsmouth	P
Barnstable	BE	Granton	GN	Port Talbot	PT
Barrow	BW	Great Yarmouth	YH	Preston	PN
Beaumaris	BS	Greenock	GK	Ramsgate	R
Belfast	B	Grimsby	GY	Rochester	RR
Berwick-on-Tweed	BK	Hartlepool	HL	Rothesay	RO
Bideford	BD	Harwich	HH	Runcorn	RN
Blyth	BH	Hull	H	Rye	RX
Borrowstoness	BO	Inverness	INS	St. Ives	SS
Boston	BN	Ipswich	IH	Salcombe	SE
Bridgwater	BR	Irvine	IE	Scarborough	SH
Bristol	BL	King's Lynn	LN	Scilly	SC
Brixham	BM	Kirkcaldy	KY	Shields, North	SN
Broadford	BRO	Kirkwall	K	Shields, South	SSS
Buckie	BCK	Lancaster	LR	Shoreham	SM
Burntisland	BU	Leith	LH	Southampton	SU
Caernarfon	CO	Lerwick	LK	Stockton	ST
Cambeltown	CN	Littlehampton	LI	Stornoway	SY
Cardiff	CF	Liverpool	LL	Stranraer	SR
Cardigan	CA	Llanelly	LA	Sunderland	SD
Carlisle	CL	London	LO	Swansea	SA
Castlebay, Barra	CY	Londonderry	LY	Tarbert, Lock Fyne	TT
Chester	CH	Lowestoft	LT	Teignmouth	TH
Colchester	CK	Maldon	MN	Troon	TN
Coleraine	CE	Manchester	MR	Truro	TO
Cowes	CS	Maryport	MT	Ullapool	UL
Dartmouth	DH	Methil	ML	Weymouth	WH
Dover	DR	Middlesbrough	MH	Whitby	WY
Dumfries	DS	Milford Haven	M	Wick	WK
Dundee	DE	Montrose	ME	Wigtown	WN
Exeter	E	Newcastle	NE	Whitehaven	WA
Falmouth	FH	Newhaven	NN	Wisbech	WI
Faversham	F	Newport, Gwent	NT	Workington	WO

Section 3

FISHING VESSEL IDENTIFICATION – PORTS OF REGISTRY

Port Name	Ident Letters	Port Name	Ident Letters	Port Name	Ident Letters
IRELAND					
Cork	C	Galway	G	Tralee	T
Drogheda	DA	Limerick	L	Waterford	W
Dublin	D	Skibbereen	S	Westport	WT
Dundalk	DK	Sligo	SO	Wexford	WD
FRANCE					
Ajaccio	AI	Douarnenez	DZ	Nice	NI
Arcachon	AC	Dunkerque	DK	Noirmoutier	NO
Audierne	AD	Fécamp	FC	Oléron	IO
Auray	AY	Ile d'Yeu	YE	Paimpol	PL
Bastia	BI	La Rochelle	LR	Port-Vendres	PV
Bayonne	BA	Le Guilvinec	GV	Rouen	RO
Bordeaux	BX	Le Havre	LH	Saint-Brieuc	SB
Boulogne	BL	Les Sables-d'Olonne	LS	Saint-Malo	SM
Brest	BR	Lorient	LO	Saint-Nazaire	SN
Caen	CN	Marennes	MN	Sète	ST
Camaret	CM	Marseille	MA	Toulon	TL
Cherbourg	CH	Martigues	MT	Vannes	VA
Concarneau	CC	Morlaix	MX		
Dieppe	DP	Nantes	NA		
NETHERLANDS					
Arnemuiden	ARM	Hontenisse	HON	Tholen	TH
Broek in Waterland	BIW	Kortgene	KG	Termunten	TM
Oostburg-Breskens	BR	Klundert	KL	Terschelling	TS
Bruinisse	BRU	Katwijk	KW	Texel	TX
Bunschoten	BU	Lemsterland-Lemmer	LE	Urk	UK
Bergen op Zoom	BZ	Ulrum-Lauwersoog	LO	Usquert	UQ
Diemen	DM	Medemblik	ME	Edam-Volendam	VD
Delfzijl	DZ	Monnickendam	MO	Vlaardingen	VL
Enkhuizen	EH	Middenschouwen	MS	Vlissingen	VLI
Finsterwolde	FL	Nieuw-Beijerland	NB	Vlieland	VLL
Genemuiden	GM	Terneuzen	NZ	Workum	WK
Goedereede	GO	Goedereede-Ouddorp	OD	Westdongeradeel	WL
Goes	GOE	Zeevang Oosthuizen	OH	Wonseradeel	WON
Harlingen	HA	Oostdongeradeel	OL	Wieringen	WR
Den Helder	HD	Amsterdam-Ranadorp	RD	Westerschouwen	WSW
Hindeloopen	HI	Den Haag Scheveningen	SCH	Reimerswaal-Yerseke	YE
Harderwijk	HK	Goedereede-Stellendam	SL	Velsen-IJmuiden	IJM
Hemelumer-Oldeferd	HL	Sloten (Friesland)	SLO	Ulrum-Zoutkamp	ZK
Hoorn	HN	Staveren	ST	Hooge en Lage Zwaluwe	ZL
				Zierikzee	ZZ
BELGIUM					
Blankenberge	B				
Nieuwpoort	N				
Oostende	O				
Zeebrugge	Z				

10

FISHING VESSEL IDENTIFICATION – PORTS OF REGISTRY

Port Name	Ident Letters	Port Name	Ident Letters	Port Name	Ident Letters
GERMANY				Kronsgaard	KRO
Dornumer-Accumersiel	ACC	Friedrichsort	FRI	Kröslin	KRÖ
Greetsiel	AG	Gager	GAG		
Ahlbeck	AHL	Geversdorf	GEV	Kühlungsborn	KÜH
Ahrenshoop	AHR	Glewitz	GLE	Klein Zicker	KZI
Anklamer Fähre	ANF	Glowe	GLO	Laboe	LAB
Anklam	ANK	Glücksburg	GLU	Langballigau	LAN
Altreddevitz	ARE	Graal-Müritz	GMU	Langholz	LANG
Arnis	ARN	Göhren	GÖH	Lassan	LAS
Assel	ASS	Gothmund	GOT	Lauterbach	LAU
Borkum	AX	Greetsiel	GRE	Leerort	LEE
Altwarp	AWA	Gristow	GRI	Lemkenhafen	LEM
Norddeich	AY	Großenbrode	GRO	Lippe	LIP
Neuharlingersiel	AZ	Grömitz	GRO	Lietzow	LIZ
Baabe	BAA	Gumbln	GUM	Lobbe	LOB
Balm	BAL	Groß Zicker	GZI	List auf Sylt	LIST
Bansin	BAN	Haffkrug	HAF	Loga	LOG
Barth	BAR	Harlesiel	HAR	Lubmin	LUB
Beidenfleth	BEI	Audeich/Kreuzdeich	HAS	Ludwigsburg	LUD
Bellin	BEL	Hatzum	HAT	Nesserdeich/Wollersum	LUN
Bensersiel	BEN	Hamburg-Kleinfahrzeuge	HBK	Lütow	LÜT
Binz	BIN	Heikendorf	HEI	Maasholm	MAA
Börgerende	BOG	Heiligenhafen	HEIL	Mahlzow	MAH
Boinsdorf	BOI	Helgoland	HEL	Meldorf	MEL
Bongsiel	BON	Hennstedt	HEN	Mönkebude	MON
Borkum	BOR	Horst	HEN	Mukran	MUK
Born	BOR	Heringsdorf	HER	List a. Sylt	MUN
Brake	BRA	HH-Finkenwerder	HF	Cuxhaven	NC
Breege	BRE	Freie und Hansestadt		Neeberg	NEE
Brokdorf	BRO	Hambu	HH	Negenmark	NEG
Büsum	BUS	Hollendorf	HOL	Neuenkirchen	NEK
Burgstaaken	BUR	Hörnum	HÖR	Neuendorf (Hiddensee)	NEU
Burhaversiel	BUR	Hohwacht	HOH	Neuharlingersiel	NEU
Buschwitz	BWS	Hooge	HOO	Neuhasu/Oste	NEU
Bremerhaven	BX	Hooksiel	HOO	Neustadt/Ostsee	NEU
Cuxhaven	CUX	Hoopte	HOO	Neukirchen	NEUK
Dahme	DAH	Horumersiel	HOR	Neuendorf (Wolgast)	NEW
Dangast	DAN	Hubertsberg	HUB	Niendorf	NIE
Dassow	DAS	Husum	HUS	Norddeich	NOR
Dierhagen	DIE	Jemgum	JEM	Neureddevitz	NRE
Dierhagen Ost	DIR	Kamminke	KAM	Bezirk Brake/Utw	OB
Ditzum	DIT	Kappeln	KAP	Oldersum	OLD
Dorum	DOR	Karlshagen	KAR	Olpenitz	OLP
Drage	DRA	Kasenort	KAS	Burhaversiel	ON
Dranske	DRA	Kellenhusen	KEL	Fedderwardersiel	ON
Oche Drecht	DRE	Ketelsby	KET	Ording	ORD
Eckernförde	ECXE	Klein Hagen	KHA	Orth	ORT
Eldena	ELD	Kiel	KIE	Otterndorf	OTT
Falshöft	FAL	Knock	KNO	Paske	PAS
Fedderwardersiel	FED	Kollmar	KOL	Peenemünde	PEE
Flensburg	FLE	Kolpinsee	KOL	Pellworm	PEL
Freest	FRE	Koserow	KOS	Pepelow	PEP
Friedrichskoog	FRI	Krakstorf	KRA	Kirchdorf	POE

Section 3

11

FISHING VESSEL IDENTIFICATION – PORTS OF REGISTRY

Port Name	Ident Letters	Port Name	Ident Letters	Port Name	Ident Letters
GERMANY (Cont)					
Poel	POE	Kiel/Heikendorf/		Ummanz	UMM
Timmendorf	POE	Laboe/ Möltenort	SK	Usedom	USE
Pogum	POG	Haffkrug	SL	Ückeritz	ÜTZ
Polchow	POL	Arnis/Schlei	SM	Varel	VAR
Prerow	PRE	Kappeln	SM	Vitt (Arkona)	VIA
Pruchten	PRU	Neustadt/Holstein	SN	Vitte (Hiddensee)	VIT
Radeland	RAD	Niedorf/O	SO	Wackerballig	WACK
Rankwitz	RAN	Spandowerhagen	SPA	Warnemünde	WAR
Redentin	RED	Spieka	SPI	Warsin	WAS
Rerik	RER	Schulau/Elbe	SS	Warte	WAT
Ribnitz	RIB	Tönning	ST	Schülpersiel	WES
Rieth	RIT	Stahlbrode	STA	Wiek	WIE
Rodenkirchen	ROD	Stein	STEI	Kaiser-Wilhelm-Koog	WIL
Rostock	ROS	Steinberghaff	STEI	Wiek (Rügen)	WIR
Schapprode (Rugen)	SAP	Stralsund	STR	Wismar	WIS
Sassnitz	SAS	Strande	STRA	Westklüsse	WKL
Burgstaaken	SB	Strukkamp	STRU	Wolgast	WOG
Büsum	SC	Husum	SU	Wremen	WRE
Schleswig	SCHLE	Hörnum	SV	Wulfen	WULF
Schlutup	SCHLU	Helgoland	SX	Wustrow	WUS
Schönberger Strand	SCHÖN	Tarnevitz	TAR	Wyk auf Föhr	WYK
Kalifornien	SCHÖN	Terborg	TER	Zecherin	ZECH
Friedrichskoog	SD	Thiessow	THI	Zempin	ZEM
Seedorf	SEE	Tönning	TÖN	Zecherin bei Wolgast	ZEW
Seester	SEE	Timmendorfer Strand	TIM	Zingst	ZID
Seestermühe	SEE	Trassenheide	TRA	Ziemitz	ZIE
Glückstadt	SG	Travemünde	TRA	Zirzewitz	ZIT
Heiligenhafen	SH	Uckermünde	UEK	Zinnowitz	ZIW
Sierksdorf	SIE	Uetersen	UET	Zudar	ZUD

Port Name	Ident Letters	Port Name	Ident Letters	Port Name	Ident Letters
DENMARK					
Aabenraa	AA	Marstal	M	Thisted	T
Aarhus	AS	Nakskov	N	Vejle	VE
Esbjerg	E	Næstved	ND	Greenland	GR
Frederikshavn	FN	Nykøbing F	NF		
Helsingør	H	Nyborg	NG		
Hirtshals	HG	Odense	O	**FAEROE ISLANDS**	
Holbæk	HK	Rønne	R		
Haderslev	HV	Ringkøbing	RI	Funglefjord	FD
Køberhavn	K	Randers	RS	Klaksvik	KG
Kalundborg	KA	Rudkøbing	RU	Sand	SA
Køge	KE	Skagen	S	Trangisvaag	TG
Korsør	KR	Svaneke	SE	Torshavn	TN
Lemvig	L	Svendborg	SG	Sandevaag	VA
Løkken	LN	Sønderborg	SØ	Vestmannahavn	VN

FISHING VESSEL IDENTIFICATION – PORTS OF REGISTRY

Port Name	Ident Letters	Port Name	Ident Letters	Port Name	Ident Letters
NORWAY					
Ålesund	ÅL	Horten	HTN	Odda	OD
Arendal	ARD	Kirkenes	KRK	Oslo	OLO
Askerøy	ASK	Kopervik	KPV	Porsgrunn	PSG
Bergen	BGN	Kragerø	KRØ	Risør	RIS
Bodø	BØ	Kristiansand S	KSA	Sandefjord	SFJ
Brevik	BVK	Kristiansund N	KSU	Sandnes	SAN
Brønnøysund	BRØ	Langesund	LAS	Sandnessjøen	SSJ
Drammen	DRM	Larvik	LVK	Sarpsborg	SBG
Drøbak	DBK	Levanger	LEV	Sigerfjord	SGF
Egersund	ESD	Lillesand	LIS	Skien	SKI
Farsund	FAS	Longyearbyen	LON	Skudemeshavn	SKH
Flekkefjord	FLF	Lyngør	LØR	Sortland	SOR
Florø	FLØ	Mandal	MDL	Stavanger	STV
Fredrikstad	FRS	Melbu	MBU	Steinkjer	STK
Grimstad	GRS	Mo i Rana	MO	Stokmarknes	STN
Halden	HDN	Molde	MOL	Svolvær	SVR
Hamar	HMR	Mosjøen	MSN	Tromsø	TBG
Hammerfest	HF	Moss	MS	Trondheim	THM
Hamnvik	HVK	Måløy	MØY	Tvedestand	TVS
Harstad	HRS	Myre	MYR	Tønsberg	VRØ
Haugesund	HSU	Namos	NOS	Vardø	VRØ
Holmestrand	HST	Narvik	NRV	Vadsø	VSØ
ICELAND					
Akranes	AK	Keflavik	KE	Siglufjördur	SI
Patreksfjördur	BA	Neskaupstadur	NK	Holmavik	ST
Akureyri Dalvik	EA	Seydisfjördur	NS	Eskifjördur	SU
Hafnarfjör	GK	Olafsfjördur	ÖF	Reydarfjördur	SU
Sandgerdi	GK	Reykjavik	RE	Vestmannaeyjar	VE
Grindavik	GK	Skaptafells Syssel	SF		
SWEDEN					
Falkenberg	FG	Kalmar	KR	Stromstad	SD
Gävle	GE	Kristianstad	ÅS	Sölvesborg	SG
Göteborg	GG	Landskrona	LA	Simrishamn	SIN
Gotland	VY	Lysekil	LL	Sundsvall	SL
Haparanda	HA	Luleå	LÅ	Stockholm	SM
Halmstad	HD	Malmö	MÖ	Söderhamn	SN
Helsingborg	HG	Nykoping	NG	Trelleborg	TG
Hårnösand	HND	Norrköping	NRG	Udevalla	UA
Hudiksvall	HL	Örnsköldsvik	ÖK	Umeå	UÅ
Karlskrona	KA	Oskarshamn	ON	Varberg	VG
Karlshamn	KN	Piteä	PÄ	Västervik	VK
				Ystad	YD

FINLAND

All Finnish fishing vessels show the prefix SF followed by the registration number

Section 3

FISHING VESSEL IDENTIFICATION – PORTS OF REGISTRY

Port Name	Ident Letters	Port Name	Ident Letters	Port Name	Ident Letters
POLAND					
Chlopy	CHY	Kuźnica	KUZ	Sarbinowo	SAR
Darlowo	DAR	Leba	LEB	Stepnica	STP
Dźwirzyno	DWI	Miloszewo	MIK	Swarzewo	SWA
Dziwnów	DZI	Miedzywodsie	MIW	Swibno	SWB
Gaski	GAS	Miedzyzdroje	MIZ	Swinoujscie	SWI
Gdańsk	GDA	Mrzeżyno	MRZ	Unieście	UNI
Gdynia	GDY	Niechorze	NIE	Ustronie Morskie	USM
Hel	HEL	Piaski	PIA	Ustka	UST
Jastarnia	JAS	Przytor	PRZ	Wiselka	WIS
Katy Rybackie	KAT	Puck	PUC	Wladyslawowo	WLA
Kolobrzeg	KOL	Rowy	ROW	Górki Wschodnie	WSG
Krynica Morska	KRM	Rewal	RWL	Górki Zachodnie	ZAG
Karsibór	KRS				
SPAIN					
Algeciras	AL	Coruna	CO	Menorca	MH
Alicante	AT	Ferrol	FE	San Sebastian	SS
Almeria	AM	Gijon	GI	Santander	ST
Barcelona	BA	Huelva	HU	Sevilla	SE
Bilbao	BI	Ibiza	IB	Tarragona	TA
Cadiz	CA	Las Palmas	GC	Tenerife	TE
Cartagena	CT	Malaga	MA	Valencia	VA
Castellon	CP	Mallorca	PM	Vigo	VI
Ceuta	CU	Melilla	MLL	Villagarcia	VILL
ITALY					
Ancona	AN	Livorno	LI	Reggio Calabria	RC
Augusta	AU	Manfredonia	MF	Rimini	RM
Bari	BA	Mazara del Vallo	MV	Roma	ROMA
Brindisi	BR	Messina	ME	Salerno	SA
Cagliari	CA	Molfetta	ML	San Benedetto del Tronto	SB
Castellammare di Stabia	CS	Monfalcone	MN	Savona	SV
Catania	CT	Napoli	NA	Siracusa	SR
Chioggia	CI	Olbia	OL	Taranto	TA
Civitavecchia	CV	Palermo	PA	Torre del Greco	TG
Crotone	CR	Pescara	PC	Trapani	TP
Gaeta	GA	Porto Empedocle	PE	Trieste	TS
Gallipoli	GL	Portoferraio	PF	Venezia	VE
Genova	GE	Porto Torres	PT	Viareggio	VG
Imperia	IM	Ravenna	RA	Vibo Valentia Marina	VM
La Spezia	SP				

SHIP MASTER'S BUSINESS

4

TONNAGE

The words 'tons' and 'tonnage' can have so many meanings that a clear indication of which tonnage is referred to is necessary. The following notes— necessarily brief—are intended as a guide to the general use of the terms.

The word tonnage is handed down from early days when dues were collected on vessels carrying wine in 'tuns' (a tun is still the recognised wine measure of 252 gallons). Since this time the words have come to be regarded as a means of indicating the size of vessels, both in terms of capacity and weight.

Registered Tonnage

Basically this is the internal capacity of a vessel; a registered ton originally being 100 cubic feet of internal measurement. Ever since this type of tonnage was introduced, over a century ago, different countries developed slightly different rules for assessing Registered Tonnages. However in 1969 an internationally agreed method for determining these tonnages was devised by the I.M.O. which came into force in July, 1982.

Under this new system every ship will continue to be assigned two tonnages (i.e. a GROSS TONNAGE and a NET TONNAGE).

The GROSS TONNAGE will be a realistic indication of the ship's size. It is based on the moulded volume of the entire ship (hull plus erections and all enclosed places) and there are no deductions, exemptions or special allowances therefrom.

The NET TONNAGE will be a general indication of the ship's earning capacity. This value is derived from a formula based upon the moulded volume of the cargo spaces, the number of passengers carried, the moulded depth of the ship and the summer draught.

These values are to be expressed simply as the GROSS TONNAGE and NET TONNAGE and the word ton should not be used in this connection.

Ships built before July 1982 may use their existing gross and net tonnages until the 17th of July, 1994.

Until there was an internationally agreed loadline, which did not come into being until 1930, these tonnages based on capacity were the only ones available. It is therefore customary for harbour and other dues to be paid on either the Gross or Net tonnage.

Displacement Tonnage

The actual weight of the ship which is equal to the weight of the water displaced by the vessel.

Light displacement refers to the weight of vessel and her equipment and machinery. Loaded displacement refers to the weight of a vessel loaded with her water, cargo, bunkers, stores and passengers.

The Displacement Tonnage is found by calculating the volume of water displaced by Simpson's Rules. The weight of the water displaced can then be determined and may be expressed in either tons or tonnes.

Deadweight Tonnage

The difference between the Light and Loaded displacements is the Dead Weight carrying capacity of the vessel in tons or tonnes.

Freight Tonnage

The freight or charge for carrying the cargo may be assessed on weight or volume. If the cargo is more than 40 cu. ft. per ton or 1 cu. metre per tonne the shipper pays on volume, e.g. cargo stowing at 80 cu. ft. to the ton would be considered as 80/40 or 2 freight tons.

THAMES MEASUREMENT TONNAGE

All small vessels and yachts are measured for the purposes of 'official' registration and Certificate of Registry.

'Thames Measurement' however is an entirely different tonnage designed as a means of obtaining much more accurate comparisons of size, as between one yacht and another, than is possible by comparing 'Registered' tonnages.

The formula is $\dfrac{(L-B) \times B \times \frac{1}{2}B}{94}$

Thus the Length (L) of the yacht (measured at deck level from the fore side of the stem to the after side of the stern post on deck); with the breadth (B) deducted; multiplied by the breadth and again by the half breadth, when divided by 94 gives the Thames Tonnage.

(B = the extreme breadth on deck - excluding rubbing strakes or belting).

Note. The sternpost in a yacht with a transom stern and an inboard rudder is the central upright timber or iron of stern incorporated in the transom.

Although tonnage details of measurement for tonnage are not international the majority of countries use similar methods to the British. Full details as to how the measurements are carried out exactly are contained in the official DpT handbook 'Instructions as to the Tonnage Measurement of Ships'.

TON CUPS

The word 'Ton' when used in relation to Ton Cups is a derivation from a French tonnage rule of 1892.

The One Ton Cup was first presented in 1898 by members of the Cercle de la Voile de Paris for match racing between France and Great Britain of small inshore keel boats rating at One Ton under the 1892 French tonnage rules.

Between 1906 and 1962, after the formation of the International Yacht Racing Union, the One Ton Cup was presented for the International Six Metre Class. In 1965, Jean Peytel, after whom the Three-Quarter Ton Trophy has been named, put the One Ton Cup for competition between yachts of 22 feet R.O.R.C. Rating with no time allowance. In 1968 the Offshore Racing Council was founded and since 1969 the One Ton Cup

has, together with other Ton Cups, been presented for world championships of yachts of a specified maximum International Offshore Rule Rating. There are now six Ton Cups, and world championships are held annually. Maximum I.O.R. rating limits are as below.

Further details can be obtained from the Offshore Racing Council, 19 St James's Place, London SW1A 1NN.

LIGHT DUES

These are payments made by ships for the maintenance of the lighthouses, lightvessels and buoys. Certain small vessels in addition to H.M. Ships and vessels in ballast (i.e. neither loading nor unloading and not earning freight) are exempted, but otherwise all vessels pay these on the tonnage of the vessel. The Light Dues Bill and Receipt should always be kept on board with the Certificate of Registry to be shown on demand to any officer of H.M. Customs.

All Yachts if 20 tons or over pay light dues annually (unless they sign an exemption form that the yacht will not be used at sea for the following 12 months).

WORLD CHAMPIONSHIPS – where to be held			
		1993	1994
TWO TON	35.05 ft	UK	Italy
ONE TON	30.55 ft	UK	France (Med.)
THREE-QUARTER TON	24.55 ft	Spain (Med.)	Sweden
HALF TON	22.05 ft	Spain (Atlantic)	-
QUARTER TON	18.55 ft	Spain (Atlantic)	Kiel, Germany
MINI TON	16.55 ft	Spain (Atlantic)	-

REGISTRATION OF SHIPS

UNITED KINGDOM

Under the Merchant Shipping Acts 1894/1988 all British-owned merchant vessels or yachts are entitled to be registered, although this is no longer compulsory. It is advisable that vessels going foreign should be registered, as most foreign administrations require this.

The Merchant Shipping Act 1983 allows an alternative mode of registration for vessels less than 24 metres (79 ft.) in length. This small ship register offers a much cheaper and simpler option. It provides evidence of nationality of the ship but not title, nor will it enable mortgages to be recorded (see section on Alternative Registration on page 5). British subjects resident overseas cannot use the small ships register.

Standard Registration for Commercial Ships:

This is a general guide to the requirements to be observed, by persons or bodies corporate entitled to own a British ship, before registry can be effected:

1. An application for registry to be made by the owner, or authorised agent, to the Registrar of British Ships at the registry port of his choice.

2. Approval of the ship's name by the Department of Transport.

3. Survey of the ship by a Department of Transport Marine Surveyor or other person appointed by organisations authorised for the purpose by that Department.

4. Satisfactory evidence of title to ownership, which for British and foreign built ships consists of the Builder's Certificate and documents of sale prior to registry if the vessel has passed through more than one owner's hands before

registry. Provision is made however for waiving of the Builder's Certificate for a foreign built ship if at the time of making his Declaration of Ownership, which all owners are required to complete, the applicant declares that the time and place of building are unknown to him or that the Builder's Certificate cannot be procured, in which case title is founded in the bill of sale by which the vessel was first acquired by a British Subject from the foreigner and any subsequent documents of sale up to that vesting ownership in the applicant for registry. For a British built ship purchased from a foreigner title is founded in the foreign bill of sale and any subsequent documents of sale between the various parties.

When these particulars have been approved a Carving Note is issued to the Owner who instructs the builder to identify the vessel according to the requirement of this form. The official Number must be cut in the vessel's main beam together with the appropriate tonnage and these normally remain constant throughout the life of the vessel. Upon completion the Note is to be signed appropriately and returned to the Registrar. Then on payment of the prescribed fee the Registrar issues the Certificate of Registry which is a most important document as it is the vessel's identification Certificate containing all details already outlined.

When a Master is appointed to the vessel his name is endorsed on the Certificate of Registry by the Registrar and his appointment is not recognised until this is done. When a vessel is issued with SIGNAL LETTERS these are endorsed on her Certificate of Registry and never alter. A vessel's Radio Call signals are now identical with her visual Signal Letters.

The Name of a British Registered vessel will only be approved provided no other vessel of that name is Registered already.

Standard Registration of Pleasure Craft under 45 feet in length

The steps which an owner has to take before a pleasure yacht can be registered are as follows:

1. He must apply in writing to the Registrar of British Ships at the registry port of his choice, for registration of the yacht. The Registrar is normally located in the Custom House. If the owner is a member of a yacht club, he should when applying so inform the Registrar, and give the name of the club.

2. He must produce to the Registrar documents of title which establish ownership. A certificate from the builder of the yacht will meet this requirement if it is in a specified form and provided the yacht has not changed hands since building. Many builders of yachts know the form of certificate required. Should a yacht have been built in stages by different builders, then a separate certificate for each stage will be required. For yachts which have changed hands since building, the Bill of Sale in respect of each transfer of ownership will also be required. Official forms of Bill of Sale can be obtained from any Registrar.

3. He must obtain approval of the pleasure yacht's name from the Registrar General of Shipping and Seamen, Department of Transport, Llantrisant Road, Cardiff CF5 2YS. Approval must be sought on the official form which can be obtained either from any Registrar or direct from the Registrar General of Shipping and Seamen.

4. He must arrange for tonnage measurement, which leads to the issue of a Certificate of Survey (Tonnage Measurement) for the yacht*.

5. He must make a declaration of ownership on the appropriate form obtainable from any Registrar.

6. When the Registrar is satisfied that all these requirements have been met he will issue a Carving and Marking Note to the owner. This Note indicates how the pleasure yacht is to be marked for identification purposes. The owner must arrange for the carving and marking to be performed in accordance with the directions on the Carving and Marking Note and when these have been so completed he should sign the Note and return it to the Registrar.

7. On request, he must pay the registry fee at the Office of H.M. Customs and Excise at which the Registrar is located. This fee is in addition to the fee payable for tonnage measurement and is chargeable at the rate in force when the Registrar is in a position to complete the

---

*As the payment of Harbour and other dues for small craft are not normally based upon cubic capacity (i.e. tonnage), during 1975 the Department of Trade simplified the survey required for pleasure craft under 45 ft length overall, and also authorised YBDSA, Lloyds and RYA measurers to carry out the necessary survey on the Department's behalf.

Most of the information now taken by the measurer is to enable the craft or yacht to be easily identified in cases of theft, etc., however, the gross and nett tonnage (both the same) are still calculated by 0.0045 x length x breadth x internal height, all measured in feet.

registration, i.e. when all the above formalities have been satisfactorily completed.

When these requirements have been met the Registrar will register the pleasure yacht and issue the Certificate of Registry.

Alternative Registration for Ships below 24 metres in length (SSR)

The application should be made in writing to: SSR, DVLA, Swansea SA99 1BX Tel: 0792 783355, who will require the owner to complete a simple form stating:

a) The overall length of the ship . . . 'self measurement' will do.

b) The name of the ship . . . there is no requirement for uniqueness of name but 'undesirable' names will not be allowed.

c) The name and address of every owner.

This registration shall be valid for a period of five years or until change of ownership and application for renewal should be made during the period of six months prior to the date of expiration.

Official Markings on Small Craft

Ships registered under the alternative system for small ships must have clearly painted or affixed to the exterior of the ship the number of its registration preceded by the letters SSR.

Pleasure yachts, barges (other than sea-going barges), pilot vessels and vessels employed solely in river navigation are exempted from having the name marked on the bows and a scale of feet on the stem and stern post. In addition, power-driven pilot vessels are exempted from having the name marked on the stern, and yachts belonging to specified clubs from having the name and port of registry marked on the stern. Royal National Lifeboats are also exempted.

IRELAND

Full registration of a yacht - which is voluntary - can be carried out by Customs & Excise.

Alternatively, the Irish Yachting Association have produced a "Certificate of Identity of Origin" to support owners when travelling outside Ireland. It should be used in conjunction with the Official Ship's Papers and is not to be considered a substitute for full registration.

Yachtsmen should note that there have been incidences where yachtsmen have been fined for not carrying proper registration documents issued by a National Government. These incidences have occurred mainly in France.

All vessels departing Ireland, bound for a destination outside the State, are obliged to clear the vessel outwards with the local Customs office. It may be helpful to have the Certificate of Identity stamped by the Customs when obtaining clearance.

The IYA does not take responsibility in circumstances where a foreign Government Agency refuse to recognise a Certificate of Identity.

Irish Yachting Association, 3 Park Road, Dun Laoghaire, Co. Dublin, Ireland. Tel: (01) 2800239.

FRANCE

It is compulsory for all pleasure craft, with the exception of 'beach toys' (which are not permitted to go more than 300m. offshore), windsurfers, jet-skis etc. to be registered with both the Customs and the Affaires Maritimes.

New craft

Written application, together with proof of buyer's identity (with ID photo), invoice and builder's or importer's certificate of construction and tonnage, should be made to the appropriate local Customs office and then to the Affaires Maritimes office.

Registration can also be applied for direct to: Affaires Maritimes de Saint-Servan, Section des Navires de Plaisance, B.P.130, 35408 Saint Malo-Cedex.

Secondhand craft

Written application, with three copies of Bill of Sale, proof of buyer's identity (with ID photo) and ship's papers to appropriate local Customs and Affaires Maritimes office.

BELGIUM

Registration is required in two categories:

I) For boats over 15m. on the water line a certificate must be produced if they are to leave Belgium waters. This should be applied for at the address below, giving details of the size of yacht, proof of ownership etc.

Administration for Maritime Affairs & Navigation, 65 rue de la Loi, 1040 Brussels. Tel: 2 233 1211. Fax: 2 230 3002.

2) Boats which are staying in Belgium waters also have to be registered. Proof of registration is to have identity letters and figures painted on the hull of the boat. Register with the Maritime Authority in either Brussels, Antwerp or Oostende.

Chief Maritime Commissioner - Oostende. Tel: 59 0925.

NOTE: New legislation is being discussed.

NETHERLANDS

For pleasure craft there is no official registration certificate.

Ships over 6 GRT (which for yachts will be a minimum length of 7-8 metres) can be registered voluntarily.

Ships over 20 GRT must be registered (unless the owner is a member of an official Yacht Club).

The law differentiates between seagoing vessels and purely inland waterway vessels when other rules apply.

To obtain the 'passport' of the ship, the so called zeebrief, one needs a meetbrief - letter of measurement (not needed for yachts), and an official statement that the ship is Dutch, to be presented with proof of ownership, ship's papers etc.

For further information contact:

Dienst van het Kadaster en de Openbare Tel: (010) 477 2377 or Directoraat-General Scheepvaart en Maritieme Tel: (070) 395 5555

GERMANY

Application should be made in writing, with proof of ownership, ship's papers etc. to the local Registration Court.

Registration at a 'Seeschiffs Register' is compulsory for vessels of 15m. LOA or more.

It is also compulsory for vessels operating on the inland waterways. If you are a member of an official Yacht Club an international boating certificate is acceptable. If not, you must apply at the next 'Binnen-Schiffs Register'. For charter vessels special safety requirements have to be met.

Vessels under 15m. LOA may be registered voluntarily to obtain an International Boating Certificate at the Deutscher Segler Verband or Deutscher Motor Yacht Verband.

For German vessels wishing to sail in French waters it is necessary to have a special Flaggen Certificate. For full details apply to: Bundesamt fur Seeschiffahrt und Hydrographie, Bernhardt Nocht Str.78, 2000 Hamburg 36.

DENMARK

Registration is voluntary for all vessels. Apply to local Customs authority, who will issue a Registration Certificate on proof of ownership.

NORWAY

Registration is voluntary for small craft. For vessels over 50 GRT it is compulsory.

Application should be made to the home area police, using the special form provided, together with proof of ownership, insurance, ship's papers etc.

SWEDEN

Official registration is necessary if your boat comes within one of three categories:

1) more than 5m. LOA.
2) sail area of 10m^2 .
3) engine power of 10 h.p. or more

Apply to the Registration Bureau in your home area. On completion of the official application form a Certificate will be issued showing the Registration Number.

NOTE: Considerable discussion are underway and the regulations are likely to be changed.

FINLAND

Sailing Yachts

It is not compulsory to register at present but the Government is considering a change in the regulations. Voluntary registration may be made through the Finnish Yachting Association (Tel: 0 1581), giving details of type of yacht, year of manufacture, name, address etc. They will issue a Certificate, but you must be a member of an official Yacht Club.

Motor Boats

Registration is compulsory if the boat has:

1) an outboard motor of more than 20 h.p.
2) an inboard engine or sterndrive over 50 h.p. capacity.

Smaller engined craft may register voluntarily.

Apply to the Boat Register in the province from where the boat will be operated. You will be asked to complete an application form and to produce the Bill of Sale or document providing proof of ownership. A Registration Certificate will then be issued.

POLAND

It is not compulsory to register sailing boats that are to be used only on inland waterways, i.e. the lakes. However, if they are to enter an official race, then they must be registered.

Sea-going sailing vessels with more than $10m^2$ of sail must register. Apply to the Maritime office of any major port, e.g. Gdynia or Swinoujscie.

For motor vessels the owner must hold a certificate of competency to handle the boat. The vessel must also be registered if it is to be sea-going.

Maritime Office, Urzedy Morski, Chrzanowskiego No: 10, Gdynia. Tel: 58 215256.

MALTA

Official registration of pleasure craft:

Provisional Registration

A vessel is first registered provisionally for a period of six months (extendable to one year) during which the documentation for permanent registration must be finalised.

Application should be made by the owner or authorised representative, providing proof of qualification to own a Maltese ship, e.g. in the case of individuals a Maltese passport or I.D. card. A Declaration of Ownership must be made before the Registrar, together with payment of initial and annual registration fees.

Permanent Registration.

The following documents must be submitted:

(1) Builder's Certificate if vessel is new.

2) Bill of Sale, if a sale has taken place, or any other document by which the vessel was transferred to the applicant for registry.

3) Cancellation certificate from last country of registry.

4) Certificate of Survey and where applicable a copy of the Maltese Tonnage Certificate.

5) An undertaking to return the provisional certificate of registry.

Further documentation is required for vessels other than pleasure craft.

Registry of Shipping and Seamen, Marina Pinto, Valletta. Tel: 228177/228997.

GIBRALTAR

The registration of any vessel in Gibraltar is termed as British and follows the same regulations as the UK.

PORTUGAL

Registration is compulsory.

For vessels less than 8m. LOA, application should be made to the Capitania do Porto of home port, with proof of ownership, builder's certificate of construction and survey certificate satisfying safety equipment requirements.

Vessels more than 8m LOA must be registered at Direccao-Geral de Navegacao e Transportes Maritimos, although this can be done through the Capitania do Porto at home port.

Written application should be accompanied by detailed log book, general and structural drawings of the vessel, stability calculations, salvage and fire precaution plans, list of electric/electronic equipment, the type of engine and engine base-plate, and drawings of the pipe structure.

Direccao-Geral de Navegacao e Transportes Maritimos, Praca Luis de Camoes No. 22-2.Dt. 1200 Lisboa.

SPAIN

Registration is compulsory for all types of vessel. There is no minimum requirement regarding LOA tonnage or engine power.

For vessels originating in a foreign country the requirements for registration are as follows:

1) Proof of ownership.

2) Import Licence.

3) Customs' Clearance.

4) Cancellation certificate from last country of registry.

Once the boat has been registered, documentation will be issued according to type or class.

Section 4

ITALY

Registration is compulsory for all vessels more than 3 GRT in two classes:

1) 3-50 GRT
2) over 50 GRT

If the builder has not already registered the vessel at the port of construction, the owner must do so. However, application can be made to the Capitanerie di Porto at any port, together with proof of ownership (builder's invoice) and Rina di Navale survey certificate.

NOTES ON MOORINGS

In many small harbours and rivers, due to the lack of space available, moorings are laid for vessels to lie to. The chains of these moorings normally foul the sea bed so that a vessel cannot use her anchor. Under these circumstances yachts are usually allotted space and put down their own moorings or they may be hired from the harbour authority.

It should be realised that these are private property and except of necessity must not be picked up and used 'as a right'. It is essential that the visiting yachtsman should carefully check that the strength of the mooring is adequate for the size of his vessel. In these circumstances it is customary for no objection to be made to the visiting yachtsman picking up an unattended mooring for a short period—indeed it is a universal custom which smooths the path of the cruising yachtsman. A point sometimes overlooked is that because of convenience an owner uses a 'mooring' instead of an anchor, but if in tidal waters he cannot claim absolute right to the stretch of water the moorings occupy; and as he has really 'obstructed' anyone else wishing to anchor there he cannot object to someone using his mooring—provided they do not damage it.

It is of course assumed that one man able to handle the vessel will remain on board and vacate the mooring immediately on request on the return of the owner. It is wrong however to pick up a mooring without authority, and leave the vessel there unattended. If an owner returns under such circumstances it is best for him either to pick up the adjacent mooring temporarily or to tie up alongside. He must not let the other vessel adrift as he would be liable for any damage done.

If difficulty exists consult the Harbour Master—if there is one—but otherwise courtesy and tolerance on both sides will make a somewhat complicated problem present no real difficulty.

The position in common law is that if another owner returns and finds an unattended vessel on his mooring he is entitled to remove it to a place of safety **provided** that due care is exercised and no damage results. He is moving another man's property and in the event of damage occurring the burden of proof will be upon him to show that he took all reasonable care to prevent such damage.

Obviously to move another man's vessel in his absence should only be undertaken as a last resort in view of the possible difficulties that could arise.

Merchant Shipping (Life Saving Appliances) Rules

These are most important as a vessel may be detained unless they are complied with. It is important to realise that the Rules apply to all vessels of any size, including fishing vessels, sea going sailing vessels, and yachts exceeding 15 tons burden. The Merchant Shipping (Life Saving Appliances) Rules do not apply to pleasure craft of less than 13.7 metres (45 feet) and such craft are subject to no equipment regulations.

However, in 1990 The Department of Transport stated that it would regard as a 'pleasure craft' only one used exclusively for the private pleasure purposes of the owner. Thus craft used for chartering or training, even if under 13.7 metres in length, may be required to comply with the 1990 Department of Transport Code of Practice.

NOTES ON TOWAGE AND SALVAGE

Towage is the amount payable to a tug or other vessel by agreement for towing a vessel anywhere.

Salvage is quite another matter however and is the act of saving or helping to save vessels or maritime property of any sort when in danger. This is a voluntary act so members of the crew cannot claim salvage for saving their own vessels, neither can passengers, pilots, or crews of tugs on ordinary duty. Salvage is not payable when life is saved only.

Provided no damage is done to the salvor's vessel we hope that Yachtsmen will always help one another without thought of monetary reward; but as any vessel may at any time need assistance through no fault of her own the following notes may be helpful to avoid an excessive claim or at least inform small craft owners of the important features of SALVAGE.

(a) The R.N.L.I. never itself claims salvage or makes a charge. Lifeboatmen, in common with anyone who saves property, are legally entitled to claim salvage for themselves, but they very rarely do so. If they did, they would forfeit any R.N.L.I. reward and be required to pay the costs of the rescue and any damage sustained by the lifeboat, irrespective of whether or not their claim was successful.

(b) If a breakdown occurs under favourable conditions always ask for a tow to a mutually agreed place and arrange the payment for this in advance if possible. Do not accept any tow unless agreement has been made in advance.

(c) Unless in physical difficulties do not allow any of the rescuers' men to board your vessel.

(d) Unless 'parish rigged' or 'schooner rigged' (means cheaply rigged), never take a salvors' rope—always pass him your rope and also always—if practicable— steer your own vessel, give orders, have your anchor ready and in fact assume command of the whole situation.

(e) Unless actually in distress do not use the recognised distress signals; but ask for assistance by flags, lamp, whistle or radio. If danger does exist, naturally the Distress Signals shown in Section 8 should be used.

(f) If salvage is claimed on the spot, always endeavour to get an agreement (and in writing if possible) or have a witness to what is said.

(g) If this cannot be arranged endeavour to get agreement to have the reward decided according to the provisions of Lloyd's Open Form.

(h) Unless danger exists, no claim can be made for Salvage, nor can claim be made in general, if the attempt is unsuccessful or if it results in the vessel being put into a worse position than she was in originally.

(i) If salvage is performed always endeavour to produce the chart with the vessel's position noted thereon and the Log Book will be excellent evidence; because a 'moderate breeze' may quickly become a 'whole gale' in a Salvage claim.

(j) If a vessel runs ashore in a narrow creek on a falling tide never accept a 'pluck off' from a stranger without saying—with thanks—that you are not in distress and do not need a tow and will run a kedge anchor away until the tide rises. Otherwise what may appear to you to be a friendly gesture may turn out unfortunately to lead to a Salvage claim.

Also if an owner accepts the 'loan' of a heavy anchor and rope he must agree a sum for its 'loan'; otherwise a Salvage claim may result.

(k) If salvage is inevitable and a bargain unobtainable—never disclose the value of your vessel or the fact of whether you are insured or not.

The laws on Towage and Salvage are governed by legal action (which is always costly) so if, by prior thought, either can be avoided (except by proper arrangements) it is a wise policy to do so. Better be sure than sorry.

CUSTOMS AND EXCISE

OWNERS AND PERSONS RESPONSIBLE FOR PLEASURE CRAFT BASED IN THE UNITED KINGDOM

I GENERAL

Pleasure craft arriving in, or departing from, the United Kingdom from or to places abroad are subject to the Pleasure Craft (Arrival and Report) Regulations, 1990. In these Regulations a pleasure craft means:

(a) A vessel which, at the time of its arrival from abroad at a port in the United Kingdom, is being used for private recreational purposes, and of which the total complement, including passengers and crew, does not exceed 12 persons; or

(b) Any vessel which an officer allows, after application is made to him in person or in writing, to be treated as a pleasure craft for the purposes of these Regulations.

The 'person responsible' means the person on board a pleasure craft under whose command or subject to whose personal direction it has arrived or will depart.

The procedures will apply throughout the United Kingdom and the Isle of Man. Compliance with the system will reduce or eliminate delays in Customs clearance.

II DEPARTURES

Registration

Pleasure craft based in the United Kingdom which proceed abroad are required to be registered under the Merchant Shipping Acts, 1894 and 1983. Information on registration can be obtained from the Registrar of British Ships

Section 4

at any registry port in the United Kingdom, or the Royal Yachting Association for inclusion on the Small Ships Register. See also section in the Almanac on Registration.

Notice of Intended Departure

As far in advance as possible, the proposed date of each intended departure from the United Kingdom must be notified to HM Customs and Excise on Part I of Form C1328, which is a three part, carbon interleaved form. When completed, Part 1, which constitutes a Notice of Intended Departure should be delivered to the Customs office nearest to the place of departure to arrive prior to the expected time of departure. Customs and Excise post boxes are available for this purpose. The Notice of Intended Departure is valid for up to 48 hours after the stated time of departure.

Failure to give notice of intended departure may result not only in delay and inconvenience on return to the United Kingdom but may in certain circumstances, lead to prosecution and a fine of up to £400 on summary conviction. The person in charge of the pleasure craft during the voyage must take with him Parts II and III of Form C1328. These will constitute the arrival documents when the return voyage is completed .

Should the voyage be abandoned after despatch or lodgement of Part I of Form C1328, Parts II and III of the form marked 'voyage abandoned' should be sent to the Customs office to which Part I was originally sent.

Shipment of Stores

In general, no restriction is placed upon the shipment of reasonable quantities of foodstuffs, fuel and other stores on which all duties and VAT have been paid. The shipment of duty free stores is normally restricted but subject to certain conditions, such stores may be shipped on yachts departing for a port beyond certain limits, viz: south of Brest or north of the north bank of the Eider. Prior application is necessary and information on the procedure for shipping stores or to reship previously landed surplus duty free stores may be obtained from any Customs office, listed in Appendix 'B' of Customs Public Notice 8.

Prohibited and Restricted goods

Certain goods such as arms, strategic goods (eg computers) and items over fifty years old are prohibited to be exported from the United Kingdom except under cover of a Department of Trade and Industry export licence. The licensing requirements will however be waived where Customs are satisfied that the goods are being shipped solely for use on board the vessel as stores, or, in the case of firearms, where the owner can produce to Customs a valid firearm or shotgun certificate and the ultimate destination is not South Africa or Namibia.

Cargo

Vessels carrying goods other than personal effects and bona fide stores do not qualify as pleasure craft. Customs Public Notice No. 69 explains the procedures to be followed by commercial vessels.

Immigration Regulations

The person responsible for the vessel must ensure that the embarkation of any non-EC nationals is notified to the Immigration Officer prior to departure, unless the vessel is proceeding to the Channel Islands, Republic of Ireland or Isle of Man. In most yachting centres, Customs officers perform the duties of Immigration officers.

Passports

The person in charge of a vessel departing for a place outside the Channel Islands, Republic of Ireland or Isle of Man is advised that to take advantage of the quick report procedure on return to the United Kingdom, all persons on board must be EC nationals carrying a valid passport.

Pleasure craft sailed by persons other than owners

Persons hiring, chartering or loaning a vessel which may depart from the United Kingdom on a foreign voyage should ensure that the person responsible for the vessel is aware of the details required in respect of the VAT status of the vessel and that these details have been completed on Part 1 of Form C1328 prior to departure. Failure to complete this section of the form will inhibit the use of the quick report procedure on the return of the vessel to the United Kingdom and may result in follow-up enquiries in respect of its VAT position.

British-owned pleasure craft visiting France (including vessels towed upon trailers or carried upon vehicles)

The French authorities require all foreign pleasure craft visiting France to carry documents identifying their nationality and ownership. In the case of British-owned vessels this document is the Certificate of British Registry.

The certificate of registration available from the Small Ships Register is an official document issued by Her Majesty's Government through the Royal Yachting Association. It constitutes the evidence of nationality required under international law and will be acceptable to authorities abroad.

Small Craft Licences

The statutory requirement to obtain a Small Craft Licence for chartered or hired pleasure craft going abroad is no longer required.

III ARRIVALS

Warning: A pleasure craft is liable to be searched by Customs officers at any time. The penalties for smuggling are severe and in some instances may include forfeiture of the pleasure craft in addition to monetary penalties or imprisonment for the person(s) concerned .

General

On arrival from abroad (including the Channel Islands and the Republic of Ireland), all pleasure craft are subject to Customs control and the person responsible must make written report on Form C1328. They may also be subject to Public and Animal Health and Immigration requirements when appropriate.

The arrival of an animal brought to the UK from the Channel Islands, Isle of Man and Republic of Ireland is not restricted provided that where an animal originated from outside these countries, it has served its full quarantine.

Persons responsible for pleasure craft who are uncertain of their responsibilities in respect of the health regulations should refer to the Health Departments of the United Kingdom Form Port 38.

PROCEDURE ON ARRIVAL

Summary: All yachts must fly the yellow 'Q' flag on arrival in territorial waters and complete the declaration on Form C1328

Yachts with *nothing to declare* must post the declaration in a Customs post-box, lodge it at a Customs office or hand it to a Customs officer. When this has been done all persons on board may go home. No telephone report is required.

Yachtsmen with *goods to declare* must telephone the nearest Customs office immediately on arrival. (Note that Freephone Customs Yachts is discontinued.) They will be told whether or not a Customs officer will board the vessel, and any Customs charges will be assessed over the phone.

All yachts, whether in ports or territorial waters, remain liable to Customs anti-smuggling checks.

Signals

On entering United Kingdom territorial waters, since 1 October 1987 twelve miles from land, a yellow flag (the 'Q' flag in the International Code of Signals), must be flown conspicuously until such time as report has been made. During the hours of darkness the flag should be suitably illuminated.

Failure to fly a yellow flag on entering United Kingdom territorial waters is an offence and may, in certain circumstances, lead to prosecution and a fine of up to £400 on summary conviction. You should also complete Form C1328 at this point. Failure to complete Form C1328 when entering territorial waters is an offence and may, in certain circumstances, lead to prosecution and a fine of up to £400 on summary conviction.

If animal or public health clearance is also required the procedure in paragraph 3 of the Health Departments of the United Kingdom Form Port 38 should be followed.

Procedure for making report

If duty and/or VAT is payable on the vessel or if the vessel:

(a) has on board any goods on which duty and/or VAT is payable; or

(b) has had any repairs, modifications or additions whilst abroad; or

(c) has on board any live animals or birds (including domestic pets); or

(d) has on board any goods the importation of which is subject to any prohibition or restriction; or

(e) has on board any person who is not a patrial or if a patrial is not carrying a valid British

Section 4

11

passport (except in the case of arrivals from the Channel Islands or Republic of Ireland); or

(f) departed on its last voyage from the United Kingdom more than a year ago; or

(g) was not on its voyage from the United Kingdom cleared outwards on Part I of Form C1328; or

(h) has any death or notifiable illness or sickness on board as defined in Form Port 38; then the person responsible must make report of the vessel by ensuring that he telephones the nearest Customs Office. You may use your Radio Telephone for this. The completed form is to be handed to the officer on his arrival.

Procedure for report with nothing to declare

This method may be used when none of the conditions above apply and animal and health clearance is NOT required.

In this case the person responsible is to complete Parts II and III of Form C1328 and, if the vessel is not visited by a Customs officer, deliver Part II to a Customs office (or post it in a Customs post box) and retain Part III for reference. All persons may then leave the vessel.

Vessel boarded on arrival

If your vessel is boarded on arrival the officer will require the person responsible to complete all reporting formalities immediately. Under these circumstances a separate notification of arrival to the Customs office will not, of course, be required

Customs duty on pleasure craft

Vessels of less than 12 metres in length arriving in the United Kingdom from outside the EC (European Community) are liable to Customs duty but a vessel built in the EC or a vessel shown to have previously departed from the EC may be admitted into the United Kingdom free of duty subject to the following conditions:

(a) the vessel is being imported within three years of the date of its departure from the EC;

(b) the vessel is being imported by or at the instance of its previous exporter;

(c) no refund of Customs duty was obtained on the vessel at export and any Customs duty previously relieved on incorporated parts has been repaid;

(d) the vessel was not exported in order to be processed or repaired; and

(e) any repair outside the EEC was unforeseen at the time of exportation and (i) merely restored the vessel to its condition at exportation; and (ii) did not enhance its export value.

A declaration certifying that these conditions are fulfilled signed by the person responsible may be called for by the Customs officer on arrival if duty free importation is claimed. Particulars of any process, repairs or alterations must be declared on Part II of Form C1328.

If a person resident in the United Kingdom buys a pleasure craft while outside the EEC or if a vessel is brought to this country for the purpose of being sold or for hire, to anyone in the United Kingdom, the vessel must be produced to the Customs officer on arrival (i.e. the full report procedure must be followed) and full details of the transaction (actual or prospective) declared.

British registration of a vessel does not in itself establish title to duty free admission into the United Kingdom.

Liability to Value Added Tax (VAT)

Vessels of less than 15 tons gross and ALL vessels designed or adapted for pleasure or recreation, whatever their tonnage or age, are liable to VAT on importation.

Major changes affecting VAT are due to take effect on 1st January, 1993. At time of going to press details are not available. Readers are advised to contact local Customs Officers for up-to-date information.

Importation of goods

All goods which may be subject to a prohibition or restriction must be declared to a Customs officer. Excess goods are to be declared on the reverse of Parts II and III of Form C1328 by each person on board. Ship's surplus stores remaining are to be declared on the reverse of Parts II and III by the owner or person responsible.

Some goods are subject to duty and/or levies and import licensing control and most goods are liable to VAT. Failure to declare goods may render them liable to forfeiture and the person(s) involved to heavy penalties. No goods must be landed or transferred to another vessel until permission is given by a Customs officer or report formalities have been completed.

Animals and Birds (including domestic pets)

Rabies susceptible mammals including dogs, cats, rabbits, mice, guinea pigs, etc, must only be landed if an agricultural department licence has previously been issued. Live birds must only be landed if an agricultural department licence has previously been issued.

Certain non-domestic species of live animals and birds (including tortoises and most species of parrot) can only be imported or exported with a valid permit – contact the Department of Environment for more information.

There are severe penalties including imprisonment and heavy fines for not meeting this requirement.

Prohibited and Restricted Goods

In order to protect health and the environment, certain goods cannot freely be imported. The main items are as follows:

Flick knives, radio transmitters (walkie-talkies, CB radios, cordless telephones, etc.) not approved for use in the United Kingdom, plants and parts thereof, plant produce including trees and shrubs, potatoes and certain other vegetables, fruit, bulbs and seeds.

If you wish to bring back articles from an overseas voyage and feel that there may be some difficulty at importation, consult a Customs officer before departure. This may save problems later!

Immigration Regulations

All non-EC nationals need the permission of an Immigration officer to enter when they arrive from outside the United Kingdom, the Channel Islands or the Republic of Ireland. The person responsible must ensure that permission is obtained.

Currency Regulations

There is no restriction on the importation of any currency notes, including United Kingdom bank notes.

Personal Duty Free Allowances

Persons arriving in the United Kingdom by pleasure craft are allowed the same personal duty free allowances as those arriving by other means of transport. These allowances, and those for paid crew members, are shown at Appendix A of Customs Notice 8.

Note. Persons under the age of 17 years are NOT allowed duty free allowances of tobacco products or alcoholic drinks.

Notices & Forms

Copies of Customs Notice 8 and Form C1328 can be obtained at most Customs offices. Where copies cannot be obtained locally, enquiries should be addressed to HM Customs & Excise, CDE1, Dorset House, Stamford Street, London SE1 9PS.

IV OWNERS AND PERSONS RESPONSIBLE FOR PLEASURE CRAFT NOT BASED IN THE UNITED KINGDOM

Slightly different procedures will apply to pleasure craft not based in the United Kingdom and these are explained in Customs Notice 8A. The main differences are that Form C1329 is to be completed instead of C1328. The automatic clearance facility is not available; clearance can only be granted by the Customs officer boarding the vessel.

Further information on points of detail and copies of Public Notice 8A and Form C1329 can be obtained at most Customs offices. Where additional copies or information cannot be obtained locally, enquiries should be addressed to HM Customs & Excise, CDE1, Dorset House, Stamford Street, London SE1 9PS.

HEALTH CLEARANCE

VESSELS ARRIVING FROM ABROAD

This is now dealt with by the Port Health Authority, and full details are set out in Form Port 38 obtainable from the local Port Health Authority or from Department of Health & Social Security, Alexander Fleming House, Elephant & Castle, London SE1 6BY. Basically if there are no indications of infectious disease on board there is no need to obtain health clearance.

Section 4

International Code of Signals

ZS or Q   My vessel is 'healthy' and I request free pratique.

*   QQ   I require health clearance.

ZU   My maritime Declaration of Health has a positive answer to question(s) . . . (indicated by appropriate number[s]).

ZW   I require Port Medical Officer. ZW1 Port Medical Officer will be available at (time indicated).

ZY   You have health clearance.

ZZ   You should proceed to anchorage for health clearance (at place indicated). ZZ1 Where is the anchorage for health clearance? I have a doctor on board. AL Have you a doctor? AM.

Health clearance may be given in three ways:
a) Wholly in plain language.
b) Partly in above signal code; remainder in plain language.
c) Wholly in the above signal code.

* By night, a red light over a white light may be shown by vessels requiring health clearance. These lights should be about 2 m. apart, should be exhibited when within the precincts of a port, and should be visible all round the horizon as nearly as possible.

GENERAL SUMMARY OF ENTRY REQUIREMENTS FOR WESTERN EUROPE

1) Most countries require evidence of ownership and in Spain, France, Malta, Italy and Greece this must be in the form of a document of Registration. However, now the Small Ships Register makes Registration so cheap and easy to obtain this is obviously the most convenient way to cover all eventualities in this area.

2) Some countries, particularly concerning their inland waterways, require that the Skipper has some recognised qualification. If the Skipper does not have a Yachtmaster or Coastal Skipper Certificate, he/she should apply to the RYA for the Helmsmans (Overseas) Certificate of Competence.

3) Prepare crew lists and ensure all crew have a valid Passport, Take the charter contract if one is involved and be prepared to 'declare your intentions' when you arrive. The French authorities interpret the expression 'Private and Pleasure Only' very strictly and even crew members contributing to voyage expenses may make them consider you a commercial craft.

4) Flying the Q flag only seems to be necessary when first entering the UK, Ireland, Belgium and Spain, unless the yacht is carrying dutiable stores, or goods, which it is intended to land.

5) Virtually all countries except France (unless the yacht is carrying dutiable stores, or goods, in excess of the personal allowance limits), require you to report to the Customs at the first port of call in that country. Because of this many countries require your first point of entry to be a port where such facilities exist.

6) The Q flag must be flown when visiting the Channel Islands from anywhere outside the UK, but when returning to the UK from the Channel Islands the usual arrival procedures must be followed.

7) The Italian authorities require all visiting craft (whether by sea or road) to carry third party insurance and to have aboard available for Inspection at all times, a certified translation of the Insurance Certificate.

See RYA booklets 'Foreign Cruising Notes' for further specific details. Available from Royal Yachting Association, RYA House, Romsey Road, Eastleigh, Hants. S05 4YA. Tel: 0703 629962. Also from Cruising Association, Ivory House, St. Katharine Dock, London E1 9AT. Tel: 071-481 0881.

Seamanship

ROPE—ITS USE AND CARE

TYPES OF CONSTRUCTION

There are three main methods of rope construction, laid or twisted ropes (cable laid), the traditional form of manufacture used when natural fibre ropes were in general use, and plaited and braided ropes. Plaited ropes, usually 4, 8 or 16 plait have the great advantage of being far less liable to kink than a traditional laid rope and are thus useful for anchor and mooring ropes where long lengths may require to be rapidly stowed in fairly small places as they will flake down with no tendency to kink. Multiplait ropes have very little tendency to kink and are smooth running. This type of construction does of course require specialist splicing techniques.

Types of Material

There are three main types of man-made fibre, nylon, polyester and polypropylene. Nylon is the strongest of the three followed by polyester and then polypropylene. Nylon, as well as being very strong is also elastic and is thus most suitable for dealing with shock loads, for example with anchors, but is unsuitable for halyards where minimum stretch is essential.

Polyester has the useful combination of strength with a low stretch characteristic which thus makes it suitable for most purposes on board— it is also available as pre-stretched which is ideal for halyards, in both plaited or three -strand construction.

The main advantage of polypropylene is that it floats and is thus the most useful rope to use for dinghy painters and mooring lines where a submerged rope could offer hazards to propellers.

A fourth material polythene is relatively cheap and has a "waxy" feel, very popular for fishing net construction but of no great interest to yachtsmen, other than for mooring lines. (Unsuitable where it is necessary to tie knots due to slippery finish.) The latest additions to the man -made fibre groups are 'Spectra' (brand name of Allied Chemicals) and 'Kevlar' (brand name of Du Pont). Both are very light with immensely strong filaments.

In their present form, both ropes are mainly of interest to the racing yachtsmen where great strength and lightness are highly desirable and cost and working life of lesser importance than they are to the cruising man. Reference should be made to the manufacturers' publications when it is proposed to use any of such new generation products in view of the varying characteristics and requirements. For example Kevlar is very susceptible to damage by chafe and bending and must be protected from sunlight whereas with Spectra, variants with adequate resistance to long term creep must be selected .

Generally speaking, man -made fibre ropes used in yachts are larger than is necessary from a strength point of view in order to facilitate ease of handling, for example the modern equivalent strengthwise of the old 1½ inch circumference manilla ropes would be far too small to handle comfortably if used for sheets. The surface of the rope also has considerable bearing on its handling properties, ropes formed with a continuous filament (never possible with natural fibres) are immensely strong and very shiny in appearance, whilst rope formed of the staple or shorter filament has slightly lower strength than the continuous filament rope but has a matt finish which is obviously more desirable where the rope is frequently handled, as in the case of sheets. With self tailers or stoppers the shiny Marlow braid should be used to facilitate long life.

Handling and Care of Ropes

The majority of man -made fibres as well as being much stronger than natural fibres are very tolerant of those factors which reduced the working life of the latter, for example the former can be stored away damp and will not rot although mildew may appear. Physical damage must be guarded against as with natural fibres, particularly bearing in mind that rope under tension is easily damaged by chafe. Ropes under tension but static (e.g. mooring lines) should be protected at any angular point or rough service by plastic tubing over the rope or parcelling with canvas, etc.

The effects of chafe from normal friction surfaces such as sheaves, fairleads and cleats is considerably reduced if the bearing surfaces are large. In the case of sheaves the diameter should be not less than five times the diameter of the rope and preferably more. The groove of a sheave should have such a radius that it supports one third of the rope's circumference. Whenever possible sharp "nips" in a rope should be avoided but if a rope has to be led through a sharp angle the bearing surface of the lead should be at least that required of a sheave and smooth. Rope can be severely damaged if led through a thin shackle or eye bolt, particularly if the angle is sharp.

When coiling a rope always commence at the end which is made fast so that any twists or kinks can be chased along and run out at the far end. It is particularly important to ensure that load is never applied to rope when there is a kink in it as this will almost inevitably damage and weaken it. Rope which has been badly overloaded in any way may indicate this by being unusually hard in parts, this hardness is caused by the heat produced by the overload friction fusing some of the filaments together.

Always avoid heavy shock loads if possible, for example when passing a tow rope between a stationary vessel and a moving one never make both ends fast at once. The resulting jerk imposes a tremendous strain on the rope which if it does not damage it, may rip a cleat or bollard out. When one end has been made fast the correct procedure at the other end is to make a figure of eight turn round the bitts, or a round turn on a bollard and allow the rope to render smoothly as the load comes on, then check steadily and make fast as the vessel gathers way.

slipping off and becoming a confused tangle. When the halyard has been made up on the cleat and coiled, hold it close to the cleat, pull a short length through the coil, twist and then loop it over the horn of the cleat (Sketch 1). Alternatively a buntline hitch can be used. After coiling and looping the last loop can be pushed through the centre of the coil, capsized over the top and drawn tight (Sketch 2). A very useful hitch to use when hanging spare warps up in a cockpit locker.

A point to remember in connection with mooring ropes is that the eye of the rope should not be dropped over any lines already on the bollard. The eye should be passed up through the eyes of lines already there and then dropped over the bollard. This will facilitate the removal of any line without disturbing the others.

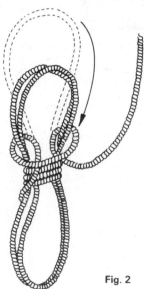

Fig. 2

It is desirable to ensure uniformity of wear in ropes whenever possible by changing end for end occasionally.

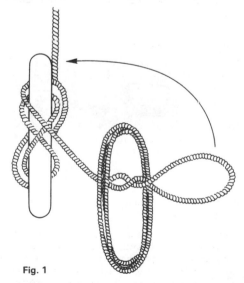

Fig. 1

Unless ropes are properly coiled kinks will occur with subsequent snags when the rope is run out. Nearly all laid ropes are right handed and should be coiled clockwise to ensure smooth running out.

In practice it is seldom that cleats on yachts are large enough to allow the fall of the halyard to be looped over the horn of the cleat without

Cleaning

The life of a rope can be extended considerably by washing in fresh water to get rid of salt crystal, grit and dirt. This should be done at the end of the season when laying up and will ensure that not only will the rope look clean but will remain soft and pliable. Detergents should not be used, soap powder only should be employed to clean the rope.

(From information supplied by Marlow Ropes)

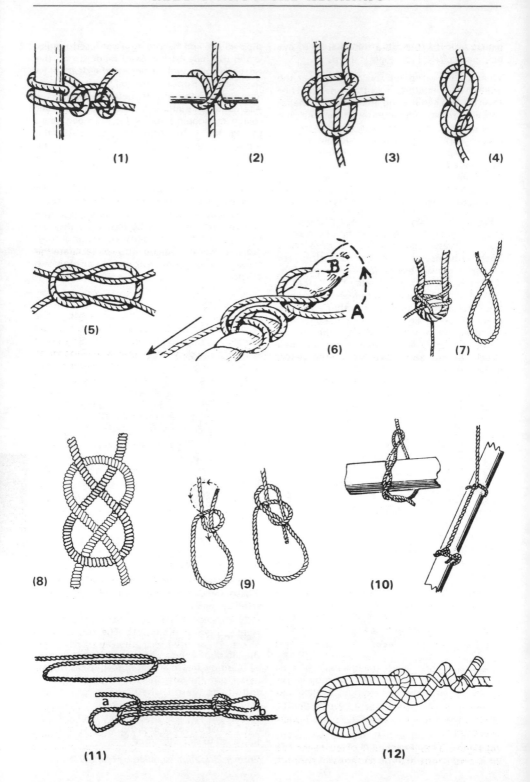

(1)

(2)

(3)

(4)

(5)

(6)

(7)

(8)

(9)

(10)

(11)

(12)

KNOTS, BENDS AND HITCHES

The following simple bends and hitches are but a few of those used by the professional seaman—they should, however, serve to meet most of the requirements of those working yachts and small boats.

A **Bend** is used to join the ends of two ropes. A **Hitch** secures a rope to another object.

The Round Turn

Although this is only the first movement in securing a rope to a permanent fixture there is much virtue in a Round Turn not always appreciated by small boat owners. Always remember that a considerable weight can be held with relatively little effort by taking a round turn about the bitts or other secure object. A round turn should always be taken about an open ended protrusion, such as bitts as this does not necessitate letting go of the rope. When in the act of coming alongside a round turn or two will take the weight without the danger of jamming.

In emergency a quick turn round some strong object on board (and the rope then held away tight), will frequently prevent the bow or stern swinging out into the tide at the wrong moment. Having stopped the vessel's movement by the round turn a judicious "slacking away" or "hauling in" using the bollard, bitt or cleat as a "hold" temporarily, is excellent seamanship—when the emergency is over, the rope can be secured or removed as desired.

(1) Round Turn and Two Half Hitches. For securing a dinghy painter to a mooring ring etc. If leaving a vessel moored to a buoy by this—the best method—have loose hitches —not too close to the buoy and lay the loose end along the standing part of the rope and frap together—it will never come adrift, but is easy to untie.

(2) Clove Hitch. A good hitch for securing a rope at intermediate points. It is not safe with a short end. Difficult to untie after being subjected to heavy strain, especially when wet.

(3) Sheet Bend. Serves many purposes. Used for making a rope fast to the bight of another—i.e. bending the sheets to the sails—securing the end of a small rope to that of a larger. If used to join ropes which are made of different materials, the ends should be seized back or the bend is liable to come adrift. (See also Double Sheet Bend.)

(4) Figure of Eight Knot. To prevent the end of a small rope from accidentally running through a block or the deck lead for jib sheets, etc.

(5) Reef Knot. Has many uses. Is excellent as a "binder" knot, joining the ends of small ropes — e.g. reef points when reefing and furling sail. Before leaving signal halliards or any "running ropes" not in use — always join both ends together in case wind blows them off the cleat and they become unrove. CAUTION: Do not use a reef knot as a bend for tying two ropes together. If the ropes are of different size, or different materials, or one is stiffer than the other, the knot is very liable to capsize.

(6) Rolling Hitch. A most practical knot much used at sea for all purposes. After commencing as a clove hitch an additional hitch is made over the first between this and the standing part of the rope which effectively jams the hitch and prevents sideways pull — the simple form is finished off with a further hitch away from the strain as shown in Fig. 6. Used for securing the tail of a block to a larger rope, hanging off a rope on a stopper, flag swivel sticks, etc. It does not slip or "roll" under normal loading but if subjected to heavy strain — as when stoppering off a mooring rope — the end (A) which does not carry the load should be "backed and dogged", i.e. backed against the hitch and twisted round the first rope (B) in long lays. The end is then held or stopped until the load can be transferred back to the larger rope.

(7) Double Sheet Bend. For securing "Bosun's Chair" and for the same purposes as the sheet bend. The working end is rove twice to give extra security.

(8) Carrick Bend. For bending two hawsers or wire ropes together. Very secure and unlikely to jam. Each end tucks under/over four times.

(9) Bowline. The most commonly used loop knot. Will never capsize if properly formed. Used to make a loop in the end of a rope without splicing—made quickly and without hesitation when sending small mooring lines ashore.

(10) Timber Hitch. Used for lifting a spar, timber, bale or plank, etc. The turns should always be dogged with the lay of the rope. When used for towing a spar, or to keep a piece of timber pointing in one direction when being lifted, it should be used with a half-hitch as illustrated.

(11) Sheepshank. Used for shortening a rope temporarily. To make more secure, especially if not subjected to a steady pull, the loops should be stopped to the standing part at points a and b.

Section 5

(12) Lighterman's Hitch. Used by lightermen to make a towing eye in the end of a barge rope. The lighterman's hitch consists of a loop secured by a half-hitch with two back tucks on the standing part, and will hold as well as any splice.

A few knots known and used correctly and instantly, shows a better seaman than one who knows all the names of the lesser used knots; but who is slow or inaccurate in their execution.

ROPE SPLICING

Eye Splice

(1) Unlay the three strands at the end of the rope enough to make at least three tucks — about one turn for each tuck — and form an eye by laying the opened strands on top of the standing part of the rope.

(2) Take the middle end (A, in Fig. 1) and tuck it, from right to left, underneath the nearest strand of the standing part.

(3) Pick up the left end (B, in Fig. 2) and tuck it — again from right to left — under the next strand to the left of the one under which (A) is tucked.

(4) Turn the whole splice over, then take the third end (C) and lead it over to the right of the third strand, so that the third tuck can, again, be made from right to left, as in Fig.3.

(5) There should now be one end coming out from under each strand on the standing part. If two ends come from under the same strand the splice is wrong.

(6) Pull each end tight enough to make a tidy and snug fit. This completes the first round of tucks.

(7) For the second round, take each end over one strand and under the next towards the left. Pull each end tight.

(8) Repeat for the third round. Never use less than three rounds of tucks if the eye is to bear any strain.

(9) If desired, for neatness, the splice can be tapered by adding additional rounds of tucks, first with halved strands and then by halving again before the final round.

Short Splicing

For joining two ropes of the same size together.

(1) Unlay the two ends to be joined—at least one turn for each round of tucks to be made.

(2) Marry these ends together, so that the strands of one rope lay alternately between the strands of the other.

(3) Hold firmly whilst making tucks. Tucks are made towards the left by passing each end, in turn, over one strand and under the next, in the same manner as described for the eye splice.

(4) If the rope is to bear any strain make at least three rounds of tucks each way.

Long Splice

Seldom used in practice but very useful as a temporary measure — i.e. until the rope can be replaced with a new one — for rope which is required to run through a block because the splice does not thicken it.

(1) Unlay the ends of two ropes to at least four times the distance required for a short splice.

(2) Marry the ends together as though about to commence a short splice.

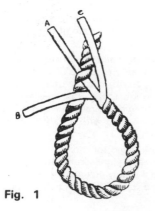

Fig. 1

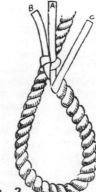

Fig. 2

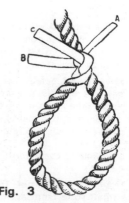

Fig. 3

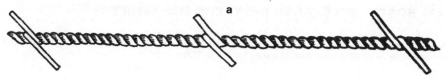

Fig. 4

(3) Select two ends which cross one another from opposite sides, unlay one of them for some length and lay into its place the opposite strand from the other rope until only a short piece is left. Cut off surplus from the end which is unlaid.

(4) Repeat with two more strands but work in the opposite direction.

(5) The third pair of strands (at 'a' in Fig. 4) are left in their original place, so that there are now three pairs of ends. Make an overhand knot with each pair so that the ends follow the lay of the rope and do not cross it.

(6) Pull very tight and then taper off by reducing the yarns in each strand.

Back Splice

Where a rope is not required to run through a block—when whippings are preferable — a back splice may be used to prevent the strands unlaying.

After unlaying the strands for the estimated distance, form a crown by interlacing the strands at the ropes end. Then tuck the strands "over one and under one" backwards towards the standing part of the rope. This splice is really only of interest with natural fibre ropes. With man-made fibres the rope ends can be fused together by heating.

Eye-Splice—Multi-Plait Rope

This double four-part rope is supple and simple to coil in either hand thus making it ideal for anchoring and mooring. The eye splice used is based upon the construction of the rope, which employs both "Z" or right-handed lay strands and "S" or left-handed strands. After whipping or stopping at the point of splice, divide the various Z and S strands as shown and tuck in two pairs front and back of the work. Thereafter the paired strands are divided and tucked separately. Finish by seizing ends as illustrated.

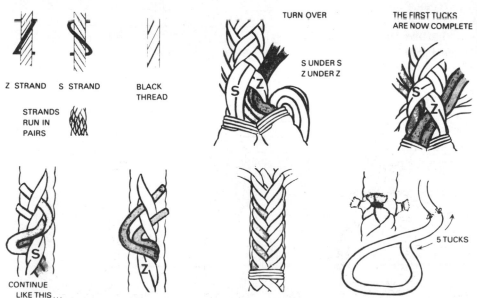

KEEL BOATS – SHEETS AND HALYARDS SIZE SELECTOR

Chart shows usual sail area in square feet for a given boat length in metres. If your boat is rigged with larger sails, use the rope size indicated for the sail area.

Overall Yacht Length m	6-8	9	10	11	12	14	16	18
Approx. Sail Area sq ft								
MAIN	90	144	171	198	252	405	540	720
GENOA/JIB	100	180	270	360	450	630	765	900
SPINNAKER	405	495	585	765	990	1260	1620	1980

SHEET SIZE mm dia								
MAIN	8	8	8	10	12	12	14	16
GENOA/JIB	10	10	12	12	14	14	16	16
SPINNAKER	8	10	10	10	12	12	12	14
SPINNAKER GUY	10	10	12	12	12	14	14	16

Suggested SHEET ropes: Marlowbraid, 16-plait matt, or KT3.

HALYARD SIZE mm dia								
MAIN	8	10	10	10	12	12	12	14
GENOA/JIB	8	10	10	12	12	12	14	16
SPINNAKER	8	8	10	10	12	12	12	14

Suggested HALYARD ropes: Marlowbraid, KT3 or super pre-stretched polyester.
Remember for KT3 Sheets or Halyards you can go down a size.

MOORING ROPES mm dia								
Displacement (approx.) tonnes	2	4	5	6.5	8	11	12	20
POLYESTER/NYLON	8-10	12	12	14	14	16	18	24
POLYPROPYLENE (Nelson)	10-12	14	16	18	20	20	24	28

Suggested MOORING ropes: 3-strand standard polyester, Multiplait nylon, Nelson or 3-strand nylon.

ANCHOR WARPS, PAINTER LINES								
NYLON	12	14	16	16	18	20	20	24
POLYESTER	14	16	18	18	20	24	24	24
NYLON (KEDGE)	8	8	10	10	10	12	12	12

Suggested ropes: Multiplait nylon, 3-strand nylon.

ANCHORS AND CHAINS								
BRUCE	5	7.5	10	10	15	20	20	30
DANFORTH & CQR	8	14	14	14	19	25	25	34
CHAIN	8	8	10	10	10	12	12	12

Bruce, Danforth and CQR anchor in kg. Other sizes are diameter in mm.

By courtesy of Marlow Ropes Limited

SIZES & BREAKING LOADS

16-plait matt polyester

Dia. mm	8	9	10	12	14	16	18	20
B/L kg.	1450	1900	2630	3470	4610	6200	7370	8300

Marlowbraid polyester

Dia. mm	6	8	9	10	12	14	16	18	20
B/L kg.	1000	1700	2000	2600	3600	4800	6300	8000	9800

KT3 100% Kevlar®/core

Dia. mm	3.5	4.5	5.5	6	8	10	12
B/L kg.	320	600	700	1200	2500	3840	5680

8-plait Marstron multifilament polypropylene

Dia. mm	5	6	8	10
B/L kg.	250	400	700	1000

3-strand super pre-stretched polyester

Dia. mm	3	4	5	6	7	8	9	10	12	14
B/L kg.	300	480	650	935	1235	1590	2010	2430	3360	4920

8-plait standard polyester

Dia. mm	1	1.5	2	3
B/L kg.	35	65	75	165

3 strand Hardyhemp polypropylene

Dia. mm	8	10	12	14	16
B/L kg.	650	1100	1600	2000	2500

3-strand standard polyester to BS 4928

Dia. mm	4	6	8	10	12	14	16	18	20	24
G.M.B.L.	400	780	1325	2025	2800	3450	4100	5100	6350	9140

3-strand Nelson spunstaple polypropylene* to BS 4928

Dia. mm	6	8	10	12	14	16	18	20	24
G.M.B.L.	550	960	1425	2030	2790	3500	4450	5370	7600

*available in multiplait

3-strand Blue Sturdee polypropylene to BS 4928

Dia. mm	4	6	8	10	12
G.M.B.L.	250	550	960	1425	2030

Multiplait nylon to BS 4928

Dia. mm	10	12	14	16	18	20	24
G.M.B.L.	2080	3000	4100	5300	6700	8300	12000

3-strand nylon to BS 4928

Dia. mm	8	10	12	14	16	18	20	24	28	32
G.M.B.L.	1350	2080	3000	4100	5300	6700	8300	12000	15800	20000

By courtesy of H&T Marlow Ltd.

Section 5

Sew and Serve Eye Splice—Plaited Rope

It is important that stoppings, sewing and finally serving are tight and neat otherwise the eye splice resulting will be loose and weak. Pass the

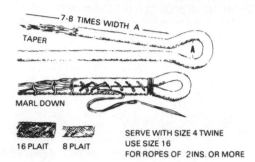

7-8 TIMES WIDTH A

TAPER

A

MARL DOWN

16 PLAIT   8 PLAIT

SERVE WITH SIZE 4 TWINE
USE SIZE 16
FOR ROPES OF 2 INS. OR MORE

sail needle right through the rope each time and tug stitch home tightly. Taper the unlaid rope yarns otherwise it will be impossible to apply a serving to the decreasing diameter of the splice. Set up taut before attempting to serve. Use No. 16 waxed whipping Polyester twine.

ROPE WHIPPINGS

Whippings are extensively used in connection with natural fibre ropes to secure the ends from unravelling but with modern man made fibres the ends of smaller ropes are usually fused together. There will always, however, be occasions when it is useful to be able to whip the end of a rope or seize an eye or thimble in the middle (e.g. double sheets).

Common Whipping.

(1) Cut off a suitable length of twine and lay one end (D in Fig. 1) along the end of the rope.

(2) Then take half a dozen or more tight turns

around the rope and the twine, working towards the end of rope and against the lay. Pull each turn tight as it is made.

(3) Now lay the other end of twine (BC in Fig. 2)

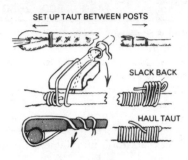

SET UP TAUT BETWEEN POSTS

SLACK BACK

HAUL TAUT

along the rope and over the turns already made.

(4) With part A of the twine, continue to pass turns round over part B.

(5) When the loop remaining at E becomes too small to pass over the rope's end, pull tight on C and cut the end off (Fig. 3).

Palm and Needle Whipping. This is more secure than the common whipping and is very suitable for reef points and all mooring ropes.

(1) Thread a suitable length of twine through a sailmaker's needle.

(2) Pass the needle under one strand and draw through most of the twine.

(3) Take about a dozen or more turns of twine round the rope, working against the lay and pulling each turn well tight as it is made.

(4) Now stitch, by following round between each strand in turn with the needle, as in Fig. 4, and thus tightly frapping the turns in between each strand.

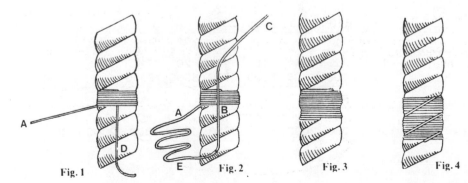

Fig. 1   Fig. 2   Fig. 3   Fig. 4

A   C   B   D   E

West Country Whipping. Useful when required to whip the bight of a rope.

(1) Place the middle of the twine against the rope, bring the two ends round in opposite directions and make a half-knot.

(2) Now bring the ends round (again, in opposite direction) to the opposite side and make another half-knot.

(3) Continue half-knotting the ends alternately on opposite sides of the rope.

(4) Finish with a reef knot when sufficient turns have been made.

MOORING ALONGSIDE

Each year a large percentage of the total damage to yachts occurs when moored alongside a quay or jetty.

When approaching the berth, make sure it is clear of overhanging obstructions which can foul the riggings or other parts of the yacht. Look also to see if there are any warning notices on the quay side, or you may return from the shore later to find your stern well jacked up by a sewer pipe, and the tide still falling.

In general, when berthed alongside, the mooring ropes should be positioned as in the diagram below, but circumstances (depending on wind, range of tide, duration of stay, possible movements of other craft, etc.) may demand some modification. It is easier to make a seamanlike job if the function of each rope is understood.

Head and Stern Ropes (1 and 2) should be strong enough to take the main load. They must also be of sufficient length to allow for the *range* of the tide. A rough rule for a range of 15 feet or less is to allow at least three times the range if the ship is berthed at half tide. If moored near High or Low Water the ropes should be adjusted later, as required. The head and stern ropes also position the ship alongside the jetty and, together with the springs, assist in checking fore and aft surging.

The diagram showing one Head rope and one Stern is only illustrative and in practice, except for a brief stay at a wharf or pier, two ropes would always be used, normally one from each bow and one from either quarter. They need not necessarily be led to the same ring or bollard ashore. With larger vessels, heavier weights being involved, several mooring ropes would always be used and with yachts in bad weather this would generally be necessary, but certainly precautionary. But connect them before dark as it is always much easier, especially if wind increases during the night.

For'rd and After Springs (4 and 3) assist the head and stern ropes in keeping the ship alongside, prevent her from surging fore and aft, and keep the bow and stern from swinging in and out.

For'rd and After Breast Ropes (5 and 6). These are seldom necessary with small craft. They are used to hold the ship alongside the jetty when boarding or loading, or to limit its distance from the jetty. Never leave breast ropes unattended in tidal waters.

Ropes which require tending with the rise and fall of the tide should, whenever possible, be made fast so that each one can be tended without disturbing another.

Slip Ropes. Mooring lines are sometimes doubled so that they can be let go from on board. A slip rope is liable to jamb when letting go if it has not been passed correctly in the first place—when only ring-bolts are available ashore, it should be passed *down* through a ring which *hangs* at the quay side and *up* through one which *lies* horizontally on top of the quay. When pulling a slip rope on board after letting the end go, haul steadily, don't *jerk*, especially when the loose end is approaching the ring or bollard. A jerk can cause the end to flip round the hauling part and jamb. A "slip" rope is only to be used as a temporary measure.

Fenders. Place with the utmost care and, when adjusting for height, bear in mind that the swell from a passing vessel can cause fenders to be toppled inboard if the lanyards are too short.

Section 5

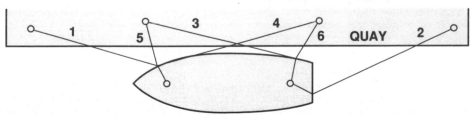

ANCHORING

Approaching anchorage. Unlash anchor from stowed position and ensure that it is ready for letting go immediately it is required.

Selecting berth. It is the duty of late arrivals to keep clear of vessels already anchored. Allow adequate clearance.

One or two anchors. A vessel moored with one anchor will swing over a much greater area than one moored with two (one upstream and one downstream) and should not be left unattended.

Making a standing or running moor. Stem the tide and motor a little way past the selected berth, drop first anchor and fall back on tide veering double the amount of chain it is intended to ride to. Drop second anchor and then haul in on first until in the selected position. Shackle second anchor cable to first and veer out until second cable is well below waterline. Vessel should then be lying midway between both anchors. Similarly with a running moor, except that the approach will be made with the tide and the first anchor will be dropped just before the selected berth is reached. Alternatively the second anchor can be laid out with the dinghy—in this case the correct amount of chain is veered with the first anchor—not double the amount.

Depth of water. Let out chain equivalent to at least three times maximum depth or five times if a warp is being used. If warp, ensure that it is connected to anchor by two fathoms of chain.

Laying out kedge. Make fast end on board and then take the coil away in dinghy, paying out from there rather than paying out from the yacht. Much easier.

Cleaning a fouled anchor. Occasions arise when the anchor becomes fouled by some underwater obstruction, usually a cable or a mooring chain. If the anchor can be hauled up to the surface a rope can be passed under the obstruction to take the weight while the anchor is being freed, and then slipped. If this is not possible and assuming that the anchor has been properly buoyed with a buoy rope attached to the crown it should not prove difficult to trip the anchor by hauling on the buoy rope in the opposite direction to the lay of the main anchor cable. It is important that this main cable should be as slack as possible, possibly by using the vessel's auxiliary engine. If the anchor has not

been buoyed remedial action may be a little more difficult.

Considering first the stockless type anchor it is a comparatively simple matter to slide a small loop of chain, attached to a warp, down the anchor cable when it will come to rest close to the crown of the anchor and the necessary pull can then be exerted.

If, however, it is a fisherman type anchor freeing may prove a little more difficult as the stock makes it difficult to get the 'retrieving' loop as far as the crown. If, however, the anchor cable is hove up as tightly as possible it will probably lift the stock off the ground and enable a chain or warp to be dragged under the stock up to the crown. A large bight of chain or weighted rope should be used, preferably towed by two dinghies spaced apart and starting from the downstream side. Once the loop has engaged with the anchor the main cable should be slacked away and tension applied by the warp in the opposite direction.

Alternatively a large bight of rope suitably weighted, 'middled' over the anchor cable and slid down to the anchor will probably engage the top arm and enable the anchor to be pulled clear provided that the angle of pull is as near horizontal as possible. In this case the main cable should not be hove in taut when the loop is slid down it.

RIDING TURN ON A WINCH

A problem which occurs sooner or later in most sailing craft is the "riding turn" on a winch. On a sheet winch the result may merely be embarrassing, on a halliard winch it creates a potentially dangerous situation with a sail that cannot be lowered. Fortunately riding turns seem to occur less frequently on halliard winches than on sheet winches.

The cause of the trouble is usually carelessness on the part of the winchman when winching in the sheet or, more likely, when "surging" it to free the sail a little.

When using the normal type of sheet winch about three turns are laid on the drum, the drum is rotated and as tension increases the winchman, who is probably also "tailing" the sheet inadvertently loses control and the sheet momentarily reverses direction. This causes the bottom turn (the one leading from the sail on to the drum) to ride down on to the skirt of the drum where it is then thrown back on to the other turns, jamming them. If the winchman does not spot this but continues winding, it will lock solid.

The first step in rectifying the situation is to heave to, thus allowing the crew to concentrate on the problem and also incidentally reducing the tension on the sheet a little. The object of the exercise is to relieve the tension on the sheet so that the riding turn can be sorted out with the aid of a large spike. This can be

achieved in several ways. If the headsail is dropped it may be possible to unhank the tack of the sail thus giving sufficient slack. Assuming that this does not work it will be necessary to apply tension to the sheet or to the clew of the sail. The latter is usually the easiest alternative. A rope is bent on to the cringle in the clew of the sail and led via a snatchblock to another winch, or a purchase is used or possibly a Spanish windlass is rigged up. Once the tension has been reduced the riding turn is easily removed.

The halliard winch, however, presents a rather different problem as it will not be possible to attach a rope to the head of the sail to reduce tension in the halliard, and it is unlikely that the tack can be unclipped because of the tension in the sail. If a wire halliard is involved, fix a Crosbie clip on to the halliard several feet above the winch, place a strop above this, bend a rope on it and lead the rope via a snatchblock to another winch or a purchase. The Crosbie clip will prevent the strop sliding down the halliard as tension is applied. In the case of a rope halliard a strop made up of 4 or 5 feet of soft rope can be used. The rope is formed into a loop which is seized on to the halliard well above the winch and each side is passed round

the halliard through the opposite side of the loop and back again. This process continues until all slack in the loop is used up when it is in effect plaited round the halliard. A purchase is attached to the bottom end of the strop and as the tension increases the strop grips the halliard. The rope used for the strop should be of smaller diameter than the halliard, otherwise it will not grip effectively.

GETTING ALOFT

At some time during his lifetime the average yachtsman may be faced with the problem of getting to the masthead in difficult circumstances. Perhaps past the first flush of youth, possibly overweight and with only his wife to assist him the situation looks difficult. Without mast steps (useful but expensive) or a rope ladder long enough to reach the masthead (unlikely to be part of the vessel's equipment) some form of mechanical assistance is required.

A counterweight is probably the most useful approach to the problem. As an example consider the use of ten-litre water carriers which

will probably be carried on board. Three, filled with water will weigh 30 kg. and will form a useful counterweight to a man weighing 63 kg. The carriers, or some other suitable weight, are attached to one end of the main halliard and the end of a spare halliard is also bent on. The weight is now hauled to the masthead and when it is up the man secures himself in a bosun's chair which is attached to the fall of the halliard. He now proceeds to haul himself up, aided by his wife on deck and the counterweight. His wife then firmly secures the halliard.

Cumbersome and slow perhaps but it offers the chance of getting aloft when no other assistance is available. It need hardly be mentioned that the person going aloft should be wearing a safety harness to clip on when working.

HEAVING TO

These few notes are not written for the experienced, long range cruising yachtsman who will already have evaluated the respective merits of heaving to, lying a'hull, towing warps and running under bare pole.

The weekend sailor, with a more modest cruising range and who prudently avoids going out in bad weather may not have contemplated the advantages of being able to leave his boat to look after itself for a short period, not necessarily in bad weather. It may be necessary to deal with a little domestic crisis below decks or merely have a peaceful meal in the cockpit and to do this, knowing that the vessel is quietly looking after itself, is greatly reassuring.

The object is to maintain a steady course at the lowest possible speed and ensure that the vessel's motion is as comfortable as possible and the principle is basically very simple.

The foresail is backed (hauled to windward), the mainsail eased slightly and the tiller lashed a little to leeward—the effect of this is that the main and foresail work against each other with the result that the vessel fore reaches slowly at probably 60°-65° off the wind and is thus under control, i.e. she does not sheer about but maintains a constant heading.

In practice, however, with modern hulls it may not be quite so simple particularly with the extreme design of a light displacement hull with narrow fin keel and transom hung rudder. The average cruising yacht, however, should perform adequately once the owner has established the sail trim required. It is well worthwhile trying out the manoeuvre initially in light winds to see how the vessel performs and then in heavier winds .

Two important points to remember: always bear in mind that although the vessel may be moving very slowly through the water, due to tidal

streams its speed over the ground may be quite appreciable so ensure that you have plenty of sea room and secondly to maintain a good lookout at regular intervals.

Remember Rule 5 of the Collision Regulations, the most important one of all.

TOWAGE—YACHTS

Towing or being towed is an eventuality which usually occurs at least once in a lifetime.

As with any emergency that is likely to occur at sea due consideration should be given to all the possibilities whilst the vessel is safely on her mooring and the owner is in a contemplative mood.

The ideal arrangement if one is being towed is to use the towed vessel's anchor cable, well secured to a strong cleat, the cable being passed to the towing vessel by means of a heaving line from either vessel. The chain must of course be secured below deck by a lashing and not shackled, in order that it can be slipped immediately if necessary. One of the advantages of using chain cable is that the weight in the bight reduces snubbing and also that being strongly

secured below deck it may not be necessary to secure it to a cleat on deck. If it is not practicable to use the anchor chain and a warp is to be used, to what is it to be secured?

In general few modern yachts carry the equivalent of the old time samson post, and whilst the cleats provided are usually adequate for their particular purpose they may be woefully inadequate to deal with the strain of a tow rope. It is important therefore to consider where and how the towing line should be attached if there are no really adequate cleats or bollards suitably positioned.

Can the tow line be secured round the foot of the mast? If the latter is stepped through the deck the problem is solved. It is important to remember however that although the mast will take the direct strain, the warp should also be secured to the deck as close to the stem head as possible. If this is not done the vessel will sheer about in a surprising manner. With the modern mast stepped on deck the situation may be somewhat different unless it is mounted in a tabernacle when the strain can normally be applied at deck level. If however the mast is merely stepped in a shoe and held in position by the compression of the rigging further thought is needed. If perhaps due to damage, the rigging is slack this method should not be used as a severe jerk on the towline when the vessel is rolling could jerk the mast out of its shoe.

If the stanchions are of reasonable strength and through bolted then a warp secured round several of them and attached to the stem head could be used as the point of attachment for the tow line. This warp should be fixed in position before the tow line is secured.

Should the stanchions prove unsuitable it may be necessary to lead a warp even farther back perhaps to the after end of the cabin, remembering that wherever this warp leads from it must be secured to the stem head before the tow line is made fast.

Having considered these various aspects the prudent owner will probably come to the conclusion that the sensible course of action is to bolt a really stout cleat or bollard to the foredeck (with an adequate backing plate under the deck) during fitting out and thus eliminate the major problem if a tow is required.

A good point to consider when being towed is the tow line itself. The legal implications of towage are dealt with under "Notes on Towage and Salvage" in Section 4 – Yachtmaster's Business and from this it will be obvious that one's own warp or anchor chain should be passed over to the towing vessel.

Consider now the other side of the picture — that of towing another vessel, and dealing with the point of tow first. If possible the attachment point of the tow line should not be at the stern, although on most yachts it will almost certainly

be the only place to secure it. A tug for example has the towing point amidships, a position which permits complete manoeuvrability of the towing vessel.

The remarks about cleats on the towed vessel apply equally well to the towing vessel and although apparently not so important as the cleats at the forward end of the vessel, strong cleats or bitts on the quarters are vital when mooring up in a tidal harbour—the moral is have strong cleats sited wherever a heavy strain is likely to be imposed on the craft.

The towing situation can vary from pulling a vessel off a lee shore in heavy weather to quietly moving a vessel in harbour in calm conditions and obviously the procedure will vary considerably. Considering the first possibility the most important point is to ensure that the vessel rendering assistance is not herself endangered, either by getting a rope around her prop or running aground and thus creating yet another problem for the rescue authorities. When within a safe distance of the distressed vessel a line can be floated down attached to an empty water carrier, fender etc., and at this point it might be prudent for the rescuing vessel to drop her anchor in case for any reason she becomes unable to manoeuvre. Having transferred a line the remainder of the operation is a matter of good seamanship on both vessels, remembering that every situation is different.

If moving another vessel in calm water, especially in harbour, it is usually easier to carry this out with the second vessel lashed alongside the towing craft, properly secured with breast ropes and springs.

A final point in connection with being towed, the remarks under Salvage Notes may sound unduly alarming and induce the owner to refuse all offers of a tow in a difficult situation unless he is practically on the point of sinking. If however the vessel is adrift within the area of a harbour authority, assistance may be offered by one of the authority's launches, and this will almost certainly not be charged for, the tow will be to a place of safety but not necessarily where the owner would wish to go.

GLOSSARY OF NAUTICAL TERMS

ABAFT
Aft of any particular point on the vessel. e.g. abaft the mast – behind the mast.

Abeam
At right angles to the line of the keel.

About
To go about, to change tack.

Aft
Towards the stern of the vessel.

Amidships
Midway between stem and stern.

Apparent wind
The wind felt aboard the boat. The speed and relative direction of the boat and speed of the wind affect the angle of the true wind.

Athwart
From side to side.

Avast
To stop, to hold fast, e.g. avast heaving.

Awash
A vessel, wreck, or shoal so low that water constantly washes over.

Aweigh
Term to indicate that the anchor has broken out of the ground.

BACK
(a) Wind shifting anti clockwise (b) To sheet a headsail out to windward making the bow bear away from the wind.

Backstay
Standing rigging from a masthead leading aft to take the strain of the mast.

Ballast
Iron or lead placed in bottom of a ship to increase her stability.

Bar
A shoal in the approach to a harbour.

Battens
Thin pieces of wood or plastic set into the leech of the sail to preserve the shape.

Beacon
Aid to navigation, lighted or unlighted, radio or racon, set on the shore or rocks.

Beam
(a) Extreme width of a vessel. (b) Athwartships timber on which the deck is laid.

Beam bearing
Direction of objects when abeam i.e. at right angles to the fore and aft line.

Bearing
Direction of an object expressed in Compass notation.

Bear away
To put the helm up, i.e. keep further away from the wind.

Beating
Sailing towards the direction of the wind by tacking.

Becket
Small rope circle, a simple eye.

Belay
To make a rope fast to a belaying pin or cleat.

Bend
Knot of various kinds.

Bight
Any part of a rope between its ends; also a curve, a cove on a coastline, or in a channel.

Binnacle
The box which houses the Mariner's Compass.

Bitter end
The last part of a cable left around the "bitts" when the rest is overboard.

Bitts
Pair of vertical wood or metal posts with a horizontal cross bar fixed on deck to which ropes may be secured.

Bluff
(a) Steep shore. (b) Full bowed vessel.

Bobstay
A stay for the bowsprit to prevent it lifting; from bowsprit end to stem at waterline.

Bollard
Heavy short post on a quay or deck to secure ship's mooring lines to.

Bolt rope
A strong rope sewn round the edge of sails to give strength and prevent tearing.

Boom
A spar for many purposes, such as to stretch out the foot of a fore and aft sail.

Boot-topping
A band of paint at the waterline between "wind and water".

Bottle screw
A screw fitting for adjusting the tension of shrouds and stays.

Bower anchor
Main anchor carried forward in a vessel.

Bow
Forward part of a vessel.

Bowsprit
Heavy spar from deck leading forward from stem head to which headsails are attached.

Breast line
Ropes forward and aft at right angles to the ship to "breast" into jetty.

Bridle
A rope attached to both ends of a boat or object to lift it. Lifting tackle is attached to middle of the rope.

Bring up	To stop, as to come to anchor.
Broach to	When running to accidentally turn and get broadside on to wind and sea.
Bulkheads	Partitions fore and aft or athwartships, forming separate compartments.
Bulwarks	A vessel's topsides that extend above the deck.
Buoy	A float, with distinguishing name, shape, colour or light.
Burgee	Pennant (pointed) shaped flag with design indicating the Yacht Club the vessel's owner belongs to.
By the head	Greater draught forward than aft.
By the lee	When running under sail, if the wind blows over the same side as the mainsail.
By the stern	Greater draught aft than forward.
CABLE	(a) $\frac{1}{10}$th Nautical mile, (b) Anchor chain.
Capstan	A vertical cylindrical machine for veering or hoisting the anchor chain.
Careen	To heel a vessel over on one side by tackles, to work on her bottom .
Carry way	To continue to move through the water.
Carvel	Edge to edge planking for a vessel's hull.
Caulk	To fill the side or deck seams with oakum or cotton to prevent leaking .
Chain plates	Metal strips fastened outside or inside the hull to take the rigging strain.
Check	To slowly stop a vessel's movement or to slowly ease a rope.
Chine	The fore and aft line of the hull where the bilge turns up towards the topsides of the hull.
Claw off	Working a vessel to windward off a lee shore.
Cleat	A two pronged device for making fast ropes.
Clew	The corner of the sail where the leech meets the foot.
Clinker	Planking when one edge overlaps the other lower plank.
Close-hauled	Sailing close to the wind.
Companion	Ladder in a ship.
Composite	A wooden vessel built with iron floors and frames.
Con	To give orders to the helmsman in narrow waters.
Counter	The overhanging portion of a stern.
Course	(a) The direction a vessel steers in. (b) The square sail set from a lower yard.
Cradle	The frame erected round and under a vessel to support her out of the water.
Cringle	Rope round a thimble, worked into a sail clew.
Crown	(a) Where the arms of an anchor meet the shank. (b) The knot when the strands of a rope are interlocked to make a backsplice.
Crutch	A stanchion with half round upper end to support the boom (also Gallows).
DAVIT	Iron crane for hoisting, lowering and holding boats in position in large vessels.
Dead reckoning	The position found by calculation from course steered and distance run.
Deadweight	Total weight of vessel, also known as the displacement.
Deckhead	Underside of a deck. The roof of a ship's cabin.
Deep	(a) Unmarked soundings of the lead line. (b) Deep water channel between shoals.
Dolphin	A built pile structure for mooring in harbour.
Downhaul	Rope or tackle used to haul down sail or yard.
Down helm	Order to helmsman to put tiller away from wind; up helm is towards wind.
Dowse	(a) To extinguish a light. (b) Lower sail or spar quickly. (c) Spray with water.
Draught	The depth of water occupied by a vessel at any time.
Drogue	A sea anchor – a cone shaped canvas bag to which the vessel lies in heavy weather to keep the bows pointing into the waves, or towed from the stern to slow the speed when running.
EARING	Rope for bending sail or head cringle to a yard or clew cringle to a boom.
Ebb	The period when the tide falls or flows from the land.
Eddy	Circular motion of the water unconnected with general water movement.

Section 5

Ensign	The flag, always carried at the stern, that denotes a vessel's nationality.
Eye of the wind	That point from which the wind is blowing towards the observer.
FAIRLEAD	A fitting for leading a rope over an obstruction to avoid friction.
Fairway	Shipping channel normally the centre of an approach channel.
Fathom	Nautical measurement of depth of six feet or 1.83m.
Fender	Soft rubber or other material to prevent chafe between vessels, or vessel and pier.
Fetch	(a) To make, arrive at a desired point. (b) The distance the wind has from weather shore to ship.
Fiddle	Wooden top, with divisions fitted to saloon table in rough weather.
Flare	The overhang of a vessel's bow; also a distress signal.
Fix	A position obtained by taking accurate bearings or by astronomical observation.
Flashing	Navigation light with duration of light less than dark, and single flash of regular intervals.
Floor	Athwartship beams supporting the cabin sole.
Foot	The lower edge of a sail.
Fore and aft	In line with the keel – lengthways of the ship.
Forward	Towards the bow.
Foul	Opposite to clear, as "foul berth", "foul anchor", "foul bottom".
Frap	To bind ropes together, or to bind a loose sail to prevent it flapping.
Freeboard	The distance from the waterline to the deck outboard edge.
Freshen	Wind freshens when increasing
Full and bye	Close hauled but with the sails well filled.
Furl	Gathering in sail and securing with gaskets to its spar.
GAFF	The spar to which the head of a fore and aft sail is bent.
Galley	The kitchen of a ship of any size.
Gallows	Frame of wood or metal with rounded top for supporting the boom .
Gimbals	Two concentric rings to hold the compass or stove horizontal at all times.
Go About	To tack.
Goose-neck	A metal fitting for securing a boom to a mast. Allows swing and topping.
Goose-winged	When running and the after mast sail is out on the side opposite to the fore sail.
Ground	(a) A ship touching bottom is said to ground. (b) Ground swell is the long coastal swell.
Gunter	A sliding gunter rig is when the gaff is hoisted vertically, reducing the necessity for a tall mast.
Gunwale	The heavy top rail of a boat.
Guy	A rope or wire used to control a spar or derrick.
Gybe	To allow a fore and aft sail to swing from one side to the other when running.
HALYARDS	Ropes or tackles used to hoist sails or flags.
Hanks	Strong clip hooks which attach head sails to the mast stays.
Hard	A place, often specially constructed, for beaching small vessels.
Harden up	To bring the vessel closer to the wind.
Hawse pipes	Pipes leading down through the bows through which the anchor cables are led.
Hawser	A heavy rope used for mooring, kedging, warping, towing or as a temporary anchor warp.
Head	Forward in a ship, headsails are those set forward of the foremast.
Head board	A triangular board sewn into the top of a sail to which the halyard is attached.
Head Sea	Sea from ahead, beam sea is caused by a wind blowing from abeam.
Heads	Toilets in a ship.
Heave the lead	To take soundings with a lead line.

Heave to	A sailing vessel is hove to when the foresail is backed thus reducing the way through the water.
Heaving Line	Light line, knotted on end to throw ashore when berthing as a messenger for a larger mooring line.
Heel	A list from the upright; the foot of a mast.
Helm	The tiller or wheel.
Hitch	To make a rope fast to a spar or stay, but not to another rope.
Holding ground	The type of bottom for anchor, i.e. good or bad holding ground.
Holiday	An unpainted or unvarnished spot in a vessel.
Horse	An iron bar parallel to the deck, running athwartship for a sail sheet to travel.
Hounds band	A band around the mast with securing eyes for attaching the lower stays.
Hull	Structure of a vessel below deck level.
INSHORE	Towards the shore
Irons	A vessel is in irons when caught head to wind and unable to pay off on either tack.
Isophase	Navigation light where duration of light and dark are equal.
JACK-STAY	A bar or rope on which anything travels e.g. a rope leading along the deck, to which safety harnesses may be clipped.
Jack staff	Small staff in the bows from which the jack is flown.
Jib	The triangular sail set as the forward headsail.
Jury	After losing mast or rudder makeshift rig to get the vessel to safety.
KEDGE	A lightweight anchor for kedging or warping.
Keel	The heavy backbone of any vessel, runs fore and aft on which the vessel sits when grounded.
King spoke	The spoke of the steering wheel which is upright when the wheel is amidships.
Knot	One nautical mile per hour.
LACING	The long line that secures the sail to a spar through eyelets.
Launch	To slide a vessel into the water. A small motor tender.
Lay	To go, i.e. lay aft or lay aloft, lay to (i.e. heave to) lay up, lay a course. The twisting of strands in a rope.
Lazy	An extra such as a lazy painter, i.e. an extra painter.
Leech	The after side of a fore and aft sail, and the outer sides of a square sail.
Lead	The lead weight at the end of the lead line used to find depth of water.
Lee side	The side away from the wind direction.
Lee tide	Tidal stream running with the wind.
Leeward (loo'ard)	Towards the sheltered side.
Leeway	The sideways drift of a vessel from her course to leeward, due to wind pressure.
Life line	Lines stretched fore and aft for crew to hold on to.
Lift	A rope or wire to support a spar as topping lift.
List	When a vessel heels through having greater weight on one side.
Log	An instrument for recording the distance run.
Log book	The record of events on board a ship, especially navigational.
Loom	The reflection on the clouds when the light is still below the horizon; also an oar handle.
Lubber line	Line on the inside of a compass bowl indicating the ship's head.
Luff	To keep closer to the wind; forward edge of a sail.
MAKE	To attain, i.e. to make harbour. Make fast is to secure. Tides that make increase. Make sail is to set sail.
Marline spike	Pointed steel tool for opening strand of rope when splicing.
Marry	To bring two ropes together.
Mast head rig	When the foresail goes up to the top of the mast.

Section 5

19

Messenger	Light line bent to a larger hawser and lead to the winch when the larger rope would be too heavy to do this.
Midships	Order to the helmsman to centralise the rudder.
Miss stays	To stay up in the wind when tacking.
Moor	To moor is to lie with two anchors down. Vessels are said to moor to a jetty when well made fast with several mooring lines.
NEAP TIDES	When the tide does not rise or fall much, when the moon is in quadrature .
Neaped	Of a grounded ship when the tide does not rise high enough to float her.
OCCULTING	Navigation light with duration of light more than dark and total eclipse at regular intervals.
Offing	To seaward.
Overhaul	To slack off a tackle.
PAY OUT	To ease a chain or rope.
Pintle	The vertical pin on which the rudder is shipped.
Pitching	A ship's movement in a seaway in a fore and aft direction.
Pooped	A term to indicate that a heavy sea has come inboard over the stern causing damage.
Port	The left hand side of a ship looking forward.
Port tack	To sail with the wind on the port side before the beam.
RACON	Beacon giving characteristic signal when triggered by ship's radar set.
Rake	The inclination of the mast in the fore and aft line from the vertical.
Ratlines	Horizontal ropes as steps affixed to the shrouds to facilitate climbing.
Reach	The courses of a sailing vessel between being sailed close hauled and running.
Reefing	To reduce sail area by taking in at the reefing points.
Round turn	To put a turn around a bollard to hold the strain on a rope under tension.
Running rigging	That rigging which is not standing e.g., halyards, sheets, purchases, etc.
SAMSON POST	Used to secure anchor or tow line.
Scantlings	The dimensions of a ship's timbers.
Scuttles	Round holes in the ship's side for ventilation and light.
Sheer	The rise of a ship's deck towards the bow or stern from amidships.
Sheer strake	The upper line of plating or planking on the hull.
Sheet	Rope or chain at lower corner of sail for regulating its tension.
Shroud	Set of ropes forming part of standing rigging and supporting mast or topmast.
Skeg	A fixed vertical fin on the after side of which the rudder is attached.
Slack water	Stationary tidal stream.
Slack in stays	When a vessel is slow in coming about.
Sole	The floor of a cabin or cockpit.
Sound	To measure the depth of water by lead line or electronic means.
Spitfire jib	A small heavy storm jib.
Spring	A mooring rope to prevent a vessel moving fore and aft when tied up alongside a quay, e.g. back spring is attached to the stern of the vessel and led to a bollard on the quay forward of the vessel to prevent it moving backwards.
Spring tides	Tides when moon is full or new, that is when range of tide is greatest.
Stand on	Maintain course.
Starboard	The right hand side of a ship facing forward.
Starboard tack	With the wind on the starboard side forward of the beam.
Stem	The forward continuation of the keel to which the planking at the fore end of the boat is affixed.
Stern sheets	The platform extending aft from the aftermost thwart.
Stern post	The after continuation of the keel to which the planking at the after end is affixed, or in the case of boats with a transom, the transom.
Stiff	Not easily inclined and when inclined returns quickly to the vertical.

Surge	To allow a rope to slip on a power windlass whilst it is revolving; to allow a rope under tension to slip whilst on a cleat or bollard.
TABERNACLE	A box-like structure on deck to hold the foot of the mast when this does not run through the deck. Usually opening aft to allow mast to be lowered.
Tackle	A purchase of ropes and blocks.
Taff-rail	A rail around stern of vessel.
Take up	To tighten.
Thwarts	Planks placed across the boat to form seats.
Tiller	Lever for turning the rudder.
Toggle	A wooden pin with one end of a line seized to its middle to make fast to an eye.
Transit	A line formed when two distant objects are in line, one behind the other.
Transom	The flat stern of a yacht, originally a board to which the after ends of the planking was secured.
Trick	A period at the wheel.
Tumble home	Where a ship's sides are inclined inwards above the water line.
Turning short round	Turning a vessel within as small a circle as possible.
UNDER WAY	When a vessel is not made fast to the ground.
Up and down	Vertical, a term used in anchor work.
VANG	A guy for steadying a gaff.
Veer	To ease out a cable. A clockwise shift of the wind.
WARPING	Moving a vessel by means of a hawser.
Weather helm	A boat has weather helm when it has a tendency to turn up into the wind.
Weather side	The side upon which the wind is blowing.
Weather tide	Where the tide is making against the wind.
Wear ship	Turning a ship around before the wind, keeping the sails full (the opposite to tacking).
Weigh	To lift the anchor off the ground.
Wind rode	Where an anchored vessel is lying to the wind rather than the tide.
YARD	A spar suspended from a mast, to spread the sails.
Yaw	When the ship's head is swung by the action of the waves.
Young flood	The first movements in a flood tide.

Section 5

SAFETY AT SEA

6

SAFETY AT SEA IN SMALL CRAFT

Safety at sea in small craft is not just a matter of carrying a packet of red flares — it is an attitude of mind and this fact should never be forgotten.

It starts with the knowledge that the ship is well found, with adequate gear and equipment and is suitable for the type of passage making that the owner contemplates. Following this should be the knowledge that the vessel is adequately provided with sufficient fuel for main or auxiliary engines and fitted with the necessary spares and equipment to deal with any situations that can be foreseen.

This — very basically deals with the vessel — what of the Skipper and crew?

The Skipper should have sufficient navigational knowledge to be aware of his position at all times and under all conditions, a basically simple requirement but one needing theoretical knowledge and the ability to put that knowledge to practical use.

He should, in addition, have sufficient knowledge of seamanship, weather forecasting, ship handling and the capabilities of his crew (and himself) to make sound judgements in difficult situations.

Having established that the ship is well-found and the Skipper and crew are competent, consideration should be given to the provision of the accepted "safety equipment.' Apart from obvious items such as personal buoyancy, safety harness, life rafts, etc, there is available an impressive range of equipment designed to assist, directly or indirectly, in avoiding or getting out of, the difficult situation. It is important to remember that all such equipment demands maintenance in some form or other together with the necessary operating knowledge. In difficult circumstances at night, lack of knowledge of the whereabouts of white flares or how to operate them, may lead rapidly to a situation in which red rocket flares are needed!

Summing up therefore, safety at sea demands a well found ship and a competent Skipper and crew who do not exceed their limitations. A rescue operation for a small craft at sea is almost invariably due to an error of judgement somewhere along the line and is therefore, an admission of failure to perform adequately under conditions that should have been foreseen.

A final word — probably the greatest danger facing the small yacht at sea, is not being run down by a supertanker, but the everyday risk of man overboard — some ideas on dealing with this situation are included further on in this section.

DEPARTMENT OF TRANSPORT (DTp) REQUIREMENTS

FOR DECK OFFICERS OF LARGE YACHTS AND SAIL TRAINING VESSELS

Yachts of 80 GRT to 200 GRT

(1) The skipper shall have an officially recognised Yachtmaster (Coastal) or RYA Yachtmaster (Offshore) Certificate for voyages within the Limited European Trading Area (E.T.A.). This area is roughly from Norway to Cape St. Vincent. (See later details).

(2) For voyages outside the Limited E.T.A. the skipper must hold an officially recognised Yachtmaster (Ocean) or RYA Yachtmaster (Ocean) Certificate.

(3) Except for voyages of less than 8 hours duration in the Limited E.T.A. the second in command must hold a similar Certificate to the skipper.

Yachts exceeding 200 GRT

Above 200 GRT the Merchant Shipping Act 1970 applies and two deck officers with DTp Certificates and a certificated engineer are required.

Sail Training Vessels

Sail training vessels registered in the U.K. and exceeding 80 GRT with or without auxiliary engines, which carry to sea persons under training or instruction, require two deck officers. One shall have a Certificate of Competency (Deck) Class I and the second a Certificate of Competency (Deck) Class II

The Trading Areas

'Limited European Trading Area' an area bounded by a line from a point on the Norwegian coast in latitude 62°N to a point 62°N 02°W; thence to a point 58°N 10°W; thence to a point 54°N 14°W; thence to a point 51°N 14°W; thence to a point 38°40'N 10°W. thence to Cape Vincent; but excluding all waters which lie to the northward and eastward of a line between Kalmar on the east coast of Sweden and a point on the west coast of Oland in latitude 56°40'N and from the southern tip of Oland to Gdansk, except between the dates of 1st May and 30th November when the remaining waters of the Baltic Sea are included.

'Extended European Trading Area' an area bounded by a line from Mys Kanin Nos Lt.Ho. on the eastern shore of the White Sea to a point 72°N 28°14′E; thence to a point 72°N 24°E; thence to a point 70°10′N 14°30′E; thence to a point 62°N 02°W; thence to a point 58°N 10°W; thence to a point 54°N 14°W; thence to a point 33°N 18°30′W; thence to a point 28°N 19°15′W; thence to a point 15°N 18°30′W, thence to Dakar; including the Limited E.T.A and the Baltic, Mediterranean and Black Seas.

EQUIPMENT

Pleasure Yachts of 13 m. in length or over are required to carry certain equipment as detailed below.

When satisfied that your vessel is equipped as required by the Rules, you may arrange for the DTp to carry out a full inspection and if satisfactory a certificate will be issued recording that the vessel is properly equipped as required under the appropriate rules. A charge is made for this service and details may be obtained from the nearest marine Survey Office.

Vessels of 13-21 metres in length

(a) If engaged on either a voyage to sea in the course of which it is more than 3 miles from the U.K. coast or a voyage to sea during the months of November to March inclusive:

(i) One or more inflatable liferafts of sufficient aggregate capacity to accommodate the total number of persons on board.
(ii) At least two lifebuoys one of which shall be fitted with a self-igniting light and self-activated smoke float.

(b) If a vessel which does not proceed to sea or which only proceeds to sea during the months of April to October, inclusive, on voyages in the course of which it is not more than 3 miles from the coast of the U.K:

(i) Lifebuoys at least equal in number to half the total number of persons on board, but, in no case, less than two lifebuoys. One lifebuoy to be fitted with self-igniting light and self-activated smoke float.

(c) A buoyant line at least 10 fathoms in length.

(d) One DTp approved lifejacket for every person on board.

(e) At least six pyrotechnic distress signals.

(f) In a position outside the machinery spaces, a hand pump with a permanent sea connection and a hose with a nozzle at least ½in. in diameter capable of producing a jet of water having a throw of not less than 20ft which can be directed on any part of the ship. (In fully decked vessels of less than 50ft and open vessels of less than 70ft, two fire buckets may be substituted for this equipment.)

(g) A spray nozzle suitable for use with the hose in (f).

(h) If fitted with oil-fired boilers or internal combustion type engines, two portable fire extinguishers suitable for extinguishing oil fires.

Vessels of 21-26 metres in length

(a) At least two inflatable liferafts of sufficient aggregate capacity to accommodate twice the total number of persons on board.

(b) At least four lifebuoys. Two of these are to be fitted with self-igniting lights and self-activating smoke signals and the other two with 15 fathom lines.

(c) One DTp approved lifejacket for every person on board.

(d) A line-throwing appliance.

(e) At least one power-operated fire pump, a fire main, water service pipes and hydrants capable of supplying at least one jet of water which can reach any part of the ship.

(f) At least two fire hoses.

(g) At least three portable fire extinguishers or fire buckets (if fire buckets are provided at least one shall be fitted with a lanyard).

(h) If a fully decked ship, a fireman's axe.

(i) At least six pyrotechnic distress signals.

Additional requirements for vessels with oil-fired boilers or internal combustion type engines.

(j) If the source of power and the sea connection to the power operated pump required by (e) are not outside the boiler or machinery spaces, an additional fire pump and its source of power and sea connection shall be provided in a position outside these spaces. This additional pump may be manually operated but, in that case, it must be capable of producing a jet having a throw of not less than 20 ft through a hose and ⅜in. diameter nozzle.

Section 6

3

Vessels of 26 metres in length or over and vessels of any size of 150 tons gross or over.

The Life Saving and Fire Appliance Rules call for comprehensive additional equipment to that laid down above. Advice on the requirements for these vessels will be given on request to the DTp.

Notes

(1) Where any equipment is required to be provided by the Rules, it should be approved equipment. It is in the Owners' interests to see that their suppliers supply the correct equipment.

(2) Lifejackets may be the Standard Kapok lifejackets or, if preferred, those complying with British Standards specification No. BS 3595: 1963, provided they do not depend wholly upon oral inflation.

(3) 4-man capacity inflatable liferafts are only permitted in vessels where the total number of persons aboard is 4 or less. If more than 4 persons are carried, the minimum capacity of any raft is to be 6.

(4) Certain items of liferaft equipment can be reduced and some omitted for vessels under 70 ft. in length. The supplier of the inflatable raft can advise.

(5) 'Length' in relation to a registered ship means registered length, and in relation to an unregistered ship means the length from the fore part of the stem to the aft side of the head of the stern post or, if no stern post is fitted to take the rudder, to the fore side of the rudder stock at the point where the rudder passes out of the hull.

DEPARTMENT OF TRANSPORT (DTp) RECOMMENDATIONS

Vessels 5.5 — 13.7 metres in length

The following recommendations are intended to guide owners and operators of seagoing pleasure craft on the safety equipment which should be carried. Needs in excess of this will vary according to the size and type of the craft and the conditions and area of the intended operations.

Owners and users must have equipped their craft as necessary with adequate navigation lights and means of giving sound signals to conform to the International Regulations for Preventing Collisions at Sea. It is assumed that the craft has been provided also with the usual equipment for its operation and safe navigation.

Because of the special considerations applicable to boats of less than 5.5 metres (18 feet) in length overall, namely their limited stowage space, fewer occupants and the wide diversity of types, the recommendations for craft in this category are shown separately from those of 5.5 metres (18 feet) to less than 13.7 metres (45 feet) in length overall.

In inland areas, the operations and equipment of craft may be subject to the requirements of local and water authorities. Other craft may be operating under organised club rules, which call for certain standards of equipment. Where these considerations do not apply or where they do not fully specify the safety equipment which should be carried, owners and users of pleasure craft operating in inland waters should also be guided by the following list of safety equipment. Needs will vary according to the size and type of the craft and the conditions and area of the intended operations. In very shallow water or on narrow canals with low banks, very little equipment may be needed.

Personal Safety Equipment

One lifejacket to BSI Specification should be carried for each person on board and should be worn at all times when there is a risk of being pitched or falling into the water. When not being worn the lifejacket should be kept in a safe but immediately accessible place.

One safety harness to BSI Specification 4224 should be carried for each person on board sailing yachts. (It may be advisable to carry one or more safety harnesses on other boats, depending on the circumstances.) It should be worn, appropriately adjusted, at all times when on deck in bad weather or at night, where there is a risk of falling overboard, except that it is inadvisable to wear it at speeds of 8 knots or more. Experience has shown that at such speeds it can be dangerous.

Sometimes it is advisable to wear both lifejacket and harness. When this is so, care should be taken to ensure that one does not interfere with the safe operation of the other.

Rescue Equipment

A minimum of 2 lifebuoys should be carried on each vessel for 'man overboard' situations. If the vessel is proceeding by night, one of the lifebuoys should have an igniting light and a 30 metres buoyant line in reserve and it should be positioned within reach of the helmsman.

Other Flotation Equipment

Additional flotation equipment should be carried according to the following:

(i) Up to 3 miles from land.

Summer (1st April to 31st October inclusive) -1 30 in. lifebuoy or buoyant seat of a pattern accepted by the DTp per 2 persons.

The lifebuoys specified above may be counted against this need, but if they are smaller than 30 in. each should be regarded as support for one person only. Alternatively the winter standard could be maintained.

Winter (1st November to 31 March inclusive) -1 inflatable liferaft of DTp accepted type, or its equivalent, sufficient in size to carry all occupants, and which should be carried on deck, or in a locker opening directly to the deck. The liferaft should be serviced annually.

For craft in sheltered waters, the scale proposed for summer may usually be regarded as adequate in winter also. Liferafts may not be necessary on angling boats operating in organised groups each vessel of which is in continuous contact with another.

(ii) Where the vessel is going beyond 3 miles from land.

1 inflatable liferaft of DTp accepted type, or its equivalent, sufficient in size to carry all occupants, and which should be carried on deck, or in a locker opening directly to the deck. The liferaft should be serviced annually.

The following are acceptable alternatives to the inflatable liferaft of DTp accepted type or equivalent:

(i) A solid dinghy carried on deck. It may be a collapsible type but should be fitted with permanent, not inflatable, buoyancy and should have oars and rowlocks secured thereto .

(ii) An inflatable dinghy built with two compartments one of which is fully inflated or with one compartment which is fully inflated. It should be carried on deck, and should have oars and rowlocks secured.

(iii) An inflatable dinghy (with two compartments) which need not be carried on deck if the yacht has enough permanent

buoyancy to float when swamped with 115 kilos (250 lb.) added weight.

In sheltered waters, the dinghy may be towed, provided the tow is secure.

Fire Fighting Appliances

Owners and builders will know that the degree of fire protection in a craft should not be limited to the fire appliances provided but can and should be considerably increased by avoiding any obvious fire hazards in the early stages of design and construction. Attention in this respect is drawn to the Home Office pamphlet 'Fire Precautions in Pleasure Craft.' Not withstanding such built-in precautions the following appliances are considered to be necessary:

For craft up to 9 m. (30 ft.) in length with cooking facilities only or with engines only, 1 fire extinguisher of not less than 1.4 kilos (3 lb.) in capacity (dry powder) is recommended. Craft having both cooking facilities and engines should carry an additional extinguisher of the same extinguishing capability. Carbon Dioxide (CO_2) or foam extinguishers of equivalent extinguishing capability are acceptable alternatives to dry powder appliances. BCF (bromo-chloro-difluoro-methane) or BTM (bromo-trifluoro-methane) extinguishers may be carried providing the owners are aware that the fumes given off are liable to be dangerous, especially in a confined space, and a notice to this effect should be prominently displayed at each such extinguisher.

For bigger craft and for those with more powerful engines requiring the carriage of large quantities of fuel, additional extinguishers of not less than 2.3 kilos (5 lb.) in capacity (dry powder) or equivalent and in some cases a fixed fire extinguishing installation, will be necessary.

Two buckets with lanyards should also be carried on all craft. A bag of sand, in addition, can be useful in containing and extinguishing burning spillages of oil or fuel.

Other Equipment

The following items are recommended for all craft:

2 Anchors, each with a warp or chain of appropriate size and length. Where warp is used at least 5.5 metres (3 fathoms) of chain should be used between anchor and warp.

Section 6

5

1 Bilge pump.

Efficient compass and a spare.

Charts covering the intended area of operations.

6 Distress flares of which two should be of the rocket parachute type. Daylight distress (smoke) signals.

An appropriate length of buoyant tow rope.

1 First aid box with anti-seasickness tablets. 1 radio receiver for weather forecasts.

1 Water resistant torch.

1 Radar reflector capable of giving a consistent, identifiable echo during any movements within a band of at least ±20 degrees of heel, through the 360 degrees of azimuth. This should be mounted or hoisted where convenient to the working of the boat and, if possible, at a height of 4 metres or more above sea level.

Line which could be used as inboard lifelines in bad weather, if necessary.

1 suitable engine tool kit.

The name, number or generally recognised sail number of the boat should be painted in a prominent position on the vessel or on dodgers in letters or figures at least 22 centimetres (9 in.) high to facilitate identification.

Vessels of less than 5.5 metres in length

Care should be taken to avoid overloading the boat by carrying more persons or equipment than the boat was designed for, which will generally be shown on a plate affixed by the constructor. Sea angling vessels should be more restricted and the following scale is recommended:

Craft of 4.9 metres (16 feet) to less than 5.5 metres (18 feet) 4 persons.

Craft of 4.3 metres (14 feet) to less than 4.9 metres (16 feet) 3 persons.

Craft of 3.7 metres (12 feet) to less than 4.3 metres (14 feet) 2 persons.

Sea-angling from craft less than 3.7 metres (12 feet) in length is hazardous.

Owners of pleasure craft in this category who intend to proceed to the open sea more than 3 miles from base or whose craft are designed for cruising should, so far as is practicable having regard to the size and carrying capacity of the vessel, follow the recommendations for craft of 5.5 metres to 13.7 metres (18 feet-45 feet) when undertaking such voyages.

DEPARTMENT OF TRANSPORT CODE OF PRACTICE FOR SAIL TRAINING BOATS

This Code of Practice is designed to ensure maximum safety for the vessel and its crew and embodies many features which must of necessity be incorporated at the design and building stage. However, there are many other useful ideas which the average handyman owner of a cruising yacht can carry out himself.

No one will deny that a sail training boat should incorporate the maximum amount of safety features reasonable for its size.

However, the sail training boat will, in general, have a young, active crew and a professional skipper. Compare this to the average cruising yacht of comparable size, with in all probability, a weak family crew. In the latter case it is obvious that the vessel should be equally well equipped from a safety point of view.

Listed below are some suggestions which are in addition to the DTp recommendations for yachts listed elsewhere in this section.

1. Bower anchor, well secured, of appropriate size and kedge anchor.

Suggested weights:

OA Length	Bower	Kedge
m.	kg.	kg.
9	15	8
10	17	9
11	20	10
12	23	12
13	26	13

2. Retaining pin in stem head fitting.

3. Companion Way — washboards 300mm. above deck level when open and when closed secured with catches that can be opened from inside as well as outside.

4. Harness attachment each side of companion way and each side of cockpit.

5. Jackstays to clip harnesses on when working on deck.

6. Dan buoy at least 2m. (6 ft.) high.

7. Remote fuel and gas shut-off.

8. Gas cooker firmly secured with flame fail/safe device.

9. Hole in engine bulkhead to discharge fire extinguisher through.

10. Engine box — flame retardant paint inside.

11. Drip tray under fuel filter.

12. Easy access to strum box.

13. Second bilge pump with long wandering pipe and strum box.

14. Locker lids so secured that they remain shut even when boat is inverted.

ROYAL YACHTING ASSOCIATION (RYA) TRAINING SCHEMES

The Royal Yachting Association designs and oversees a variety of training schemes for cruising yachtsmen — for both motor and sail. A beginner can move through his chosen scheme step by step, whilst of course gaining further practical experience along the way. Both practical and shore-based courses are included.

A training scheme can be entered at any appropriate level, and there is no compulsion to follow strictly the normal progression of courses. The beginner starts with an elementary course and may end the scheme, some enjoyable years later, passing the examination for Ocean Yachtmaster.

Certificates are awarded on successful completion of courses, both shore-based and practical. In the future it is possible that some form of certification will be required by people who wish to skipper a cruising boat. Even today, many countries require documentary evidence of ability. The RYA covers this by the award of the Helmsman's Overseas Certificate of Competence. This can be obtained, without further testing, by holders of a Day Skipper Practical Course Completion Certificate; others have to take a practical test at a recognised centre.

The information overleaf covers, in outline, the training schemes for motor and sail.

Section 6

7

ROYAL YACHTING ASSOCIATION NATIONAL CRUISING SCHEME

Course	Content	Ability after Course	Duration
MOTOR CRUISING COURSES			
Introduction to motor cruising	Safety and basic seamanship	Useful crew member	2 days
Helmsman's, practical	Safety,helmsmanship, boat handling, intro to engine maintenance	Competent to handle a motor cruiser of specific type in sheltered waters	2 days
Day Skipper, shore-based	Basic seamanship and intro to navigation and meteorology		About 60 hours
Day Skipper, practical	Pilotage, boat handling, seamanship and navigation. Engine maintenance	Competent to skipper a motor cruiser, by day, in familiar waters	4 days
Coastal Skipper/ Yachtmaster (Offshore), shore-based	Offshore and coastal navigation, pilotage, meteorology		About 60 hours
Coastal Skipper, practical	Skippering techniques for coastal and offshore passages	Competent to skipper a motor cruiser on coastal passages by day and night	5 days
SAIL CRUISING COURSES			
Competent Crew, practical	Basic seamanship and helmsmanship. Safety	Useful crew member	5 days
Day Skipper, shore-based	Basic seamanship and intro to navigation and meteorology		About 60 hours
Day Skipper, practical	Pilotage, boat handling, seamanship and navigation	Competent to skipper a small sailing yacht by day, in familiar waters	5 days
Coastal Skipper/ Yachtmaster (Offshore), shore-based	Offshore and coastal navigation, pilotage, meteorology		About 60 hours
Coastal Skipper/ practical	Skippering techniques for coastal and offshore passages	Competent to skipper a sailing yacht on coastal passages by day and night	5 days

Most readers of Reed's Nautical Almanac will already be experienced sailors. We hope however, that these pages will help to inform beginners, as well as other sailors looking for more advanced training, what opportunities exist.

SAFETY IS A STATE OF MIND. TRAINING AND EXPERIENCE ENGENDER THE RIGHT STATE.

Further information from:

The Royal Yachting Association,
RYA House,
Romsey Road,
Eastleigh,
Hampshire SO5 4YA.
Telephone: (0703) 629 962

National Federation of Sea Schools,
Staddlestones,
Fletchwood Lane,
Totton, Southampton,
Hampshire SO4 2DZ.
Telephone: (0703) 869 956.

8

TRAINING SCHEMES ELSEWHERE

Motor and sail training courses are also available in certain other countries in Europe: Details are available from the following:

IRELAND

Irish Sailing Association,
3 Park Road,
Dun Laoghaire,
Co. Dublin.
Tel: (1) 2800239.

FRANCE

Federation Francais de Volle,
55 Avenue Kleber,
75784 Paris, Cedex 16.
Tel: (1) 45 53 68 00.
Fax: (1) 47 04 90 12.

NETHERLANDS

Royal Netherlands Yachting Union,
Runnenburg 12,
Postbus 87,
3981 Az Bunnik.
Tel: (03405) 70524.

GERMANY

Deutscher Segler Verband e.V.
Grundgenstr 18,
2000 Hamburg 60.
Tel: 040 632 0090.

Deutscher Motoryacht Verband e.V.
Grundgenstr. 18,
2000 Hamburg 60.
Tel: 040 630 8011

DENMARK

Dansk Sejlunion,
Idraettens Hus,
Brondby Stadion 20,
Dk-2600 Glostrup.
Tel: (42) 455555.

NORWAY

Norwegian Navigation & Sailing School,
Th. Kittelsens Vei 144,
1415 Oppegård.
Tel: (2) 992652.
Fax: (2) 562385.

SWEDEN

Courses are run by individual Yacht Clubs.

FINLAND

Suomen Purjehtyulitto
and
Suomen Moottorivenelitto,
Radiokatu 20.
00240 Helsinki.
Tel: (9) 0-1581.

POLAND

Polski Zwiazek Zeglarski
Chocimska 14,
Warsaw.
Tel: 22495731.

Section 6

BLIND ARC FROM THE BRIDGE OF A VESSEL WITH BRIDGE AFT

There is a blind area ahead of and on each bow of any commercial vessel, the larger the vessel the larger the blind area. Simple mathematics will prove the point but as a general guide line,

APPLICATION OF COLLISION REGULATIONS

In applying the Collision Regulations and Harbour By-laws the following practical considerations may be of use;

ANY vessel which is of deeper draft than you is

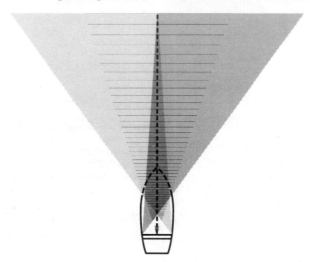

if you are within a mile of a medium to large vessel i.e. 10,000 to 15,000 tons then you are in the blind arc. Again a simple test is, if you cannot see his bridge then the chances are he cannot see you.

Avoid either remaining in, or crossing the bow within, the blind arc. The actual area of the arc is a function of the size of the vessel, the size of the yacht, the height of eye of the vessel and it's beam. It is the yacht hull that has to be seen, not the mast.

"restricted in her ability to manoeuvre" being restricted to the deeper water, whether in a narrow channel or close to shore, sand banks, etc. and therefore cannot necessarily get out of your way.

Few commercial vessels can manoeuvre as easily as a yacht so they are also "restricted".

Blind arc under the bow. Doubled if vessel is container or timber carrier.

The Distance/Speed ratio should also be appreciated.

Closing speed	60 kts.	Distance	1 mile.	Meet in	1 minute
" "	30 "	"	1 "	" "	2 minutes
" "	15 "	"	1 "	" "	4 "
" "	7½ "	"	1 "	" "	8 "

Which is not a lot of time even at the lower speeds

NAVIGATION IN FOG

Basically there is no difference between navigating in fog or daylight but the envelopment of a small craft in dense fog, preventing the navigator from seeing more than a few yards ahead, has a psychological effect which is quite surprising to who have not experienced it before. The following checkpoints are suggested as a standard drill in the event of fog:

1. All crew to don safety harness and personal buoyancy and ensure that liferaft is attached to vessel but free to float clear. A man overboard situation in clear weather can be difficult, the same situation in dense fog could easily become catastrophic.

2. Immediately update the E.P. on the chart and then maintain an accurate check at say ½ hour intervals.

3. If under power, immediately reduce speed in order that avoiding action is easily taken if there appears to be imminent danger of collision.

4. Remember to use your fog signal in accordance with the Collision Regulations.

Note: Power vessel making way through the water — 1 prolonged blast ev. 2 min. Power vessel under way but stopped — 2 prolonged blasts with 2 sec. intervals ev. 2 min. Sailing vessel — one prolonged and two short blasts ev. 2 min.

5. When coasting — if possible get out of the shipping lanes into shallow water where there is no possibility of being run down by a large vessel and if circumstances render it advisable, anchor until it is safe to resume passage.

It is doubly important that a radar reflector is hoisted when in fog.

SEA EMERGENCIES

Emergencies inevitably occur at sea (as they do in every other context) but the prudent skipper will make every effort to see that they do not occur as a result of his own carelessness or unpreparedness. Every effort should be made to overcome emergency situations and to plan how best to overcome them if they should occur. What sort of emergencies can happen? What action will be necessary? Are the right spares and equipment carried on board? Have the crew members been properly briefed? Do they know where the flares are stowed? (and do they know how to use them?

These and many other questions should be given serious consideration — tragedies in yachts are fortunately rare, bearing in mind the numbers that put to sea — but those that do happen can usually be traced to carelessness or human error, perhaps even the simple one of neglecting to listen to the shipping forecast before departure.

Man overboard

This is one of the most difficult situations that can confront the small craft sailor and one which usually results from someone's carelessness. Every crew member should have a safety harness and it is the skipper's responsibility to ensure that they are worn when weather conditions demand it. Are there adequate attachment points on board and are the crew properly briefed on their location?

There is a general tendency for safety precautions to be rather more casual when rowing out in the dinghy than when underway at sea and it is salutary to reflect that amongst cruising people probably more drowning tragedies occur when rowing out to the parent vessel than when underway in her. Life jackets should always be worn (especially by children) if there is the slightest danger. (See on for man overboard drill).

Collision at Sea

Fortunately a rare occurrence but nowadays a very real danger in those areas of high density of shipping such as the Straits of Dover. A sound knowledge of the Collision Regulations is necessary to evaluate any possible close quarters situation which may arise — can the sound signals in restricted visibility be instantly remembered? Is the vessel on the correct course for crossing a shipping lane? And is the speed adequate? Remember Collision Regs. Rule No. 10 — 'a vessel of less than 20m in length or a sailing vessel shall not impede the safe passage of a power driven vessel following a traffic lane'. Even outside a traffic lane a large vessel operating in confined waters (which may not appear to be 'confined waters' to a small vessel) may be quite unable to take avoiding action and the responsibility for taking such action then lies squarely with the small vessel. It is important that such action should be taken in good time and is obvious to all vessels involved in the close quarters situation.

Severe Weather

The advent of rough weather should not necessarily be regarded as an emergency. Assuming that the vessel is well found and her crew are prepared, rough weather may pose problems in navigation but the situation, unless it gets badly out of hand, is not an emergency. The prudent skipper will have reefed down in adequate time, firmly secured all deck gear and have thermos flasks of hot water ready for the preparation of soup later, when conditions in the galley may become difficult. The navigator should ensure that his E.P. on the chart is up to date and consider whether it would be wise to alter course for an alternative destination, bearing in mind the probable conditions to be expected on arrival. For example, certain ports on the French and Belgian coasts can be dangerous for small craft with strong on shore winds.

In severe conditions the skipper may eventually be faced with the alternatives of heaving to, running under bare pole or lying a hull. He should have given careful consideration to these possibilities before the need arises and will certainly have practised heaving to in moderate conditions and assessed how his boat is likely to behave in more severe conditions. It is of course important to consider how much room there is to leeward when contemplating heaving to.

Finally remember to take action in good time. A dry, warm and well fed crew can deal much more easily with trouble than can the wet, cold and exhausted crew.

Gas Hazards

Gas explosions in small craft are fortunately rare and providing certain precautions are taken should never happen. The installation should be properly carried out and maintained; it is most important to regularly check all flexible connections and always to turn off gas at the cylinder when the cooker is not in use. Inevitably small quantities of gas escape each time the cooker is lit, and being heavier than air sinks down to the bilges where it accumulates. Pumping the bilges daily will evacuate any such accumulation .

Miscellaneous

Engine failure in a well found sailing yacht should not under normal circumstances be regarded as an emergency. If, however, it occurs for example when the vessel is entering a port with frequent fast moving cross channel ferries entering and leaving, then the situation may become difficult if there is insufficient wind to set sail. It is therefore important to regularly maintain the engine even if only occasionally used, filters should be changed at the appropriate intervals and if as sometimes happens, no sediment trap is fitted in the fuel line, it would be wise to consider installing one.

Failure due to fuel line trouble should not therefore occur in a well maintained craft. However, a blocked water inlet or worse, a rope round the propeller, can easily occur at any time particularly when in the vicinity of a large port and the prudent skipper will have considered how he would deal with the situation in the circumstances prevailing at the time. Occasionally with luck, it is possible to clear a rope round the prop by rotating it backwards. Unfortunately the incidence of rubbish in the sea is a growing problem and the installation of line cutting equipment on the propeller shaft is well worth considering.

On any passage at sea, the anchor, if stowed on deck, should be very firmly secured but should always be easily dropped when entering port.

Perhaps fire at sea is the worst emergency which can occur in small craft due to the incredible speed with which it can spread. Fortunately it is the most unusual disaster to occur but here again thought should be given to dealing with a fire in one's boat (see on for fire precautions). It need hardly be said that personal accidents which may occur ashore within easy reach of medical aid assume a very different complexion when the vessel is perhaps a day or more sailing distance away from medical aid. A working knowledge of first aid and the presence on board of an adequate first aid kit can be a very reassuring factor when dealing with accidents which may occur despite sensible precautions. (See First Aid Section 9)

FIRE PRECAUTIONS IN SMALL VESSELS

Small vessels normally use diesel or petrol in their main or auxiliary engines and paraffin or Calor gas for cooking purposes. Each fuel has its own particular hazards, but petrol and Calor gas must be treated with the greatest respect.

The flashpoint, i.e. the temperature at which a liquid gives off an inflammable gas, is much higher in Diesel and paraffin than it is with petrol, and the two former fuels are therefore, safer under normal working conditions. Both, however, are a fire risk if they come into contact with very hot metal, for example, an unlagged or uncooled exhaust pipe.

Considering first the engine installation, the fuel tank, especially if petrol, should be situated well away from the engine and exhaust pipe. Particular care should have been taken in the installation if, due to lack of space, it was necessary to place the tank close to the engine. The exhaust pipe should be well lagged and, if possible, fireproof thermal insulation placed between the engine and fuel tank to reduce the temperature rise in the fuel. The tank should have a vent pipe exhausting on deck to ensure that any fuel vapour is discharged well clear of the installation. The fuel pipe to the engine should be carefully installed and properly secured, the greatest danger in this connection is that of fracturing due to vibration. There is a great temptation in certain circumstances to use thin plastic piping for fuel pipe, mainly due to its flexibility and ease of installation in confined spaces. This should, of course, never be allowed. If a flexible connection is needed, it should be a proper armoured flexible pipe to British Standards Specification.

Apart from an actual spillage of petrol and the consequent possibility of fire, it will be appreciated that the great danger in small vessels is the accumulation of an explosive mixture in the bilges, caused by a mixture of air and either petrol vapour or Calor gas. There are various gas detecting devices on the market which will give adequate warning of a dangerous condition in the bilges. In addition, or perhaps as a substitute if no detector is carried, the bilges should be pumped daily. The average bilge pump, especially the diaphragm type, will pump air without the need for priming and will therefore, effectively evacuate any gases from the bilges.

The galley installation, particularly if a gas one, should be well designed and carefully maintained. Starting with the gas bottle, this should be installed in a separate compartment with a drain out through the ship's side so that any leakage from the valve or regulator is safely disposed of overside. As the gas is heavier than air, it will be appreciated that this compartment does not need a gas tight lid. This compartment should also accommodate the spare bottle if one is carried.

Pipework from the bottle to the cooker should be properly installed, being clipped at regular intervals to lessen the possibility of damage. Flexible connections to the cooker, particularly if the latter is in gimbals, should be inspected regularly for damage, slack nuts, etc. When the cooker is not in use, the gas should be turned off at the regulator, thus reducing the possibility of leaks.

Summarising, the following points should always be borne in mind:

1. Keep all compartments, where gas can accumulate, clear and well ventilated.

2. Maintain all installations, both gas and liquid fuel, in a good condition — this means regular inspection. It also means inspection of electrical equipment installed in a position where a spark could ignite an accumulation of gas.

3. When filling fuel tanks, ensure that there are no naked lights, smoking, etc, and that the quantity required is known, thus reducing the risk of fuel overflowing.

4. Make sure that the fire extinguishers are in good order, properly positioned and everyone on board knows how to use them.

FIRE FIGHTING

The following points in connection with fire fighting are intended primarily for small vessels. An officer of a merchant ship is expected to have a good knowledge of fire drill in general and any particular precautions or methods of fire fighting required by a specific type of vessel or cargo.

In case of fire:

1. Alert all on board and tackle the fire, no matter how small as a major incident. A fire can get out of hand with astonishing rapidity. Extinguisher should be aimed at the base or centre of the fire where it will probably have the greatest hold.

2. Detail one crew member to alter course or stop the ship so that the wind is prevented from spreading the fire, and to move the life raft to a safe position and ensure it is ready for launching.

3. Close any hatches, ports, etc. that will reduce the draught through the ship.

4. If you can transmit either by radio or visual signalling, inform the nearest ship or shore station of your predicament. It is better to cancel an alarm than to be too late to send one.

5. Launch the dinghy or life raft as soon as it is obvious that it will be required and if a dinghy, make sure that the 'survival kit', i.e. water, flares, etc, is placed aboard.

The above points may be dismissed as painfully obvious and indeed, they are, but they are intended to make the skipper of the small vessel consider his equipment and the general preparedness of himself and his crew to deal with a

Section 6

13

danger that may confront all of us at some time or other. Finally, again very obvious if water is used successfully to combat a fire — remember to pump the bilges as soon as possible.

MAN OVERBOARD

Sailing is probably one of the safest sports (certainly going to sea is safer than driving along the motorway) but there are certain risks which can be evaluated and provision made to deal with them. The greatest of these and one which in all probability will never happen in the life of the average yachtsman is 'Man Overboard'.

The rare chance of it happening and the rather awe-inspiring problems tends to induce the 'It won't happen to me' reaction in the average skipper. Probably it will not, but this is no excuse for neglecting seamanlike precautions — if it does happen it can easily prove fatal if the crew members have not practiced their drill — it is the Skipper's responsibility ultimately if an accident happens.

In many of the published articles on the subject the boats carrying out the exercise generally appear to be strongly crewed with three or four men on board. In the following notes it is assumed that the vessel concerned has a man and woman crew, perhaps with two small children — the real life family cruising situation. It is strongly recommended that a 'Man Overboard' exercise should be carried out at reasonable intervals to familiarise all crew members with the problems and their solutions.

It is reasonable to assume that the vessel will have a reliable auxiliary engine and in all probability a VHF radio set, two items which can play an important part in the exercise.

There are three main stages in the M.O.B. Operation. First stop the vessel and return to the casualty, secondly secure him alongside and finally recover him aboard. All three stages must be carried out quickly and effectively. Mental concentration on these three stages will greatly help to discipline and steady the mind during the period when panic can rapidly develop and slow the whole operation down.

The immediate reaction to 'Man Overboard' must be to release the danbuoy (with life buoy attached) from its position on the push pit in order to pinpoint the casualty's position.

There are two generally accepted methods of returning to the casualty — the reach tack reach method and the quick stop method.

The first consists of sailing off on a broad reach for four or five boat lengths, tacking and sailing

back on a reciprocal course. When downwind of the casualty tack again, leave the jib backed and fore reach up to the casualty.

The second method, the quick step method is simple and rapid and tailored to a weak and less experienced crew.

After the danbuoy has been released, tack and leave the jib backed (adjusting the sheets if necessary) to enable the vessel to be forereached back to the casualty. After tacking ensure that no ropes are overside and start the auxiliary, furl the jib and motor up-wind to the casualty

This is one stage in fact where previous exercises in different wind strengths can literally mean the difference between life and death to the casualty.

After the immediate dropping of the danbuoy and with the vessel heading back to the casualty the opportunity should be taken to drop astern a 30 metre flotation line attached to the vessel with a lifebuoy at the end. This may prove useful in getting a line to the casualty if difficulties arise when the vessel has been brought back to him. The flotation line and small buoy or lifebuoy should be permanently rigged on the pushpit in such a way that it can be easily released.

The next stage on arrival at the casualty is to secure him alongside. There are various pieces of equipment now available to assist the operation. One type consists of a pole with a stiff plastic loop on the end which can be dropped over the head and shoulders of the casualty. When suitably positioned the loop can be tightened from the inboard end, thus enabling him to be firmly secured alongside. (The construction of a suitable piece of equipment, small enough to stow on board should be within the capability of the average handyman).

The third and final stage of the operation, getting the man aboard, is undoubtedly the most difficult. A useful piece of equipment is a scrambling net as used by the R.N.L.I. This consists of a strong net six feet by eight feet with four or five inch mesh. This is suspended from the guard wire or stanchion bases and apart from providing a comparatively easy method of scrambling aboard it also enables the crew member to stand in the net and assist the casualty aboard. One occasionally hears references to transom hung boarding ladders being useful — nothing could be less useful if there is a heavy sea running. Whilst suitable as a bathing ladder in calm conditions, in anything of a seaway the transom will be rising and

falling a matter of feet and anyone in the water underneath it would be in a dangerous position. Recovery must be effected amidships where the vessel's movement is at a minimum.

At this stage a decision must be made about the use of VHF if this is available. If the casualty is conscious and obviously able, with assistance, to scramble aboard — get him aboard. If however, he is unconscious or there is any doubt about getting him on board, immediately send out a Pan Pan signal giving the vessel's name, position and brief details of emergency, eg. 'Pan Pan Yacht XYZ, Position six miles East of North Foreland, man overboard, request immediate assistance.' It is far better to make a Pan Pan call in good time and then cancel it if recovery is successful than wait until it has proved impossible to recover the casualty. If it is obvious that the crew stand no chance of getting the casualty aboard unaided then a May Day call should be sent immediately.

Assuming that the person is unable to get back on board unaided, some form of mechanical aid is essential. The use of a halliard winch single handed offers no chance of success — the average woman without someone to tail the

fall would certainly not be able to lift a heavy weight. Additional power must be available and probably the easiest way of providing this is by means of a three-fold purchase which can be hoisted up on the main halliard to a pre-determined position then used as a tackle to hoist the casualty aboard. This purchase consists of two treble blocks giving the very useful advantage of 4:1. The tackle should be suspended from the main halliard by means of a swivel snap shackle and the fall taken from the tip block via a foresail sheet winch.

Two points to remember, firstly the point to which the tackle must be hoisted must be determined by trial and error and then carefully noted. Secondly the stowage of the tackle — inevitably a piece of equipment which may never be used will probably be stowed in some inaccessible position and when required will be found to be a tangled mass of blocks and rope — leading to delays. Probably the best way to stow the gear is in a tight polythene sleeve of sufficient length to allow the tackle to be stowed in it in the fully extended position with a block at each end of the sleeve. This will prevent the rope tangling and ensure that the tackle can be used immediately without having to overrun the turns. The bottom guard wire should always be set up with pelican hooks or lashings so that it can be quickly cut adrift without any trouble, thus enabling a casualty to be rolled aboard without having to be lifted over the top guard rail.

It is hoped that the foregoing notes may assist the family crew to work out their own approach to the problem, practice the drill and should it ever become necessary in real life, to successfully recover the man overboard. Summing up it must be stressed that it is the skipper's responsibility to first ensure that any equipment needed is available on board, second that the crew are practised in the method to be employed and thirdly that the skipper at least is familiar with the vessel's behaviour in varying sea conditions.

ABANDONING SHIP

These notes apply to home waters in the Northern hemisphere where one is unlikely to be adrift for more than 5-7 days. All small vessels should have:

1. A simple list of 'Procedure on Abandoning Ship' on permanent display near the chart table/navigation area.

2. An Abandon Ship Waterproof Box/Bag near the liferaft or cabin entrance. The following suggestions regarding contents, may provide a useful guide:

BASIC SURVIVAL KIT

1. Container(s) of fresh water (with some air so they float) 2 litres per head.
2. Flares/rockets/smoke signals .
3. 'Space' Rescue blanket.
4. Glucose sweets — 500 grammes per head.
5. Torch.
6. Compass.
7. Plastic bucket — bailer.
8. 5 fathom warp.
9. Emergency radio.

If time allows

10. Extra warm clothing, sleeping bags, sweaters, etc.
11. First aid box.
12. Ship's Papers, money, passports — kept permanently in plastic folder.
13. Chart(s).
14. Rescue quoit with line.
15. Sheath knife and other tools.
16. Pencils and paper.
17. Food — bread, chocolate, canned food plus opener.

TWO CRAFT ARE BETTER THAN ONE — IF POSSIBLE TAKE LIFERAFT AND DINGHY.

PROCEDURE ON ABANDONING SHIP

Put on all possible waterproof clothing including gloves, headgear and lifejacket. Collect survival kit. Note present position. Send out MAYDAY. Launch liferaft — attached to ship. Launch dinghy — attached to liferaft. Try to enter liferaft direct (if impossible, use minimal swimming effort to get aboard).

IN THE LIFERAFT/DINGHY

Get a safe distance from the sinking vessel. Collect all flotsam — the most unlikely articles can be adapted for use under survival conditions. Keep warm — bodies together. Remove all clothing from dead bodies and share between survivors. Keep dry — especially feet. Stream sea anchor. Arrange lookout watches. Use flares only on skipper's orders — when there is a real chance of being seen. Arrange for collection of rainwater. Ration water to maximum $\frac{1}{2}$ litre per person per day — issued in small doses. Do not drink sea water or urine. If water in short supply only eat sweets from survival rations.

THE WIND CHILL FACTOR

The chart below shows the limitations imposed by winds at low temperatures. Although compiled primarily for use in arctic conditions, it will be of use for those sailing in areas covered by this almanac in winter months.

The point at which the temperature and wind speed intersect on the graph indicates the wind chill factor. The practical implications of the wind chill factors are given below the graph. It must be noted that 'proper clothing' means protecting all skin areas from direct wind with sufficient thickness to prevent undue coldness. If clothing becomes wet or frost forms on it, it should be dried as soon as possible.

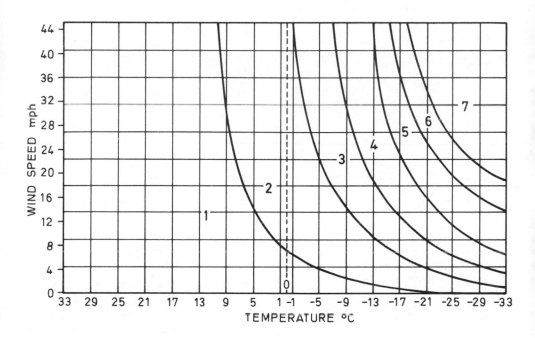

1. Comfortable with normal precautions.

2. Can become uncomfortable on overcast days unless properly clothed.

3. Heavy outer clothing necessary even on clear days.

4. Heavy clothing is mandatory. Unprotected skin will freeze over prolonged period of exposure.

5. Multiple layers of clothing mandatory, especially protection for the face.

6. Proper face protection becomes mandatory. One should not venture on deck alone, exposure must be controlled by careful scheduling.

7. Survival conditions. Crew can become easily fatigued and mutual observation of fellow crew members is mandatory.

RUBBISH DUMPING AT SEA

In addition to it being an offence to discharge oil, oily waste or any noxious liquid into the sea or rivers (MARPOL 73/78 Annex I & II), it is also an offence to discharge any garbage into the sea or rivers. Plastic/synthetic materials are totally prohibited. Food wastes, paper, bottles, metal etc. 3 M from nearest land (baseline of territorial waters) if passed through a grinder, otherwise 11 M. Dunnage, linings etc. which float – 25 M. For most yachts coasting this will mean taking your rubbish back to the yacht club or home for disposal. (MARPOL 73/78 Annex V). Marinas and Port Authorities should provide facilities for disposal of rubbish.

Section 6

EMERGENCY REPAIRS

7

JURY STEERING

All boats should be fitted with an alternative means of steering in case the rudder, tiller or wheel is damaged. The simplest form of emergency steering, which was standard issue in ships' lifeboats, was an oar, which could be put into a crutch, rowlock or strop at the stern, and used in the manner of the Viking ships. When planning a long cruise it is advisable to equip the boat with a lifeboat oar or similar for this purpose. If an oar is not carried, then it is worth spending some time in advance working out how a jury steering system is to be set up, and if necessary, putting extra fittings on the boat in readiness.

When the rudder or tiller breaks, the first thing to do is stop the boat, by handing all sail or stopping the engines, and then investigate the cause. If the rudder is thrashing around, immediate steps must be taken to control it, or it is likely to damage its gudgeons and pintles. Again there is a lesson to be learned from ship's lifeboats, which had a hole drilled through the outer lower end of the rudder blade through which a line was led from each side of the gunwale, and knotted either side of the hole. This served as an emergency steering system. Yachts will not want to sail around with lines hanging over the stern, but it is worth considering having the hole drilled in the rudder blade at the next re-fit, so that it is there if necessary.

If there is no hole in the rudder, one method of restraining it is to put a rope over the stern, secured on each side of the stern, and haul it tight against the rudder blade. If figure-of-eight knots are put into the rope, the blade will not be able to slip beyond the nearest knots. An alternative is to put lines on each side of a large shackle, from which the pin has been removed, and haul the shackle in tight over the aft end of the rudder blade. This method can be used as a rudimentary steering system, provided the shackle can be held in place, easing on one line as the other is taken up to alter the rudder angle. In a dire situation, even the anchor can be used to restrain the rudder by putting one line on one arm, and another on the cable ring, and lowering the anchor down the rudder so that the blade is caught between the shank and arm.

If the tiller has broken, an emergency tiller can be set up by lashing any suitable piece of wood or metal to the rudder head. Where the boat has wheel steering, the usual cause of failure is one of the tiller lines. A spare wire, already spliced to fit the system, should be carried but if not, a replacement will have to be made up on board. With hydraulic steering systems, the usual cause of failure is a leak in the hydraulic pipe lines. If insufficient spare oil is available, the manual back-up system should be installed. All hydraulic steering systems should have stop valves in the pipe lines, and a method of isolating the wheel from the hydraulic rams, so that if the failure is due to some other cause, the wheel can be disconnected.

The most difficult repair is where the rudder stock has broken, as any jury system of steering is going to have to be rigged directly to the rudder blade, and this means using one of the methods described earlier to control the angle of the blade.

Where the entire rudder is lost, it is most unlikely that the modern fin keel and skeg yacht will be able to steer herself by balancing the sails, as was occasionally possible with the older, long keel yachts, or with two masted boats. However it may be possible to control direction by setting the jib, and hanking a small jib or storm sail to the backstay. The jib will provide power and hold the bow off the wind. By trimming the sheet on the small sail, the boat will tend to come into the wind, by easing the sheet, the boat will pay off. If the boat is fitted with self-steering gear which has an auxiliary rudder, this might just work, but it would be unwise to put too much strain on it, and sail should be reduced to keep the speed down.

The most obvious jury rudder is made up by using a spinnaker pole, or a similar spar, over the stern like a steering oar. The inner end of the pole should be lashed to the backstay which then acts as a pivot. Two lines should be led from the outer end of the pole, one to each side of the stern, where they pass through a block and then into the cockpit. Experimentation will show whether these lines need to be led to winches, or whether they can be pulled and eased manually. If the pole is long enough, it may be possible to lash it to the backstay at a point on its length which allows the inner end of the pole to be operated like a crude tiller, with the fulcrum being at the backstay.

Jury Steering and Jury Rigs are extracted from "Seamanship" by Robin Knox-Johnston with the permission of Hodder & Stoughton Limited.

2

However, this is hard work and the lines should be rigged for back-up. The pole on its own will steer the boat as it is moved from side to side (this is how punts are steered) but it will be much more effective if a plank, such as the ubiquitous bunk board, is bolted or lashed to it.

Where the stern of the boat is narrow, and the angle of the lines from the spinnaker pole back to the stern is acute, the tension required to pull the pole from side to side will be considerable. It can be lessened by widening the angle, and the easiest way to do this is to lash another spinnaker pole square across the stern of the boat, with blocks at each end, and lead the tiller lines through these blocks instead of the ones on the boat's gunwale.

JURY RIGS

Being dismasted is a serious misfortune for a sailing boat, because the rig provides her motive power. It will tend to occur in extremely heavy weather, but could equally be due to the failure of some part of the rigging. In the quest for aerodynamic efficiency some modern racing boats are rigged rather too lightly, and whilst modern materials are immensely strong they are not indestructible. It is important to avoid personal injury when the mast breaks or falls wholesale over the side. One consequence of the loss of the mast in a monohull will be a much quicker motion of the boat, due to the loss of the inertia aloft; this makes remedial work all the more difficult. If you are not far offshore, then it is best to make for port under power, once you have sorted out the mess, but if this occasion arises when you are in mid-ocean and beyond the reach of outside help, then you have got to improvise some kind of jury, or temporary, rig. Even if you have large fuel tanks, restoring some sail area will steady the motion of the boat and provide a modicum of sail-power.

If the boat is a ketch, yawl or schooner and the mainmast breaks, it may be possible to move the other mast into its position. Before my singlehanded circumnavigation I replaced *Suhaili*'s wooden mizzen with a lighter aluminium spar, so that if I broke the mainmast, I would have an easier task of moving the mizzen up into its place. Provided one mast is left standing, the task of stepping a jury mast in the other position is made much easier because there is already a high point to attach a line to take the jury mast up to a parallel upright position from where tackles can be used on the stays to finish off the job.

Of course, in a ketch or yawl, it may not be necessary to replace a broken mizzen mast, as the boat may sail perfectly well under the sails on the mainmast alone.

In the event that the only mast has broken, and been lost, than a jury mast will have to be set up from what remains on board, such as the main boom, spinnaker poles or bowsprit. If there is a stump of the mast remaining, a spar, previously dressed with its shrouds, stays and halyards,can be lashed upright to this stump.

A reasonable mast can be made by using two spars as sheer legs, and setting up fore and back stays, but this rig is only suited to a square sail, and another spar will be needed as a yard of sorts.

Jury Masts.

When a mast breaks the first job to tackle is clearing the wreckage, and recovering as much usable rigging and bits of the mast as possible as these may come in handy for making a jury rig.

If part or all of the mast has gone overside, it will be attached to the boat by shrouds and stays, so check that it is not endangering the hull of the boat. The next move is dependent upon the sea state. In anything worse than a small chop, it will be difficult or impossible to try to haul the mast on board, and the wreckage cannot be left lying alongside as it is likely to knock a hole in the hull. If conditions permit, try to recover the sails intact and release all the rigging, but leave a stout line attached to a part of the mast or rigging, and then let go. A wood mast should float clear of the boat, an aluminium one will sink beneath the boat. Either way, the mast should be well clear of the boat, but still attached so that it can be re-covered to be used as part of the jury rig when the sea conditions improve.

Where the sea conditions are bad, and it is therefore dangerous to try and keep the mast attached, all the wreckage will have to be let go completely, and other items that remain on board used to make up the jury rig.

When conditions allow, or if the mast breaks in a reasonable sea, haul the mast in alongside.

Start by putting fenders overside between the mast and the hull and lash the mast to the boat to reduce the relative movement between them. Next remove the rigging by disconnecting it from the mast and then from the deck by undoing the rigging screws and coil it down. This reduces the weight hanging overside, and makes the load to be heaved on board less; it also tidies up the deck and makes working easier.

Hauling the mast on board, unless it is small and light, is not an easy task, and so should be tackled methodically. Move the mast fore and aft until its centre of gravity is level with the midship section of the boat. Pass strops from the deck, down round the mast and back onto the deck again, and attach tackles to the upper end of the strops to form a simple parbuckle.

If no suitable tackles are available, take a line from the upper part of the strop to a snatch block on deck in line with the strop's position and back to a winch. Alternatively, instead of using a strop, take a line from the winch, through a snatch block, and then down over the mast and up from beneath the mast to be secured to some strong point on deck.

On a large boat, more than two strops could be used, but on a boat of, say 30 feet in length, two should be sufficient; the strops should be placed between 6 and 10 feet either side of midships, depending on how the hull curves. If the hull is fairly straight, the strops may be further apart.

Having rigged the tackles, start to take up the weight. If the mast refuses to come up the side easily, the job can be made easier by fitting a temporary ramp, angled down from the deck into the water, up which the mast can slide. Spinnaker poles, or the main boom will do for the ramp They should be dropped down overside between the hull and the mast, and then the top end hauled inboard. This will have the effect of moving the mast upwards and away from the hull. The ramps should be fitted with fore and aft guys so that they cannot slip. Once the ramps are in place, hauling the mast on board with the parbuckles should be a lot easier. Once the mast is aboard, lash it down to the deck, and start to work out what you have with which to set up your jury rig.

Mast intact. If the mast is deck-stepped and has only gone overside because of some rigging failure, then it will probably still be intact. First repair or replace the the broken rigging. Even if

the only material available is rope, set up temporary rigging replacements with this rope, and make it as tight as possible. It is unlikely to be as strong as the original rigging, but it will provide some support, and if reduced sail is subsequently set, it should take the strain.

Mast broken. If the mast has been broken, the first decision is which part of the mast should be used for the jury rig. Normally it would be sensible to use the longest remaining section, as more sail could be set, but sometimes it is advisable to use a shorter section because it will be easier to set up, as when, for instance, the top part of the mast is available, as it has halyard sheaves and tangs intact for the rigging.

When a lower section of the mast is to be used, if the break is just above a spreader, then the spreader level will make a convenient point for the attachment of the fore and backstays. They can either be knotted directly to the mast just above the spreader, or tied off to a strop placed around the mast above the spreaders. Either way, the spreaders will prevent the stays from slipping downwards.

Where the temporary hounds are to be put clear of an obvious point like the spreaders, a jury mast knot will serve to provide good holding points for shrouds and stays. If you are worried that the jury mast knot might slip downwards, you can always put a turk's head around the mast just below the jury mast knot.

Once the temporary hounds are set up, put on shrouds and stays. Blocks will also have to be secured to the hounds to take the temporary headsail and mainsail halyards.

Where the mast has broken close to the deck, thus leaving a stump, it is usually advisable to leave this stump, and lash the jury mast to it. When stepping the mast, make a secure lashing to hold the foot of the jury mast to the bottom of the stump at deck level, and, once the mast is upright, lash it to the stump. The best system of lashing is to take at least a dozen tight turns around the two pieces of the spar, and finish by frapping the lashing between the two spars and tying it off. If there is space, put more than one such lashing around the spars.

Stepping the mast. There are two alternative methods when re-stepping the mast. The first is to push the mast forward, its head projecting out over the bow, and its heel lashed to hold it at the mast step. Set up two spinnaker poles, or a spinnaker pole and main boom, as sheer legs over the deck, aft of the mast step, and hang a block from the apex of the sheer legs. To avoid damaging the deck, place pieces of wood beneath the heels of the spinnaker poles. Next, put lashings around the bottom of the poles and take them to secure points fore and aft so that the heels cannot slide. Lead a line from the masthead, or a point on the mast that would be the same height as the top of the sheer legs block when the mast is upright, through the block on the sheer legs, and down to a winch on deck. Attach the shrouds and the forestay to their rigging screws and then winch up the mast. The moment it is upright, secure the backstays and then dismantle the sheer legs.

The alternative method, which will almost certainly have to be used if the mast is intact because it will be too long to extend safely over the bows, is to lay the mast on deck with its head over the stern. Rig sheer legs again, just forward of the mast step, and follow the same procedure, but this time it is the forestay that will have to be attached once the mast is upright.

In both systems, all the standing rigging, halyards, running backstays etc., should be secured to the mast before it is stepped.

Topmast broken. Where the upper part of the mast breaks off, leaving a substantial length of the mast still standing, the remaining length can be used to set sail. First remove the wreckage, and, if it has not already fallen, lower the broken piece of the mast as gently as possible to the deck. If the break is clean it may be worth keeping this broken section, as a mast maker might be able to repair the mast, which will be cheaper than buying a new one.

If there are no halyards left below the break, it is going to be necessary to make a means of getting aloft to rig temporary stays and halyards. Where there are two lower shrouds, the simplest system is to make ratlines. Where the mast has only a single lower shroud, make a ladder by tying off lines between the mast and this shroud. This task may not be easy, as the boat will become more stiff without the extra weight aloft and this will reduce her rolling period, making her motion more jerky.

Once it is possible to climb to the top of the broken mast, either put a jury mast knot around the top to attach stays, shrouds and halyard blocks, or where the break is close above a spreader, attach these to the mast on a strop around the mast just above the spreader.

Sprit and Gunter Jury Rigs.

A very handy jury rig can be set up once a mast is stepped, using either the sprit or gunter rigs. In the case of the sprit rig, this is practical when the lower part of the mainsail is intact. Any suitable spar can be lashed roughly in the position of the main boom gooseneck, so that it can rotate a little, and then its outer end lashed to a suitable point on the leech of the mainsail. The mainsail should be sewn along its new head, and, if necessary, a rope should be sewn along this seam to provide extra strength.

The gunter rig is slightly more difficult to set up, but will work when the upper part of the mainsail survives, and there is more length of mainsail than the mast remaining or the jury mast. The gunter rig is simple to handle and allows a higher sail to be set where the jury mast is short and it is not possible to put parrels on the upper part of the sail because they could not be hoisted above the spreaders.

Jury Sails.

If you are lucky, sufficient of the mast will remain to allow the mainsail, suitably reefed, to be set. However, if the mainsail is so badly torn that it cannot be repaired, some other sail will have to be set as a mainsail.

On a ketch, this could be the mizzen. On any boat, a jib or staysail can be used, and set loose footed, with the clew taken out to the end of the main boom. Where possible, the sail should have its luff secured to the mast, be this its usual luff or its leech if it happens to fit better back to front. If the mast track remains, it is a simple job to sew the sail slides onto the jury sail. If the track is unusable, it will be necessary to make up parrels to go around the mast; however, this will only work if there are no obstructions, such as spreaders, in the way.

Where it is not possible to make up any form of fore and aft sail, a square sail, or a lateen sail may be the only answer. In both cases a spar will be necessary. It is advisable to rig up a halyard for this yard, and secure the halyard directly to the pivot point of the yard, or onto slings, so that both the sail and the yard can be lowered easily to the deck when necessary.

If none of the sails left on board will fit as a mainsail, it may be necessary to adapt them for the new rig. No-one likes to cut up a perfectly good sail, but there may be no alternative.

Section 7

DEALING WITH WATER INGRESS

The discovery of a significant quantity of water in the bilges or, worse still, emerging above the floorboards in the cabin naturally leads to one reaction – panic. This is an unhelpful instinct at a time when quick but careful thought and action is required.

FINDING THE SOURCE

Whilst it may initially seem to be a good idea to devote all energies to bailing, this is not the case. Other than switching on any non-automatic bilge pumps and putting spare crew to manual pumps and buckets, the first priority must be to find the source, not always an easy job.

If the water is originating from a hole upwards of 1 in (25 mm) square below the waterline, there is only a short time available to locate the leak and stem it before the boat becomes unstable and capsizes, or sinks.

Is the water fresh or salt? If it is the former, a domestic supply tank or pipe has split (turn off the domestic electric water pump if fitted), or rainwater has been entering into a compartment in the boat unnoticed over a period of time, In either case, there is no immediate danger. If the boat is on a fresh water navigation, there may not be a salt taste, so carry on checking.

Any boat already has a number of holes below the waterline in the form of skin fittings, sea cocks, instrument transducers, shaft logs, rudder shafts, keel bolts, anode studs and prop shaft bracket fixings and these should be suspected before impact damage unless it is obvious that the boat has made contact with something capable of holing it.

Systematically work around all sea cocks and close them until the leak has been found, unless essential and deemed to be sound. Fractured hoses can be difficult to detect. On a well-heeled yacht sea toilet pipework and submersible bilge pump skin fittings below the heeled waterline could be the source.

If the propeller shaft has been partially or completely pulled out of the boat, ensure the integrity of the rudder and shaft bracket fixings.

Check the cooling water circuit and exhaust on any working engines – the cooling pump is capable of pumping a large quantity of water straight into the bilge via any fractured lines. On motorboats fitted with outdrives, do not forget to look at the transom area in the engine compartment for failure of the rubber bellows sealing the drive to the leg.

If the boat has been taking heavy spray or green water, openings above the waterline such as anchor fittings, hatches, portholes, windows, throughdeck chainplates and blocked cockpit drains may be suspect.

If no immediate cause is found, hull damage is a possibility and all internal parts of the hull so far uninspected should be examined as quickly as possible. If furnishings, fixed floors or interior mouldings conspire to hide certain areas, look further down towards the keel where possible to see if water is flooding from that direction.

TAKING ACTION

Most small craft bilge pump systems can rarely stem the flow of a major leak unaided. Likewise, the proverbial panicked man and bucket is not the saviour that popular fable makes him out to be, while manual pumping will quickly tire the operator to below the pump's theoretical maximum capacity.

Once a leak is located, the first course of action is to reduce the ingress of water to a level which the pumps can easily manage. Time has then been bought to bring about a proper repair if possible, effect a temporary solution sufficient to make port, or in the worst case, commence an orderly call for assistance.

The easiest method of stopping a broken below-waterline skin fitting, sea cock, hose or shaft which is completely missing is to drive a round, tapered softwood plug into the hole. Packs of these are available from most major chandlers. To be most effective, suitable-sized examples can be secured near to all skin fittings, with spares carried in a handy locker well above the bilges. Remember that water pressure will try to force these temporary plugs out, so they need to be tended until secured in some way.

Instrument transducers often come with a spare solid plug to fill the hole while the fitting is being cleaned and these too should be kept in an easily found and accessible place in case of emergencies.

If the hole is uneven, rag wrapped around a plug may provide a solution, or cloth alone, forced into place will reduce the flow to manageable levels.

It may seem obvious, but even if it is going to take a relatively short time to locate suitable materials, try to constrict the flow with a hand if possible – a 2 in (50 mm) hole 30 in (0.75 m) below the waterline will let in around 40 gal (180 lts) every minute.

If the propeller shaft has become detached, but is still inside the shaft log, the best answer is to push it back if at all possible, holding it in place with a spare jubilee clip until more effective repairs can be effected.

For hull damage, one solution is to rig a collision mat, a cloth (canopy, sail or even a deflated inflatable without floorboards for instance) which can be secured over the hole from the outside with ropes secured to the corners. Water pressure holds the cloth against the hull, substantially reducing the flow. Patented devices are also available which work like an umbrella, pushed through the hold from the inside and opened outside.

In the absence of a collision mat or the time to rig such a device, bunk cushions pressed against the damaged area from the inside will again reduce the flow. These can also be used to reduce water ingress from shattered windows, or failed hatches and portholes.

A change of tack with a yacht may reduce the pressure on any damage. Likewise on fast motorboats, the hole may be in a region where, if the boat stays on the plane, the leak is stopped or at least reduced. A change of course or speed on all craft will also assist if the leak is above the waterline. Again, by initially stemming the leak in any way possible, time has been gained to solve the problem.

Section 7

DISTRESS & RESCUE

8

DISTRESS & EMERGENCY SIGNALS – EMERGENCY ACTION

RADIO TELEPHONE PROCEDURE

Set to International Distress Frequency 2182 kHz, or Ch. 16 (VHF).

First transmit alarm signal

(If equipment available) for 30 seconds to 1 minute.

THEN transmit distress call

(a) 'MAYDAY' spoken 3 times
(b) 'THIS IS (or DE spoken 'DELTA ECHO' if language difficulties)
(c) Name of ship spoken three times

THEN transmit distress message

(a) Distress signal 'MAYDAY'
(b) Name of ship and call sign
(c) Position
(d) Number of crew
(e) Nature of emergency and assistance desired
(f) Any other information which might facilitate rescue, and your intentions.

Acknowledgement will be

(a) Name of ship sending distress call—spoken three times
(b) 'THIS IS' (or 'DELTA ECHO')
(c) Name or identification of station acknowledging distress call

Visual signals

Full details of all distress signals are given in Annex IV of the Collision Regulations but the following ones are most likely to be of use on small vessels (assuming VHF is not available).

By night

(1) Parachute Flares
(2) Very Pistol (Red Flares)
(3) Hand held Red Flare

By Day

(1) Parachute Flares
(2) Orange Coloured Smoke Signal
(3) Slowly and repeatedly raising and lowering the arms outstretched to the sides.
(4) An article of clothing on an oar
(5) The flag signal N.C. (I am in distress and require immediate assistance)
(6) A square flag having anything resembling a ball above or below it.

Note: If a distress signal is not justified the appropriate International Code signal should be sent by Flag or Morse, i.e.

'V' I require assistance.
'W' I require medical assistance.

RADIO TELEPHONE PROCEDURES

DISTRESS, EMERGENCY AND SAFETY

All Distress and Emergency signals should be sent on 2182 kHz or 156.8 MHz (Ch. 16 on VHF sets). However any other frequency may be used at any time if it appears probable that assistance may thereby be obtained more promptly.

Certain of the larger types of radio telephone sets are equipped with an alarm signal which may be used to precede the actual distress message. It is a two-tone alarm signal which activates the auto alarm fitted in the larger types of shipping.

It may also be used to precede an urgency Pan Pan signal in cases such as man overboard.

Silence Period. Vessels fitted with equipment capable of receiving 2182 kHz should maintain a listening watch during the 3 minute silence period commencing at each hour and half hour.

Types of Priority Signals. There are three types of priority signals—Mayday, Pan Pan and Securité (pronounced SAY-CURE-E-TAY).

DISTRESS SIGNALS

A Mayday Call or a Distress Flare may be used only when there is grave and imminent danger to a ship, aircraft or person and, immediate assistance is required.

If for some reason there is an element of doubt about the necessity for sending a Mayday signal then an urgency Pan Pan signal (see on) should be sent. This will alert vessels in the vicinity and any coastal station or Coastguard Station within range. In the light of subsequent events the signal can either be cancelled or a Mayday call sent out. In this connection there are two important points to remember, firstly it is far better to give as much advance warning of trouble as possible to the Coast Radio Stations and secondly that if the situation becomes less urgent and help is no longer required then the Distress or Urgency signal must be immediately cancelled.

Mayday Relay Signals. Any vessel hearing a distress call must listen for a short period to see if it is acknowledged by a Coast Radio Station. If this does not occur then the vessel which has received the Mayday signal must re-transmit the signal but prefacing the distress call with the words Mayday Relay three times followed by the name or call sign of the vessel re-transmitting the distress message three times.

Communications Control during the Distress Incident. In Coastal waters the primary responsibility for control of distress incidents lies with the Coastguards who initiate S.A.R. (Search and Rescue). The control of the distress traffic communications may lie either with the Coastguard Station or a Coast Radio Station who will impose silence on all vessels in the vicinity by transmitting the signal SEELONCE MAYDAY, followed by its own name or call-sign. (The signal will be transmitted on the frequency being used to control the incident.) When complete radio silence is no longer necessary the controlling station will transmit the following message:

MAYDAY

Hello all stations (repeated 3 times)

This is .... (name of control station)

Name of vessel in distress

PRUDONCE

Essential communications may then be resumed but it is vital to avoid interference with any signals relating to the MAYDAY incident. When all traffic relating to the incident is concluded the controlling station will send out a general signal SEELONCE FEENEE which permits resumption of normal working.

URGENCY SIGNALS

Pan Pan Signals The words Pan Pan repeated three times are used where it is necessary to transmit a very urgent message concerning the safety of the ship or some person on board or within sight. It does not imply that the vessel herself is in immediate danger. Examples are cases of injury where urgent medical assistance or advice is required, man overboard when there is doubt about the ability of the vessel to rescue him. Pan Pan signals should, where possible, be addressed to a specific shore station or ship but if any doubt exists about the nearest shore station the urgency Pan Pan should be transmitted as a general call.

The Urgency Signal and message should normally be sent on 2182 kHz or Ch. 16 but if the message itself is a long one the urgency signal should be transmitted on the Distress Frequency together with a statement that the

message will be transmitted on a working frequency. Any vessel hearing an urgency signal must immediately cease transmitting and listen to check whether the urgency signal is acknowledged by a Coast Radio Station. After a short period of three minutes, if no acknowledgement is heard, the listening vessel must endeavour to contact a shore station and relay the message.

SAFETY MESSAGES

Securité pronounced SAY-CURE-E-TAY repeated three times precedes any important navigational or meteorological warning. The safety signal is sent on a distress frequency, either 2182 kHz or Ch. 16, together with an announcement giving the working channel on which the safety message will be broadcast. Any vessel hearing the safety message must at once cease working on the frequency chosen for the safety message and listen until they are satisfied that it does not concern them.

VHF Ch. 67 is allocated for the exchange of safety messages between small! craft and H.M. Coastguard when the message does not warrant the use of the Distress Channels. Small craft should contact the Coastguard station on Ch. 16, stating they have safety traffic, when they will be instructed to change to Ch. 67. Small craft should not endeavour to contact the Coastguard station initially on Ch. 67 as they normally only maintain a listening watch on Ch 16.

Emergency Transmitters for Small Craft. Two types of emergency transmitters are available for small craft, the VHF Distress Beacon Buoy and the Distress Radio Telephone. The former is a buoyant battery operated automatic radio beacon transmitter giving continuous transmission for at least 48 hours on the Distress frequency and thus provides 'homing' facilities for aircraft engaged in the search. The transmitter can be operated from the deck of the vessel or in the sea, attached to the life raft by a small line. The Radio Telephone is also completely self contained and portable but is not submersible. As communication is by radio telephone it can be used for Pan Pan and Securité messages as well as distress calls.

PYROTECHNIC DISTRESS SIGNALS

All small craft should carry some means of indicating distress and preventing collision at night.

PYROTECHNIC SIGNALS

These are internationally recognised ways of indicating distress or risk of collision, using red flares or stars (hand-held, projected, or parachute-suspended), or orange smokes (hand-held or buoyant) for distress, and white flares for collision warning.

Distress flares should be used only when there is grave and imminent danger. If not in distress but needing assistance, signal "V" in morse (· · · –) or hoist flag "V". The distress signals you should carry depends not on the size of your boat, but on the distance from land you are likely to go.

Different types of distress flares are needed to raise the alarm and pin-point your position to rescuers. All craft sailing at night should carry white flares to attract the attention of larger vessels when there is risk of collision. Learn how to use your flares and teach your crew, so you will not be caught in distress, possibly at night, trying to read the labels.

INSHORE

Up to 3 miles from land or within sight of potential help carry 2 red handflares and 2 hand-held orange smoke signals.

To raise the alarm and later pin-point your position to rescuers use red handflares in conditions of poor visibility, high wind or darkness. In daylight with good visibility and a light wind hand-held orange smokes will be more distinctive.

COASTAL

Up to 7 miles from land or in conditions of low cloud carry 4 rockets discharging red stars, 4 red handflares and 2 hand-held orange smoke signals.

Beyond 3 miles hand-held signals may not be sighted, being below the visible horizon of potential help. Therefore, attract attention by firing flares which project red stars to 45m. These flares are particularly useful when low cloud might obscure a more powerful rocket. It is recommended that the first two signals be fired within 2 minutes of each other. When rescuers are within visual range, use red handflares or hand-held orange smokes.

OFFSHORE

Over 7 miles from land carry 4 red parachute rockets, 4 red handflares and 2 buoyant orange smokes.

Beyond 7 miles, red star signals may not be sighted. Therefore fire rockets which project a very bright parachute-suspended flare to a height of over 300m. This is the most powerful type of flare. It is recommended that the first two rockets are fired within 2 minutes of each other. When rescuers are within visual range but in conditions of poor visibility, high winds or darkness use red handflares. In daylight with good visibility and a light wind a 3 minute buoyant orange smoke will be more distinctive.

COLLISION WARNING

Carry 4 white handflares within easy reach from the cockpit. If a vessel is sighted on a collision course at night and shows no sign of seeing you, use a white handflare to draw attention to your position. Alternatively a Very pistol projecting white flares is extremely useful.

LIFE SAVING STATION SIGNALS

Replies from life saving stations or maritime rescue units to distress signals made by ship or person:

SIGNALS

By day – Orange smoke signal or combined light and sound signal (thunderlight) consisting of three single signals fired at approx. one minute intervals.

By night – White star rocket consisting of three single signals at approx. one minute intervals.

Signification

'You are seen – assistance will be given as soon as possible.' (may be repeated)

If necessary the day signals may be given at night or the night signals by day.

LANDING SIGNALS

(For guidance of small boats with crews or persons in distress.)

SIGNALS

(a) By day – Vertical motion of a white flag or the arms or green star signal or K (– · –). By night – Vertical motion of a white light or flare; a green star signal by day or night; or code letter K (– · –) by light or sound signal.

Signification

'This is the best place to land.'

4

Section 8

(A range, indication of direction, may be given by placing a steady white light or flare lower and in line with the observer).

(b) By day – Horizontal motion of a white flag or arms extended horizontally.

By day or night – Horizontal motion of a white light or flare or firing of a red star signal or code letter S (· · ·) by light or sound signal.

Signification

'Landing here highly dangerous.'

(c) By day – Horizontal motion of a white flag, followed by the placing of the white flag on the ground and the carrying of another white flag in the direction to be indicated.

By day or night – Horizontal motion of a white light or flare, followed by the placing of the white light or flare on the ground and the carrying of another white light or flare in the direction to be indicated or firing red star vertically and a white star in direction towards a better landing place or using Code letter S (· · ·) followed by Code letter R (· – ·) if better landing is more to the right or letter L (· – · ·) if more to the left of approach line.

Signification

'Landing here highly dangerous. A more favourable location to land is in the direction indicated.'

Note: Distress answering from lighthouses and light vessels is being phased out.

SEARCH AND RESCUE PROCEDURE

GENERAL ARRANGEMENTS

Around the coasts of the United Kingdom (and extending to Long. 30°W between Lat. 45°N and 61 °N) it is the responsibility of HM Coastguard to initiate and coordinate the appropriate search and rescue procedure (SAR) for vessels in distress.

Coast Radio Stations, on receiving a distress message, either directly or relayed via another vessel, immediately alert the Coastguard and then transmit the Distress Signal on the distress frequencies 500 kHz and 2182 kHz (and Channel 16 after consultation with HM Coastguard) to vessels at sea, after which it ensures radio silence on the appropriate frequency by all vessels not involved in the emergency.

HM Coastguard have responsibility for and maintain 24 hour coverage on Channel 16 VHF. In addition there are Auxiliary Coastguard

stations which can keep visual watch in periods of high casualty risk and which have a rescue capability.

When a vessel is in distress and the Coastguard have been informed, they will call upon the Lifeboat Service and/or the Royal Air Force and Royal Navy depending on the nature and size of the emergency. The Air Rescue Coordination Centres at Edinburgh and Plymouth are responsible for providing rescue facilities for military and civil aircraft, but may also assist ships in distress at the request of the appropriate Coastguard station. In addition the Royal Navy may also provide helicopters, and if appropriate, Royal Navy surface vessels may assist. In the event of an emergency a considerable distance from land the Coastguard may request assistance from the Air Traffic Control centre covering that area, thus ensuring that any low flying aircraft in the vicinity of the incident keep watch for life rafts etc.

Distress signals re-transmitted or intercepted by satellites are relayed to Falmouth MRCC which takes appropriate action.

SEA RESCUE BY HELICOPTER

GENERAL PROCEDURE

Once the helicopter has become airborne, how soon it locates the ship and how effective its work can be depends to a large extent on the ship herself.

LARGE VESSELS

From the air, especially if there is a lot of shipping in the area, it is very difficult for the pilot of a helicopter to pick out the particular ship he is looking for, from the many he can see, unless that ship uses a distinctive distress signal which can be clearly seen by him. One such signal is the daylight orange coloured smoke signal. This is very distinct from the air. A well-trained Aldis lamp can also be seen except in very bright sunlight. Display of these signals may mean all the difference between success and failure in the helicopter locating the casualty.

It is essential that the ship's position should be given as accurately as possible if the original distress signal is made by radio. The bearing (mag. or true) and distance from a fixed object, like a headland or lighthouse should be given if possible. The type of ship or yacht, colour of sails and hull should be included if time allows, along with brief details of lifesaving equipment, e.g., liferaft.

Because of their operational limitations, helicopters should not be unnecessarily delayed at the scene of the rescue. Every effort should be made to provide a clear stretch of deck or hatchway and to mark this area with a large letter 'H' in white, prior to the arrival of the helicopter. A helicopter will approach the ship from astern and come to the hover over the cleared area, heading into wind. In order that the helicopter pilot and crewman may have as large an area of the ship as possible on which to operate consistent with the helicopter remaining heading into the wind, the ship should steam at a constant speed heading 30° to starboard of the prevailing wind direction. If this is not possible the ship should remain stationary head to wind. If these conditions are met the helicopter can lower on to or lift from the clear area, the maximum length of the winch cable being about 200ft. On no account should the strop on the end of the winch cable, when lowered to the vessel, be secured to any part of the vessel or allowed to become entangled in any rigging or fixtures. If the ship cannot comply with these conditions the helicopter may be able to lift a man from a boat towed astern on a long painter. If the vessel is on fire and making smoke it is of advantage to have the wind two points off the bow. In all cases an indication of wind direction is useful. Pennants and flags are acceptable for this purpose and possible smoke from the galley funnel, provided that there is not too much smoke.

Helicopters are well practised in rescuing survivors from either a deck or the sea and two methods are employed. These are:

(1) The survivor, whether on deck or in the water, is rescued by means of the strop. The crewman is lowered from the helicopter together with the strop which is secured around the survivor's back and chest, and both are winched up into the helicopter.

(2) If a survivor on a deck is injured to the extent that the use of a strop around his back and chest would aggravate the injury or cause suffering, a crewman is lowered on to the deck with a stretcher. The survivor is placed in the stretcher, strapped in in such a manner that it is impossible for him to slip or fall out, and both stretcher and crewman are winched up into the helicopter. If possible, the helicopter will be carrying a doctor who will be lowered to the deck and will assist the survivors as necessary.

If from the ship in trouble it is observed that the helicopter is going to pass by, or is on a course which will take it away, continued use should be made of visual distress signals, and at the same time, if fitted with radio, the fact reported to the Coastguard stating the present bearing and distance of the helicopter. The Coastguard will pass this information direct to the helicopter.

YACHTS AND SMALL VESSELS

A yacht in distress may not anticipate a helicopter rescue, particularly in view of the increasing number of inshore rescue boats, but it is always advantageous to be prepared for this type of operation. A yacht, particularly a small one, is not always easily identified from the air.

The necessary precautions to ensure easy identification should form part of the normal sea-going equipment of every yacht, e.g. sail numbers should be clearly marked, canvas dodgers with the vessel's name clearly marked on them, and, if the dinghy is carried upside down on the deck, the name should be clearly painted on its bottom.

Failing these precautions a large strip of canvas with the vessel's name on should be carried and in the event of an emergency it can be lashed on deck.

When the emergency occurs the use of a flare or smoke signal when the helicopter is sighted may materially speed up the rescue. DO NOT FIRE PARACHUTE FLARES WHILST THE HELICOPTER IS EITHER DIRECTLY OVERHEAD OR CLOSE BY. Once it is obvious that rescue is being carried out by this means, a sea anchor if available, should be streamed in order to reduce drift. Alternatively the main anchor and cable may be paid out to help reduce surface drift.

It is most important to remember that the helicopter crew will not under any circumstances risk the winching cable becoming entangled with the yacht's mast and rigging. A sailing yacht must therefore prepare for its crew to be picked up from the water a safe distance from the vessel. A life raft or inflatable dinghy should be made ready and on the approach of the helicopter it should be streamed, complete with crew, on the end of at least a 100ft warp firmly secured to the parent vessel (unless of course there is the danger of the latter foundering).

The winchman can then operate in safety, well clear of the yacht and her rigging. In the unfortunate event of the vessel having no life-raft or inflatable dinghy it will be necessary for the crew to take to the water when the helicopter has located them. Again a long warp should be streamed, the crew with life jackets firmly secured can then drift to leeward attached to the warp in a bunch. In the unlikely event of some members of the crew having to be left in the water for a further period they will have means of returning to the yacht by means of the warp.

The 'pick up' problem does not arise in the case of the small sailing dinghy or the motor cruiser with no mast. In these cases the crew should remain on board unless otherwise instructed by the winchman. Finally, remember that a helicopter cannot remain airborne indefinitely, watch for and carry out the winchman's instructions exactly and immediately.

HIGH LINE TECHNIQUE

In very bad weather, it may not be possible to lower the crewman and strop directly on to the deck. In such a case, a rope extension of the winch line may be lowered to the ship. This should be handed by a member of the ship's crew and taken in as the helicopter pays out her wire. Coil down the line on deck clear of snags, but do not make it fast. The helicopter will pay out the full scope of wire and descend, while the ship's crew continue to take in the slack until the winch hook and strop are on board. The casualty will then be secured in the strop and, when he or another member of the ship's crew signifies that he is ready, the helicopter will ascend and take in the wire. Pay out the extension rope, keeping enough weight on it to keep it taut, until the end is reached, then cast the end clear of the ship's side; unless further evacuation of crew is intended when, if possible, the end of the line should be retained on board to make recovery of the strop for the next man easier—but do not make the line fast.

Rescue helicopters are fitted with marine VHF and may wish to communicate on Channel 6 (on scene co-ordination channel for SAR) during transfer. Yachts with VHF should however monitor Channel 16 (or other channel designated by HM Coastguard) and await instructions.

Remember—Keep clear of the main and tail rotors.

AIRCRAFT SEARCHES AND PATTERNS

NIGHT SEARCHES

In general night visual searches are dependant upon the ability of the survivors to indicate their positions using Pyrotechnics, Lights, Fires, etc. The searching aircraft can only hope to illuminate an accurately defined area, i.e. on sighting red flares, or flashing lights.

There are several patterns of searches, but the ones most likely to be used for missing craft/persons are the following:

Expanding Square Search: This procedure begins at a given point and expands in concentric squares, used to cover a limited area usually when survivors are known to be in a relatively small area. To execute a Square Search, the aircraft is flown in such a way as to make good the tracks shown in the diagram that follows.

EXPANDING SQUARE SEARCH

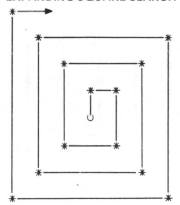

Note: The GREEN flares are used at night only by aircraft to indicate to the survivors that the aircraft is turning. Survivors should, on seeing the flares, WAIT until the flare has died out and then fire a red flare to indicate the position of the casualty. When the aircraft fire the green flares the aircrews will not look out until the length of time it takes the flare to expire. This is to enable them to retain their night vision.

Track Crawl Search: The procedure for this search is to fly along the known course from the last known position towards the intended destination and return on a parallel track at the sweep width distance to one side of the original track; then to return parallel to the original

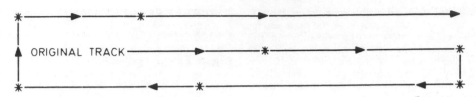

track on the other side again at the sweep width distance.

Note: Green Flares will be fired by the aircraft at each turning point and also if the legs are long at intervals of approximately five minutes. If the aircrew see a visual aid marking the survivors position several green flares will be fired in quick succession.

Creeping Line Ahead Search: This procedure is used for search of a rectangular area by a single aircraft. The aircraft proceeds to a corner of the search area and flying at the allotted height sweeps the area maintaining parallel tracks.

(a) The search area is long and narrow.

(b) The search based on a first priority of the track.

Note: Green flares will be fired along each leg at approximately five minute intervals and also at the turning point.

SIGNALS BY AIRCRAFT

DIRECTING SHIPS TOWARDS AN AIRCRAFT, SHIP OR PERSON IN DISTRESS

(A) Procedures performed in sequence by an AIRCRAFT

1. Aircraft circles the surface craft at least once.
2. Aircraft crosses the surface craft course close ahead at low altitude while rocking the wings, or by opening and closing the throttle or changing the propeller pitch.
3. Aircraft leads in the direction in which the surface craft is to be directed.

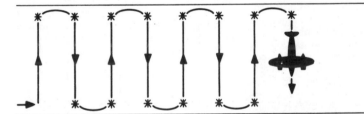

Note: Green flares will be fired by the aircraft at each turning point.

Parallel Track Search: This procedure is normally used when the search area is large and only the approximate location of the casualty is known. A uniform coverage is desired. The aircraft proceeds to a corner of the search area and flying at the allotted height, sweeps the area maintaining parallel tracks. Successive tracks are flown parallel to each other until the area is covered.

All three aircraft signals* above mean: The aircraft is directing a surface craft towards an aircraft or surface craft in distress.

(B) Aircraft crossing the surface craft's wake close astern at low altitude while rocking the wings, or by opening and closing the throttle or changing propeller pitch.

The above signal* means: The assistance of the surface craft is no longer required.

*(Repetition of signals have the same meaning.)

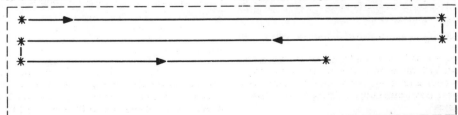

YACHT AND BOAT SAFETY SCHEME

Every year, Coastguards are alerted to more than 1,000 small craft overdue or in distress. But often they do not have enough information (such as the appearance, equipment and sailing plans of the missing craft) to concentrate a search in the right area

AS THE OWNER OR USER OF A SMALL CRAFT YOU CAN HELP THE COASTGUARD (AND YOURSELF) BY JOINING THE YACHT AND BOAT SAFETY SCHEME. It costs nothing, and one day might save your life as well as the lives of your family or friends.

How do you join?

All you need to do is fill in a simple postcard. You can get one from Coastguard stations, marinas, yacht clubs, harbour masters' offices and wherever you see the circular "Issuing Authority" sign. Describe your craft, its equipment and your normal sailing area, and then drop the card into a post-box. Remember to up-date the information whenever details change.

What information do the Coastguards need?

The following details will be helpful: the name of your club or association; type of craft or rig; name of craft, how and where displayed; colours of hull, topsides, sail; sailing/fishing number; speed and endurance under power; special identification features; life-raft and serial number; dinghy type and colour, lifejackets carried, radio— HF/MF trans/rec, VHF channels and call sign; type of distress signals carried; usual base, mooring, activity and sea areas; shore contact's name, address, telephone number; owner's name, address, telephone number; date.

Proceeding on a cruise

To facilitate the efficient operation of the Yacht Safety Scheme, the skipper should inform his contact of the details of the trip and his ETA at a specified point. In the event of his failure to report his safe arrival within an agreed time, the contact can alert the Coastguard who will then take the necessary action.

Keeping in touch – VHF radio

You will sail more safely if your craft is fitted with VHF radio, so that you can pass distress, urgency and safety messages (including your latest position reports) direct to the Coastguards.

Pass distress and urgency messages on Channel 16. If you want to report your position, or change your plans, you should call up on Channel 16 and say you have "safety traffic". You will be asked to switch to Channel 67 (the small boat safety frequency) to pass your message.

When passing reports you should pass your vessel's name, call sign, departure and destination points and, if possible, your estimated time of arrival, the total number of persons on board and the Coastguard Rescue Centre which holds your safety scheme card.

Keeping in touch – MF radio

Yachts or boats fitted with MF radio transceivers only, or outside coastal VHF range, should contact the British Telecom Coast Radio Stations periodically to give their TR (position report); then, if it becomes necessary, Coastguards can use the last known TR to establish a search datum.

Passages outside coastal waters

If you intend to sail outside UK waters you are recommended to contact your nearest Coastguard station and give details. These can then be noted, and through their contact with overseas rescue organisations the Coastguards will be able to advise you of any measures which could improve your safety.

MISSING OR OVERDUE VESSELS

LLOYD'S SERVICES FOR DEEP-SEA YACHTSMEN

Reporting of yachts on overseas voyages

Yachtsmen intending to undertake overseas voyages and wishing to keep their relatives or families informed of their whereabouts should signal to passing merchant vessels with the International Code Signal ZD2 (Please report me to Lloyds, London) and are invited to contact the Intelligence Department, telephone No. 0260 772277, Ext. 2410 in order that the necessary arrangements can be made. Charges are made for any expenses incurred such as telephone calls, postage etc.

In addition, those relatives or friends who feel concerned for the safety of a yacht on an overseas voyage are advised to contact the above number at any time of the day or night.

If the yacht is considered to be outside the British Coastguard area of responsibility Lloyds will arrange for a general broadcast to shipping in the area or make inquiries of their agents along the vessel's route for later news. A person making an inquiry for an overdue yacht which is considered to be in the Coastguard area of responsibility will either be given the telephone number of the appropriate Coastguard Liaison Station to contact or Lloyds will pass the facts direct to that Station.

Reporting arrival of small vessels

If only yachtsmen (and others who put to sea) communicated with their relatives ashore, if only relatives could give worthwhile information about the vessels and their proposed itineraries—such lapses are all too typical when coastguards and others are asked to instigate inquiries.

It is very necessary in our crowded waterways to report to ports which vessels may enter and when delayed or stormbound always to telephone details to relatives or business. This may save endless trouble to overworked Lifeboat Crews, Coastguard, or harbour authorities. ALWAYS REPORT ARRIVAL TO SOMEONE AFTER A PASSAGE

STATUTORY DUTIES OF MASTERS

Under International Law the Master or person in charge of any vessel shall, so far as he can do so without serious danger to his own vessel, her crew and passengers (if any), render assistance to every person, who is found at sea in danger of being lost. If he fails to do so, he is guilty of a misdemeanour.

The Master of a ship, on receiving at sea a distress signal or information from any source that a vessel or aircraft is in distress, must proceed with all speed to the assistance of the person in distress (informing them, if possible, that he is so doing), unless he is unable, or in the special circumstances of the case considers it unreasonable or unnecessary to do so, or unless he is released from this obligation under certain conditions. If the Master of any ship in distress requisitions any ship that has answered his call, it is the duty of the Master of the requisitioned ship to comply with the requisition by continuing to proceed with all speed to the assistance of the persons in distress.

A Master is released from the obligation to render assistance as soon as he is informed of the requisition of one or more ships other than his own and that the requisition is being complied with by the ship or ships requisitioned, or if he is informed by the Master of any ship that has reached the persons in distress that assistance is no longer required.

IN CASES OF COLLISION

In every case of collision between two vessels, it shall be the duty of the Master or person in charge of each vessel, if and so far as he can do so without danger to his own vessel, crew and passengers:

(a) to render to the other vessel, her Master, crew and passengers such assistance as may be practicable, and may be necessary to save them from any danger caused by the collision, and to stay by the other vessel until he has ascertained that she has no need of further assistance, and also

(b) to give to the Master or person in charge of the other vessel the name of his own vessel and of the port to which she belongs, and also the names of the ports from which she comes and to which she is bound.

GMDSS – A NEW ERA OF SAFETY AT SEA

Advanced digital communications techniques are heralding a new era of safety for the mariner. These new technologies are making safety equipment easier to use and more affordable than before.

With the modern mobile satellite communications terminals that are now available, simply the press of a button alerts the nearest rescue coordination centre (RCC) instantly, wherever you are sailing in the world. Many of these communications systems weigh only a few kilograms and can be fitted on even very small yachts.

Having such equipment on board helps you not only during an emergency but also ensures that you are in touch with people on shore however far you are from land and whatever the weather. The facilities available on-board range from data communications to direct-dial telephone, facsimile, telex and electronic mail and live video and audio broadcasts.

A set of safety regulations is in force, specifying the equipment ships must carry for disaster communications. The regulations form part of the Global Maritime Distress and Safety System (GMDSS) that has been formulated by the

International Maritime Organization. These regulations apply to all passenger ships and cargo vessels of 300 gross tonnage or more and ships have until February 1999 to comply with the rules.

What is GMDSS? GMDSS takes advantage of the major technical advances in modern radio and satellite communications. The basic concept of GMDSS is that not only ships in the vicinity of the emergency, but also search and rescue authorities on shore, should be alerted instantly to an emergency at sea, so that a rescue operation may be launched without delay.

To achieve this, GMDSS mandates the use of automated communications equipment for rapid and reliable links with shore. In addition, GMDSS provides for the dissemination of maritime safety information warnings. Every ship will be able, irrespective of the area in which it operates, to perform the communications that are essential for the safety of not only the ship itself, but of other ships operating in the same area.

IMO has specified nine principal communications functions which need to be performed by all ships and then specified the equipment that would meet these requirements depending on the zones in which they operate. These functions are ship-to-shore, shore-to-ship, ship-to-ship distress alerting; search and rescue coordination communications; on-scene communications; transmitting and receiving position signals and maritime safety information; general radiocommunications; and bridge-to-bridge communications.

To specify the communications equipment which must be carried to perform these functions, GMDSS divides the seas into four different operating zones.

Sea Area A1: An area usually within 20-30 miles from land, within the range of shore-based VHF radio having digital selective calling (DSC) capability.

Sea Area A2: An area excluding A1 but within the range of shore-based MF radio (about 100 miles from shore), having DSC capability.

Sea Area A3: An area excluding A1 and A2 but within the range of services provided by the Inmarsat geostationary satellite system which covers the whole globe except small areas of navigable water in the polar regions.

Sea Area A4: All other areas outside areas A1, A2 and A3.

GMDSS requires that distress alerts reach a rescue coordination centre uncorrupted and without delay; the alerts should pinpoint the tragedy at sea, provide the identity of the ship in distress, the nature of the emergency and other relevant information. Initiation of an alert should be automatic or by the push of a button.

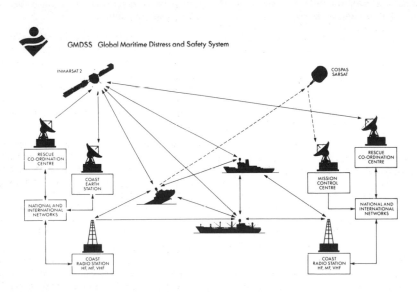

GMDSS Global Maritime Distress and Safety System

Proven reliability of Satcoms: The geostationary satellite system operated by Inmarsat, the 64-member-country cooperative based in London, offers the most reliable means of communication now available to mariners. It is available 24 hours a day, regardless of weather and atmospheric conditions, and offers clear communications links without fading and interference no matter how far the ship is from shore.

Inmarsat satellite terminals that provide access to the network require no special training to use. All of these terminals have a distress alert facility, often integrated with automatic message generators that give the vessels' position and other vital information.

Ships in distress can use the "Priority 3" channel on these terminals to guarantee automatic top priority over all other messages. No charge is made for use of Inmarsat space segment for:

Distress alerts;

Search and rescue coordination with associate RCCs, including communications subsequent to initial distress alerts relating to the immediate assistance required by a ship which is in grave and imminent danger;

Urgent navigational/ meteorological danger reports;

Medical assistance for those caught on a ship in distress.

Added advantages: Inmarsat coverage provides the mariner with the security of trustworthy communications over virtually all of the world's navigable waters, with satellites positioned over four ocean-regions – the Indian, Pacific, and the Atlantic East and West Oceans – arranged to give duplicated, overlapping coverage for most of the world's major shipping areas.

In addition, the Inmarsat system now offers a new emergency position-indicating radio beacon (EPIRB) system, Inmarsat-E, that operates via its satellites. Until now, EPIRBs have been used to transmit distress signals only to the Cospas-Sarsat satellite system. In a distress situation, the free floating EPIRB, which is linked to the ship's electronics system, automatically transmits the ship's identification and position. These beacons can also be activated manually.

A typical transfer time between the activation of the alert and the reception at the nearest rescue coordination centre is just about two minutes.

Satellite communications via Inmarsat thus provide the best answer to GMDSS medium and long-range communications requirements, particularly in sea areas A2 and A3, and the availability of a reliable, round-the-clock communications system for other commercial applications is an added bonus. With an Inmarsat telephone, facsimile or data terminal, you can communicate with the world as you sail — receive electronic 'newspapers', the results of the latest races, up-to-date stock market data — and make your journey more enjoyable, more productive and, definitely, safer.

FIRST AID AT SEA

9

MEDICAL ADVICE

In case of SERIOUS ILLNESS OR ACCIDENT AT SEA Masters of small vessels can get prompt medical advice by either:

1. RADIO – Contact nearest shore station OR
   Put out a call 'PAN PAN'

2. DIRECT SIGNALLING to other vessels by:
   Flag W
   OR
   Morse W · – – } = I require medical assistance

The principles of First Aid are to sustain life and prevent the condition becoming worse until expert help is available.

ALWAYS KEEP CALM AND REASSURE THE PATIENT.

FIRST AID BOX

The following suggestions apply to a vessel expecting to be at sea for not more than 72 hours. Dressings and drugs are preferably kept in separate polythene boxes with airtight lids.

DRESSINGS

Sterile non-adhesive dressings
(1 pack of 10 5cm x 5cm)
Gauze packs—6 large, 6 small
Cotton wool—30 grammes
Triangular bandage—2
Crepe bandage—1m x 7.5cm
Adhesive plaster—5m x 2.5cm
Transparent waterproof adhesive tape 5m x 5cm
Wound dressings, 3 large, 3 medium, 3 small

OTHER ITEMS

Airway
Scissors
Assorted safety pins
Disposable syringe and needle (13 gauge)
Reflective blanket ('Space' Rescue Blanket)
Clinical thermometer—Sub normal and normal.
Splinter forceps

BASIC MEDICINE KIT

Seasickness Pills
Pain Relievers
Antacid Tablets/Liquid
Anti-diarrhoeal Tablets
Laxative
Antiseptic Cream/Lotion
Multi-Vitamins
Eye Wash/Drops

SUPPLEMENTARY KIT

Sun Screen
Waterproof Adhesive Plasters
Splints – 2 45cc. x 7.5cc.
         2 45cc. x 15cc.
Foot Cream/Powder

HYPOTHERMIA—EXPOSURE

Cold is dangerous—most people who die following immersion in Northern latitudes die from cold injury and not from drowning. Hypothermia is the medical name given to the condition which is often called 'exposure'.

TREATMENT OF SEVERE HYPOTHERMIA

IF ON RECOVERY FROM THE WATER A BODY FEELS ICE COLD:

1. If unconscious, open airway and check breathing. Complete the ABC of Resuscitation (described opposite) if necessary, and place in Recovery Position (see p. 6)

2. Remove the outer clothing, and replace any wet clothing with dry.

3. Place casualty in sleeping bag, cover with blankets, etc.

4. Place a suitably covered hot-water bottle in left armpit or over breast bone—to warm 'core' circulation.

5. Give hot drinks and high energy food when conscious.

DO NOT place hot water bottles at extremities as this increases blood flow through the limbs and may result in a dangerous fall in 'core temperature'.

Note: Never presume that the casualty is dead simply because you cannot detect breathing or a pulse.

Note: It is best to rewarm a casualty at the speed cooling took place. Therefore, a person immersed in the sea should be rewarmed rapidly.

PREVENTION OF HYPOTHERMIA

ON BOARD THE EFFECTS OF COLD ARE INSIDIOUS AND MAY AFFECT ANY CREW MEMBER. They are more likely to occur at night and skippers should be aware of this risk if the temperature drops.

SYMPTOMS

Casualty's skin cold, pale and dry.
Body temperature below 35°C.
Slowing of physical and mental responses.
Irritability or unreasonable behaviour.
Cramps or shivering.
Unconsciousness may develop.
Difficulties with speech or vision.

NONE OF THESE WARNINGS SHOULD BE
IGNORED

SHOCK

This medical condition accompanies severe injury and illness. The blood circulation fails because blood pressure or volume of blood is reduced, thus failing to supply sufficient oxygen to the vital organs. The condition may prove fatal.

Signs and Symptoms

Skin becomes pale, cold and clammy.
Casualty may feel weak, faint or giddy.
Pulse is weak and rapid.
Breathing shallow and fast.
Possible unconsciousness.

Treatment

1. Treat any serious injury.
2. Lay him down, keep head low and turn to one side.
3. Raise legs, unless fracture of leg suspected.
4. Loosen tight clothing at neck, chest and waist.
5. Shelter from extremes of temperature—cover with blanket if cold.
6. Monitor condition of pulse, breathing, consciousness.
7. Arrange urgent removal to hospital.
    DO NOT give casualty anything to eat or drink.
    DO NOT use hot water bottles.

RESUSCITATION

When a casualty is not breathing and if the heart is not beating, it is vital to resuscitate the patient. The general rule is the ABC of resuscitation:
A—Airway
B—Breathing
C—Circulation

AIRWAY

When a casualty is unconscious the airway may be blocked or narrowed, making breathing noisy or impossible. Urgent action is needed to open the airway.

1. Lift the casualty's chin forward with the index and middle fingers of one hand while pressing the forehead backwards with the other hand. The patients jaw will lift the tongue forward, clear of the airway.

2. The casualty may start to breathe, if so, place in the recovery position.

3. Place your ear above the casualty's mouth and nose, look along chest to determine if breathing .

4. Clear the airway of any obstruction, such as food or vomit. Turn head to side, hook two fingers into mouth and sweep out any obstructions.

5. Check if casualty is breathing, if so, place in the recovery position.

BREATHING

Following checks of the airway, if the casualty is found not to be breathing, undertake mouth to mouth resuscitation.

1. Open your mouth and take a deep breath, pinch casualty's nostrils with your fingers and support the jaw.

2. Seal your lips around the patient's mouth and blow into the lungs. Watch the chest rise.

3. If chest does not rise, check airway not obstructed.

4. Remove your mouth well away from casualty's and watch his chest fall. Take a deep breath and repeat inflation.

5. After two inflations, check the carotid pulse. If pulse is beating, continue giving inflations at a rate of 12-16 times per minute, until natural breathing is restored.

6. When natural breathing returns, place casualty in the recovery position.

CIRCULATION

Check the carotid pulse after the first two inflations of the lungs. If it is not present, External Chest Compression must be performed in conjunction with mouth to mouth resuscitation.

1. Lay the casualty on his back on a firm surface. Kneel alongside the patient facing the chest, in line with the heart.

2. Find the junction of the rib margins at the bottom of the breastbone. Place the heel of one hand along the line of the breastbone, two fingers width above this point.

3. Cover this hand with the heel of the other hand and interlock fingers.

4. Keep arms straight and press down vertically on the lower half of the breastbone.

5. Press down about 4 to 5cm in the average adult, then release pressure. Complete 15 compressions at the rate of 80 compressions per minute.

6. Move to the patient's mouth and give two breaths of mouth to mouth ventilation.

7. Continue with 15 compressions followed by two inflations.

8. Check the pulse after one minute, if pulse present then cease External Chest Compression, but continue mouth to mouth until breathing returns.

9. If no pulse present, continue with 15 compressions and two inflations. Check pulse every three minutes.

As soon as the pulse returns, stop compressions, but continue with mouth to mouth ventilation until the breathing is restored. Place casualty in recovery position.

RESUSCITATION FOR CHILDREN

The method and rate varies slightly from the adult cycle shown above.

BABIES AND CHILDREN UNDER TWO—For mouth to mouth ventilation, seal your lips around baby's mouth and nose. Gently puff into lungs about 20 breaths per minute.
—For External Chest Compression, use two fingers only, at rate of 100 times per minute, pressing 1.5 to 2.5cm.

CHILDREN—For mouth to mouth ventilation, seal lips around mouth and nose, gently breathe at 20 times per minute.
—For External Compression, use one hand only, pressing 2.5 to 3.5cm at rate of 100 times per minute.

Most people using this head-tilt oral method find in the excitement of the moment that it is not distasteful, but the few who are repulsed by

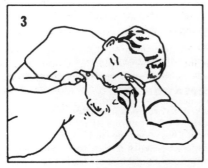

1   Neck is lifted

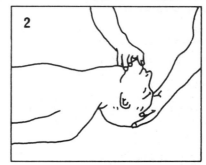

2   Head is tilted back

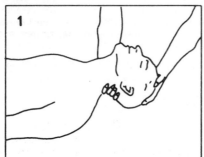

3   Lungs are inflated via nose or
    mouth
    Chest should be seen to rise

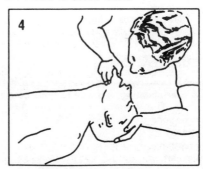

4   Victim exhales by himself, if
    necessary, through his mouth.
    Chest falls

the thought of physical contact with the patient can use a special mask, or a simple device with a nylon mouthpiece and valve set in a small plastic sheet. Use of these devices should also reassure any persons worried about the risk of infection from direct mouth to mouth contact.

SEASICKNESS

Prevention is much better and easier than cure. Avoid large meals and alcohol before sailing. Keep warm at all times.

Anti-seasickness Pills. Take early—at least 1 hour before sailing or at the first indication of deteriorating weather conditions. The best preparations contain Hyoscine in a dose up to 0.6 mgm. which in excess causes a dry mouth. Some people prefer anti-histamines but they are more likely to cause drowsiness. Consult the pharmacist or your doctor for suggestions.

Sailors should experiment. Small doses repeated every few hours are often more effective than large doses and cause less side effects.

Start treatment while still feeling 100%. All treatments are much less effective after symptoms have appeared.

Responsibility of a job to do (e.g. taking the helm) will often prevent seasickness and an observant skipper should consider this when a member of the crew becomes pale or unusually quiet.

Frequent small feeds of dry tack, dry bread, barley sugar, hot soup or other foods according to taste should be taken as appropriate with sips of water or tea.

Treatment. Prolonged sickness is dangerous. Mild attacks will respond slowly to the measures outlined above under Prevention but more severe attacks will require sedation (by injection if necessary).

Seasick crew should be kept warm in a bunk, if possible near fresh air, and given frequent sips of fluid when awake.

ANY PERSON VOMITING OVER THE SHIP'S SIDE MUST BE ATTACHED BY SAFETY HARNESS OR LINE.

ACCIDENTS

THE ATTENDANT MUST KEEP CALM AND CONSTANTLY REASSURE THE INJURED PERSON.

BURNS AND SCALDS

Principles. If clothing is alight, lay person down to prevent flames reaching facial area, and quench the flames with blanket or cold water. Continue cooling the damaged area for at least ten minutes with fresh or salt water.

Remove only loose clothing from burnt area. Do not attempt to pull off clothing stuck to skin. Cover lightly with sterile dressing. Keep patient warm. If burns severe, seek help.

Chemical Burns Remove affected clothing and wash with water. If acid burn wash with diluted bicarbonate of soda if available. Dry and treat as above.

Electrical Burns Switch off the current. If this is impossible stand on some dry insulating material such as wood or rubber and try to push the supply away from the patient, or the patient's limbs away from the supply with a piece of wood. If the patient is not breathing clear the airway and start artificial respiration and cardiac massage. Treat burn as above.

CUTS AND BLEEDING

A small quantity of blood can look excessive. Most bleeding can easily be controlled by direct pressure and the majority of wounds will stop bleeding within 5 or 10 minutes. Apply pressure directly over the wound with a dressing and bandage firmly. Keep the patient lying down but if possible ELEVATE THE BLEEDING PART. If blood continues to soak through the dressing add gauze pads and bandage firmly. Repeat if necessary. Do not remove the original bandage.

FRACTURES

A fracture is a broken or cracked bone.

Damage to the surrounding tissues and organs may outweigh the importance of the fracture itself.

Symptoms PAIN. SWELLING. DEFORMITY. LOSS OF POWER. ABNORMAL MOVEMENT.

In case of doubt always treat the condition as a fracture.

Bleeding into the surrounding tissues may be severe. If there is excessive swelling do not bandage too tightly as this can stop the circulation to the rest of the limb.

Treatment

Gently correct any deformity if the skin is tightly stretched over the bone or if there is evidence that the circulation is impeded.

Splint the limb using a proper splint, by bandaging to the sound limb or to the trunk or

Section 9

5

support the limb in a comfortable position with cushions, rolled clothing, etc.

Loosen any clothing which might affect the circulation and watch for signs of constriction, e.g. if the hand or foot below the fracture becomes cold, blue and swollen, loosen the bandage.

Keep the limb raised above chest height.

Open Fracture

This is a severe injury in which part of a broken bone pierces the skin. The wound must be covered by a sterile dressing.

If a patient sustains a fracture when in an inaccessible position it is often better to let him move out of it under his own power if he can.

Once the legs are bandaged together movement of the patient may be very difficult.

SPRAINS

A sprain occurs when the ligaments supporting a joint are damaged, usually by a twist injury of the ankle, wrist or knee.

Treatment

Apply a pressure bandage by wrapping the joint and the area above and below in a good layer of cotton wool and then bandage firmly, preferably with a crepe bandage. If an arm joint is sprained support the arm in a sling.

IF IN DOUBT TREAT AS A FRACTURE.

HEAD INJURY

Keep the patient flat and quiet in his bunk if possible. Scalp wounds bleed profusely. Wash with plenty of water and then apply prolonged pressure with a sterile dressing covered by gauze.

Loss of consciousness following a blow on the head suggests concussion. Vomiting or increasing drowsiness are serious signs. Ensure complete rest in the recovery position shown below until seen by a doctor.

Blood or straw-coloured fluid seeping from ear or nose may indicate a fractured skull. Place patient in recovery position with leaking side down to allow fluid to escape. Do not bandage or plug which could cause a build-up in the skull and pressure on the brain. Immobilise and maintain a check on patient's breathing.

WARNING

If a spinal injury is suspected do NOT place patient in recovery position. Use an airway to maintain respiration and as a means of giving mouth to mouth resuscitation. Warn patient to lie still. Soft, solid items such as luggage or padded objects can be placed to prevent movement of head or body.

SYMPTOMS SUGGESTING
SERIOUS ILLNESS

Medical help is required urgently in the following situations:

CONTINUOUS SEVERE PAIN IN THE CENTRE OF THE CHEST.

This suggests a heart attack. The patient should be rested and propped up in his bunk with three or four pillows.

CONTINUOUS SEVERE PAIN IN THE ABDOMEN.

If associated with vomiting and shock, this suggests a serious internal disorder such as a perforated bowel. Lay the patient down flat, if acceptable, or with one pillow if more comfortable. Give nothing by mouth. A pillow under the knees may help.

SICKNESS, PALLOR, SWEATING AND RAPID BREATHING.

This suggests internal bleeding. Confirmation of this may come from the patient vomiting blood or passing black motions. Keep him lying flat with no pillow and as quiet and comfortable as possible.

LOSS OF CONSCIOUSNESS—COMA.

This has many causes but is always serious. MAINTAIN A CLEAR AIRWAY.

The recovery position.

Treatment

Remove dentures.

Clear the back of the mouth and throat with the finger and wipe away any liquid which has accumulated.

If patient not breathing start artificial respiration.

Once satisfied with the patient's breathing turn him onto his side with his uppermost knee drawn up to a right angle—RECOVERY POSITION.

Keep patient's mouth downwards so that any liquid can run out. Loosen all clothing and keep him warm. Give nothing by mouth. Someone should remain with patient to ensure the airway remains clear.

OTHER EMERGENCIES

HEATSTROKE

This is due to high temperature and high humidity.

The patient may collapse suddenly with a high temperature — 41°C (106°F) or more or appear confused and complain of headache or dizziness.

Treatment

Strip the patient. Cover him with sheets or towels soaked in cold water and keep them wet and cold till the patient's temperature is 39°C (102°F). Open all ventilators. Cool as rapidly as possible.

FITS, EPILEPSY

Try to prevent the patient injuring himself. Keep him horizontal.

After the attack, keep him quiet and resting for a few hours.

FAINTING

Either—with the patient sitting, hold his head between his knees.

Or — lay him down and raise legs.

In either case — loosen tight clothing and ensure he can breathe.

NOSE BLEEDS

SIT CASUALTY WITH HEAD WELL FORWARD.

Casualty to breathe through mouth, then pinch soft part of nose.

Bleeding should cease within 10 minutes, if not, continue pressure.

If bleeding persists, seek medical aid.

FOREIGN BODIES IN THE EYE

If the foreign body can be seen beneath the lower lids it can be removed with the moistened corner of a handkerchief. This can also be tried if it can be seen on the white of the eye.

Do not remove anything that adheres to the clear part of the eye.

If the foreign body cannot be seen, it is probably under the top lid.

In this case pulling the top lid over the bottom lid may cause the bottom lashes to sweep it clear.

The patient may try opening and closing his eye with his face in a bowl of clean water.

Should the eye be burned with splashes of caustic chemicals:

Lay the patient down.

Open the eye with your finger.

Wash the eye with large amounts of clean tepid water.

WEIL'S DISEASE—LEPTOSPIROSIS

This is caught through contact with water infected by animal urine. All those using waterways and river banks are at risk, since the disease can exist on wet vegetation and enters through cuts, grazes and the mucous membranes of the mouth, nose and eyes. Take the following simple precautions:

1) Cover any cuts or grazes with waterproof dressings BEFORE sailing.

2) If skin injury occurs during contact with untreated water wash with clean water, treat with antiseptic and cover.

3) Avoid immersion and swallowing of untreated water.

4) After water activity, wash hands thoroughly (or shower if immersed) before eating, drinking or smoking.

First symptoms can be confused with 'flu, e.g. fever, pain in joints or muscles. If you develop these symptoms after spending time in or by water, tell your doctor immediately. Antibiotics are effective in the early stages of infection, but if left more serious problems develop.

Section 9

EMERGENCY CHILDBIRTH

Send for medical aid. If not available keep calm, and let nature take its course.

Labour may begin with either:

1. Backache and regular pains in the abdomen.
2. A "show" of blood-stained mucus.
3. A gush of water from the birth canal.

Reassure mother. Get basket or drawer and blanket ready for baby.

Boil a pair of scissors and three pieces of string about nine inches long, for about 15 minutes. These are to cut and tie the cord. Prepare a bed for the mother by covering the mattress with a plastic sheet or newspapers, then a clean sheet. Have a supply of hot water, jugs and basins available.

Scrub hands thoroughly and keep crew members with any infection well away.

The first stage of labour, during which the neck of the womb opens, usually lasts several hours. The abdominal pains are usually every 15 to 20 minutes, becoming more frequent as labour progresses.

In the second stage the baby's head descends the birth canal and it may be preceded by a gush of water.

Turn the mother onto her side with her knees drawn up, and cover the top half of her body with a blanket to keep her warm. Encourage her to relax as much as possible when the pains occur. Should a bowel movement appear, wipe it away and wipe from the birth canal.

The baby's head will appear, more of it becoming visible with each contraction. At this stage ask the mother not to bear down, but to try to relax and breathe through her mouth .

Once the baby's head is born, support it with one hand and gently feel if the cord is wrapped around the baby's neck. If it is, ease it gently over the baby's head or shoulders. If a membrane is over the face, remove it.

Do not pull on baby or the cord. The shoulders are usually born with the next pain: then gently lift baby under its armpits, towards mother's abdomen.

Immediately attend to the baby's breathing. Hold it upside down supporting it by the ankles and shoulders. It is slippery so preferably wrap a cloth around the ankles. Wipe the mouth out with a clean handkerchief over the little finger. If the baby does not cry begin gentle artificial respiration.

When the baby cries lay it down against its mother's legs, with the head down, to allow any fluid to drain from the mouth.

If there is excessive bleeding, massage of the lower abdomen will often stimulate the womb to contract.

The afterbirth will be expelled with a pain in about five to fifteen minutes. Then tie the cord, or tie it if the afterbirth has not been expelled in fifteen minutes. Tie one boiled piece of string tightly and firmly about six inches, and the second piece of string about eight inches, from the baby's navel.

Cut the cord between the ligatures. Cover the baby's end of the cord with a sterile dressing and do not apply any antiseptics, etc., to the cord.

Wrap the baby lightly in a blanket and place it in the temporary cot. Inspect the cord for bleeding ten minutes later and, if suspected, tie another piece of boiled string an inch below the first one.

If the afterbirth has not been expelled, cover the mother's end of the cord with a sterile dressing. Keep the afterbirth for the doctor to inspect.

Wash the mother. Replace the sheets and newspapers with dry ones. Give the mother a hot drink and biscuits, and then encourage her to sleep.

RADIO & SATELLITE COMMUNICATIONS

10

RADIO LICENSING
AND ALLIED INFORMATION

Under International Rules all Marine Radios must be licensed and the operator must have a Certificate of Competency.

The following applies to the U.K.;

(1) The Radiocommunications Agency, Room 804, Waterloo Bridge House,SE1 8VA Tel: (071) 215 2292 is the regulatory authority for radio communications in the U.K. Various Acts of Parliament provide for and require that every installation is licensed.

(2) Three types of licence are provided for (a) Ship's Radio (b) Ship's Radio VHF (c) Ship's Radio Transportable Licence.

(a) covers all installations of any type.

(b) covers VHF and radar and EPIRBS and is the usual licence for small craft.

(c) covers Transportable (Portable) equipment, A call sign is not issued with this equipment. If it is used on the one vessel only then a separate license is not required. If however the equipment is to be used on more than one vessel or location then a licence is required.

3. In order to get a licence, the equipment must be Type Approved so that it meets the equipment standards requirements. Do not buy suspect equipment.

4. The operator must also be licensed and this, for the Restricted (VHF) licence, can be done through the Royal Yachting Association, RYA House, Romsey Road, Eastleigh, Hampshire, S05 4YA. Tel: (0703) 629962 or through DVLA Swansea SA99 1BX (0792) 783355, for the Small Ships Register.

5. A Call Sign/Visual Signal Letters (VSL) is allocated when the vessel is first licensed and will remain with the vessel throughout its life. A vessel that already has a VSL will retain this for the radio call sign.

6. Registration is not a prerequisite for Licensing but may and often is required for other purposes.

7. Maritime VHF channels may only be used for their designated purpose i.e. Intership, Port Operations, Public Correspondence.

8. Channel 16 VHF is the Distress and Calling Channel. Use working channel wherever possible.

Channel 67 is used by the U.K. Coastguards for small ships safety and working channel.

Maritime VHF may be used on Inland Waterways in the same manner as on the open sea.

9. Channel 37(M) or M2 (157.850 & 161.425 MHz respectively) are private channels for licenced pleasure craft only. Marinas wishing to use these channels and Channel 80 must apply for a Business Radio (base only) Licence.

10. Selective Calling (Selcall) is an automatic alerting system for business use. The Selcall number must be requested on applying for your license. Your radio must be capable of receiving the automatic signal.

11. Maritime Mobile Service Identity (MMSI) are numbers which uniquely identify vessels and coast stations. They are used by Telephone and Telex subscribers to call vessels automatically. All Digital Selective Calling equipment will use MMSI's.

12. Link Calls. Any vessel (U.K. resident) making a link call through the British Telecom network to telephones in the U.K., Channel Islands or Isle of Man must have the call charged to their home U.K. telephone number. Otherwise you must have an Accounting Authority number/code or have requested British Telecom to act as your Accounting Authority. To make an International call you must have an Accounting Authority code. This is necessary so that e.g. the Swedish/ Spanish/Italian coast station can check your vessel against a list of vessels/codes to know where to send the bill.

All countries have similar rules and regulations in order to comply with the International Rules under the International Maritime Organisation (I.M.O.).

QUESTIONS AND ANSWERS

Some of the more common questions asked concerning Ship's VHF Radio. These clarify the International Rules.

Do I still require a licence if I decide to keep my vessel outside UK territorial waters?
Yes, the WT Act covers all vessels registered in the UK and indeed all unregistered vessels permanently moored in the UK.

Do I need a licence if I am not using my radio for a period, i.e. during the winter when my vessel is not in use?
Yes. The licence is for establishing a station irrespective of whether it is in constant use.

Do I require a licence if I remove the radio equipment and store it?

No, but prior to refitting the equipment you should apply for a licence.

Can I obtain a call sign prior to getting a licence?
No. A call sign is allocated only on issue of a licence and remains valid only while the licence is current.

What happens to my call sign if I purchase another vessel?
Callsigns are not transferable. You will need to apply for a new licence (and therefore call sign) each time you change vessels.

What should I do if I sell my vessel and do not purchase another one?
Write to us giving details of the new owner's name and address and return the old licence to us. As soon as we receive this information we will cancel the licence and contact the new owner.

What should I do if I want to purchase another vessel?
As, above, but additionally we will send you an application form for your new vessel.

What happens to the fee if the vessel is sold prior to the renewal date of the licence?
Licence fees are not transferable as the fee is regarded as a charge upon granting permission to use the radio rather than as a hire or rental spread across the period of the licence.

Do I require a separate licence for the Marina Channels 37M and M2?
No. The owners of pleasure vessels are automatically granted an Authority to use the Marina Channels on issue of a licence.

I have purchased a vessel and the radio equipment is not type approved, what should I do?
Consideration can only be given in instances where the vessel and non-type approved equipment has previously been licensed by another administration, for example, if a vessel had been purchased from a French owner who held a radio licence for that vessel with that equipment issued by the French radio administration. If this is not the case then it will be necessary for you to submit a letter from the other administration to that effect or a copy of the previous radio licence. If this is not the case then the non-type approved equipment must be removed.

Can I use a marine radio from shore to contact a vessel?
No. You may only use your VHF when afloat. Any use on land is illegal and will leave you liable to prosecution

I only want a VHF radio for distress purposes –(i) do I need a full VHF licence?
(ii) do I need a Certificate of Competence?
(i) Yes. VHF radio is capable of being used for many purposes and therefore needs a Ship Radio (VHF) licence.
(ii) Yes.

What does the Public Correspondence category on my licence mean?
It indicates the number of hours of watch-keeping to be kept by a particular class of vessel. A key to the different classifications is given below (please note - dispensation for commercial vessels may be given by the Department of Transport).

HX (voluntary fitted vessels, including pleasure craft) – there is no fixed hours of service.

H8 (compulsory fitted vessels, I.e commercial vessels) – eight hour radio watch must be kept.

H16 (passenger vessels) – a sixteen hour radio watch must be kept.

H24 (passenger vessels) – a 24 hour radio watch must be kept.

INTERNATIONAL ACCOUNTING AUTHORITIES

ACCOUNTING AUTHORITY INDICATOR CODES (AAIC'S)
Note – some authorities only deal with their own or commercial vessels.

A.V. Stagnetto, 186 Main Street, Gibraltar. GK08
Abdel Mohty Attiah, 42 Talaat Harb Street, Cairo, Egypt. UN02
Abdelkrim Bel Hadj Salah et Cie, Jara, Gabès, Tunisie. TN04
Administration & Gestion S.A., 40 Rue du Rhône, P.O. Box Stand 341, CH-1211 Genève 11, Suisse
....CH03
Administration des P. et T., Division des Télécommunications, Section Comptabilité, K-2999 Luxembourg.....................................LU01
Adriano Antonio Lima, Av 5 de Julho 27, S. Vicente de Cabo Verde, Cap-Vert.............CV13
Agence Glemot, B.P. 49, 06402 Cannes Cédex, France FR04
Alberto Pancrácio Lopes, Mindelo, S. Vicente de Cabo Verde, Cap-Vert. CV04
Alexandria Ports General Organisation, Alexandria, Egypt. UN05
Ali El Ghoul et Cie, 11 Rue Mohamed Snan, Mahdia, Tunisie TN29
Andgate (International) Ltd, P.O. Box 399, Suite 52, Victoria House, 26 Main Street, Gibraltar. GK12

Aporvela-Ass. Portuguesa de Treino de Vela, Museu da Marinha, Praça do Imperio, 1400 Lisboa, Portugal..PO11

Arab Maritime Co., P.O. Box 39, Alexandria, Egypt. UN13

Arab Union for Marine Transport (FAMCO), 5 Gabtry Street, Alexandria, Egypt. UN15

Arfaoui Khaled, 218 Avenue H. Bourguiba, Le Kram, Tunisie TN26

Arklow Shipping Co., North Quay, Arklow (Co. Wicklow), Ireland. EI02

Associaçáo Naval de Lisboa, Doca de Belém, 1300 Lisboa, Portugal. PO10

Associaçáo Portuguesa dos Armadores da Marinha Mercante, Rua de S. Juliáo, 80 20, 1100 Lisboa, Portugal. PO02

Attias & Levy, Suite 1 & 3, 3 Irish Place, Gibraltar. GK19

Attitallah Myoussef Amilcar, 3 VII, 15 Rue Patrice Lumumba, Sfax, Tunisie. TN13

Azores Radio Communications Services, 20 Ifigenias Street, Limassol, Cyprus. CY02

Bachmann Marine Services Ltd, P.O. Box 175, Frances House, Sir William Place, St Peter Port, Guernsey, Channel Islands. 0481-23573 ......GB12

Bell Lines Ltd, 7 Montague Street, Dublin 2, Ireland. EI03

Bezeq, The Israel Telecommunication Corp. Ltd, Finance Division, P.O. Box 1175, 91010 Jerusalem. Israel. IL02

Brian Perez LL.B., Suite 4 & 5, 4 Giro's Passage, Gibraltar...GK07

British Telecom, NIA Maritime Accounts, 3rd Floor, Barbican Computer Centre, 26/28 Glasshouse Yard, London EC1A 4JY, United Kingdom. 071-492-4954.........................GB14

Bureau de la Comptabilité Internationale des P.T.T., H-1525 Budapest Pf 3, Hongrie. HU01

BATELCO, P.O. Box 14, Manama, Bahrain. ...BN01

C.C.A., 5 Bd Abdellah Ben Yassine, Casablanca, Maroc...MP20

C.I. Maritime Services, P.O. Box 601, St Peter Port, Guernsey, Channel Islands. 0481-54506. ......GB19

C.I. Shipping Ltd, Holland House, 1-4 Bury Street, London EC3A 5AT, United Kingdom. GB15

Cable & Wireless PLC, Mercury House, 110-114 Theobalds Road, London WC1X 8RX United Kingdom GB02

Cap Bon, Société de Pêche, Ennahdha Port de Pêche, Kelibia, Tunisie. TN27

Celestino Lopes de Conceiçáo, S. Vicente de Cabo Verde, Cap-Vert. CV08

Chaari Mohamed Annibal, 3 VII El Bousten, Route d'El Mahdia, Km 2, Sfax, Tunisie. TN24

Clube Internacional da Marinha de Vilamours, Centro Comercial da Marinha, 8125 Vilamoura, Portugal. PO14

Comanav, 7 Bd de la Résistance, Casablanca, Maroc..MP02

Comapêche, Immeuble Air France, 28 Avenue Mohamed V, Rabat, Maroc. MP32

Comapêche, 8 Place Mirabeau, Casablanca, Maroc. MP30

Comarit, 13 Rue d'Artois, Casablanca, Maroc. MP06

Comex Services, F-13275 Marseille Cédex 9, France FR05

Comissáo de Gestáo Transportes Marítimos, S. Vicente de Cabo Verde, Cap-Vert.............CV10

Compagnia Generale Telemar, Viale Tiziano 19, I-00196 Roma, Italie IU03

Compagnie de Navigation Denis Frères, 25 Rue du General Foy, F-75008 Paris, France. FR14

Compagnie Générale pour les Développements Opérationnels des Richesses Sous-Marines, 58 Rue du Dessous des Berges, F-75013 Paris, France. FR12

Compagnie Morbihannaise et Nantaise de Navigation, 4 bis Place du Sanitat, F-44040 Nantes Cédex 01, France.........................FR08

Compagnie Tunisienne de Navigation, 5 Avenue Dag Hammarskjoeld, Tunis, Tunisie............TN02

Companhia de Navegaçáo Estrela Negra Ltda., Mindelo, S. Vicente de Cabo Verde, Cap-Vert CV01

Companhia Nacional de Navegaçáo Arca Verde, Praia, Cap-Vert. CV05

Comptabilitié de l'Office monégasque des téléphones, 21 Avenue de la Costa, Monte-Carlo, Monaco. MC01

Conselho Administrativo da Administraçáo Central da Marinha, Praça do Comério, 1188 Lisboa Codex, Portugal. PO01

Cotrama, 42 Avenue Hassan Es-Seghir, Casablanca, Maroc. MP05

Crescent Shipping, c/o Ships Electronic Services Ltd, 23-27 High Street Greenhithe (Kent) DA9 9PA, United Kingdom. GB04

Czechoslavak Ocean Shipping, Pocernicka 168, 10 099 Praha 10, Czechoslavakia.....................CS02

Cámara Portuguesa dos Armadores da Marinha Mercante, Edif. "Bartolomeu Dias" 2o., Doca de Alcántara, 1300 Lisboa, Portugal. PO15

CONGEL, S Vicente de Cabo Verde, Cap-Vert. CV03

CONTAG-Arístides Lima Silva-António, Pedro Silva-Rui Lima e Lúcio, S. Vicente de Cabo Verde, Cap-Vert. CV12

D.G.N.T.M. - Inspecçáo de Navios e Seguranca Marítima, Av. Brasilia, Pavilháo Central, 1300 Lisboa, Portugal. PO13

Dabinovic (Monaco) S.A.M., 74 Boulevard d'Italie, Monaco. MC02

Demitry Honin Ratl, 14 Ard Sherif Street, Cairo, Egypt. UN31

Deutsche Post der Deutschen Demokratischen Republik, Zentrales Post-und Fernmeldeverk-ehrsamt, Postfach 100 (Postelcentre Berlin), DDR-1085 Berlin, Germany. DD01

Direccíon General de Correos y Telégrafos, Subdirección General de Explotación, Sección de Cuentas, 28070 Madrid, España...................ES01

Direction de la Marine Marchande, 10 Avenue de la République, 1011 Tunis, Tunisie TN21

Direction des télécommunications des réseaux extérieurs, D.T.R.E., Immeuble P.T.T. Bercy, 246 Rue de Bercy, F-75584 Paris Cédex, France. ...FR01

Direction générale des douanes, 12 Avenue Jean Jaurès, Tunis, Tunisie TN21

Direction générale des postes et des télégraphes, Postgasse 8, A-1011 Wien, Autriche. AU01

Direction générale des postes et télécomm-unications, Department des finances, Tiranë, Albanie. AB01

Direction générale des postes et télécomm-unications, Service de trafic et décomptes internationaux, 38 B-dul D. Golescu, 77113 Bucarest, Roumanie. RM01

Direction générale des postes, télégraphes et téléphones, Service des finances, Ch-3030 Berne, Suisse. CH01

Director General, Sudan Shipping Line, P.O. Box 426, Port Sudan, Sudan. SD01

Directorate General of the Syrian Telecomm-unications Establishment, Saadallah Jabiri Street, Damascus, Syria. SY01

Directorate General of Posts and Telecomm-unications of Iceland, Reykjavik, Iceland. IS01

Domingos António Duarte, S. Vicente de Cabo Verde, Cap-Vert CV06

Dredging International N.V., Scheldedijk 30, B-2730 Zwijndrecht, Belgique. BE03

Dublin Shipping Ltd, Beechill. Clonskeagh, Dublin 6, Ireland. EI04

DEBEG GmbH, Funkverkehrsabrechnung, Postfach 50 03 29, D-2000 Hamburg 50, Allemagne. DP02

DML Data Marine Ltd, 1 Stadium Street, Gzira, Malta...MW04

E.B. Communications (Great Britain) Ltd, 20 Imperial Way, Croydon CR0 4RR, United Kingdom. 081-686 5701 ....GB11

E.M. Russo, 12B College Lane, Gibraltar.......GK04

Eastern Petroleum Co., Cairo, Egypt. UN07

Ecole de la Marine Marchande, Sousse, Tunisie. TN01

Egyptian Spanish Maritime Co. (EGYSPAN), 95, 26th July Street, Mazarita, Alexandria, Egypt.UN16

Electro-Nav. International Ltd, Marine Electronics, 208-211 Gardiner House, London Production Centre, Broomhill Road, London SW18 4JQ United Kingdom. 081-8709755 ...GB10

Equicor Limited, 5 Cannon Lane, Gibraltar. GK20

Esso Standard Cédex No. 2, 6 Avenue Andrés Prothin, F-92080 Paris La Défense, France. ...FR11

EB Nachrichtentechnik GmbH, Postfach 70 05 02, D-2000 Hamburg 70, Allemagne. DP04

ETISALAT, P.O. Box 3838, Abu Dhabi, United Arab Emirates. EM01

Finshipyards S.A.M., Le Parc Palace, Avenue de la Costa, MC 98000 Monaco.......................MC03

France Shipmanagement, 4 bis Palace du Sanitat 21 X, F-44040 Nantes Cédex 01, France. FR10

FLAMAR PVBA, Visserstraat 33, B-8380 Brugge 5, Belgique. BE08

FT Everard & Son Ltd, c/o Ships Electronic Services Ltd, 23-27 High Street, Greenhithe (Kent) DA9 9PA, United Kingdom. GB17

General Directorate of Posts and Telecomm-unications, Tripoli, Libya. LY01

General Manager, Bahamas Telecommunications Corp., P.O. Box N-3048, Nassau, Bahamas. ...BS01

General National Maritime Transport Co., (GNMTC) P.O. Box 4673, Tripoli, Libya.........LY02

General Petroleum Co., 14 Talaat Harb Street, Cairo, Egypt UN30

Goutaland (Gib) Ltd, The Lighthouse, 48 Europa Flats, Europa Point, Gibraltar. GK18

Hagenuk GmbH, Funkgebuehrenabrechnung, Postfach 1149, D-2300 Kiel 1, Allemagne. ...DP03

Hecosar Co., 16 Rue Profitou Ilia, Agia Paraskevi, Athinai, Grèce. GR03

Helexco Co., Ltd, 31 High Street, Colliers Wood. London SW19 2JE, United Kingdom. 081-0542 4916. ....GB13

Hellenic Radio Services Ltd, Iroon Politechniou 59, Piraeus 185, 35 Grèce. GR05

Houlder Bros. & Co. Ltd, Head of Radio Traffic Services, 53 Brighton Road, Redhill, Surrey RH1 6YL, United Kingdom. GB01

Inter Shipping Co., Ltd, 131 East Street, Valletta, Malta...MW05

International Accounting Centre, Ministry of Communications, 2-oi Smolensky pereulok, d. I/4, Moscow 121099, Russia. (For SATSU02 or SU03) SU01

International Posts and Telecommunications Accounts Office, Fibichova 21, 130 00, Praha 3 - Zizkov, Czechoslovakia. CS01

International Radio Traffic Services Ltd, 90 Marlborough Road, Dublin 4, Ireland. E106

Isola & Isola, 3 Bell Lane, Gibraltar. GK02

John I. Azopardi LL.B., 31/2 Irish Town, Gibraltar. Gk11

Joâo Bossuet Gomes de Pina, S. Vicente de Cabo Verde, Cap-Vert. CV07

Junta Autónoma dos Portos do Arquipélago de Cabo Verde, Mindelo, S. Vicente de Cabo, Cap-Vert. CV02

Kelvin Hughes Ltd, New North Road, Hainault, Ilford (Essex) IG6 2UR, United Kingdom. 081-500 1020...GB05

Libyan Algerian Maritime Transport Co., P.O. Box 12957, Tripoli, Libya...............................LY03

Libyan-Turkish Maritime Transport Co., 216 Alfateh Street, P.O. Box 12400, Tripoli, Libya. LY04

Limadet, 3 Rue Regnault, Tanger, Maroc. ...MP24

Lord Maritime Enterprises, 43 Ramses Street, P.O. Box 476, Cairo, Egypt. UN14

LIMAGES, S. Vicente de Cabo Verde, Cap-Vert. CV16

Section 10

5

Magnav, 30 Avenue des FAR, Casablanca, Maroc MP09

Mahmoud Omar, 93 El Qasr El Iny Street, Cairo, Egypt. UN08

Marcos Lopes, S. Vicente de Cabo Verde, Cap-Vert. CV14

Marine Investments, 123 Main Street, Gibraltar. GK03

Marine Nationale, Bizerte, Tunisie. TN07

Marphocean, Angle Bd La Grande et Route D'El Jadida, Casablanca, Maroc. MP03

Mecopex SARL, 44 Lot Guynamer, Casablanca, Maroc. MP22

Medwest Shipping Agency Ltd, 3 Library Ramp, P.O. Box 199, Gibraltar. GK09

Ministry of Communications, P.O. Box 5929, Ruwi, Muscat, Oman. ON01

Ministry of Communications, P.O. Box 16, Safat, Kuwait KT01

Ministry of Communications, Finance Division, 23 Jaffa Road, 91999 Jerusalem, Israel. IL01

Ministry of Defence, IT (FIN) 3, Room 7119, St. Christopher House, Southwark Street, London SE1 0TD, United Kingdom. GB09

Ministère d'Etat chargé des postes et télécommunications, Division des abonnements et réseaux TE2, Avenue Moulay Hassan, Rabat, Maroc. MP01

Ministère des postes et des télécommunications, Direction centrale des services radioélectriques, Div. I- Section III, I-00100 Roma, Italie. IU01

Ministère des postes et télécommunications, Bureau de la comptabilité internationale, Sofia, Bulgarie. BG01

Ministère des postes et télécommunications, Direction générale des télécommunications, Bureau des radiocommunications, Alger, Algérie. DZ01

Misr Edco Co., 42 Abdel Kadar Ragab Street, Rochdy, Alexandria, Egypt..........................UN11

N.V. Jan de Nul, Tragel 27, B-9308 Aalst, Belgique. BE06

Nakhodka Coast Earth Station, 70 pereulok Koltsevaya, Primorsky Krai 692900 Nakhodka, Russia . (Via SAT only). SU03

Navale & Commerciale Havraise Péninsulaire, c/o Euronavis - Départment Personnel Navigant, Tour Fiat, 1 Place de la Coupole, 92084 Paris La Défense Cédex 16, France. FR21

Navimar, 42 Avenue Hassan Es-Seghir, Casablanca, Maroc. MP14

Norwegian Telecommunications Administration, Postboks 6701, St. Olavs Plass, N-Oslo 1, Norway. NO01

Nouvelle Compagnie des Paquebots, 33 Rue J.F. Leca, F-13221 Marseille Cédex 1, France. FR25

Odessa Coast Earth Station, 1 pereulok Lastochkina, 2-70026 Odessa, Russia. (Via SAT only) SU02

Office des ports nationaux, Port de La Goulette, Tunis, Tunisie...TN19

Omnium Marocaine de Pêche, Tour Habous, 19/20 ème étage, Avenue des FAR, Casablanca, Maroc MP10

Organisme Héllénique des Télécommunications S.A., (OTE), 15 Rue Stadiou, Athinai 124, Grèce. GR01

P.&T. - Tele, Radio Services, P.O. Box 98, SF-00511 Helsinki, Finland..SF01

Pecos, Avenue Hassan II, Immeuble Tarik Announon, Agadir, Maroc. MP27

Penav Maroc, Tour Habous, 19/20ème étage, Avenue des FAR, Casablanca, Maroc. MP16

Peninsular Electronics, 13-17 Long Lane, London EC1A 9PN, United Kingdom. 071-726 2464...GB06

Petramar, Bd de la Résistance, Casablanca, Maroc. MP15

Petrocab, 24 Bd Brahim Roudani, Casablanca, Maroc. MP17

Ports and Lighthouse Administration, Alexandria, Egypt. UN03

Postal Headquarters, 104 Main Street, Gibraltar. GK06

Posttechnisches Zentralami (PTZ), Bureau de la comptabilité internationale, Postfach 1180, D-6100 Darmstadt, Allemagne. DP01

PTT Centralny Osrodek Rozliczenjowy, Ul. Bernardynska 15, 85-029 Bydgoszcz, Pologne. ...PL01

PTT Isletme Genel Müdürlügü, Milletlerarsi Illiskiler Daire Baskanligi, 06101 Ankara, Turkey TR01

PTT Telecom Scheveningenradio, P.O. Box 468, 1970 Al Ymuiden, Netherlands. NL01

Radio and Electronic Services, Cunard Building, Ground Floor, Water Street, Liverpool L3 1Ds, United Kingdom. GB03

Radio Holland Group Traffic Accounting, P.O. Box 5860, 3008 AB Rotterdam, Netherlands, ...NL02

Roinn Na Gaeltachta, Dublin 2, Ireland. EI08

Rowbotham Tankships Ltd, c/o Ships Electronic Services Ltd, 23-27 High Street, Greenhithe (Kent) DA9 9PA, United Kingdom. GB18

Royal Netherlands Navy, c/o Fibekm Pers. Ultgaven, P.O. Box 20702, 2500 ES The Hague, Netherlands. NL04

Régie des transports maritimes, Natienkaai 5, B-8400 Oostende, Belgique. BE05

Régie des télégraphes et des téléphones, Département Relations publique et Service commercial, 2ème Bureau, Bd. E. Jacqmain 166, B-1210 Bruxelles, Belgique. BE01

Saetma, 45 Bd d'Anfa, B.P. 12574, Casablanca, Maroc. MP21

Schelde Sleepvaartmaatschappij N.V. Noorderlaan 139, B-2030 Anvers, Belgique. BE07

Sea Malta Co., Ltd, P.O. Box 555, Valletta Flagstone Wharf, Marsa, Malta. MW01

Sema Electrónicas - Soc. Elect. Marítima e

Aéronautica, Av, 24 de Julho, 60-1o, 1200 Lisboa, Portugal. PO05

Sociedade Nacional dos Armadores de Bacalhau, SARL, Rua do Ferragial, 33-lo. e 4o., 1200 Lisboa, Portugal. PO88

Società Italiana Radio Marittima, Piazzale G. Douhet 25, 00144 Roma, Italie. 396-5910441 IU02

Société Anonyme Le Golfe, Le Kram, Tunisie. TN11

Société Boulonnaise d'Armement Le Garrec et Cie. B.P. 287, 62204 Boulogne-sur-Mer Cédex, France FR19

Société Chimie Gabès Transport, 7 Rue Khartoum, 1002 Tunis Belvédère, Tunisie. ...TN08

Société Générale Industrielle, KM 3, 2 Djebel Djelloud, Tunis, Tunisie. TN23

Société Imem El Mezri Teboulba, Tunisie. ...TN30

Société Le Cosoup, 50 Rue Patrice Lumumba, Sfax, Tunisie. TN20

Société Marocaine de Navigation, 81 Avenue Houmane El Ftwaki, Casablanca, Maroc. ...MP31

Société Navale de l'Ouest, Tour Franklin Cédex 11, F-92081 Paris La Défense, France. FR03

Société Navale des Chargeurs Delmas Vieljeux, 16 Avenue Matignon, F-75008 Paris, France. ...FR22

Société Sarost, Immeuble Saadi, Route Ariana, Tour C-D, Tunis, Tunisie. TN31

Société Tunisienne de Remorquage, d'Assistance et de Travaux Maritimes, 16 Rue de Remada, Sfax, Tunisie. TN06

Sofruma, 27 Avenue des FAR, Casablanca, Maroc. MP07

Sogema, 15 Rue Foucauld, Casablanca, Maroc. MP04

Somama, 12 Rue Foucauld, Casablanca, Maroc. MP08

Somamer, 97 Bd El Massira El Khdra, Casablanca, Maroc. MP12

Somapes, 1 Rue de Madrid, Agadir, Maroc MP34

Somathom, 1 Résidence Ben Omar, 2ème étage, Casablanca, Maroc. MP18

Sonarp, 8 Rue Voltaire, Casablanca, Maroc. MP11

Sosema S.A., Société de services maritimes, Zone industrielle Ouest, CH-1260 Nyon, Suisse. ...CH05

Starcom Systems ltd, Fortuna Court, Block B, 284 Arc. Makarios Ave., Limassol, Cyprus. CY04

Stephenson Clark Shipping Ltd, c/o Ships Electronic Services Ltd, 23-27 High Street, Greenhithe (Kent) DA9 9PA, United Kingdom. GB16

Suez Canal Authority, Suez, Egypt. UN09

Swedish Telecommunications Administration, International Accounts Office, S-123 86 Farsta, Sweden. SW01

SAIT Electronics Marine, Chausée de Ruysbroeck 66, B-1990 Bruxelles, Belgique. 322-370 5480 BE02

SOMVIK, Rue Alexandre Dumas, Sfax, Tunisie TN14

STC International Marine Ltd, Intelco House, 302 Commonside East, Mitcham (Surrey) CR4 1YT, United Kingdom. 081-640 3400 ....GB07

Telaccount Overseas ltd, P.O. Box 132, Limassol, Cyprus. CY03

Telecom Denmark, Telecommunications Accounts, Telegade 2, DK-2630, Taastrup, Denmark...DK01

Telecom Eireann Gaiety Centre, South King Street, Dublin 2, Ireland. EI01

Telecommunications Organization, Ramses Street Cairo, Egypt. UN01

Temsah Ship Construction Co., Cairo, Egypt. UN10

Teodoro José Nascimento e José Isidoro Almeida, Rua do Sol 47, S. Vicente de Cabo Verde, Cap-Vert. CV09

The Egyptian Navigation Co., 2 El Nasr Street, Alexandria, Egypt. UN04

The Marconi International Marine Co., Ltd, Elettra House, Westway, Chelmsford (Essex) CM1 3BH, United Kingdom. 2045-261701............GB08

Thenamaris Ellas EPE, Filonos 107-109, Le Pirée, Grèce. GR10

Totoheo Radiocommunication Services Ltd, 114A Omonia Ave., P.O. Box 1449, Limasol, Cyprus. CY05

Transinsular-Transportes Marítimos Insulares, SARL, Av. Santos Dumond 57-8o., 1000 Lisboa, Portugal. PO12

Trevisan Peter, Ringstrasse 10, CH-3117 Kiesen, Suisse. CH04

Triay & Triay, 28 Irish Town, Gibraltar. GK01

Troodes Radio Communications Services, 3 Ioannis Marsellos Street, Larnaca, Cyprus. ...CY01

TOTAL, Compagnie Française de Navigation, 24 Rue du Pont, F-92521 Neuilly-sur-Seine Cédex, France. FR16

TRANSMAR - Carlos Albertino Barreto de Carvalho, Veiga-Praia, Cap-Vert. CV15

U.M.M., 5 Bd Abdellah Ben Yassine, Casablanca, Maroc. MP13

Umimar, 12 Rue Foucauld, Casablanca, Maroc. MP13

Unie van Redding en Sleepdienst N.V. Antwerpen, Jordaenskaai 15, B-2000 Anvers, Belgique. BE04

Union Navale, 3 Bouevard Malesherbes, B.P. 9808, Paris Cédex 08, France. FR18

Ustanova za odrzavanje pomorskih puteva, PLOVPUT, Obala Lazareta 1, 58000 Split, Yugoslavia. YU02

Younsi Faouzi Jamaa, El Haoua 1008, Tunis, Tunisie. TN28

Section 10

LICENSING AUTHORITIES

The following is a list of Government Departments who deal with the licensing of equipment and persons in the countries indicated. Contact either the Department or the Agency indicated for full details of the necessary procedures.

Norwegian Telecommunications Regulatory Authority (NTRA), P.O. Box 2592, Solli N-0203 OSLO 2, Norway.

Ministry of Communications, Vilnius, LITHUANIA, Tel: +7 12 62 44 02.

Ministry of Transport and Public Works, Telecommunications and Post Department, P.O. Box 450, 9700 AL GRONINGEN, The Netherlands, Pays Bas.

Ministero Poste & Telecomunicazioni, Direzione Generale, Officio Relazioni Internazionali, Viale America, 1-00100 ROMA-EUR, ITALY

Ministry of Communications, International Relations, P.O. Box 29515, 61294 TEL AVIV, Israel.

Ministry of Transport and Communications, Vasagatan 8-10, S-10333 STOCKHOLM, Sweden.

Ministere des Postes et Telecommunications, Direction du Service public, S/Direction industrielle et Internatale, 20 Avenue de Segur, F-75700 PARIS, France.

State Telecom Inspection, Riga, LATVIA. Tel: +7 132 32 30 36.

Inspection of Telecomm, Telbium, ESTONIA. Tel: +7 142 422 15.7

Minsviaz Moscow,
Telex 411120.
Tel: +7 095 925 5108.
Fax: 07095 230.

Ministere des Transports et des Communications, Administration des Postes et des Communications, 49 Avenue Syngrou, GR-11780 ATHENS, Greece.

The Chairman Board of Directors, National Telecommunications Organisation (ARENTO), P.O. Box 2271, CAIRO 11511, Egypt.

Ministerstwo Lacznosci, Pl Malachowskiego 2, 00-940 WARSAW, Poland.

Ministerio de Obras Publicas Y Transporte, Secretaria General de Comunicaciones, 28070 MADRID. Spain.

Directorate General of PTT, Department of Telegraphs and Telephones, ANKARA, Turkey.

Ministere des Postes et des Telecommunications, Boulevard Moulay AL Hassan, RABAT, Morocco.

Der Bundesminister Fur Post und Telekommunikation, Referat 201, Postfach 8001, D-5300 BONN 1, Germany.

Instituto das Comunicacoes de Portugal, Avenida Jose Malhoa, Lote 1683-7°, 1000 LISBON, Portugal.

Direction Generale des Postes, Telegraphes et Telephones, 42 Rue Myslym Shyri, TIRANA Albania.

General Directorate of Posts and Telegraphs, Director General, Tietgensgade 37, DK-1530 COPENHAGEN V, Denmark.

Radio & Broadcasting Branch, Department of Tourism, Transport and Communications, Scotch House, Hawkins Street, DUBLIN 2, Ireland. Tel: (01) 718211, Ext. 1124. Fax: (01) 679 2934.

Community of Yugoslav Posts, Telegraphs and Telephones, Palmoticeva 2, 11001 BEOGRAD, Yugoslavia.

AGENCIES

The Netherlands.

Hoofddirectie Telecommunications en Post, Bureau Maritime Machtigingen, Postbus 450, 9700 Al Groningen, The Netherlands.

Information about the training of operators is via the same address. Tel. 50222170.

Germany

In the Federal Republic of Germany the Federal Minister of Posts and Telecommunications takes responsibility for the licensing of ship stations and for the granting of ship radiotelegraph operators' certificates. The public maritime mobile service is operated by the coast stations of Deutsche Bundespost TELEKOM.

The Federal Minister of Posts and Telecommunications issues the rules and regulations concerning operators' certificates (Verordnung über Seefunkzeugnisse) which regulates the responsibility for the conduct of examinations for obtaining ship radiotelegraph certificates. For further enquiries contact:

Bundesamt at für Post und Telecommunikation, Templerstr. 2-4, Postfach 80 01, D-W-6500 Mainz.

The licensing of German ship stations falls within the sole responsibility of the Hamburg branch of the Federal Office for Posts and Telecommunications. The address is:

Bundesamt für Post und Telecommunikation,
Außenstells Hamburg
Sachsenstr. 12 + 11,
D-W-2000 HAMBURG 1.

Licences can only be granted for ship stations which have been type approved for the maritime mobile service.

Denmark

The following licences are necessary in Denmark and onboard Danish ships to operate radio equipment in the maritime mobile radio services:

a) a licence for the equipment (Ship Station Licence);
b) a licence for the operator (Operator's Certificate).

The issuing organisation for both the above mentioned licences is the National Telecom Agency, Holsteinegade 63, DX-2100 Copenhagen East.

To issue a Ship Station Licence, an application is required with the necessary information such as shipowner's name and address, radio-operator's name and licence number and also the make(s) and type(s) of the radio equipment onboard. Application forms are available from the National Telecom Agency.

To issue an Operator's Certificate, it is necessary that an applicant has passed a test in front of an examiner from the National Telecom Agency and the applicant has to sign a solemn declaration, placing him under obligation to preserve secrecy in accordance with the International Radio Regulations.

The test (examination) normally takes place at the school or institution, where the applicant has been trained.

An Operator's Certificate cannot be issued without the compulsory test (examination). There is however no obligation to have received training.

If someone has an Operator's Certificate issued by a foreign Authority, this certificate has to be approved by the National Telecom Agency, before it is valid to operate radio equipment onboard Danish ships.

Sweden

Frequency Management–Swedish Telecom,
Box 700, 136 27 Haninge,
Sweden.
Tel: 8 707 35 00.

Poland

The National Radiocommunications Agency Headquarters, Ranstowa Agencja Radio-komumikacyjna, ul. Kaspranza 18/20, Rzeczpos-polita, Pollska. Zarzad Krajowy 01-211-Warszawa.
Tel: +48 22 32 78 05.
Fax: +48 22 32 80 44.

Latvia

Application must be made in writing, stating the basic technical characteristics of the proposed equipment, frequencies, power output, type of modulation, antenna, terms of operation and also name, address, phone and if available fax. number of the applicant. The applicant will be sent a questionnaire.

Apply for licenses through:

Latvia State Telecommunication Inspection, 41/43 Elizabeth Street, Riga, Latvia.
Tel: 013 2 333034.
Fax: 013 2 323036.
Telex: 02 161311 TEXCT.

SATELLITE NAVIGATION

TRANSIT SATELLITE SYSTEM

Originally developed for the U.S. Navy, the system consists of five satellites orbiting the earth at a height of 1000 km and transmitting data on frequencies of 400MHz and 150MHz.

The transmission frequency received by an observer decreases as the satellite passes overhead due to the Doppler effect. The rotation of the earth brings the receiver under each satellite orbit in turn, and as the receiver 'sights' the satellite, it computes its position from the data transmitted.

The time between suitable satellite 'passes' varies between 90 minutes in the low latitudes and 30 minutes in the high latitudes. The actual time of the satellite pass overhead varies between 10 and 15 minutes, during which time the receiver calculates the navigator's position.

SatNav does not provide continuous position-fixing like Decca and Loran C, and it is therefore necessary to maintain a D.R. Position on the chart between fixes. The accuracy of the system is basically good—of the order of ± 100m—but correct input of the vessel's speed is necessary for this accuracy. The speed of the vessel will affect the Doppler effect and therefore the calculated position. This error can be of the order of ± 400m for every knot of velocity error.

In some sets speed and compass course can be keyed in manually and in the more sophisticated sets it can be done automatically by interfacing with automatic log and compass units.

Satellite fixes are based on the World Geodetic System (WGS72) Datum and for the best accuracy the receiver coordinates should be amended by the local 'shift' where mentioned on a particular chart.

GLOBAL POSITIONING SYSTEM (GPS)

GPS has been developed in the USA for military purposes by the Department of Defense, and by arrangement with the Department of Transportation a degraded version is utilized for civilian use. The system will eventually consist of 21 satellites with 3 spares in orbit at an altitude of 20,000km, each satellite rotating round the earth at 12-hour intervals. There are at least 4 satellites visible to a receiver at sea level at any one time, thus providing continuous position fixing.

The method of operation, basically is that each satellite broadcasts its exact position at an exact time, the receiver then notes the time taken for the transmission to reach it and converts that time into the distance from the satellite. This operation is carried out on 4 satellites and the receiver obtains 4 'position lines' or circles, the point of intersection being the navigator's position. The timing is of extreme importance and this is achieved by equipping the satellites with atomic clocks with an error of ± 1 second in 300,000 years.

Each satellite transmits data on two frequencies, the first designed for military purposes and not available for civilian use, giving extremely accurate position-fixing, probably of the order of 6 to 8 metres error. The transmission available to civilian users is deliberately degraded and the error will be of the order of ± 100m.

It should be noted that the position obtained by GPS should be amended for chart datum in exactly the same way as SatNav positions are amended.

Differential Transmissions (GPS)

The accuracy of satellite navigation systems (e.g GPS) can be improved considerably by the transmission of differential corrections obtained from suitably located stations. These stations can be radiobeacons operating on the maritime radiobeacon frequencies.

The differential corrections are transmitted on an additional signal (within 0·5 kHz of the radiobeacon frequency), with Minimum Shift Keying (MSK) and G1D class of emission. This additional signal should not affect the radiobeacon.

Radiobeacon stations may also be used to transmit supplementary navigational information using narrow-band techniques, provided that the prime function of the beacon is not significantly affected.

Reference is made in the footnotes to the list of radiobeacons in the annual Almanac where such transmissions are made.

INMARSAT SYSTEMS

The idyllic remoteness of the high seas is one of the attractions of sailing, but as any ocean-going yachtsman knows, this isolation can have serious disadvantages.

The high seas can be an unpredictable and dangerous environment where reliable communications for information and assistance are indispensable and for some in the business world, the possibility of being cut off for even a few hours from their offices might prevent them from going to sea at all. Access to a reliable, easy to use communications link can make any voyage better, more enjoyable and safer. Today, a growing number of yachts of 80 ft. and beyond, are being fitted with mobile

Fig 1

satcoms equipment that enables world-wide direct-dial telephone, fax and data communications.

Known as Inmarsat-A, this global communications system is available around the clock for ocean-going yachts wherever they may be sailing. Fig. 1 shows a yacht fitted with an Inmarsat-A terminal, the white radome antenna visible at the top. Each satellite terminal has a unique number, and making a call either to or from is as simple as using the telephone in the office or at home. The facsimile, telex and data communications facilities are just as easy to use. Inmarsat-A also connects easily into the world's electronic mail networks, using a built-in personal computer.

A range of specialized services is also offered, e.g. using modern data compression techniques it is possible to send and receive high quality photographs to and from an on-board terminal. These techniques can also enable the system to be used for transmitting still and moving video images. A video signal coming from a camera can be manipulated by a computer as an ordinary graphic. This graphic can in turn be enlarged or decreased in size or rotated; colours and contrasts can be changed and then the graphic is saved as a file, compressed and transmitted via Inmarsat-A to an office onshore where, for instance, it can be imported into desk top publishing software. Ships at sea can receive instant advice on the repair of engines and other critical parts by faxing a photograph of the faulty section to an on-shore agent who can then pinpoint the defect and suggest methods of repair immediately.

The ability to transmit text, graphics and photographs via the system has enabled news networks on shore to reach a ship on the high seas and many yacht owners have up-to-date electronic 'newspapers' and weather charts delivered to them.

Even with all of these advanced capabilities, Inmarsat-A is extremely easy to operate and does not require the skills of a radio officer. Thirteen terminal models are available. Essentially, these consist of an above-the-deck parabolic antenna encased in a weatherproof radome. Below decks is the electronics and peripheral equipment such as a telephone, facsimile and computer. Terminals are available with up to four channels. Some large yachts are fitted with two separate terminals for different applications.

SATCOMS FOR SMALL YACHTS

The size and cost of Inmarsat-A equipment means that smaller yachts may not find it suitable to their requirements. Many yachtsmen with craft as small as 30 ft. and those for whom voice communications are not critical, need an affordable communications system that can fit on to even the smallest yacht. Until recently, no such communication link existed for those small boat owners and operators who ventured into high seas.

The alternative for the small boat owner is Inmarsat-C, a store-and-forward data messaging system, which is able to send messages in any language or character set. These messages can be originated or delivered in many forms such as telex, electronic mail, switched data, or a message forwarded as a fax from your yacht to a shore destination. Fig. 2 shows a sailing yacht fitted with this equipment.

Fig 2

Fig 3

Inmarsat-C antennas are small enough to be fitted to a vessel of any size or even to be carried in one hand. They are also light, omni-directional and the terminals have low power requirements. Below-decks equipment is neat, compact and simple to install on any boat. Fig. 3 shows a typical below-decks installation.

Section 10

The system's simplicity extends to its operation. Anyone who has used a personal computer, word processor or a telex machine can use Inmarsat-C and touchscreen computers can be connected to send handwritten messages.

Every terminal in the system is allocated a discrete identity number and only messages addressed to that number are received. This, along with its digital transmission mode, automatically provides a high level of security for users.

While Inmarsat-C is a store-and-forward communications system, it can deliver messages in a very short time to anybody in the world, possible because of its connectibility into international data networks. It also makes possible a range of services such as data reporting, position reporting and polling.

Yacht captains can programme their terminals to transmit regular data reports of the condition of vessels and other operational information to shore-based offices. Alternatively, shore-based managers and yacht owners can 'poll' or interrogate ships, automatically or manually, for receiving the same information.

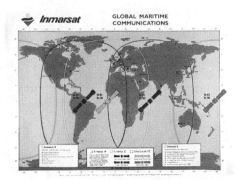

Fig 4

Inmarsat-C can also be connected to positioning devices like GPS receivers to enable ships at sea to send periodic position reports to shore. The terminals can be programmed to do this automatically at regular intervals or they can transmit position reports manually. Besides GPS, Inmarsat-C can also use inputs from other positioning systems such as Glonass, Decca and Loran.

While Inmarsat-C is used primarily for two-way messaging communications between mobile terminals and fixed communications points on shore, its flexibility is such that it can support many value-added services. Shore based service providers offer regularly updated weather reports, stock market information. news and electronic mail services.

Terminals fitted with an optional Enhanced Group Call capability, are able to receive two categories of messages known As SafetyNET™ and FleetNET™. SafetyNET™ is specifically designed for the distribution of safety information provided by hydrographic, meteorological, coastguard and search and rescue coordination authorities. Messages can be targeted to boats in or approaching specific geographic regions, such as the area around a hazard or a ship in distress.

FleetNET™ can be used to transmit trade information, such as company news or market prices, simultaneously to selected groups of ships. Using FleetNET™, subscription services can provide ships with up-to-the-minute news and stock prices.

Fig.4 depicts the global satellite coverage operated by Inmarsat, a London-based international enterprise with 64 member countries. The satellites are in orbit over the equator, providing communications to all of the earth's surface except the extreme polar regions.

Users can also choose to route their calls through any of a growing number of Coast Earth Stations around the world which act as gateways, delivering messages into public telephone and data networks on shore, and also channelling calls from shore onward to mobile terminals.

Significantly, fitting Inmarsat-C and/or Inmarsat-A terminals on yachts is also an efficient way for boats operating outside of coastal radio coverage, to meet the long range communications requirement of the Global Maritime Distress and Safety Systems (GMDSS). See Section 8. The Inmarsat-C SafetyNET™ service meets GMDSS requirements for shore-to-ship distress alerting.

A further system. Inmarsat-M will provide satellite telephone services through lightweight, low-cost terminals, offering all-digital telephony and facsimile services. Inmarsat-M specifications will allow the customer terminals to be smaller than Inmarsat-A, have lower power requirements, and low terminal and operating costs.

For those who require it, combinations of Inmarsat-C with Inmarsat-M/A will allow for substantial flexibility of Satcoms to suit individual needs. Satellite communications will be available to more boats than ever before and the idyll of the high seas will never be ominous again.

SEA SIGNALLING

INTERNATIONAL CODE OF SIGNALS

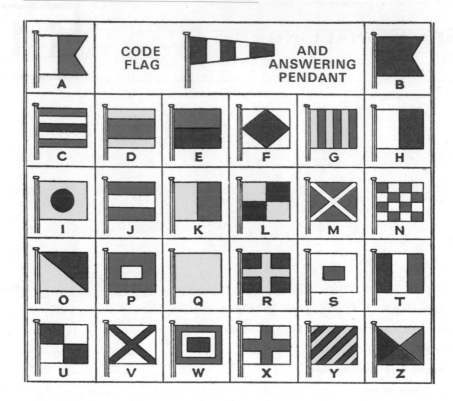

NUMERAL PENDANTS

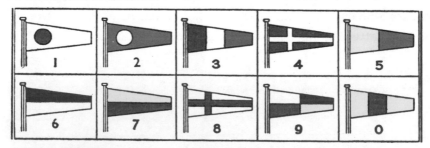

SUBSTITUTES

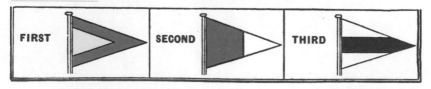

The meanings of all Single Letter Flags, A to Z, are shown on the opposite page.

INTERNATIONAL CODE OF SIGNALS

SINGLE LETTER SIGNALS BY FLAG, LIGHT, OR SOUND

The most important Code signals of all – the single letter signals – consist of Very Urgent signals or those in common use. Seamen should know these by heart, so that there may be no hesitation in acting on them.

The following may be made by any method of signalling, but those marked (*) when made by sound may only be made in compliance with the International Regulations for Preventing Collisions at Sea, Rules 34 and 35.

A • — I have a diver down; keep well clear at slow speed.

*B — • • • I am taking in, or discharging, or carrying dangerous goods.

*C — • — • Yes, affirmative or "The significance of the previous group should be read in the affirmative."

*D — • • Keep clear of me – I am manoeuvring with difficulty.

*E • I am altering my course to starboard.

F • • — • I am disabled. Communicate with me.

*G — — • I require a Pilot. When made by fishing vessels operating in close proximity on the fishing grounds it means: "I am hauling nets."

*H • • • • I have a Pilot on board.

*I • • I am altering my course to port.

J • — — — I am on fire and have a dangerous cargo on board: keep well clear of me

†K — • — I wish to communicate with you.

L • — • • You should stop your vessel instantly.

*M — — My vessel is stopped and making no way through the water.

N — • No, negative or "The significance of the previous group should be read in the negative." This signal may be given only visually or by sound. For voice or radio transmission the signal should be "No."

O — — — Man overboard.

P • — — • In harbour (Blue Peter) hoisted at the foremast head. "All persons should report on board as the vessel is about to proceed to sea." At sea. It may be used by fishing vessels to mean "my nets have come fast upon an obstruction." It may also be used as a sound signal to mean "I require a pilot".

Q — — • — My vessel is healthy and I request free pratique.

‡R • — •

†*S • • • I am operating astern propulsion.

*T — Keep clear of me I am engaged in pair trawling.

U • • — You are running into danger.

V • • • — I require assistance.

W • — — I require medical assistance.

X — • • — Stop carrying out your intentions and watch for my signals.

Y — • — — I am dragging my anchor.

*Z — — • • I require a tug. When made by fishing vessels operating in close proximity on the fishing grounds it means: "I am shooting nets."

1 • — — — —	6 — • • • •
2 • • — — —	7 — — • • •
3 • • • — —	8 — — — • •
4 • • • • —	9 — — — — •
5 • • • • •	0 — — — — —

†Signals "K" and "S" have special meanings as landing signals for small boats with crews or persons in distress. ‡Single letter Signal R has so far not been allocated a Signal meaning as this already has a meaning in Rule 35 of the Collision Regulations.

Section 11

INTERNATIONAL PORT TRAFFIC SIGNALS

(to be introduced worldwide as circumstances permit)

MAIN MESSAGE

No.	Signal		Message
1	● ● ●	FLASHING	SERIOUS EMERGENCY—ALL VESSELS TO STOP OR DIVERT ACCORDING TO INSTRUCTIONS
2	● ● ●	FIXED OR SLOW OCCULTING	VESSELS SHALL NOT PROCEED
3	● ● ●		VESSELS MAY PROCEED. ONE WAY TRAFFIC
4	● ● ○		VESSELS MAY PROCEED. TWO WAY TRAFFIC
5	● ○ ●		A VESSEL MAY PROCEED ONLY WHEN IT HAS RECEIVED SPECIFIC ORDERS TO DO SO

EXEMPTION SIGNALS AND MESSAGES

No.	Signal		Message
2a	◌ ● ● ●	FIXED OR SLOW OCCULTING	VESSELS SHALL NOT PROCEED, EXCEPT THAT VESSELS WHICH NAVIGATE OUTSIDE THE MAIN CHANNEL NEED NOT COMPLY WITH THE MAIN MESSAGE.
5a	◌ ● ○ ●		A VESSEL MAY PROCEED ONLY WHEN IT HAS RECEIVED SPECIFIC ORDERS TO DO SO; EXCEPT THAT VESSELS WHICH NAVIGATE OUTSIDE THE MAIN CHANNEL NEED NOT COMPLY WITH THE MAIN MESSAGE.

IMPORTANT SOUND SIGNALS

Although signalling between vessels may be carried out by whistle or siren using the Morse Code, it is a slow method, and unless in open waters should never be resorted to. Confusion as to any Sound Signals given or its misinterpretation can have most disastrous results, so Sound Signals should be used with the utmost discretion.

On the other hand they should be used decisively and correctly whenever they are required by the Collision Regulations or when the circumstances of the occasion require. The following Sound Signals occur in ordinary Navigation:

FOG SIGNALS BY LIGHTHOUSES, LIGHT VESSELS, BUOYS, ETC.

These cannot of course be memorised – except by Pilots in their own Pilotage area – but should be consulted as required in the annual edition.

SOUND SIGNALS BY YOUR OWN AND OTHER VESSELS IN FOG OR THICK WEATHER

These must be known instinctively as described in the Collision Regulations, Rule 35*

SOUND SIGNALS BY VESSELS MANOEUVRING

These are not given in fog, but must be used by vessels manoeuvring in sight of other vessels, so must be known without hesitation. See the Collision Regulations, Rule 34.*

Note carefully the provision under Rule 34 of the "in doubt " or "wake up" signal of five or more short and rapid blasts.

DISTRESS SIGNALS

Shown fully in Annex IV of the Collision Regulations.*

PILOT SIGNALS IN FOG

In a majority of U.K. ports, but by no means all, vessels make the Morse letter G (– – •) when requiring a Pilot and the Pilot vessel waiting to put the Pilot on board sounds four short blasts (• • • •) as prescribed by Rule 35 of the Collision Regulations.*

RIVER APPROACH SIGNAL

A prolonged warning blast by a vessel approaching a bend in a river as described in Rule 9 of the Collision Regulations

URGENT AND IMPORTANT SIGNALS

For single-letter signals which may be made by any method of signalling see page 11.3.It is of the utmost importance that all Owners or Masters in charge of small craft should commit these signals to memory so that they can be used or recognised instantly, without reference.

FOG CLOSE QUARTERS WARNING SIGNAL

"R" (• – •), made by sound signal only, may be used by a vessel at anchor in fog to give warning of her position to an approaching vessel. This signal would be made in addition to her normal sound signal. See Rule 35*

"U" DANGER WARNING SIGNAL

"U" (• • –) should never be neglected – many vessels "standing" towards a sandbank or rocky coast have been saved from disaster by the vigilance of others.

SIGNAL FOR VESSEL TURNING

Although not contained in the Collision Regulations It is the "ordinary practice of seamen" in crowded waterways – to use a special signal for "turning" (either when turning completely round or simply turning athwart the channel) of – four short blasts followed after a very short interval by one short blast if turning to Starboard or two short blasts if turning to Port.

KEEP CLEAR OF ME – I AM MANOEUVRING WITH DIFFICULTY

The Sound Signal D (– • •) "keep clear of me – I am manoeuvring with difficulty" – is a single letter Code Signal, which should be used if necessary in crowded waters.

IMPORTANT DAY AND NIGHT SIGNALS, U.K.LIFESAVING STATION SIGNALS

These most important signals between lifesaving personnel ashore, and a shipwrecked vessel or crew, are fully described in Section 8 and should be well understood.

---

* The International Regulations for Preventing Collisions are given in Section 2

Section 11

DISTRESS SIGNALS BY VESSELS AT SEA

Hardly a day goes by without the ever watchful Coastguard or another vessel sighting a genuine distress signal, and it is true to say that without this signal being given, many vessels would not be rescued, and lives lost needlessly. So, all seagoing personnel in charge of vessels of every size must know what these signals are and how to use them. Section 8 gives most valuable information on this subject.

COASTGUARD RESCUE EQUIPMENT

It is vital that the Master of any vessel – and this includes all fishing vessels and yachts – should know precisely what to do in an emergency – which most probably could occur at night. The rules are simple, but must be clearly understood. Consult Section 8 for this information.

INTERNATIONAL DIVING FLAG

The International Code flag A means:

"I HAVE A DIVER DOWN; KEEP WELL CLEAR AT SLOW SPEED."

In view of the increasing number of underwater swimmers and diving parties operating on the coasts and in harbour approaches, Mariners are asked to keep well clear whenever they see this DIVING FLAG – which is the International Code flag A. Give the vessel flying this flag a very wide berth at slow speed as it means that divers are down.

All persons in charge of craft are asked to keep well clear of the immediate area where this flag is flown, so that divers' lives may not be put in hazard and so that their own craft may not become fouled on lifelines, ropes or other temporary underwater obstructions ancillary to diving.

Club diving parties will do their best to avoid all recognised fairways, although some diving may be expected in fairways when the object is a survey or recovery operation. Local branches of Sub-Aqua Clubs are often able to assist other organisations in such work.

SIGNALLING AT SEA

Signalling at sea in all large vessels is normally carried on by radio, and only when signalling to vessels close to or to small vessels would other means be employed.

Small vessels do not always carry radio and, although many are equipped with radio-telephones, these may be out of order or other circumstances may make the use of visual signalling necessary.

Vessels in sight or hearing of one another may use Sound Signals, Code Flags, or Flashing.

CODE FLAGS

All signals are given in one, two or three letter hoists. The International Code Book is published in the nine most commonly used languages and thus communication between different nationals presents no difficulty. As all urgent or important signals are now made with one or two flags it is practicable for small vessels to carry a few flags which would enable them to make essential distress signals.

FLASHING

Signalling by flashing is carried out by using Morse Code – which is also International – so it is only necessary to learn the symbols and their meanings and to practice sending and receiving by this method to be able to talk to any other vessel, up to several miles range by day and night.

The signalling lamp – generally the Aldis lamp – is of great use to small vessels. It is portable and may be plugged into any 12 volt battery or the vessel's 24 volt main supply.

The lamp is held in the crook of the arm and pointed in any direction by movement of the operator"s body. Sights are attached to secure the correct "line" of vision on the target for the signal. It has a good range of several miles both by day and night. It may also be used for rescues or for picking up a mooring at night.

INTERNATIONAL CODE OF SIGNALS

A VESSEL'S IDENTITY

It is often necessary, to inform other vessels of your vessel's name and nationality, for identification purposes. The Ensign ordinarily indicates the nationality of the signalling vessel, but in addition, most registered vessels, warships, and certain other vessels are allotted a combination signal of four flags, the top flag or flags indicating their nationality. For example in

British vessels the top flag is either G,M,or 2, in the Netherlands P, in Germany D, while in vessels of the United States of America the top flag is either A, K, N or W. The four flags are always kept bent together on the Bridge for instant use and are known as the vessel's "number". The same four letters or numbers are also the vessel's radio call sign.

THE CODE FLAG AND ANSWERING PENNANT (OR PENDANT)

Known as Code Flag, when flown singly – indicates International Code being used. When used to answer hoists of flags from another vessel it is termed the Answering Pennant.

INTERNATIONAL MORSE CODE

Letter	Character	Letter	Character
A	· —	N	— ·
B	— · · ·	O	— — —
C	— · — ·	P	· — — ·
D	— · ·	Q	— — · —
E	·	R	· — ·
F	· · — ·	S	· · ·
G	— — ·	T	—
H	· · · ·	U	· · —
I	· ·	V	· · · —
J	· — — —	W	· — —
K	— · —	X	— · · —
L	· — · ·	Y	— · — —
M	— —	Z	— — · ·

Num'l	Character	Num'l	Character
1	· — — — —	6	— · · · ·
2	· · — — —	7	— — · · ·
3	· · · — —	8	— — — · ·
4	· · · · —	9	— — — — ·
5	· · · · ·	0	— — — — —

Ä (German) = AE (Danish) · — · —
Á or Å (Spanish or Scandinavian) · — — · —
Ch (German or Scandinavian) — — — —
É (French) · · — · ·
Ñ (Spanish) — — · — —
Ö (German) = Ø (Danish) — — — ·
Ü (German) · · — —

When any flag hoist is sighted, the Answering Pennant should be hoisted immediately at the "dip" (about half-way up the halliards) and when the Code Book has been consulted and the Signal thoroughly understood, the Answering Pennant is at once hoisted "close up" (at the top of the halliards). After the other vessel has hauled down her hoist the Answering Pennant is lowered to the "dip" again to await another hoist from the other signalling vessel. It may be used also as a decimal point.

THE THREE SUBSTITUTES

To avoid the necessity of carrying more than one set of Flags, Substitutes are used. The first substitute always repeats the uppermost flag of that class of flag which immediately precedes it. The second and third substitutes similarly repeat the second or third flag of that class of flags which immediately precede them. No substitute can be used more than once in a hoist

Example. Longitude 11°11' = G Numeral 1 first substitute; second substitute; third substitute. Example. MTT = MT second substitute.

SINGLE-LETTER SIGNALS WITH COMPLEMENTS.

A (with three numerals)– AZIMUTH or BEARING

C (with three numerals)– COURSE

D (with two, four or six numerals)	– DATE
G (with four or five numerals)	– LONGITUDE (last two mins, rest deg.)
K (with one numeral)	– I wish to COMMUNICATE by ..... (Semaphore)
L (with four numerals)	– LATITUDE (first two deg., rest mins.)
R (with one or more numerals.)	– DISTANCE in nautical miles.
S (with one or more numerals)	– SPEED in knots.
T (with four numerals)	– LOCAL TIME (first two hours, rest minutes)
V (with one or more numerals)	– SPEED in kilometres per hour.
Z (with four numerals.)	– GMT (first two hours, rest mins.)

Section 11

7

PROCEDURE SIGNALS

A bar over the letters composing a signal denotes that the letters are to be made as one symbol.

SIGNALS FOR VOICE TRANSMISSION

Signal	Pronounced as	Meaning
Interco Code	IN-TER-CO	International group(s) follow(s)
Stop	STOP	Full Stop.
Decimal	DAY-SEE-MAL	Decimal point.
Correction	KOR-REK-SHUN	Cancel my last word or group. The correct word or group follows.

SIGNALS FOR FLASHING-LIGHT TRANSMISSION

AA AA AA etc.	Call for unknown station or general call.
EEEE etc.	Erase signal.
AAA	Full stop or decimal point.
TTTT etc	Answering signal.
T	Word or group received.

SIGNALS FOR FLAGS, RADIO-TELEPHONY AND RADIO-TELEGRAPHY TRANSMISSIONS.

CQ	Call for unknown station(s) or general call to all stations

When this signal is used in voice transmission, it should be pronounced in accordance with the letter-spelling table.

SIGNALS FOR USE WHERE APPROPRIATE IN ALL FORMS OF TRANSMISSION.

AA	"All after ..." (used after the "Repeat signal" (RPT) means "Repeat all after...".
AB	"All before ..." (used after the "Repeat signal" (RPT) means "Repeat all before ..."
AR	Ending signal or End of Transmission or signal.
AS	Waiting signal or period
BN	"All between ... and ..." (used after the "Repeat signal" (RPT)) means "Repeat all between ... and ...".
C	Affirmative – YES or "The significance of the previous group should be read in the affirmative".
CS	"What is the name or identity signal of your vessel (or station)?"
DE	"From ..." (used to precede the name or identity signal of the calling station).
K	"I wish to communicate with you"or "Invitation to transmit".
NO	Negative –NO or "The significance of the previous group should be read in the negative". When used in voice transmission the pronunciation should be "NO".
OK	Acknowledging a correct repetition or "It is correct:"
RQ	Interrogative, or, "The significance of the previous group should be read as a question".
R	"Received" or "I have received your last signal".
RPT	Repeat signal "I repeat" or "Repeat what you have sent" or "Repeat what you have received".
WA	"Word or group after ..." (used after the "Repeat signal" (RPT) means "Repeat word or group after ... ".
WB	"Word or group before ..." (used after the "Repeat signal" (RPT) means "Repeat word or group before .... ".

The procedure signals "C", "NO" and "RQ" cannot be used in conjunction with single letter signals.

SOME TWO LETTER SIGNALS

AC	I am abandoning my vessel.
AN	I need a doctor.
AQ	I have injured/sick person (or number of persons indicated)) to be taken off urgently.
CB	I require immediate assistance.
CK	Assistance is not (or is no longer) required by me (or vessel indicated).

SOME TWO LETTER SIGNALS – Cont.

CP   I am (or vessel indicated is) proceeding to your assistance.

DV   I am drifting.

DX   I am sinking (lat...long...if necessary).

ED   Your distress signals are understood.

EL   Repeat the distress position.

FA   Will you give me my position?

FO   I will keep close to you.

GW   Man overboard. Please take action to pick him up (position to be indicated if necessary).

IL   I can only proceed at slow speed.

IT   I am on fire.

JG   I am aground; I am in dangerous situation.

JH   I am aground; I am not in danger.

JW   I have sprung a leak.

KJ   I am towing a submerged object.

KM   I can take you (or vessel indicated) in tow.

KQ   Prepare to be taken in tow.

KT1   I am sending a towing hawser.

LBI   Towing hawser is fast to chain cable.

NC   I am in distress and require immediate assistance.

NF   You are running into danger.

NG   You are in a dangerous position.

OQ   I am calibrating radio direction finder or adjusting compasses.

PN   You should keep to leeward of me (or vessel indicated).

PP   Keep well clear of me.

QD   I am going ahead.

QI   I am going astern.

QQ   I require health clearance.

QU   Anchoring is prohibited.

RB   I am dragging my anchor.

RU   Keep clear of me. I am manoeuvring with difficulty.

TP   Fishing gear has fouled my propeller.

UW   I wish you a pleasant voyage.

UY   I am carrying out exercises – keep clear of me.

XP   I am stopped in thick fog.

YG   You appear not to be complying with the traffic separation scheme.

ZD1   Please report me to Coast Guard New York.

ZD2   Please report me to Lloyds London.

ZM   You should send (or speak) more slowly.

ZS   My vessel is healthy and I request free pratique.

ZV   I believe I have been in an infected area during the last 30 days.

ZW   I require Port Medical Officer.

Section 11

FLAGS AND FLAG ETIQUETTE

12

SOME ENSIGNS AND FLAGS OF THE WORLD

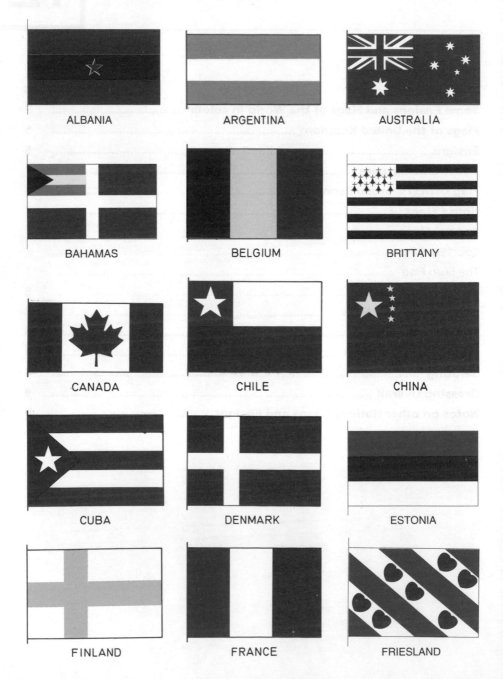

ALBANIA	ARGENTINA	AUSTRALIA
BAHAMAS	BELGIUM	BRITTANY
CANADA	CHILE	CHINA
CUBA	DENMARK	ESTONIA
FINLAND	FRANCE	FRIESLAND

SOME ENSIGNS AND FLAGS OF THE WORLD

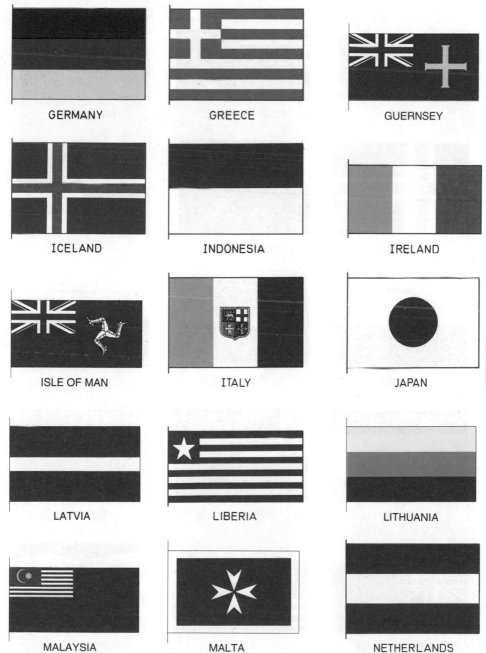

GERMANY	GREECE	GUERNSEY
ICELAND	INDONESIA	IRELAND
ISLE OF MAN	ITALY	JAPAN
LATVIA	LIBERIA	LITHUANIA
MALAYSIA	MALTA	NETHERLANDS

Section 12

3

SOME ENSIGNS AND FLAGS OF THE WORLD

NIGERIA	NEW ZEALAND	NORMANDY
NORWAY	PAKISTAN	PANAMA
POLAND	PORTUGAL	RUSSIA
SPAIN	SRI LANKA	SWEDEN
UNITED KINGDOM	U.S.A.	ZEELAND

FLAGS OF THE UNITED KINGDOM

THE ROYAL BANNER

The Royal Banner, generally but incorrectly known as the Royal Standard, is the personal flag of the Sovereign.

Other immediate members of the Sovereign's family have a similar banner which is defaced with their personal emblem. This defacement consists of a narrow white strip from fly to hoist, down to the first horizontal. For example, Prince Edward has a banner on which the white horizontal is divided into three "tabs" on the centre one of which is a red rose with a yellow centre and green barbs.

THE NATIONAL FLAG

The Union Flag, frequently but incorrectly referred to as the Union Jack, is never worn at sea except by Royalty or specified officers of the Royal Navy.

ENSIGNS

1. White— Red Cross of St George on a white field. Union Flag in upper canton. Worn by the Royal Yacht, Royal Navy and Royal Squadron, and sometimes with Royal Cypher used as a Standard.

2. Blue— Dark blue field with Union Flag in upper canton. The fly is frequently defaced by badge of the office or organisation wearing it, e.g: Royal Fleet Auxiliary, H.M. Customs etc. An Admiralty warrant for the vessel is required before an undefaced or defaced Blue Ensign may be worn. Many Yacht Club members have this privilege, some with defaced and some with undefaced Ensigns.

3. Red— Red field with Union Flag in the upper canton. Worn by Merchant Navy and private craft of British subjects. Sometimes defaced in fly. Worn with defacement in fly by some Yacht Clubs (e.g. Lloyd's Y.C.) with Admiralty Warrant.

4. Royal Air Force vessels wear a Light Blue Ensign with the Union Flag in the upper canton and with a defacement of Red, White and Dark Blue Roundels (small red in the centre).

5. Civil Air. Dark Blue St. George's Cross with White border on a Light Blue field with the Union Flag in the upper canton.

ROYAL NAVY

1. All Ships and Establishments— White Ensign.

2. Lord High Admiral and Lords Commissioners. Crimson (Maroon) field charged with gold anchor and cable., Also worn on foremast of Royal Yacht when the Sovereign is aboard.

3. Admiral of the Fleet— Union Flag.

4. Admiral— White field charged with Red Cross of St George.

5. Vice Admiral— As Admiral plus red ball in the upper canton.

6. Rear Admiral— As Vice Admiral plus red ball in the lower canton.

7. Commodore— As Vice Admiral but slight taper ending with swallow tail.

8. Commanding Officer Small Craft— White pendant with Red Cross of St. George in the hoist.

TRINITY HOUSE

1. Jack— Red Cross of St. George, old sailing ships in quarters.

2. Ensign— Red Ensign, defaced by Jack in fly.

3. Burgee— As Jack on a red field.

H.M. CUSTOMS

1. Ensign— Blue defaced by crown over portcullis.

2. Burgee— White with red border on upper and lower edges, defaced crown over portcullis.

MISCELLANEOUS

1. Queen's Harbour Master— Union Flag with white border, charged with white circle with Q.H.M. in black; Imperial Crown over.

2. Thames Conservancy— St. George's Cross charged with arms of T.C.

3. Port of London Authority— St. George's Cross charged with arms of P.L.A. or Blue Ensign defaced.

4. Examination Service Vessels— Blue or White Ensign and Special flag White over Red horizontal surrounded by a Blue border.

Section 12

5

5. Royal Mail— White pendant charged with "ROYAL MAIL" cypher and horn.

6. North Sea Fisheries— Pendant quartered, Blue above Yellow in hoist, reverse in fly.

7. Pilots— Pilot Flag, upper half White, lower half Red.

8. The Jack— A small flag worn on a jackstaff on the stern of Naval Vessels. The Royal Navy wears the Union Flag and other Commonwealth countries wear their National Colours. Only worn at anchor or in harbour. This is the only occasion when it is correct to describe the flag as the Union Jack.

9. The Pilot Jack— This consists of the Union Flag having a White border one fifth of the size of the flag. Originally the International signal for a Pilot it was discontinued as such when the International Code of Signals was introduced. It is rarely used nowadays but may be flown by any registered British ship from a Jackstaff in the bows when the vessel is at anchor or in harbour and wearing her Ensign. It should be raised and lowered at the same time as colours.

SEA FLAG ETIQUETTE

Flags worn at sea by British vessels comprise:

1. Ensigns

(a) The Royal Navy and Royal Yacht Squadron wear the White Ensign. Red and Blue Ensigns, either undefaced or defaced, are worn by all other British vessels.

The Red Ensign undefaced is the correct wear for any British vessel unless she has been granted an Admiralty Warrant (or in the case of a yacht — a Yacht Certificate) for a privilege Ensign.

The Blue Ensign undefaced may be worn by a Merchant vessel providing she fulfils certain conditions laid down by the Ministry of Defence regarding the presence of Naval Reserve officers in her complement, when an Admiralty Warrant will be issued to this ship. Blue Ensigns undefaced are also worn by a few Yacht Clubs such as the Royal Cruising Club which have in the past been granted an Ensign Warrant for this purpose.

Under the terms of the Merchant Shipping Act a vessel of 50 tons gross or larger is compelled to wear her colours when entering or leaving a British port and all vessels (unless registered as fishermen) must wear their National colours when entering or leaving a foreign port.

(b) Individual Yacht Permits are issued which permit the holder to wear a privilege Ensign (White, Blue defaced or plain and Red defaced). The owner must first be a member of a Yacht Club which holds a special Ensign Warrant issued by the Ministry of Defence. This warrant empowers the Secretary of the Club to issue a Yacht Permit to a member whose yacht satisfies the qualifying conditions of the Small Ships Register or those yachts registered under the Merchant Shipping Act 1894. Yachts qualifying by virtue of entry on the S.S.R. must measure not less than 7m in length. Yachts which are the property of a Limited Company are eligible for a Yacht Permit provided that they are not used for business, professional or commercial purposes and that the name does not incorporate a name, product or trade mark used for business or commercial purposes. This applies only to yachts registered under the Merchant Shipping Act 1894 as the S.S.R. is not open to yachts owned by Limited Companies. A permit may be issued for a yacht under charter to a club member for a period at the discretion of the Club. Yachts registered under the Merchant Shipping Act will be issued with a permit which is valid until such time as the ownership of the vessel changes, when a new permit will be required (assuming the new owner is a member of an approved Club). The permit issued to a yacht registered on the S.S.R. *will* be valid until the expiry of the Registration Certificate. *i.e.* for a maximum of five years, or until change of ownership occurs. Warrants already issued for vessels registered under the Merchant Shipping Act will continue to be valid until such time as the ownership of the vessel changes. The new owner will then have to apply to the appropriate Yacht Club Secretary for a permit. It is important to remember that the privilege Ensign may only be worn when the particular Yacht Club Burgee is flown. A yacht tender, provided it can be hoisted on board, may wear the special Ensign as long as the parent vessel is wearing hers. Severe penalties exist for the improper use of privilege Ensigns. Under the Merchant Shipping Act 1894 the illegal wearing of a Privilage Ensign renders the vessel's owner liable to a fine not exceeding £1,000. A Naval Officer or Customs Officer is entitled to demand sight of the Admiralty Warrant granting the right to wear the Ensign. If this is not forthcoming the Ensign will be confiscated and the matter referred to the Civil Courts.

2. Yacht Club Burgees and Flag Officers' Broad Pennants

A Burgee is a triangular flag with a design adopted by the particular Yacht Club, the design of which must be such that it cannot be confused with any other Burgee, flag or Ensign. The Burgee should be worn at the masthead but nowadays the increasing amount of instrumentation at the truck renders this very difficult and it is becoming increasingly common to wear it at the starboard yard arm. It should be worn with a Red Ensign except in the case of very small yachts or those yachts which have an Admiralty Warrant for a special Ensign.

When an owner is a member of several clubs the first rule is that the senior club's Burgee has precedence over the others and also that a "Royal" club is senior to a "non Royal" club. In the owner's home waters it is however a matter of courtesy to wear the Burgee of his local club. In this case if his local club does not have an Admiralty Warrant for a special Ensign then the Red Ensign must be worn with the local Burgee. If an owner belongs to a Yacht Club and an Association and wishes to fly both Burgees the Yacht Club should take precedence and its Burgee should be worn at the masthead with the other at the starboard yard arm. An exception to this rule is the Cruising Association, a very old established Yacht Club with London headquarters, and which has an Admiralty Warrant for a defaced Blue Ensign. When a yachtsman belongs to a foreign Yacht Club and wishes to wear its Burgee in the club's home port, it must displace his British Yacht Club's Burgee at the masthead, unless his yacht has two masts when the foreign Burgee should be worn at the foremast and the British Burgee at the aftermast.

The Flag Officers of a club normally comprise the Commodore, Vice Commodore and Rear Commodore (in some clubs there may be more than one Rear Commodore). The Commodore wears a swallow tail flag incorporating the club's Burgee design, the Vice Commodore wears a similar flag with a ball of distinctive colour in the upper canton, while the Rear Commodore has a similar flag with two balls which may be side by side or more usually one in the upper canton and one in the lower. These swallow tail flags are known as Broad Pennants and in a sailing yacht must always be flown at the masthead.

Some Yacht Clubs have special appointments such as Admiral, President, or Past Commodore, and these officers fly a rectangular flag with similar design to the club Burgee. In some clubs the Secretary is regarded as a Flag Officer and usually wears a triangular club Burgee with some additional distinguishing marks on it, such as one ball in the upper canton.

3. House Flags

A House flag is a rectangular flag of special design and is in effect the personal flag of the owner. It may be of any design as long as it cannot be confused with any existing Ensign, flag or Burgee. In the Merchant Navy it is customary for each shipping line to have its own house flag.

House flags are seldom used in sailing yachts, being usually confined to the larger power yachts. An exception to this is the Royal Yachting Association flag flown by members of the R.Y.A. when in harbour. It does not denote ownership but indicates that the owner is a member of the R.Y.A.

4. Special Flags

(a) *Courtesy Ensigns:* It is traditional for a vessel visiting a foreign country to show her respect by flying the maritime flag of that country in a conspicuous position, usually the starboard yard arm. The courtesy Ensign is usually about one third the size of the vessel's National Ensign.

The correct Courtesy Ensign for foreign yachts visiting the United Kingdom is the Red Ensign — not the Union Flag.

(b) *The Euro flag:* It is important to understand that the Euro flag is not a National flag but a flag representing an association of nations, in other words an association flag.

Some Continental nations are using it as a defaced Ensign, i.e. a Euro flag with a small edition of their National flag in the upper canton (similar to a Red Ensign with the small Union flag in the upper canton).

While this may be permissable under their particular constitution, it would not be so in the United Kingdom. The Merchant Shipping Act of 1894 specifically states that the Red Ensign is the proper National flag for British ships. (This is amended by Admiralty Warrants for Red and Blue defaced Ensigns).

The wearing of a Euro flag as an Ensign in a British ship, whether defaced or not, is therefore prohibited and can lead to a fine of £500.

Section 12

7

Its use as a courtesy flag is rather different. A courtesy flag is the flag of a foreign nation worn on the starboard yard arm of a yacht when visiting that particular country. It cannot be replaced by the Euro flag as this is not the flag of any particular country.

However, it would be regarded as a pleasant gesture if the Euro flag was worn inferior to (below) the correct courtesy flag when visiting a foreign country which is a member of the European Community.

(c) *Racing Flags:* When a yacht is racing the club Burgee is replaced with the owner's racing flag, square in shape and of any design and colour. It is not now obligatory to fly a racing flag unless prescribed by the club rules due to the difficulties incurred with instrumentation at the masthead. The Ensign is never worn while racing, being handed down at the 5 minute gun and rehoisted at the conclusion of the race, or if the yacht withdraws, to indicate that she is no longer racing.

The prize flag is usually a smaller version of the owner's racing flag. The second prize flag is triangular, blue with a white 2 marked on it and the third prize is a red triangular flag with a white 3.

The protest flag may be specified by the organising club (the R.Y.A. does not specify any particular flag), the International Yacht Racing Union suggests the use of International Code Flag B.

(d) *International Code Flags:* These flags, together with the International Code Book enable vessels of any nationality to communicate with each other irrespective of language difficulties. It is unusual for the smaller cruising yacht to carry the full set unless she wishes to "dress overall" on ceremonial occasions but it is useful for certain flags with single letter meanings to be carried on board. An example is "W" — I require medical assistance. It is important to remember that the flags must be of such a size as to be clearly visible at a reasonable distance. Any registered British vessel may be allotted a four flag hoist — known as her "number" and which is the same as her radio call sign. This hoist is used when she wishes to identify herself at sea.

The code flag most frequently used by yachts is the "Q" flag meaning: My vessel is healthy and I request free pratique. This is used universally as a request for Customs clearance when a vessel is entering a foreign port from another country and also when returning to her own country from abroad.

When Flags are Worn

Flags worn at sea comprise the Ensign, club Burgee or house flag. The Ensign may be hauled down at night and when on passage out of sight of land or other ships, but should be hoisted when passing another vessel.

When entering or leaving a foreign port a British vessel must wear her "colours" and those of 50 tons gross and upwards must do likewise when entering or leaving a British port.

In harbour the Burgee and special Ensigns are worn when the owner is on board or in effective control of the vessel (similarly with any house flag which the owner may fly).

Ensigns, Burgees and house flags are hoisted at 0800 in summer and 0900 in winter and lowered at sunset or 2100 hours whichever is earlier. Flag Officers' Broad pennants, following the Royal Navy custom, are flown throughout the 24 hours when the owner is on board. There is no strict rule regarding the raising and lowering of Burgees and it is now common practice to fly the Burgee throughout the 24 hours. The times in some foreign countries may vary and whenever possible the time should be taken from any Naval vessel in port or the local Yacht Club.

Where Flags are Worn

The Ensign, being the most important flag on board, must always be worn in the after part of the vessel on its own staff on the taffrail. If for any reason this is impossible it may be worn at a position ⅔ up the leech of the mainsail in the case of single masted vessels and in similar position in two masted vessels where the aftermast is as tall or taller than the foremast. Where the aftermast is shorter than the foremast the Ensign may be worn on a staff at the mizzen masthead.

The Burgee or Flag Officer's Pennant should be flown from the main masthead although if the masthead is cluttered with instrumentation the Burgee may be flown from the starboard yard arm but a Flag Officer's Pennant must never be flown from any position other than the main masthead.

Saluting

It has always been traditional for Ensigns to be "dipped" when passing any Naval vessel, Royal yacht, or the flag officer of a yacht club when the yacht saluting is wearing the Burgee of the

Flag officer's club. The salute is made by lowering the Ensign to a position about ⅓ from the lower end of the hoist and rehoisting when the vessel being saluted rehoists hers.

Nowadays, this is hardly practicable in certain situations, e.g. a crowded summer weekend on the Solent. When at sea, however, it is pleasant and courteous to maintain this ancient tradition.

Dressing Ship

Dressing overall can take place on three types of occasions, a British national festival, a foreign festival and local occasions such as regattas, and there are minor variations in the flag arrangements for each. Ships only dress overall when in harbour or anchored. The International code flags are worn on a line stretching from stem to stern, over the masthead or heads. The order in which the flags are attached is as follows and commences at the Stern (the reason for a particular order is to ensure variety of shape and colour):

E Q p3 G p8 Z p4 W p6 P p1 1 CODE T Y B X 1st H 3rd D F 2nd U A O M R p2 J p0 N p9 K p7 V p5 L C S

If the vessel is two masted the line between the mastheads starts with Y and finishes with 0.

In the case of a British national festival the Ensign will be worn in its usual place, i.e. taffrail or mizzen masthead with the addition of an Ensign at the masthead, with the Club Burgee side by side. In the case of a Flag Officer his personal Pennant only will be flown from the masthead.

For foreign national festivals the appropriate National flag should be flown at the masthead with the Club Burgee alongside. If however the vessel is two masted the foreign national flag is flown at the lower masthead. In the event of the owner being a Flag Officer his personal Pennant only is flown at the main masthead the foreign Ensign being flown at the starboard crosstree if the vessel is single masted.

When the owner is entitled to wear the special Ensign of a privileged yacht club he may fly either the Red Ensign or the privilege Ensign but if the latter, the same privilege Ensign must be worn at the taffrail or at the masthead.

In the case of local festivals, regattas, etc. no Ensign is flown from the masthead, only the Club Burgee or Flag Officer's Pennant.

NOTES ON SOME OTHER NATIONAL FLAGS AND ENSIGNS

The main maritime nations such as the Netherlands, France, Germany etc. have in general a similar pattern of flag arrangements to the UK, i.e. National flags for shore based use and Ensigns and Jacks for marine use. The marine Ensign is similar to the National flag but with major or minor additions. A notable exception to this is Norway where the National and Merchant flags are identical. The Naval Ensign with its swallow tail and the square Jack also have the same design.

Some countries including Belgium, Denmark, Italy, France, the Netherlands, Norway and Ireland, grant the privilege of a special Ensign to certain of their Yacht Clubs, usually the National Ensign with the addition of the Club's insignia as an embellishment.

The rules governing this privilege vary in different countries. It may be a Government Department controlling it as in the UK or a specially authorised national or principal Yacht Club, e.g. the Royal Norwegian Yacht Club and the Yacht Club Italia. These clubs usually control yachting in their respective countries and in some respects are similar to the Royal Yachting Association in the UK.

In addition to their National flags and Ensigns many countries have provincial flags, some of great antiquity, of which they are very proud. In countries with a great maritime tradition these provincial flags are often worn by their yachts in preference to the National Ensign when in home waters. Two particular examples of this are the Zeeland and Friesland flags in the Netherlands. Foreign yachts visiting either of these provinces should be particularly careful to wear these flags inferior to the courtesy flag.

Some countries also have a Jack, a special flag normally worn on a Jackstaff in the bows of the vessel and usually square in shape. Probably the most widely used Jack in Europe is from the Netherlands, a square flag with alternating triangles of the national colours and worn by many Netherlands motor cruisers.

Section 12

BASIC NAVIGATION

13

BASIC NAVIGATION

The widespread use of position fixing systems such as Decca and G.P.S. make the work of the navigator very easy. It is tempting to rely entirely on this method but very unwise – instruments are fallible and it is essential for the navigator to understand the basic principles of navigation.

This section is not intended to be an advanced or even an elementary course on coastal navigation. Those readers who wish to study the subject should read *Coastal Navigation* in the Reed's Yacht Master Series which is aimed at preparing the student for the Yacht Master Certificate examination and consequently contains all the information required by the aspiring coastal navigator.

The primary object of this section is to act as a general *aide memoire* for the inexperienced navigator, with the hope that the more experienced one may find it useful at times.

The essence of good navigation in small ships is adequate preparation before the start of the voyage, careful observation and recording, thus enabling the dead reckoning to be kept up to date at regular intervals.

THE NAVIGATOR'S EQUIPMENT

The following list should be regarded as the minimum for navigation.

Charts

The basic essential for navigation – dealt with more fully later.

Tidal Atlas

Available from all good chart agents, various editions for different areas give hour by hour diagrams of tidal stream direction and strength. Extremely useful for the small ship navigator.

Sailing Directions

Many available, issued by the various hydrographic offices, and many commercially published ones. Highly desirable for reading before a trip into unfamiliar waters and should be available on passage.

Nautical Almanac

Is essential to provide all the information required relating to tides, lights, buoys, radio aids and navigational tables, etc.

Ship's Log Book

It is important to record all the information relating to the navigation of the ship as well as the D.R. position on the chart. A ship's position about which the navigator is subsequently doubtful can thus be rechecked if the facts and calculations are readily available. It is customary to keep a rough or "deck" log, entering it up in the ship's log at the end of the day or other suitable interval. Reed's Log Book embodies preplanning sheets which enable important information to be readily available.

Dividers and Pencil Compasses

Essential for chart work.

Parallel Ruler or Patent Protractor

The traditional instrument for laying off courses on the chart is the parallel ruler, but for small ship navigation where motion may be violent and space restricted the patent protractor is more convenient with less chance of error. The patent protractor consists of a compass rose on a perspex base with a rotating arm which permits a course to be read or laid off without reference to the chart rose.

Chart Magnifier

An illuminated chart magnifier can be extremely useful for reading fine detail on a chart under difficult conditions.

Clock

A good marine clock is a useful item of equipment as is a stopwatch for timing the frequency of lights.

Barometer

A good marine barometer is necessary to maintain a check on the weather situation. Remember that shipping forecasts are invaluable in that they cover a large area – it is useful and it may be vital to know the trend of pressure locally.

Compass

A good compass is an essential piece of equipment in any vessel. A particularly useful type for small vessels with possible inexperienced helmsmen is the grid compass. In this type the compass bowl is surmounted by a perspex plate with an annular ring marked with 0 360°. The course is set by rotating the annular ring on to the desired heading and the helmsman then keeps the N-S line on the compass card parallel to two lines engraved on the perspex grid. This renders the helmsman's task much easier, especially at night and when fatigue sets in.

A small hand bearing compass is invaluable for position fixing from fixed objects and lights.

Patent Log

A towed or hull fitted log will help immeasurably with the dead reckoning calculations.

Pocket Calculators

Useful for rapid calculations. The scientific type, programmed for calculating SIN, COS and TAN are especially useful in navigation provided the navigator understands the fundamentals involved.

Echo Sounder

Apart from the useful ability to predict when the ship is likely to run aground, the electronic echo sounder is a very useful aid to navigation, especially in fog.

Sextant

Not an essential item of equipment for the coastal navigator but useful for measuring horizontal and vertical angles for fixing positions. Dealt with more fully later.

Radio Aids

A radio set for weather forecasts is really essential. R.D.F. sets are of considerable assistance to navigators but should never be relied on to the exclusion of normal navigation methods.

THE CHART

The chart is obviously the key piece of equipment required by the navigator and should be treated as such and kept up to date.

Notices to Mariners are issued weekly and can be obtained from chart agents. This weekly notice contains navigational warnings – amendments to dangerous areas, corrections to Lists of Lights, fog signals, radio signals and any important navigational alterations or additions necessary to safe navigation. The navigator should always carry a number of charts to cover the area of the projected voyage, together with those necessary to cover any area to which the vessel may be driven by reason of bad weather. In the case of a fairly lengthy trip, for example from Burnham to Ijmuiden in Holland, one small scale passage chart to cover the whole trip is required together with larger scale charts covering the coastline and port approaches.

TYPES OF CHARTS AND DETAILS

There are basically two different types of navigational chart, the difference being in the method of construction or "projection". These two projections are called the Mercator and the Gnomonic projections, the latter being used for large scale charts covering small areas. From the small ship navigator's point of view, the projection has no practical significance in coastal navigation.

The British Admiralty publish a chart catalogue covering the whole of the world's surface and listing the charts covering the various areas. The charts can be roughly divided into three main groups, general charts on a small scale covering large areas, i.e. the North Sea; coastal charts of larger scale and detailed charts of harbours and estuaries, etc. A "home" section of this chart catalogue covering the British Isles and the N.W. coast of Europe as far as the Kiel Canal is issued separately. It is important when ordering charts to quote the number as well as the title. Other maritime nations publish their own chart catalogues which are useful when charts of a particular country are required.

In addition to navigational charts, charts for special purposes such as Decca, Consol and Loran charts are also issued which deal with commercial radio navigational systems. Various other specialised charts such as magnetic variation, track charts and tidal stream are also obtainable.

Compass Rose

Compass Roses are True 0°-360° – very large and clear with a small line with half an arrow head reaching out from the centre of the rose pointing to the N. Magnetic Pole with the legend printed – Mag. Var. 5°W. decreasing about 8' annually. (Note: These figures will vary according to the particular area covered by the Charts.)

Section 13

3

Depths

All depths are given below Chart Datum and the units are stated under the title. In places where there is no appreciable tide, depths are given below sea level. Chart datum, originally M.L.W.S. is now adjusted to the level of the predicted lowest astronomical tide (L.A.T.)

Depths of more than 21 are always given in whole metres, whereas depths of less than 21 are given in metres and decimetres – e.g., 5_3 which means 5.3 metres.

Heights

Heights, other than drying heights are given in metres above M.H.W.S., except in places where there is no appreciable tide, in such cases heights are referred to sea level.

Drying Heights are given in metres and decimetres above Chart Datum and underlined, thus $\underline{1}_6$, $\underline{0}_9$, etc. Should there be insufficient space for printing the figures in the drying area, such height may be stated alongside the area; e.g., "Dries 1.6 m."

Depth Contours

Depth contours are drawn in fine firm lines, broken in places where there are figures indicating the depth in metres, e.g. 30, 100, 1,000, 2,000, etc.

Vertical Clearances

Vertical clearances (under bridges, etc.) are given in metres, the figures are printed with a line over the top and in brackets, thus ($\overline{10}$).

Submerged Wrecks

Sounded or swept depths over wrecks are given in metres, or metres and decimetres. The criterion for dangerous wrecks is less than 28 m. clearance.

Tints and Colours

The land tint is buff and drying areas are green on British charts but vary on other nationality charts. The 10 metres contour is edged on the inside with a narrow blue ribbon, and all sea areas contained within the 5 metre contour are blue. Blue tints however, may be shown to different limits according to the scale of the chart.

CHART SYMBOLS

For a full understanding of all symbols used in British Admiralty charts, reference should be made to Admiralty Chart No. 5011 now published in book form. This gives full details of every symbol and abbreviation used and should be included in the equipment of everyone who takes their navigation seriously. Some useful chart symbols and abbreviations are included in this section. Charts of other nationalities may have varying symbols and the appropriate key should always be consulted.

Notices to Mariners

Each maritime nation issues notices giving the latest navigation information. The British Admiralty issue Notices to Mariners weekly giving world-wide information and quarterly notices for yachtsmen covering the area from the Elbe to the Gironde. These exclude information of items applicable to large vessels.

USEFUL CHART SYMBOLS

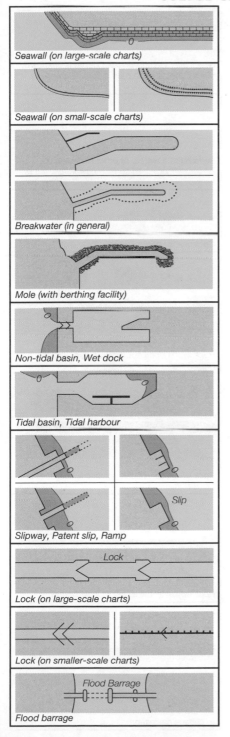

Seawall (on large-scale charts)

Seawall (on small-scale charts)

Breakwater (in general)

Mole (with berthing facility)

Non-tidal basin, Wet dock

Tidal basin, Tidal harbour

Slip

Slipway, Patent slip, Ramp

Lock (on large-scale charts)

Lock (on smaller-scale charts)

Flood barrage

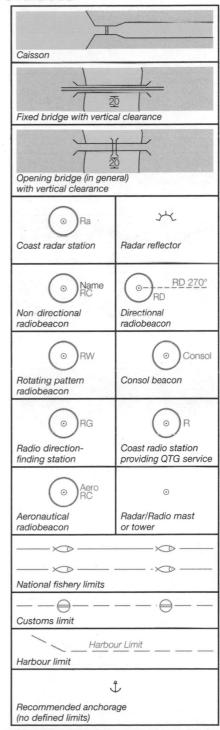

Caisson

Fixed bridge with vertical clearance

Opening bridge (in general) with vertical clearance

Coast radar station

Radar reflector

Non-directional radiobeacon

Directional radiobeacon

Rotating pattern radiobeacon

Consol beacon

Radio direction-finding station

Coast radio station providing QTG service

Aeronautical radiobeacon

Radar/Radio mast or tower

National fishery limits

Customs limit

Harbour limit

Recommended anchorage (no defined limits)

Section 13

5

USEFUL CHART SYMBOLS

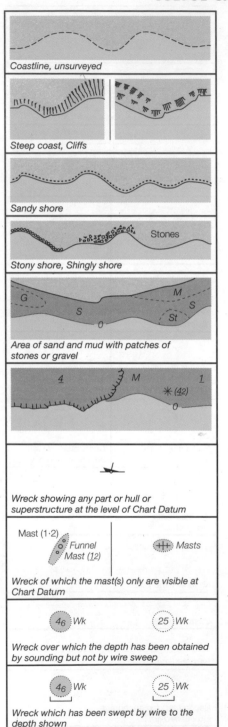

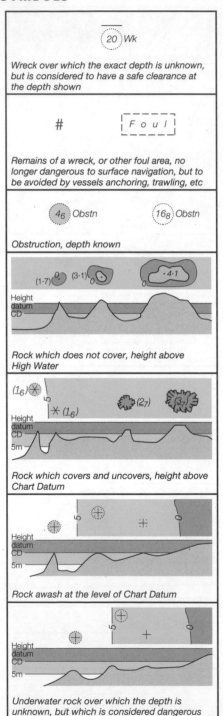

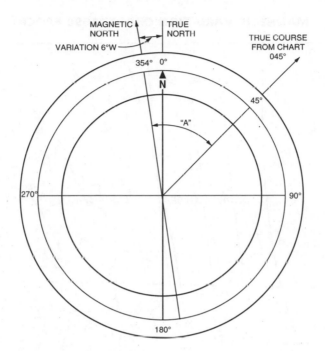

VARIATION AND DEVIATION

Basically variation is the angle between the Magnetic North Pole and the True Pole – which could perhaps be described as the Geometric Pole. This angle varies over the earth's surface and at present is of the order of 5° W in the North Sea area and is decreasing about 8' annually.

Deviation is an error induced in a vessel's compass by local conditions, i.e., magnetic material near to the compass. This error varies with the ship's heading and should therefore be known on all points of the compass for which purpose a deviation card is required. This card can be prepared by a professional compass adjuster or, with care, by the mariner himself. One method of preparing such a card is described later.

METHOD OF APPLYING VARIATION

When the *True* course has been laid on the chart, it is then necessary to convert it to a *Magnetic* course for use on the mariner's compass. Consider the diagram above and assume a course of 045° *True* is required. It will be observed that the *Variation* angle in this example is 6° West, i.e., *Magnetic North* is 6° West of *True North*.

The angle between the *True* course of 45° and the *Magnetic North* is therefore 45° + 6° = 51° (angle A). The course to be steered on the compass is therefore 51° Magnetic. Similarly, if the Variation angle was to be East of *True North* it will be seen that the Variation is subtracted from the True Course, i.e., if the variation was 6° East the above-mentioned course of 45° True would become 45° True – 6° = 39° Magnetic.

To assist in remembering this fact when converting from True to Magnetic courses under difficult conditions the following may help:

"West is best (i.e. greater); East is least (i.e. less)."

Applying Variation and Deviation

The same rule applies to Deviation. For example a True Course of 254° T, Variation 6° W; Magnetic Course will be 254° T + 6° W = 260° M, and from the Deviation Card (page 10) Dev. for this course will be 4° E. ∴ Compass Course will be 254° T + 6° W Var. = 260° – 4° E. Dev. = 256° C.

The two components, Var. and Dev. can be combined, i.e., + 6° W. – 4° E = 2° Compass error for the particular course. 254° T + 2° = 256° C.

It is essential when converting from True to Compass to apply Var. and Dev. in that order.

MAGNETIC VARIATION CHART (1990 EPOCH)

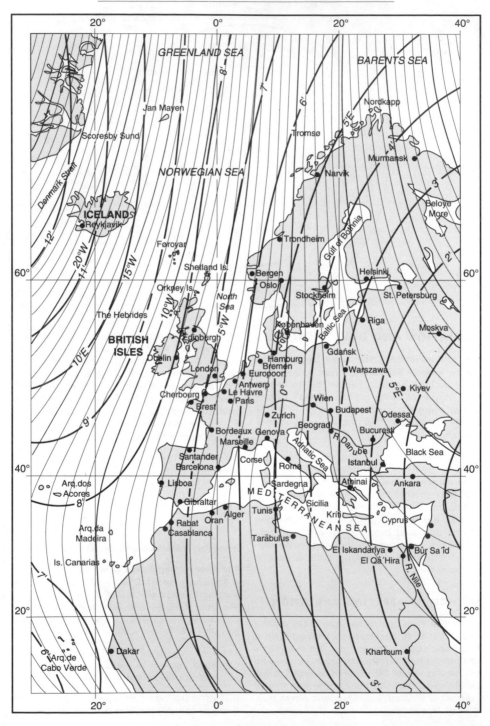

PREPARING A DEVIATION CARD

It is important that the navigator should know the deviation of the ship's compass (unless it is a gyro compass where this error does not arise). It is also very useful if the owner of the smaller vessel has sufficient knowledge and confidence in his ability to produce his own deviation card. One useful method for producing a reasonably accurate deviation card when no known transit is readily available is described below.

A Pelorus is required for the exercise but if not available, with reasonable care can easily be constructed with materials readily to hand. A sheet of plywood approximately 12" to 18" square is prepared with a lubber line clearly marked along the centre. On the centre of this square is glued a compass rose from an old Admiralty chart with the magnetic North and South lines accurately lined up on the lubber line. A circle of say 12" diameter is then marked on the plywood square using the centre of the compass rose for the purpose. Lines are then drawn through each 5° point on the rose to the outer circle mentioned above. The degree marks then obtained on the outer ring can be further subdivided but it will probably be found that readings can be quite accurately estimated by eye. A small wooden pointer about 9" long with the appropriate sighting marks is then mounted in the centre of the rose and the Pelorus is complete.

The Pelorus is then mounted in such a position that the lubber line is on the fore and aft line of the vessel and sights can be taken all round. It will be appreciated that the purpose of the Pelorus is to take bearings of an object relative to the ship's head.

A position is then selected where the vessel can be manoeuvred through 360° as far as possible in the same position, for example near a buoy, and bearings taken on a distant object, ideally at least 5 miles away. The magnetic bearing of this object is immaterial at this stage. The procedure is as follows:

The ship is swung until her head is on due North (Compass) and the bearing of the object is noted on the Pelorus. This procedure is repeated for each quadrant of the compass so that 8 bearings of the object are obtained relative to the main compass headings. The compass bearings of the object with the ship's head on the different compass headings can then be calculated and the deviation card prepared in the usual way. For example, with the ship's head on compass North, the Pelorus reading will be the actual bearing of the object as it would be read from the ship's compass. Assume that this figure is 250°. The ship's head would then be swung to 45° and the Pelorus bearing would become say 200°. The compass bearing of the object would thus be 200° + 45° = 245°. Carrying on in this way a series of roughly similar Pelorus bearings would be obtained and the average of these would give the correct magnetic bearing of the object, i.e., in effect a transit.

By adjustment, i.e., adding or subtracting each ship's head bearing from the Pelorus bearing (it will be obvious when the figures are obtained what to do) corrected bearings are obtained which when compared with the mean bearing give the difference necessary on each heading to enable the deviation curve to be prepared.

THE SEXTANT

The sextant is an optical instrument used for measuring angles and is an essential item of equipment for the ocean navigator. It is, however, of considerable assistance to the coastal navigator, mainly in the field of position fixing by means of vertical and horizontal angles of terrestrial objects such as lighthouses, etc. Position fixing by observations of celestial bodies is dealt with in Section 20. Like most instruments practice is necessary to achieve proficiency in its use – coastal navigation will afford plenty of opportunity. Those wishing to attain a high standard of proficiency should refer to *The Sextant Simplified* by Captain O.M. Watts, published by Reed's

INDEX ERROR

Any residual error left in the sextant after it has been properly adjusted is called *Index Error* and this value should be applied as a correction to all sextant readings. There are several methods by which Index Error can be found, one simple method is:

To find Index Error by the sea horizon

1. Clamp the index at approximately zero.
2. Hold the sextant vertically and look through the telescope at the sea horizon.
3. Turn the tangent screw until the true and reflected horizons together form an unbroken line.
4. The *reading* on the sextant now indicates the Index Error which should be applied as a subtractive correction if the reading is on the arc, and additive if off the arc.

A clear horizon is essential to ensure accurate results.

DEVIATION CARD

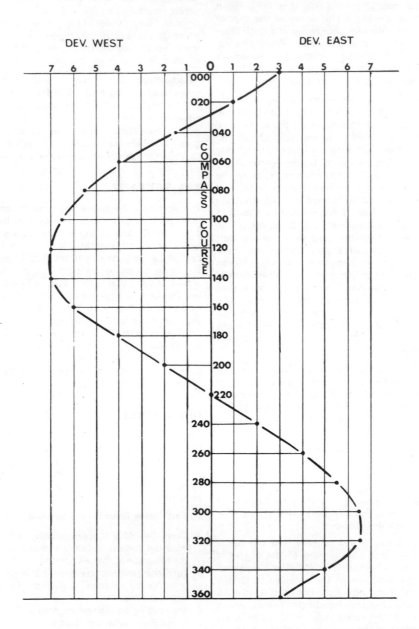

DEV. WEST   DEV. EAST

A typical deviation card which shows the method of construction.

TAKING HORIZONTAL AND VERTICAL SEXTANT ANGLES

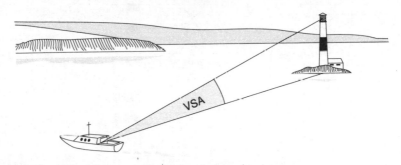

Fig. A. Vertical Sextant Angle

TO MEASURE VERTICAL SEXTANT ANGLES (e.g. those of the lighthouse in Fig. A)

The Telescope is shipped in its collar and the Index is set to zero. Hold the Sextant vertically and view the centre of the light through the Telescope. The light will be seen direct through the plane (or unsilvered) part of the Horizon Glass, i.e., the TRUE image. It will also be seen as a REFLECTED image in the silvered part. (Figs. B and C.) Both True and Reflected images should coincide.

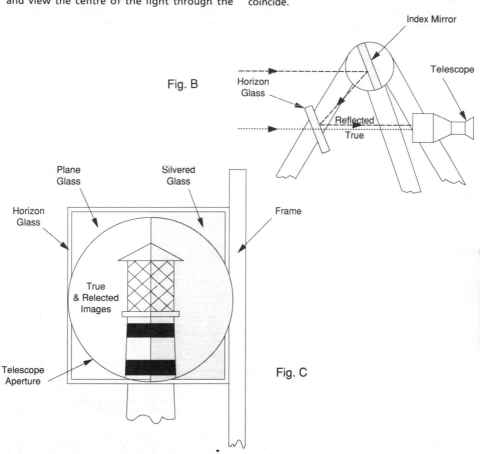

Fig. B

Index Mirror

Telescope

Horizon Glass

Reflected

True

Plane Glass

Silvered Glass

Frame

Horizon Glass

True & Relected Images

Telescope Aperture

Fig. C

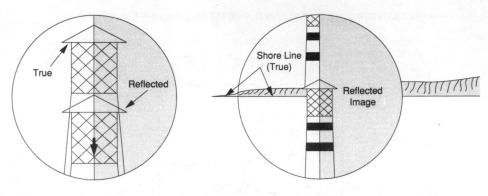

Fig. D   Fig. E

The Micrometer Head is now turned with the left hand so that the Index moves along the Arc, away from the Telescope end. As soon as the Micrometer is turned the True and Reflected images will separate, the Reflected image moving downwards. (Fig. D). As the Reflected image of the light "falls" the Sextant is tilted downwards to follow its movement. When the centre of the light reaches the shoreline the reading is noted. (Fig. E.)

Using the sextant should first be practised on dry land and then on a yacht. Try bringing a chimney top down to the base of a wall to begin with.

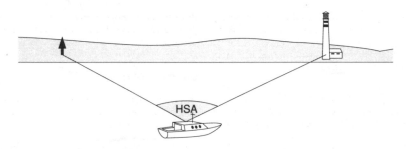

Fig. F Horizontal Sextant Angle

TO MEASURE HORIZONTAL SEXTANT ANGLES (Fig. F)

The Horizontal Sextant Angle between, say, a lighthouse and a beacon is measured by holding the Sextant horizontally with the Handle downwards. As with the Vertical Sextant Angle the Index is set to zero. The Telescope is now pointed at the right hand object, in Fig. G, the Lighthouse.

Fig. G

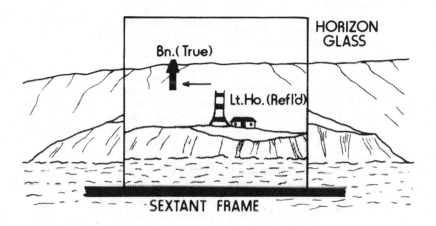

Fig. H

Since the angle to be measured will be relatively large the Index is now moved along the Arc by means of the Quick Release Clamp. Make sure a firm pressure is exerted on the clamp otherwise the gear teeth may be damaged.

The Reflected image of the Lighthouse will appear to move towards the LEFT, so that by letting it follow the True coastline in the unsilvered part of the Horizon Glass it will eventually approach the beacon (Bn.) (Fig. H). The Sextant must be swung towards the LEFT to keep the Reflected lighthouse in view.

As soon as the beacon is seen in the Horizon Glass the clamp is released. The Micrometer Head is now turned until the Reflected image of the lighthouse is superimposed on the True image of the beacon. The angle may then be read.

Some navigators prefer to point the sextant initially at the left hand object and move the index bar forward so that the right hand object eventually comes into view.

NAVIGATOR'S CHECK LIST

The following check list may be helpful to those making a coastal passage for the first time. Remember that pre-sailing planning materially reduces the possibility of making a navigational error when the situation is difficult. The use of

Reed's Log Book with its facilities for preplanning will be very helpful in this connection.

BEFORE YOU SAIL

Have you made a quick reference list of lights and buoys with their ranges, etc., for use in the cockpit if necessary?

Check that all charts required are available on board and corrected up to date.

Are the desired course lines marked on the charts to assist navigation at sea?

Have alternative courses been considered in case stress of weather dictates a departure from the planned trip?

Have you an up to date copy of Reed's Nautical Almanac on board? (Don't forget the Spring Supplement.}

A Tidal Atlas for the area is a most useful addition to the reference books. If not available the information is shown on the tidal stream charts in this Almanac but of necessity the scale is much smaller.

Do you know your compass deviation and have you prepared a deviation card?

Section 13

13

POINTS TO CONSIDER WHEN ON PASSAGE

(i) In yachts equipped with Decca etc., there is always the temptation to rely on it entirely but the prudent navigator will always maintain an E.P. on the chart at say hourly intervals. In the event of equipment failure he will then have a good starting point for the basic navigation that becomes necessary

(ii) Never pass a light or buoy without identifying it if reasonably possible. Remember that dangers such as sandbanks may have several buoys with the same name but different prefixes.

(iii) Remember that tidal streams vary in force and direction from place to place and also according to the time relative to HW. It is also important to remember the effect of Springs and Neaps on the force of the tidal stream.

(iv) Do not forget leeway angle when setting courses and do not overlook the effect of surface drift which may occur due to a hard and prolonged blow.

(v) When navigating in fog if it is not possible to anchor in safety out of shipping lanes try to maintain a constant speed – it makes calculations easier.

(vi) Remember the copy book approach to an unfamiliar but well lighted shore – close the coast before dawn to obtain an accurate fix from lights and then make your entry with daylight.

(vii) Finally – when approaching an unfamiliar destination, if uncertain of your position and there is a possibility of danger as a result – heave to or stand out to sea again until you have sorted out the situation.

THE VESSEL'S COURSE

One of the first essentials before commencing a trip is to decide upon the different courses to be made good between the start and the finishing point. The standard terms used in connection with the vessel's course are given below and it is recommended that these should always be used, particularly in discussions between the navigator and helmsman.

The word "course" by itself can have several quite different meanings. It may refer to a course to steer, a leeway course, a required course, or a course to make good, which is not always the same thing as the required course.

Heading refers only to the vessel's fore-and-aft line. It is the direction in which she is pointing, regardless of her actual track, and is designated as True (T), Magnetic (M) or Compass (C), as appropriate. Whenever the true heading is plotted on the chart, the line should be marked for identification with a single arrow head pointing in the appropriate direction.

Track refers to the direction of the ship's track over the sea bed. It may be designated as True (T) or Magnetic (M), as convenient, and when drawn on the chart should be marked for identification with two arrow heads and clearly labelled, e.g., 286° (T). The Required Track is the direction of the intended track between two points. The line drawn on the chart to indicate the required track is often referred to as the "course line".

Tidal Stream – when plotted on the chart should be marked with three arrow heads.

Course to Steer is the heading required to make good a specified track.

Course Steered refers to the heading that was steered over a specified time.

Leeway is the angle between the ship's fore-and-aft line and her line of movement through the water.

Leeway Course or Wake Course is the direction of the vessel's line of movement through the water. Thus when she is making leeway the wake course always lies to leeward of the true heading; and if there is a significant current, too, the track may be different to both the heading and wake course.

PLOTTING THE REQUIRED TRACK

Any reader wishing to use a calculator should, after studying the following basic information, refer to the use of the electronic calculator later in this section.

On a coastal passage the configuration of the coastline may necessitate many changes of course and it is a wise practice to plot all the required courses on the chart before the commencement of the passage. The prudent navigator will also plot the courses of any "escape route" that may be necessitated by bad weather.

A close examination of the course lines should then be made to ensure that adequate clearance is given to all possible dangers. The courses can be marked in on the course lines or preferably noted separately. The reason for not writing them on the chart is to ensure that it is as uncluttered as possible before the normal chartwork of recording estimated positions, etc., commences as the passage progresses.

SETTING THE COURSE

With Allowance for Leeway only:

Some sea-going experience and a knowledge of the ship's likely behaviour under existing conditions is required when estimating the allowance to be made for leeway. For any one course this allowance must be adjusted from time to time as dictated by change in the force and/or direction of the wind.

The leeway angle is the angle between the fore and aft line of the vessel and her wake and should be measured or estimated for various speeds and sea conditions.

To determine the true course to steer: apply leeway to windward of the required true track.

To determine the true track being made good: apply leeway to leeward of the true course being steered.

Always apply leeway angle before variation and deviation have been applied to the course to steer.

When there is no current or tidal effect, the track and the wake course are the same.

Allowance for Tide or Current and Leeway

The term speed refers always to the ship's speed through the water; her speed over the sea bed is called effective speed.

EXAMPLE: It is required to set course to make good a track of 080° (T) when the tidal stream is

setting 180° at 3 knots, wind northerly and leeway 5°. If the vessel's speed is 9 knots, what course should she steer, and what will be her effective speed?

In the diagram AB represents the required track drawn on the chart.

1. Take any convenient point C and lay off the current vector CD representing 3 kts. (using units from any convenient scale) at 180° (T).

2. With centre D and radius equal to ship's speed of 9 kts. strike an arc cutting AB at E.

3. DE represents True Course required, i.e., 061° (T).

4. Apply Southerly leeway angle of 5°; course will be 056° (T).

5. Compass course will be 056° + 6° Var. W. –3° Dev. E. = 059° (C).

6. CE measured in the same units as CD gives 8 kts. – the effective speed.

When out of sight of land or in low visibility with no navigational fixing aids available, allowance for leeway and tide should be adjusted continually, as required, so as to "make good" the required track over the sea bed. In continued low visibility, soundings taken at regular intervals often provide a useful check on the distance off the coast.

COURSE CORRECTION

Every prudent navigator when setting a course makes allowance for leeway, and the effects of a tidal stream or current.

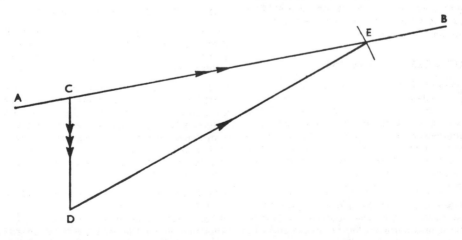

The following Table has been designed to save the navigator of a small vessel having to work the problem on the chart to find out what course allowance he should make to counteract the effect of a tidal stream or current of an estimated speed and taking into account the speed of his vessel.

It will be realised, of course, that the slower the vessel's speed the more it will be affected by any current; and the more this tidal stream or current is abeam, the more it will push the vessel sideways from her course, and, therefore, the more allowance that must be made. Should the stream be directly ahead or astern, no course allowance need be made, but the speed will be advanced or retarded according to the speed of the current.

The Table – in addition to giving in the shortest time the allowance to be made to the course – gives also the speed made good over the ground. Whilst this latter may sometimes be required, it is more necessary in practical navigation to find the course allowance to be made at frequent intervals.

This Table saves any chart plotting and enables the course allowance for tidal stream or current to be found mentally in the quickest possible manner.

HOW TO FIND THE COURSE TO STEER TO COUNTERACT THE EFFECT OF TIDE OR CURRENT

(1). Find the speed of tidal stream (or current) at the top of the page and with the relative angle of the tidal stream (or current) from the desired track to be made good in the left hand column, C, read value from the Table.

(2) Find at the top of the Table the speed of the vessel (through the water) and look down this column until the value in (1) above is found (or closely approximated). Then read off in the left hand column C, the number of degrees allowance to be made to the course.

(3) Allow this course correction to the same side, port or starboard, as the tidal stream or current; i.e., in order to counteract a current setting towards the vessel on the starboard side, you naturally make the course allowance towards the starboard side.

Example I. Vessel steering 060° (T) at 10 knots estimates a current will set 290° (T) at 3½ knots. What allowance should be made, and what course should be steered?

1) Find speed of current, 3½ knots, in column at top of page, and 50° (relative angle of the current to the vessel's course) on the left hand side of the page giving a value of 2.681.

(2) Find speed of vessel, 10 knots, at the top of the Table and value 2.681 in this column – 2,760 is the nearest. The course allowance in column C on this line is seen to be 16° C.

(3) As the current is on the starboard bow, the 16° must be allowed to starboard to counteract its effect. Therefore, the course to steer is 076° (T).

Example II. Vessel steering 200° (T), speed 8 knots, tidal stream estimated to set 230° (T) at 1½ knots (i.e., 30° from dead astern). With 1.5 knots on top and 30° in column C, value is 0.750. With 8 knots on top and value 0.750 in same column, in column C is found 5°.

Tidal stream is on port quarter, so allow 5° to port, i.e., the course to steer is 195° (T).

Example III. Vessel steering 337° at 14½ knots, tidal stream setting 247° at 2½ knots. What course should the vessel steer to counteract the effect of the tidal stream?

With 2½ knots on top and 90° in column C value is 2.500. With 14½ knots on top and value 2.500 in the same column, in column C is found 10°.

Tidal stream is abeam to starboard so allow 10° to starboard. Course to steer therefore is 347°.

HOW TO FIND THE SPEED MADE GOOD OVER THE GROUND (EFFECTIVE SPEED)

(1) Enter the Table from the top with speed of tidal stream (or current) and from the right hand column S with relative angle of the stream. Read from the Table the factor and name it T.C. (Tidal Contribution to vessel's speed over ground).

(2) Enter Table from the top with ship's speed (through the water) and from the right hand column S with course correction. Read from the Table the factor and name it S.C. (Ship's Contribution to vessel's speed over ground).

(3) If tidal stream (or current) is on the bow, (i.e., before the beam), the vessel's effective speed is the sum of S.C. and T.C.

If tidal stream (or current) is on the quarter (i.e., abaft the beam), the vessel's effective speed is the sum of S.C. and T.C.

COURSE CORRECTION TABLE
(Designed by R. C. Fisher)

SPEED OF TIDAL STREAM (OR CURRENT) OVER THE GROUND AND SHIP'S SPEED THROUGH THE WATER

C	Knots 0.5	1.0	1.5	2.0	Knots 2.5	3.0	3.5	4.0	4.5	Knots 5.0	S
0	0	0	0	0	0	0	0	0	0	0	90
1	0.009	0.019	0.026	0.035	0.044	0.052	0.061	0.070	0.079	0.087	89
2	0.017	0.035	0.052	0.070	0.087	0.105	0.122	0.139	0.157	0.174	88
3	0.026	0.052	0.079	0.105	0.131	0.157	0.183	0.209	0.236	0.262	87
4	0.035	0.070	0.105	0.140	0.174	0.209	0.244	0.279	0.314	0.349	86
5	0.044	0.087	0.131	0.174	0.218	0.261	0.305	0.349	0.392	0.436	85
6	0.052	0.105	0.157	0.209	0.261	0.314	0.366	0.418	0.470	0.523	84
8	0.070	0.139	0.209	0.278	0.348	0.418	0.487	0.557	0.626	0.696	82
10	0.087	0.174	0.200	0.347	0.434	0.521	0.608	0.696	0.781	0.868	80
12	0.104	0.208	0.312	0.416	0.520	0.624	0.728	0.832	0.936	1.040	78
14	0.121	0.242	0.363	0.484	0.605	0.726	0.847	0.968	1.089	1.210	76
16	0.138	0.276	0.413	0.551	0.689	0.827	0.965	1.103	1.240	1.378	74
18	0.155	0.309	0.464	0.618	0.773	0.927	1.082	1.236	1.391	1.545	72
21	0.179	0.358	0.538	0.717	0.896	1.075	1.254	1.433	1.613	1.792	69
24	0.203	0.407	0.610	0.813	1.017	1.220	1.424	1.627	1.830	2.034	66
27	0.227	0.454	0.681	0.908	1.135	1.362	1.589	1.816	2.043	2.270	63
30	0.250	0.500	0.750	1.000	1.250	1.500	1.750	2.000	2.250	2.500	60
33	0.272	0.545	0.817	1.089	1.362	1.634	1.906	2.179	2.451	2.723	57
36	0.294	0.588	0.882	1.176	1.469	1.763	2.057	2.351	2.645	2.939	54
39	0.315	0.629	0.944	1.259	1.573	1.888	2.203	2.517	2.832	3.147	51
42	0.335	0.669	1.004	1.338	1.673	2.007	2.342	2.667	3.011	3.346	48
46	0.360	0.719	1.079	1.439	1.798	2.158	2.518	2.877	3.237	3.597	44
50	0.383	0.766	1.149	1.532	1.916	2.298	2.681	3.064	3.447	3.830	40
54	0.405	0.809	1.214	1.618	2.023	2.427	2.832	3.236	3.641	4.045	36
58	0.424	0.848	1.272	1.696	2.120	2.540	2.986	3.392	3.816	4.240	32
62	0.442	0.883	1.324	1.766	2.207	2.649	3.090	3.532	3.973	4.415	28
66	0.457	0.914	1.370	1.827	2.284	2.741	3.197	3.754	4.111	4.568	24
70	0.470	0.940	1.410	1.879	2.349	2.819	3.289	3.759	4.229	4.698	20
75	0.483	0.966	1.449	1.932	2.415	2.898	3.381	3.864	4.347	4.830	15
80	0.492	0.985	1.477	1.970	2.462	2.954	3.447	3.939	4.432	4.924	10
85	0.498	0.996	1.494	1.992	2.490	2.989	3.487	3.985	4.483	4.981	5
90	0.500	1.000	1.500	2.000	2.500	3.000	3.500	4.000	4.500	5.000	0
C	0.5	1.0	1.5	2.0	2.5 Knots	3.0	3.5	4.0	4.5	5.0	S

C	Knots 6	7	8	9	Knots 10	12	14	16	18	Knots 20	S
0	0	0	0	0	0	0	0	0	0	0	90
1	0.105	0.120	0.140	0.160	0.170	0.210	0.240	0.280	0.310	0.350	89
2	0.209	0.240	0.280	0.310	0.340	0.420	0.490	0.560	0.630	0.700	88
3	0.314	0.370	0.420	0.470	0.520	0.630	0.730	0.840	0.940	1.050	87
4	0.419	0.490	0.560	0.630	0.700	0.840	0.980	1.120	1.260	1.400	86
5	0.523	0.610	0.700	0.780	0.870	1.050	1.220	1.390	1.570	1.740	85
6	0.627	0.730	0.840	0.940	1.050	1.250	1.460	1.670	1.880	2.080	84
8	0.835	0.970	1.110	1.250	1.390	1.670	1.950	2.230	2.510	2.780	82
10	1.040	1.220	1.390	1.560	1.740	2.080	2.430	2.780	3.130	3.470	80
12	1.247	1.460	1.660	1.870	2.080	2.490	2.910	3.330	3.740	4.160	78
14	1.452	1.690	1.940	2.180	2.420	2.900	3.390	3.870	4.350	4.840	76
16	1.654	1.930	2.210	2.480	2.760	3.310	3.860	4.410	4.960	5.510	74
18	1.854	2.160	2.470	2.780	3.090	3.710	4.330	4.940	5.560	6.180	72
21	2.150	2.510	2.870	3.230	3.580	4.300	5.020	5.730	6.450	7.170	69
24	2.440	2.850	3.250	3.660	4.070	4.880	5.690	6.510	7.320	8.130	66
27	2.724	3.180	3.630	4.090	4.540	5.450	6.360	7.260	8.170	9.080	63
30	3.000	3.500	4.000	4.500	5.000	6.000	7.000	8.300	9.000	10.00	60
33	3.268	3.810	4.360	4.900	5.450	6.540	7.620	8.710	9.800	10.89	57
36	3.527	4.110	4.700	5.290	5.880	7.050	8.230	9.400	10.58	11.76	54
39	3.776	4.410	5.030	5.660	6.290	7.550	8.810	10.07	11.33	12.59	51
42	4.015	4.680	5.350	6.020	6.690	8.030	9.370	10.71	12.04	13.38	48
46	4.316	5.040	5.750	6.470	7.190	8.630	10.07	11.51	12.95	14.39	44
50	4.596	5.360	6.130	6.890	7.660	9.190	10.72	12.26	13.79	15.32	40
54	4.854	5.660	6.470	7.280	8.090	9.710	11.33	12.94	14.56	16.18	36
58	5.088	5.940	6.780	7.630	8.480	10.18	11.87	13.57	15.26	16.96	32
62	5.298	6.180	7.060	7.950	8.830	10.60	12.36	14.13	15.89	17.66	28
66	5.481	6.390	7.310	8.220	9.140	10.96	12.79	14.62	16.44	18.27	24
70	5.638	6.580	7.520	8.460	9.400	11.28	13.16	15.04	16.91	18.79	20
75	5.796	6.760	7.730	8.690	9.660	11.59	13.52	15.45	17.39	19.32	15
80	5.909	6.890	7.880	8.860	9.850	11.82	13.76	15.76	17.73	19.70	10
85	5.977	6.970	7.970	8.970	9.960	11.95	13.95	15.94	17.93	19.92	5
90	6.000	7.000	8.000	9.000	10.00	12.00	14.00	16.00	18.00	20.00	0
C	6	7	8	9	10 Knots	12	14	16	18	20	S

Section 13

Example I. (as page 16). Vessel's speed 10 knots, current 3½ knots, 50° on the starboard bow. What is the vessel's speed over the ground?

(1) With 3½ knots at top and 50° on the right in column S, gives (by interpolation) 2.249.

(2) With 10 knots at the top and 16° course correction on the T.C. right in column S gives (by interpolation) S.C. 9.608.

(3) As the current is ahead of the vessel (i.e., 50° on the starboard bow) and pushing her back, the difference between S.C. and T.C. – 9.608 and 2.249 gives 7.359* knots, the vessel's effective speed.

Should the current have been on the starboard quarter (i.e., helping the vessel along) the sum of T.C. and S.C. i.e., 11.857 knots, would have been the effective speed.

*If interpolation had not been done but the nearest tabulated figures used, i.e., T.C. 2.203 and S.C. 9.660, the result would be 7.457, which is quite accurate enough for ordinary purposes.

Example II. (as page 16). Vessel's speed, 8 knots, tidal stream speed 1½ knots, 30° on the quarter. Course allowance 5°. What speed did the vessel make good over the ground?

1. With 1½ knots and 30° T.C. equals 1.300.

2. With 8 knots and 5° S.C. equals 7.970.

3. As stream is behind vessel, the sum 9.27 is the effective speed.

Example III. (page 16). Vessel's speed 14½ knots. Tidal stream 2½ knots abeam. Course allowance 10°. What was the vessel's effective speed?

1. With 2½ knots and 90° T.C. equals 0.

2. With 14½ knots and 10° S.C. equals 14¼.

As stream is abeam the sum (or difference) is 14¼, so vessel's speed over the ground is 14¼ knots.

POSITION FIXING

A "Fix" is obtained by the intersection of two or more position lines; more than two should be used whenever possible. If the position lines are obtained all at the same time it is commonly called a Simultaneous Fix. If, however, there is a significant time interval between the observations, so that the first position time has to be transferred up to the time of the last one, it is termed a Running Fix. All other things being equal, a simultaneous fix is more reliable than a running fix.

There are various types of position lines; but those which are normally available to the average yacht are obtained by:

(1) A compass bearing of a fixed object ashore.

(2) A transit bearing i.e., two fixed objects seen in line with one another, e.g., a point of land in line with a conspicuous chimney – very accurate.

(3) A vertical sextant angle of an object of known height coupled with its compass bearing – very accurate.

(4) A horizontal sextant angle between two fixed objects – very accurate.

(5) A dipping range.

(6) A sounding corresponding to a clearly defined fathom line (e.g., 20 m) on the chart.

(7) A radio D/F bearing;

(8) An astronomical observation.

A fix can be obtained by any combination of the position lines listed above. A quick and accurate method by day is to combine the distance of an object (e.g., headland or lighthouse) obtained from a vertical sextant angle with the simultaneous bearing of the object.

Compass bearings are obtained with the use of an Azimuth Mirror on the main compass or, in the case of smaller vessels, by means of a Hand Bearing Compass.

There are many occasions when a single position line may prove useful, for example:

(a) A position line which is parallel or nearly parallel to the required track shows whether or not the vessel is maintaining that track.

(b) A position line which cuts the track at or near 90° will often provide a good check on effective speed and ETA at the next point.

(c) Two marks or beacons in transit may provide a leading line into a harbour, or clear a danger.

(d) A single bearing may be used as a clearing line – danger being avoided by keeping to one side of the bearing line.

When making a passage it is necessary to have an accurate assessment of the vessel's position at all times – especially important in coastal navigation. The ocean navigator may only plot his position at noon each day – the coastal

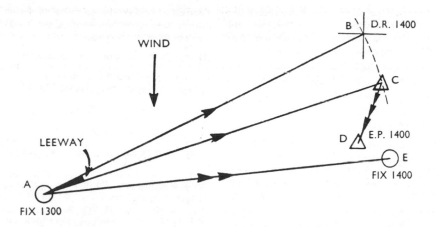

navigator should plot his at least once each hour. The standard terms used in position fixing are:

DEAD RECKONING (DR) – a position obtained from the course steered by the vessel and her speed through the water and no other factors. The distance run through the water is laid off along the course line steered and the position so obtained marked with a small cross, the letters DR and the time, thus – + DR 1030.

ESTIMATED POSITION (EP) – a position obtained by adjusting the DR position for the effects of leeway and current. It is marked on the chart by means of a dot in a triangle thus △ EP 1030.

A FIX – provided by reliable observations of terrestrial or celestial bodies and is shown thus ⊙ Fix 1030.

With practice the symbols only should be used – clarity on the chart reduces the chances of error.

The figure above illustrates the different kinds of position as defined above. Assuming point A to be the last reliable fix (obtained at, say, 1300 hours), AB the course steered and the log distance for one hour; then B is the DR position for 1400 hours – i.e., the position the vessel would be in if there was no leeway, no current, the course had been accurately steered and the distance run through the water accurately indicated.

If the ship had been making leeway (angle BAC) due to a northerly wind, but was not affected by current, then C would be the EP at 1400 hours. Note that the distance AB and AC are always the same.

If, however, a current setting (say) 200° (T) at 3 knots was encountered, then the set and drift

for one hour (200° (T) – 3 miles) would be laid off on the chart from point C – i.e., CD, and point D is now the EP for 1400 hours. Note that the effect of current is marked by three arrow heads.

Should a reliable fix, E, be obtained at 1400 hours, the current actually experienced during the last hour would be determined by measuring the direction and distance from C to E (not drawn in figure). The track and distance made good, and the effective speed, would be determined by the straight line AE.

THE RUNNING FIX

A Running Fix is primarily for use on those frequent occasions (particularly during night passage) when only one known object is visible, so that simultaneous cross bearings cannot be obtained. Although less reliable than a simultaneous fix, it does have many valuable applications which should never be neglected.

To obtain a Running Fix from bearings of the same object with a time interval between them:

(1) Take the first bearing and note the reading of the log, plot the position line on the chart and mark it with a single arrowhead at one end and also the time at which the observation was made.

(2) When the bearing has altered enough to make a good angle of "cut" with the first position line repeat the procedure.

(3) From any convenient point on the first position line lay off the "run" (the run being the track and the distance made good over the ground during the time interval between the bearings) – AB.

19

(4) Through the end of the run draw a line parallel to the first position line. This line is the first position line "transferred", and it should be marked by two arrow heads at each end.

(5) The point where the transferred position line cuts the second bearing is the "fix" and should be marked accordingly.

Important Notes:

(a) The accuracy of this method of fixing is dependent, not only on the accuracy of the bearings and their angle of cut, but also on the accuracy with which the "run" between the bearings has been estimated – remember leeway and effect of tide.

(b) The reliability of a running fix can be better assessed when two bearings are transferred up to the time of a third. A small "cocked hat" thus formed can generally be treated with a greater degree of confidence than a running fix from only two bearings.

(c) The principle of the running fix applies whether or not the position lines are obtained from the same point of origin. A bearing of one object may be transferred to cross with a bearing of a different object which was not sighted until after the first one was lost to view.

Example of a Running fix with no tide Fig. 1:
Vessel steering 270° (T) and making no leeway. At 2300 hrs. a lighthouse, P, bore 315° (T), Patent Log read 86.2. At 2330 hrs. the same light bore 040° (T), Patent Log read 90.7. If the

tidal effect was estimated to be nil during the interval between the bearings, what was the ship's position at 2330 hours?

(1) Plot the two position lines as described.

(2) From any convenient point A on the first position line lay off the run (AB) 270° 4.5 miles.

(3) Through B draw the transferred position line parallel to PA, and the point where it cuts the second bearing is the fix.

Example of a Running fix in a tidal stream Fig. 2:

Vessel steering 270° (T) and making 5° leeway due to a northerly wind. At 2300 hours a Lighthouse, P, bore 315° (T), Patent Log reading 86.2. At 2330 hours the same light bore 040° (T), Patent Log reading 90.7. The tidal stream was estimated to be setting 010° at 2 knots. Required: the vessel's position at 2330.

Referring to the figure overleaf:

(1) Plot the two position lines as described above.

(2) From any convenient point A on the first position line lay off AB (4.5 miles along the Wake Course – 265°).

(3) From point B lay off BC the tidal effect for 30 minutes (set 010°, drift 1 mile). The estimated run then is AC.

(4) Through point C draw the transferred position line parallel to PA, and the point where it cuts the second bearing is the fix.

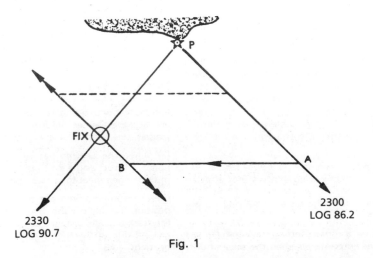

2300
LOG 86.2

2330
LOG 90.7

Fig. 1

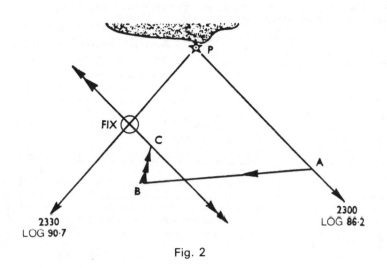

Fig. 2

SOME USEFUL VARIATIONS IN THE RUNNING FIX METHOD

One particular advantage of any of the methods which follow is that the approximate distance off a terrestrial object can be found before it comes abeam and, if necessary, the track can be altered at once to avoid passing too close to a danger.

Another important feature is that the approximate "distance off" any fixed object can be found even though the observed object cannot be located and identified on the chart.

Running Fix Table: To avoid having to plot these bearings on the chart, a special table has been included overleaf.

Bearing-Angles on the Bow. If, through bad weather or other cause, it is not possible to use tables the following special bow bearings may be very valuable.

Provided the same track is maintained and the distance run over the ground during the interval between the two bearings is known, the "distance off" that the vessel will pass the object (of which the bearings were taken) when it is abeam can be determined by observing any pair of the following angles on the bow:

Pairs of angles: (a) 22° and 34° ; (b) 25° and 41° ; (c) 26½° and 45° ; (d) 32° and 59° ; (e) 35° and 67° ; (f) 37° and 72° ; (g) 45° and 90°.

The distance off when abeam of the object will be equal to the distance run (over the ground) between the bearings in any one pair.

Caution: These methods (including the special cases described below are accurate only when: (a) there is no tidal effect; (b) no leeway; (c) the bearings are accurate; (d) the course is accurately steered from the instant of the first bearing until the vessel is abeam of the object; and (e) the distance run over the ground between the bearings is accurately known.

In tidal waters and/or when the vessel is making leeway the "angle on the bow" should be substituted by the "angle between the true bearing of the object and the true track", because in these circumstances the heading is likely to be very different to the track. The "abeam" bearing should always be at 90° to the track.

When the track and/or effective speed is uncertain, running fixes should be treated with the utmost caution.

RUNNING FIX TABLE

DISTANCE OFF (at Second Bearing) By TWO BEARINGS AND RUN BETWEEN THEM

EXAMPLE OF USING TABLES. At 0600 steering East (Magnetic) a vessel takes a bearing of a lighthouse 160° (M). Patent Log 56. half an hour later the Patent Log reads 60 and the bearing is found to be 210° (M). Find the distance off at the second bearing. Angle between Course Line and First bearing equals 70°. Angle between First and Second bearing equals 50°. Using Table, with above angles 70° at top and 50° at side, gives 1.2M.

Distance run between bearings (PL 60 – 56) = 4 miles. Therefore, 1.2 × 4 = 4.8 miles.

Vessel's bearing and distance from the lighthouse is therefore 210°, distance 4.8 miles.

Speed must be estimated as accurately as possible if Patent Log is not available.

Angle between Course Line (i.e. Ship's Head) and First Bearing

Angle between 1st and 2nd Bearings	20°	25°	30°	35°	40°	45°	50°	55°	60°	65°	70°	75°	80°	85°	90°	Angle between 1st and 2nd Bearings
10°	2·0	2·4	2·9	3·3	3·7	4·1	4·4	4·7	5·0	5·2	5·4	5·5	5·7	5·7	5·8	160°
15°	1·3	1·6	1·9	2·2	2·5	2·7	3·0	3·2	3·3	3·5	3·7	3·8	4·0	4·0	4·0	155°
20°	1·0	1·2	1·5	1·7	1·9	2·1	2·2	2·4	2·5	2·6	2·8	2·8	2·9	2·9	2·9	150°
25°	0·8	1·0	1·2	1·4	1·6	1·7	1·8	1·9	2·0	2·1	2·2	2·3	2·3	2·4	2·4	145°
30°	0·7	0·9	1·0	1·1	1·3	1·4	1·5	1·6	1·7	1·8	1·9	1·9	2·0	2·0	2·0	140°
35°	0·6	0·8	0·9	1·0	1·1	1·3	1·4	1·5	1·5	1·6	1·7	1·7	1·7	1·7	1·7	135°
40°	0·5	0·7	0·8	0·9	1·0	1·1	1·2	1·3	1·4	1·4	1·5	1·5	1·5	1·6	1·6	130°
45°	0·5	0·6	0·7	0·8	0·9	1·0	1·1	1·2	1·2	1·3	1·3	1·4	1·4	1·3	1·4	125°
50°	0·4	0·6	0·7	0·7	0·8	0·9	1·0	1·1	1·1	1·2	1·2	1·3	1·3	1·2	1·3	120°
55°	0·4	0·5	0·6	0·6	0·7	0·8	0·9	1·0	1·0	1·1	1·1	1·1	1·2	1·2	1·2	115°
60°	0·4	0·5	0·6	0·6	0·7	0·8	0·9	0·9	1·0	1·0	1·1	1·1	1·1	1·1	1·2	110°
65°	0·4	0·5	0·5	0·6	0·7	0·7	0·8	0·9	0·9	0·9	1·0	1·0	1·0	1·1		105°
70°	0·3	0·4	0·5	0·6	0·6	0·7	0·8	0·9	0·9	0·9	1·0	1·0	1·0	1·0		100°
75°	0·3	0·4	0·5	0·6	0·6	0·7	0·8	0·8	0·9	0·9	0·9	1·0				95°
80°	0·3	0·4	0·5	0·5	0·6	0·7	0·8	0·8	0·9	0·9	0·9					90°
85°	0·3	0·4	0·5	0·6	0·6	0·7	0·8	0·8	0·9	0·9						
90°	0·3	0·4	0·5	0·5	0·6	0·7	0·8	0·8	0·8	0·9						
Angle between 1st and 2nd Bearings	160°	155°	150°	145°	140°	135°	130°	125°	120°	115°	110°	105°	100°	95°	90°	

Angle between Course Line (i.e. Ship's Head) and First Bearing

Note: When the angles exceed 90° use the right vertical column for the difference between bearings and the bottom horizontal row for the angle between Course Line and First Bearing. Interpolate for accuracy.

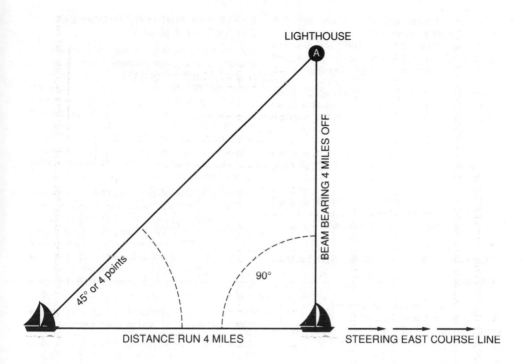

LIGHTHOUSE

A

BEAM BEARING 4 MILES OFF

45° or 4 points

90°

DISTANCE RUN 4 MILES

STEERING EAST COURSE LINE

SPECIAL CASES OF RUNNING FIXES

Although tables will give the distance off for any bearing, it requires pencil, paper, and, of course, the table itself. The following well-known methods of fixing a vessel's position can be used mentally hence their great value in small vessels.

(1) The Four Point Bearing.

(2) Doubling the Angle on the Bow.

The term "4 Points" derives its name from the old sailing ship days. A course in degrees was too difficult to steer to so the compass rose was divided into 30 points and courses were given in points and half points, each point being 11¼°. Hence, 45° = 4 Points.

1. The Four Point Bearing

It is customary in Coastal Navigation (where no special dangers lie near the Course Line) to fix the position when a point of land or a light is abeam, as it is then the Track is usually altered.

Method. Take a bearing of an object when it bears 4 points (i.e., 45°) on the bow (assuming there is no leeway or current, otherwise take

the bearing when it makes an angle of 45° with the track) and note the time and Log. Again take the time and log when it is abeam (i.e., at 90° to the track). Then – the distance made good over the ground in the interval between the two bearings equals the distance off when abeam.

Example. Steering 022° at 8½ knots, a lighthouse bears 067° at 1638 Log 36. At 1704 it came abeam (Log 39½). What was the distance off when abeam? At 8½ knots in 26 mins. vessel goes 3.7 miles (see Time Speed and Distance Tables) check by the Log which shows 3½ miles has been run. Therefore the vessel is 3½ miles off.

2. Doubling the Angle on the Bow

The 4 point bearing method gives the distance off when abeam, but by "doubling the angle on the bow" the vessel's position may be found in advance, and therefore how far off a point the vessel will be when it comes abeam.

Method. Take a bearing of an object when more than 2 points (22½°) on the bow and take the time and Log. Note down this angle and

23

watch the compass bearing carefully until it is exactly doubled then note the log and time again. Then the distance made good over the ground between the bearings is the distance off at the time of taking the second bearing.

Example Steering 231° at 5 knots a lighthouse bears 259°. One hour 13 minutes later it bears 287°. What is the position at the second bearing?

As the first angle on the bow had been doubled, i.e., 28° to 56° the distance run must be the distance off.

In 1hr. 13 min. at 5 knots the vessel steams 6.1 miles therefore the vessel's position is with the lighthouse bearing 287° 6.1 miles off.

POSITION BY VERTICAL SEXTANT ANGLE

If the height of any object is known, its distance off can be measured by a vertical sextant angle and if a bearing of the object is taken at the same time the result is an accurate fix.

When measuring the vertical angle remember that the height is measured to the centre of the light – not to the top of the lighthouse.

In practice no allowance is made for height of tide or observer's eye unless the object is very low, any error will produce a shorter distance off – giving a margin of safety.

TABLE FOR FINDING "DISTANCE OFF" UP TO 7 MILES

The following table gives the "distance off" by inspection of an object whose height is known and of which a sextant angle has been obtained. Where the height of the object is small, the distances cannot be found beyond 6 miles, so for this reason the first page extends only to 6 miles. The columns are for every 3m. (10ft.) up to 122m (400ft.) and every 15m. (50ft.) thence to 213m. (700ft.) The distance column is for every cable up to 3 miles and every 2 cables from 3 to 6 miles.

Example 1. The sextant angle of a lighthouse 40m. above HW was taken and found to be 0° 24'. Required, the distance off. First find the column for 40m. Glance down this column until the "angle off" is sighted, i.e., 24'. Cast the eye along this line to the left when the "Distance off" in miles and cables will be seen – in this case 3 miles exactly. The distance off is therefore 3 miles.

Example 2. The vertical angle of a lighthouse 70m. high was 1° 26' and compass bearing 022°.

Under 70m. the nearest figure given for 1° 26' is 1° 27' which gives 1 mile 5 cables. The position of the vessel is therefore on a bearing of 202° from the lighthouse, 1.5 miles off – a reliable fix if the bearing is reasonably accurate.

If it is desired to keep 1 mile off this lighthouse, the necessary sextant angle to do so can be found from the table, 70m. high, 1 mile off is 2° 10'.

TABLE FOR FINDING DISTANCE OFF WITH SEXTANT UP TO 6 MILES

Distance in Miles & Cables	HEIGHT OF OBJECT, TOP LINE METRES – LOWER LINE FEET												Distance in Miles & Cables
	12 / 40	15 / 50	18 / 60	21 / 70	24 / 80	27 / 90	30 / 100	33 / 110	37 / 120	40 / 130	43 / 140	46 / 150	
m c	° '	° '	° '	° '	° '	° '	° '	° '	° '	° '	° '	° '	m c
0 1	3 46	4 42	5 38	6 34	7 30	8 25	9 20	10 15	11 10	12 04	12 58	13 52	0 1
0 2	1 53	2 21	2 49	3 18	3 46	4 14	4 42	5 10	5 38	6 06	6 34	7 02	0 2
0 3	1 15	1 34	1 53	2 12	2 31	2 49	3 08	3 27	3 46	4 05	4 23	4 42	0 3
0 4	0 57	1 11	1 25	1 39	1 53	2 07	2 21	2 35	2 49	3 04	3 18	3 32	0 4
0 5	0 45	0 57	1 08	1 19	1 30	1 42	1 53	2 04	2 16	2 27	2 38	2 49	0 5
0 6	0 38	0 47	0 57	1 06	1 15	1 25	1 34	1 44	1 53	2 02	2 12	2 21	0 6
0 7	0 32	0 40	0 48	0 57	1 05	1 13	1 21	1 29	1 37	1 45	1 53	2 01	0 7
0 8	0 28	0 35	0 42	0 49	0 57	1 04	1 11	1 18	1 25	1 32	1 39	1 46	0 8
0 9	0 25	0 31	0 38	0 44	0 50	0 57	1 03	1 09	1 15	1 22	1 28	1 34	0 9
1 0	0 23	0 28	0 34	0 40	0 45	0 51	0 57	1 02	1 08	1 14	1 19	1 25	1 0
1 1	0 21	0 26	0 31	0 36	0 41	0 46	0 51	0 57	1 02	1 07	1 12	1 17	1 1
1 2	0 19	0 24	0 28	0 33	0 38	0 42	0 47	0 52	0 57	1 01	1 06	1 11	1 2
1 3	0 17	0 22	0 26	0 30	0 35	0 39	0 44	0 48	0 52	0 57	1 01	1 05	1 3
1 4	0 16	0 20	0 24	0 28	0 32	0 36	0 40	0 44	0 48	0 53	0 57	1 01	1 4
1 5	0 15	0 19	0 23	0 26	0 30	0 34	0 38	0 41	0 45	0 49	0 53	0 57	1 5
1 6	0 14	0 18	0 21	0 25	0 28	0 32	0 35	0 39	0 42	0 46	0 49	0 53	1 6
1 7	0 13	0 17	0 20	0 23	0 27	0 30	0 33	0 37	0 40	0 43	0 47	0 50	1 7
1 8	0 13	0 16	0 19	0 22	0 25	0 28	0 31	0 35	0 38	0 41	0 44	0 47	1 8
1 9	0 12	0 15	0 18	0 21	0 24	0 27	0 30	0 33	0 36	0 39	0 42	0 45	1 9
2 0	0 11	0 14	0 17	0 20	0 23	0 25	0 28	0 31	0 34	0 37	0 40	0 42	2 0
2 1	0 10	0 14	0 16	0 19	0 22	0 24	0 27	0 30	0 32	0 35	0 38	0 40	2 1
2 2	0 10	0 13	0 15	0 18	0 21	0 23	0 26	0 28	0 31	0 33	0 36	0 39	2 2
2 3	0 10	0 12	0 14	0 17	0 20	0 22	0 25	0 27	0 30	0 32	0 34	0 37	2 3
2 4	0 10	0 12	0 14	0 17	0 19	0 21	0 24	0 26	0 28	0 31	0 33	0 35	2 4
2 5	0 9	0 11	0 13	0 16	0 18	0 20	0 23	0 25	0 27	0 29	0 32	0 34	2 5
2 6	0 9	0 11	0 13	0 15	0 17	0 20	0 22	0 24	0 26	0 28	0 30	0 33	2 6
2 7	0 9	0 10	0 12	0 15	0 17	0 19	0 21	0 23	0 25	0 27	0 29	0 31	2 7
2 8	0 8	0 10	0 12	0 14	0 16	0 18	0 20	0 22	0 24	0 26	0 28	0 30	2 8
2 9	0 8	0 10	0 11	0 14	0 16	0 18	0 20	0 21	0 23	0 25	0 27	0 29	2 9
3 0	0 8	0 9	0 10	0 13	0 15	0 17	0 19	0 21	0 23	0 24	0 26	0 28	3 0
3 2				0 12	0 14	0 16	0 18	0 19	0 21	0 23	0 25	0 27	3 2
3 4				0 12	0 13	0 15	0 17	0 18	0 20	0 22	0 23	0 25	3 4
3 6				0 11	0 13	0 14	0 16	0 17	0 19	0 20	0 22	0 24	3 6
3 8				0 10	0 12	0 13	0 15	0 16	0 18	0 19	0 21	0 22	3 8
4 0				0 10	0 11	0 13	0 14	0 16	0 17	0 18	0 20	0 21	4 0
4 2						0 12	0 14	0 15	0 16	0 17	0 19	0 20	4 2
4 4						0 12	0 13	0 14	0 15	0 17	0 18	0 19	4 4
4 6						0 11	0 13	0 14	0 15	0 16	0 17	0 18	4 6
4 8						0 11	0 12	0 13	0 14	0 15	0 16	0 18	4 8
5 0						0 10	0 11	0 12	0 14	0 15	0 16	0 17	5 0
5 2								0 12	0 13	0 14	0 15	0 16	5 2
5 4								0 12	0 13	0 14	0 15	0 16	5 4
5 6								0 11	0 12	0 13	0 14	0 15	5 6
5 8								0 11	0 12	0 13	0 14	0 15	5 8
6 0								0 10	0 11	0 12	0 13	0 14	6 0

Section 13

TABLE FOR FINDING DISTANCE OFF WITH SEXTANT UP TO 7 MILES

Distance in Miles & Cables	HEIGHT OF OBJECT, TOP LINE METRES — LOWER LINE FEET												Distance in Miles & Cables
	49 160	52 170	55 180	58 190	61 200	64 210	67 220	70 230	73 240	76 250	79 260	82 270	
m c	° ′	° ′	° ′	° ′	° ′	° ′	° ′	° ′	° ′	° ′	° ′	° ′	m c
0 1	14 45	15 37	16 29	17 21	18 13	19 03	19 54	20 43	21 32	22 21	23 09	23 57	0 1
0 2	7 30	7 58	8 25	8 53	9 20	9 48	10 15	10 43	11 10	11 37	12 04	12 31	0 2
0 3	5 01	5 19	5 38	5 57	6 15	6 34	6 53	7 11	7 30	7 48	8 07	8 25	0 3
0 4	3 46	4 00	4 14	4 28	4 42	4 56	5 10	5 24	5 38	5 52	6 06	6 20	0 4
0 5	3 01	3 12	3 23	3 35	3 46	3 57	4 08	4 20	4 31	4 42	4 53	5 05	0 5
0 6	2 31	2 40	2 49	2 59	3 08	3 18	3 27	3 36	3 46	3 55	4 05	4 14	0 6
0 7	2 09	2 17	2 25	2 33	2 41	2 49	2 58	3 06	3 14	3 22	3 30	3 38	0 7
0 8	1 53	2 00	2 07	2 14	2 21	2 28	2 35	2 42	2 49	2 57	3 04	3 11	0 8
0 9	1 40	1 47	1 53	1 59	2 06	2 12	2 18	2 24	2 31	2 37	2 43	2 49	0 9
1 0	1 30	1 36	1 42	1 47	1 53	1 59	2 04	2 10	2 16	2 21	2 27	2 33	1 0
1 1	1 22	1 27	1 33	1 38	1 43	1 48	1 53	1 58	2 03	2 08	2 14	2 19	1 1
1 2	1 15	1 20	1 25	1 30	1 34	1 39	1 44	1 48	1 53	1 58	2 02	2 07	1 2
1 3	1 10	1 14	1 18	1 23	1 27	1 31	1 36	1 40	1 44	1 49	1 53	1 57	1 3
1 4	1 05	1 09	1 13	1 17	1 21	1 25	1 29	1 33	1 37	1 41	1 45	1 49	1 4
1 5	1 00	1 04	1 8	1 12	1 15	1 19	1 23	1 27	1 30	1 34	1 38	1 42	1 5
1 6	0 57	1 00	1 04	1 07	1 11	1 14	1 18	1 21	1 25	1 28	1 32	1 35	1 6
1 7	0 53	0 57	1 00	1 03	1 07	1 10	1 13	1 16	1 20	1 23	1 26	1 30	1 7
1 8	0 50	0 53	0 57	1 00	1 03	1 06	1 09	1 12	1 15	1 19	1 22	1 25	1 8
1 9	0 48	0 51	0 54	0 57	1 00	1 02	1 05	1 08	1 11	1 14	1 17	1 20	1 9
2 0	0 45	0 48	0 51	0 54	0 57	0 59	1 02	1 05	1 08	1 11	1 14	1 16	2 0
2 1	0 43	0 46	0 48	0 51	0 54	0 57	0 59	1 02	1 05	1 07	1 10	1 13	2 1
2 2	0 41	0 44	0 46	0 49	0 51	0 54	0 57	0 59	1 02	1 04	1 07	1 09	2 2
2 3	0 39	0 42	0 44	0 47	0 49	0 52	0 54	0 57	0 59	1 01	1 04	1 06	2 3
2 4	0 38	0 40	0 42	0 45	0 47	0 49	0 52	0 54	0 57	0 59	1 01	1 04	2 4
2 5	0 36	0 38	0 41	0 43	0 45	0 48	0 50	0 52	0 54	0 57	0 59	1 01	2 5
2 6	0 35	0 37	0 39	0 41	0 44	0 46	0 48	0 50	0 52	0 54	0 57	0 59	2 6
2 7	0 34	0 36	0 38	0 40	0 42	0 44	0 46	0 48	0 50	0 52	0 54	0 57	2 7
2 8	0 32	0 34	0 36	0 38	0 40	0 42	0 44	0 46	0 48	0 50	0 53	0 55	2 8
2 9	0 31	0 33	0 35	0 37	0 39	0 41	0 43	0 45	0 47	0 49	0 51	0 53	2 9
3 0	0 30	0 32	0 34	0 36	0 38	0 40	0 41	0 43	0 45	0 47	0 49	0 51	3 0
3 2	0 28	0 30	0 32	0 34	0 35	0 37	0 39	0 41	0 42	0 44	0 46	0 48	3 2
3 4	0 27	0 28	0 30	0 32	0 33	0 35	0 37	0 38	0 40	0 42	0 43	0 45	3 4
3 6	0 25	0 27	0 28	0 30	0 31	0 33	0 35	0 36	0 38	0 39	0 41	0 42	3 6
3 8	0 24	0 25	0 27	0 28	0 30	0 31	0 33	0 34	0 36	0 37	0 39	0 40	3 8
4 0	0 23	0 24	0 25	0 27	0 28	0 30	0 31	0 33	0 34	0 35	0 37	0 38	4 0
4 2	0 22	0 23	0 24	0 26	0 27	0 28	0 30	0 31	0 32	0 34	0 35	0 36	4 2
4 4	0 21	0 22	0 23	0 24	0 26	0 27	0 28	0 30	0 31	0 32	0 33	0 35	4 4
4 6	0 20	0 21	0 22	0 23	0 25	0 26	0 27	0 28	0 30	0 31	0 32	0 33	4 6
4 8	0 19	0 20	0 21	0 22	0 24	0 25	0 26	0 27	0 28	0 30	0 31	0 32	4 8
5 0	0 18	0 19	0 20	0 21	0 23	0 24	0 25	0 26	0 27	0 28	0 29	0 31	5 0
5 2	0 17	0 18	0 20	0 21	0 22	0 23	0 24	0 25	0 26	0 27	0 28	0 29	5 2
5 4	0 17	0 18	0 19	0 20	0 21	0 22	0 23	0 24	0 25	0 26	0 27	0 28	5 4
5 6	0 16	0 17	0 18	0 19	0 20	0 21	0 22	0 23	0 24	0 25	0 26	0 27	5 6
5 8	0 16	0 17	0 18	0 19	0 19	0 20	0 21	0 22	0 23	0 24	0 25	0 26	5 8
6 0	0 15	0 16	0 17	0 18	0 19	0 20	0 21	0 22	0 23	0 24	0 25	0 25	6 0
6 2					0 18	0 19	0 20	0 21	0 22	0 23	0 24	0 25	6 2
6 4					0 18	0 19	0 20	0 21	0 21	0 22	0 23	0 24	6 4
6 6					0 17	0 18	0 19	0 20	0 21	0 21	0 22	0 23	6 6
6 8					0 17	0 18	0 18	0 19	0 20	0 21	0 22	0 22	6 8
7 0					0 16	0 17	0 18	0 19	0 19	0 20	0 21	0 22	7 0

TABLE FOR FINDING DISTANCE OFF WITH SEXTANT UP TO 7 MILES

Distance in Miles & Cables	HEIGHT OF OBJECT, TOP LINE METRES—LOWER LINE FEET												Distance in Miles & Cables
m c	85 280	88 290	91 300	94 310	97 320	101 330	104 340	107 350	110 360	113 370	116 380	119 390	m c
0 1	24 44	25 30	26 16	26 01	27 46	28 29	29 13	29 56	30 38	31 19	32 00	32 41	0 1
0 2	12 58	13 25	13 52	14 08	14 45	15 11	15 37	16 03	16 29	16 55	17 21	17 47	0 2
0 3	8 44	9 02	9 20	9 39	9 57	10 15	10 34	10 52	11 10	11 28	11 46	12 04	0 3
0 4	6 34	6 48	7 02	7 16	7 30	7 44	7 58	8 11	8 25	8 39	8 53	9 07	0 4
0 5	5 16	5 27	5 38	5 49	6 01	6 12	6 23	6 34	6 45	6 56	7 08	7 19	0 5
0 6	4 23	4 33	4 42	4 51	5 01	5 10	5 19	5 29	5 38	5 47	5 47	6 06	0 6
0 7	3 46	3 54	4 02	5 10	4 18	4 26	4 43	4 42	4 50	4 58	5 06	5 14	0 7
0 8	3 18	3 25	3 32	3 39	3 46	3 53	4 00	4 07	4 14	4 21	4 28	4 35	0 8
0 9	2 56	3 02	3 08	3 15	3 21	3 27	3 33	3 40	3 46	3 52	3 58	4 05	0 9
1 0	2 38	2 44	2 49	2 55	3 01	3 06	3 12	3 18	3 23	3 29	3 35	3 40	1 0
1 1	2 24	2 29	2 34	2 39	2 44	2 49	2 55	3 00	3 05	3 10	3 15	3 20	1 1
1 2	2 12	2 17	2 21	2 26	2 31	2 35	2 40	2 45	2 49	2 54	2 59	3 04	1 2
1 3	2 02	2 06	2 10	2 15	2 19	2 23	2 28	2 32	2 36	2 41	2 45	2 49	1 3
1 4	1 53	1 57	2 01	2 05	2 09	2 13	2 17	2 21	2 25	2 29	2 37	2 37	1 4
1 5	1 46	1 49	1 53	1 57	2 01	2 04	2 08	2 12	2 16	2 19	2 23	2 27	1 5
1 6	1 39	1 42	1 46	1 50	1 53	1 57	2 00	2 04	2 07	2 11	2 14	2 18	1 6
1 7	1 33	1 36	1 40	1 43	1 46	1 50	1 53	1 56	2 00	2 03	2 06	2 10	1 7
1 8	1 28	1 31	1 34	1 37	1 40	1 44	1 47	1 50	1 53	1 56	1 59	2 02	1 8
1 9	1 23	1 26	1 29	1 32	1 35	1 38	1 41	1 44	1 47	1 50	1 53	1 56	1 9
2 0	1 19	1 22	1 25	1 28	1 30	1 33	1 36	1 39	1 42	1 45	1 47	1 50	2 0
2 1	1 15	1 18	1 21	1 23	1 26	1 29	1 32	1 34	1 37	1 40	1 42	1 45	2 1
2 2	1 12	1 15	1 17	1 20	1 22	1 25	1 27	1 30	1 33	1 35	1 38	1 40	2 2
2 3	1 09	1 11	1 14	1 16	1 19	1 21	1 24	1 26	1 29	1 31	1 33	1 36	2 3
2 4	1 06	1 08	1 11	1 13	1 15	1 18	1 20	1 22	1 25	1 27	1 30	1 32	2 4
2 5	1 03	1 06	1 08	1 10	1 12	1 15	1 17	1 19	1 21	1 24	1 26	1 28	2 5
2 6	1 01	1 03	1 05	1 07	1 10	1 12	1 14	1 16	1 18	1 20	1 23	1 25	2 6
2 7	0 59	1 01	1 03	1 05	1 07	1 09	1 11	1 13	1 15	1 17	1 20	1 23	2 7
2 8	0 57	0 59	1 01	1 03	1 05	1 07	1 09	1 11	1 13	1 15	1 17	1 19	2 8
2 9	0 55	0 57	0 58	1 00	1 02	1 04	1 06	1 08	1 10	1 12	1 14	1 16	2 9
3 0	0 53	0 55	0 57	0 58	1 00	1 02	1 04	1 06	1 08	1 10	1 12	1 14	3 0
3 2	0 49	0 51	0 53	0 55	0 57	0 58	1 00	1 02	1 04	1 05	1 07	1 09	3 2
3 4	0 47	0 48	0 50	0 52	0 53	0 55	0 57	0 58	1 00	1 02	1 03	1 05	3 4
3 6	0 44	0 46	0 47	0 49	0 50	0 52	0 53	0 55	0 57	0 58	1 00	1 01	3 6
3 8	0 42	0 43	0 45	0 46	0 48	0 49	0 51	0 52	0 54	0 55	0 57	0 58	3 8
4 0	0 40	0 41	0 42	0 44	0 45	0 47	0 48	0 49	0 51	0 52	0 54	0 55	4 0
4 2	0 38	0 39	0 40	0 42	0 43	0 44	0 46	0 47	0 48	0 50	0 51	0 53	4 2
4 4	0 36	0 37	0 39	0 40	0 41	0 42	0 44	0 45	0 46	0 48	0 49	0 50	4 4
4 6	0 34	0 36	0 37	0 38	0 39	0 41	0 42	0 43	0 44	0 45	0 47	0 48	4 6
4 8	0 33	0 34	0 35	0 37	0 38	0 39	0 40	0 41	0 42	0 44	0 45	0 46	4 8
5 0	0 32	0 33	0 34	0 35	0 36	0 37	0 38	0 40	0 41	0 42	0 43	0 44	5 0
5 2	0 30	0 32	0 33	0 34	0 35	0 36	0 37	0 38	0 39	0 40	0 41	0 42	5 2
5 4	0 29	0 30	0 31	0 32	0 34	0 34	0 36	0 37	0 38	0 39	0 40	0 41	5 4
5 6	0 28	0 29	0 30	0 31	0 32	0 33	0 34	0 35	0 36	0 37	0 38	0 39	5 6
5 8	0 27	0 28	0 29	0 30	0 31	0 32	0 33	0 34	0 35	0 36	0 37	0 38	5 8
6 0	0 26	0 27	0 28	0 29	0 30	0 31	0 32	0 33	0 34	0 35	0 36	0 37	6 0
6 2	0 26	0 26	0 27	0 28	0 29	0 30	0 31	0 32	0 33	0 34	0 35	3 06	6 2
6 4	0 25	0 26	0 27	0 27	0 28	0 29	0 30	0 31	0 32	0 33	0 34	0 34	6 4
6 6	0 24	0 25	0 26	0 27	0 27	0 28	0 29	0 30	0 31	0 32	0 33	0 33	6 6
6 8	0 23	0 24	0 25	0 26	0 27	0 27	0 28	0 29	0 30	0 31	0 32	0 32	6 8
7 0	0 23	0 23	0 24	0 25	0 26	0 27	0 37	0 38	0 29	0 30	0 31	0 31	7 0

Section 13

TABLE FOR FINDING DISTANCE OFF WITH SEXTANT UP TO 7 MILES

Distance in Miles & Cables	122 / 400	137 / 450	152 / 500	168 / 550	183 / 600	198 / 650	213 / 700	244 / 800	274 / 900	305 / 1000	457 / 1500	610 / 2000	Distance in Miles & Cables
m c	° ′	° ′	° ′	° ′	° ′	° ′	° ′	° ′	° ′	° ′	° ′	° ′	m c
0 1	33 20	36 30	39 26	42 08	44 37								0 1
0 2	18 13	20 18	22 21	24 20	26 16	28 08	29 56	33 20	36 30	39 26			0 2
0 3	12 22	13 52	15 20	16 47	18 13	19 37	21 00	23 41	26 16	28 44			0 3
0 4	9 20	10 29	11 37	12 45	13 52	14 58	16 03	18 13	20 18	22 21			0 4
0 5	7 30	8 25	9 20	10 15	11 10	12 04	12 58	14 45	16 30	18 13	26 15		0 5
0 6	6 15	7 02	7 48	8 34	9 20	10 06	10 52	12 22	13 52	15 20	22 20	28 44	0 6
0 7	5 22	6 02	6 42	7 22	8 01	8 41	9 20	10 39	11 56	13 13	19 25	25 10	0 7
0 8	4 42	5 17	5 52	6 27	7 02	7 37	8 11	9 20	10 29	11 37	17 08	22 21	0 8
0 9	4 11	4 42	5 13	5 44	6 15	6 46	7 17	8 19	9 20	10 21	15 19	20 05	0 9
1 0	3 46	4 14	4 42	5 10	5 38	6 06	6 34	7 30	8 25	9 20	13 51	18 13	1 0
1 1	3 25	3 51	4 17	4 42	5 08	5 33	5 59	6 49	7 40	8 30	12 38	16 39	1 1
1 2	3 08	3 32	3 55	4 19	4 42	5 05	5 29	6 15	7 02	7 48	11 37	15 20	1 2
1 3	2 54	3 16	3 37	3 59	4 20	4 42	5 04	5 47	6 30	7 13	10 45	14 12	1 3
1 4	2 41	3 02	3 22	3 42	4 02	4 22	4 42	5 22	6 02	6 42	10 00	13 13	1 4
1 5	2 31	2 49	3 08	3 27	3 46	4 05	4 23	5 01	5 38	6 15	9 20	12 22	1 5
1 6	2 21	2 39	2 57	3 14	3 32	3 49	4 07	4 42	5 17	5 52	8 46	11 37	1 6
1 7	2 13	2 30	2 46	3 03	3 19	3 36	3 52	4 26	4 59	5 32	8 15	10 57	1 7
1 8	2 06	2 21	2 37	2 53	3 08	3 24	3 40	4 11	4 42	5 13	7 48	10 21	1 8
1 9	1 59	2 14	2 29	2 44	2 58	3 13	3 28	3 58	4 27	4 57	7 25	9 50	1 9
2 0	1 53	2 07	2 21	2 35	2 49	3 04	3 18	3 46	4 14	4 42	7 02	9 20	2 0
2 1	1 48	2 01	2 15	2 28	2 41	2 55	3 08	3 35	4 02	4 29	6 41	8 53	2 1
2 2	1 43	1 56	2 08	2 21	2 34	2 47	3 00	3 25	3 51	4 17	6 23	8 30	2 2
2 3	1 38	1 51	2 03	2 15	2 27	2 40	2 52	3 16	3 41	4 05	6 07	8 09	2 3
2 4	1 34	1 46	1 58	2 10	2 21	2 33	2 45	3 08	3 32	3 55	5 52	7 48	2 4
2 5	1 30	1 42	1 53	2 04	2 16	2 27	2 38	3 01	3 23	3 46	5 38	7 30	2 5
2 6	1 27	1 38	1 49	2 00	2 10	2 21	2 32	2 54	3 16	3 37	5 25	7 13	2 6
2 7	1 24	1 34	1 45	1 55	2 06	2 16	2 27	2 47	3 08	3 29	5 13	6 57	2 7
2 8	1 21	1 31	1 41	1 51	2 01	2 11	2 21	2 41	3 02	3 22	5 02	6 42	2 8
2 9	1 18	1 28	1 37	1 47	1 57	2 07	2 16	2 36	2 55	3 15	4 52	6 28	2 9
3 0	1 15	1 25	1 34	1 44	1 53	2 02	2 12	2 31	2 49	3 08	4 42	6 15	3 0
3 2	1 11	1 20	1 28	1 37	1 46	1 55	2 04	2 21	2 39	2 57	4 24	5 52	3 2
3 4	1 07	1 15	1 23	1 31	1 40	1 48	1 56	2 13	2 30	2 46	4 09	5 32	3 4
3 6	1 03	1 11	1 19	1 26	1 34	1 42	1 50	2 06	2 21	2 37	3 55	5 13	3 6
3 8	1 00	1 07	1 14	1 22	1 29	1 37	1 44	1 59	2 14	2 29	3 43	4 57	3 8
4 0	0 57	1 04	1 11	1 18	1 25	1 32	1 39	1 53	2 07	2 21	3 31	4 42	4 0
4 2	0 54	1 01	1 07	1 14	1 21	1 28	1 34	1 48	2 01	2 15	3 21	4 29	4 2
4 4	0 51	0 58	1 04	1 11	1 17	1 24	1 30	1 43	1 56	2 08	3 12	4 17	4 4
4 6	0 49	0 55	1 01	1 08	1 14	1 20	1 26	1 38	1 51	2 03	3 04	4 05	4 6
4 8	0 47	0 53	0 59	1 05	1 11	1 17	1 22	1 34	1 46	1 58	2 57	3 55	4 8
5 0	0 45	0 51	0 57	1 02	1 08	1 14	1 19	1 30	1 42	1 53	2 50	3 46	5 0
5 2	0 43	0 49	0 54	1 00	1 05	1 11	1 16	1 27	1 38	1 49	2 44	3 38	5 2
5 4	0 42	0 47	0 52	0 58	1 03	1 08	1 13	1 24	1 34	1 45	2 28	3 30	5 4
5 6	0 40	0 45	0 50	0 56	1 01	1 06	1 11	1 21	1 31	1 41	2 32	3 22	5 6
5 8	0 39	0 44	0 49	0 54	0 58	1 03	1 08	1 18	1 28	1 37	2 26	3 15	5 8
6 0	0 38	0 42	0 47	0 52	0 57	1 01	1 06	1 15	1 25	1 34	2 21	3 09	6 0
6 2	0 36	0 41	0 46	0 50	0 55	0 59	1 04	1 13	1 22	1 31	2 16	3 02	6 2
6 4	0 35	0 40	0 44	0 49	0 53	0 57	1 02	1 11	1 20	1 28	2 12	2 57	6 4
6 6	0 34	0 38	0 43	0 47	0 51	0 56	1 00	1 09	1 17	1 26	2 08	2 51	6 6
6 8	0 33	0 37	0 42	0 46	0 50	0 54	0 58	1 07	1 15	1 23	2 04	2 46	6 8
7 0	0 32	0 36	0 40	0 44	0 48	0 53	0 57	1 05	1 13	1 21	2 01	2 42	7 0

HEIGHT OF OBJECT, TOP LINE METRES – LOWER LINE FEET

HORIZONTAL SEXTANT ANGLE FIX

An accurate fix can be obtained by measuring the angles between three objects marked on the chart and using the tables overleaf to fix the vessel's position. The best results are obtained when the objects are roughly in a straight line and the angles separating them are at least 30°.

Explanation and examples of how to use the Tables.

The diagram illustrates a vessel (S) whose navigator, when coasting, has taken simultaneous (or nearly so) horizontal sextant angles. The first angle taken was between the centre object a Church (✝) and the right hand object – a high Rock (R); and the second angle was taken immediately between the same centre object, a Church (✝) and the left hand object, a Lighthouse (L), all marked conspicuously on the chart and clearly visible to the navigator.

Angle between Rock (R) and Church (C) (right hand angle) = 30°. Distance between R and C =

3.2 miles. Angle between Lighthouse (L) and Church (C) (left hand angle) = 45°, and Distance between L and C = 7.1 miles.

Instructions

With the angle RSC (30°), subtended by the right hand and centre objects enter the table on page 30 from the side and find the Radius of one of the Position Circles in the column headed by the Distance between the objects. In this case with 30° at the side and 3.2 miles at the top the Radius (by simple interpolation) is 3.2. Therefore with 3.2 miles in the compasses as Radius strike short arcs from both R and C and mark P – their point of intersection. With the same radius describe round P the circle RCS.

Proceeding in a similar way, describe arcs LQ and CQ and draw circle LCS.

The intersection of the two circles (S in the figure) gives the desired Fix and the Ship's position.

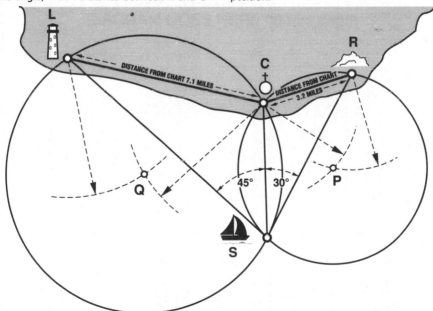

Note: The distances, tabulated at the top of the table are for full miles. For tenfolds and decimals of full miles use ten times or tenths respectively, of the tabulated radii and add, thus:
Subtended Angle 50°

Distance between objects 23.7 miles.

For 20 miles (ten times two) 10 x 1.31	13.1 miles
For 3 miles (from table)	1.96 miles
For 0.7 miles (column 7 divided by 10)	0.46 miles
Radius	15.5 miles

In general no interpolation between the tabulated angles will be necessary and in any case most Navigators would prefer to interpolate at sight.

HORIZONTAL SEXTANT ANGLE FIX

Angle Subtended by Objects °	'	1	2	3	4	5	6	7	8	9	Angle Subtended by Objects °	'
30		1.00	2.00	3.00	4.00	5.00	6.00	7.00	8.00	9.00	150	
	10	1.00	1.99	2.99	3.98	4.98	5.97	6.97	7.96	8.96		50
	20	0.99	1.98	2.97	3.96	4.95	5.94	6.93	7.92	8.91		40
	30	0.99	1.97	2.96	3.94	4.93	5.91	6.90	7.88	8.87		30
	40	0.98	1.96	2.94	3.92	4.90	5.88	6.86	7.84	8.83		20
	50	0.98	1.95	2.93	3.90	4.88	5.85	6.83	7.80	8.78		10
31		0.97	1.94	2.91	3.88	4.86	5.83	6.80	7.77	8.74	149	
	10	0.97	1.93	2.90	3.86	4.83	5.80	6.76	7.73	8.70		
	20	0.96	1.92	2.89	3.85	4.81	5.77	6.73	7.70	8.65		50
	30	0.96	1.91	2.87	3.83	4.79	5.74	6.70	7.66	8.61		40
	40	0.95	1.91	2.86	3.81	4.76	5.72	6.67	7.62	8.57		30
	50	0.95	1.90	2.84	3.79	4.74	5.69	6.64	7.58	8.53		20
												10
32		0.94	1.89	2.83	3.77	4.72	5.66	6.61	7.55	8.49	148	
	10	0.94	1.88	2.82	3.76	4.70	5.63	6.57	7.51	8.45		50
	20	0.94	1.87	2.81	3.74	4.68	5.61	6.55	7.48	8.42		40
	30	0.93	1.86	2.79	3.72	4.65	5.58	6.51	7.44	8.38		30
	40	0.93	1.85	2.78	3.71	4.63	5.56	6.49	7.41	8.34		20
	50	0.92	1.84	2.77	3.69	4.61	5.53	6.45	7.38	8.30		10
33		0.92	1.84	2.75	3.67	4.59	5.51	6.43	7.34	8.26	147	
	10	0.92	1.83	2.75	3.66	4.58	5.49	6.41	7.32	8.24		50
	20	0.91	1.82	2.73	3.64	4.55	5.46	6.37	7.28	8.19		40
	30	0.91	1.81	2.72	3.62	4.53	5.44	6.34	7.25	8.15		30
	40	0.90	1.80	2.71	3.61	4.51	5.41	6.31	7.22	8.12		20
	50	0.90	1.80	2.69	3.59	4.49	5.39	6.29	7.18	8.08		10
34		0.89	1.79	2.68	3.58	4.47	5.36	6.26	7.15	8.05	146	
	10	0.89	1.78	2.67	3.56	4.45	5.34	6.23	7.12	8.02		50
	20	0.89	1.77	2.66	3.55	4.43	5.32	6.21	7.09	7.98		40
	30	0.88	1.77	2.65	3.53	4.42	5.30	6.18	7.06	7.95		30
	40	0.88	1.76	2.64	3.52	4.40	5.27	6.15	7.03	7.91		20
	50	0.88	1.75	2.63	3.50	4.38	5.25	6.13	7.00	7.88		10
35		0.87	1.74	2.62	3.49	4.36	5.23	6.10	6.97	7.84	145	
	12	0.87	1.74	2.60	3.47	4.34	5.21	6.07	6.94	7.81		48
	24	0.86	1.73	2.59	3.45	4.32	5.18	6.04	6.90	7.77		36
	36	0.86	1.72	2.58	3.44	4.30	5.15	6.01	6.87	7.73		24
	48	0.86	1.71	2.57	3.42	4.28	5.13	5.99	6.84	7.70		12
36		0.85	1.70	2.55	3.40	4.25	5.10	5.95	6.80	7.66	144	
	12	0.85	1.69	2.54	3.39	4.23	5.08	5.93	6.77	7.62		48
	24	0.84	1.69	2.53	3.37	4.21	5.06	5.90	6.74	7.58		36
	36	0.84	1.68	2.52	3.35	4.19	5.03	5.87	6.71	7.55		24
	48	0.83	1.67	2.50	3.34	4.17	5.01	5.84	6.68	7.51		12
37		0.83	1.66	2.49	3.32	4.16	4.99	5.82	6.65	7.48	143	
	12	0.83	1.65	2.48	3.31	4.14	4.96	5.79	6.62	7.44		48
	24	0.82	1.65	2.47	3.29	4.12	4.94	5.76	6.58	7.41		36
	36	0.82	1.64	2.46	3.28	4.10	4.92	5.74	6.56	7.38		24
	48	0.82	1.63	2.45	3.26	4.08	4.90	5.71	6.53	7.34		12
38		0.81	1.62	2.44	3.25	4.06	4.87	5.68	6.50	7.31	142	
	12	0.81	1.62	2.43	3.23	4.04	4.85	5.66	6.47	7.28		48
	24	0.81	1.61	2.42	3.22	4.03	4.83	5.64	6.44	7.25		36
	36	0.80	1.60	2.41	3.21	4.01	4.81	5.61	6.41	7.21		24
	48	0.80	1.60	2.39	3.19	3.99	4.79	5.59	6.38	7.18		12
39		0.79	1.59	2.38	3.18	3.97	4.77	5.56	6.36	7.15	141	
	12	0.79	1.58	2.37	3.16	3.96	4.75	5.54	6.33	7.12		48
	24	0.79	1.58	2.36	3.15	3.94	4.73	5.52	6.30	7.09		36
	36	0.79	1.57	2.35	3.14	3.92	4.71	5.49	6.28	7.06		24
	48	0.78	1.56	2.34	3.12	3.91	4.69	5.47	6.25	7.03		12
40		0.78	1.56	2.33	3.11	3.89	4.67	5.45	6.22	7.00	140	
	20	0.77	1.55	2.32	3.09	3.86	4.64	5.41	6.18	6.95		40
	40	0.77	1.54	2.30	3.07	3.84	4.61	5.37	6.14	6.91		20
41		0.76	1.52	2.29	3.05	3.81	4.57	5.33	6.10	6.86	139	
	20	0.76	1.51	2.27	3.03	3.79	4.54	5.30	6.06	6.81		40
	40	0.75	1.50	2.26	3.01	3.76	4.51	5.26	6.02	6.77		20
42		0.75	1.50	2.24	2.99	3.74	4.49	5.23	5.98	6.73	138	
	20	0.74	1.49	2.23	2.97	3.71	4.46	5.20	5.94	6.68		40
	40	0.74	1.48	2.21	2.95	3.69	4.43	5.17	5.90	6.64		20
43		0.73	1.47	2.20	2.93	3.67	4.40	5.13	5.86	6.60	137	

HORIZONTAL SEXTANT ANGLE FIX

Angle Subtended by Objects °	'	1	2	3	4	5	6	7	8	9	Angle Subtended by Objects °	'
43		0.73	1.47	2.20	2.93	3.67	4.40	5.13	5.86	6.60	137	
	20	0.73	1.46	2.19	2.91	3.64	4.37	5.10	5.83	6.56		40
	40	0.72	1.45	2.17	2.90	3.62	4.34	5.07	5.79	6.52		20
44		0.72	1.44	2.16	2.88	3.60	4.32	5.04	5.76	6.48	136	
	20	0.72	1.43	2.15	2.86	3.58	4.29	5.01	5.72	6.44		40
	40	0.71	1.42	2.14	2.85	3.56	4.27	4.98	5.69	6.40		20
45		0.71	1.41	2.12	2.83	3.54	4.24	4.95	5.66	6.36	135	
	20	0.70	1.41	2.11	2.81	3.52	4.22	4.92	5.62	6.33		40
	40	0.70	1.40	2.10	2.80	3.50	4.19	4.89	5.59	6.29		20
46		0.70	1.39	2.09	2.78	3.48	4.17	4.87	5.56	6.26	134	
	20	0.69	1.38	2.07	2.76	3.46	4.15	4.84	5.53	6.22		40
	40	0.69	1.38	2.06	2.75	3.44	4.13	4.81	5.50	6.19		20
47		0.68	1.37	2.05	2.73	3.42	4.10	4.79	5.47	6.15	133	
	20	0.68	1.36	2.04	2.72	3.40	4.08	4.76	5.44	6.12		40
	40	0.68	1.35	2.03	2.71	3.38	4.06	4.74	5.41	6.09		20
48		0.67	1.35	2.02	2.69	3.37	4.04	4.71	5.38	6.06	132	
	20	0.67	1.34	2.01	2.68	3.35	4.02	4.69	5.36	6.03		40
	40	0.67	1.33	2.00	2.66	3.33	4.00	4.66	5.33	5.99		20
49		0.66	1.33	2.00	2.65	3.31	3.98	4.64	5.30	5.96	131	
	20	0.66	1.32	1.98	2.64	3.30	3.95	4.61	5.27	5.93		40
	40	0.66	1.31	1.97	2.62	3.28	3.94	4.59	5.25	5.90		20
50		0.65	1.31	1.96	2.61	3.26	3.92	4.57	5.22	5.87	130	
	30	0.65	1.30	1.94	2.59	3.24	3.89	4.54	5.18	5.83		30
51		0.64	1.29	1.93	2.57	3.22	3.86	4.51	5.15	5.79	129	
	30	0.64	1.28	1.92	2.56	3.20	3.83	4.47	5.11	5.75		30
52		0.63	1.27	1.90	2.54	3.17	3.81	4.44	5.08	5.71	128	
	30	0.63	1.26	1.89	2.52	3.15	3.78	4.41	5.04	5.68		30
53		0.63	1.25	1.88	2.50	3.13	3.76	4.38	5.01	5.63	127	
	30	0.62	1.24	1.87	2.49	3.11	3.73	4.35	4.98	5.60		30
54		0.62	1.24	1.85	2.47	3.09	3.71	4.33	4.94	5.56	126	
	30	0.61	1.23	1.84	2.46	3.07	3.68	4.30	4.91	5.53		30
55		0.61	1.22	1.83	2.44	3.05	3.66	4.27	4.88	5.50	125	
	30	0.61	1.21	1.82	2.43	3.03	3.64	4.25	4.85	5.46		30
56		0.60	1.21	1.81	2.41	3.02	3.62	4.22	4.82	5.43	124	
	30	0.60	1.20	1.80	2.40	3.00	3.60	4.20	4.80	5.40		30
57		0.60	1.19	1.79	2.38	2.98	3.58	4.17	4.77	5.36	123	
	30	0.59	1.19	1.78	2.37	2.97	3.56	4.15	4.74	5.34		30
58		0.59	1.18	1.77	2.36	2.95	3.54	4.13	4.72	5.31	122	
	30	0.59	1.17	1.76	2.35	2.93	3.52	4.11	4.69	5.28		30
59		0.58	1.17	1.75	2.33	2.92	3.50	4.09	4.67	5.25	121	
	30	0.58	1.16	1.74	3.32	2.90	3.48	4.06	4.64	5.23		30
60		0.58	1.16	1.73	2.31	2.89	3.47	4.04	4.62	5.20	120	
61		0.57	1.14	1.72	2.29	2.86	3.43	4.00	4.57	5.14	119	
62		0.57	1.13	1.70	2.27	2.83	3.40	3.97	4.53	5.10	118	
63		0.56	1.12	1.68	2.24	2.81	3.37	3.93	4.49	5.05	117	
64		0.56	1.11	1.67	2.23	2.78	3.34	3.90	4.45	5.01	116	
65		0.55	1.10	1.66	2.21	2.76	3.31	3.86	4.41	4.96	115	
66		0.55	1.10	1.64	2.19	2.74	3.29	3.83	4.38	4.93	114	
67		0.54	1.09	1.63	2.17	2.72	3.26	3.80	4.34	4.89	113	
68		0.54	1.08	1.62	2.16	2.70	3.24	3.78	4.32	4.86	112	
69		0.54	1.07	1.61	2.14	2.68	3.21	3.75	4.28	4.82	111	
70		0.53	1.06	1.60	2.13	2.66	3.19	3.72	4.26	4.79	110	
71		0.53	1.06	1.59	2.12	2.65	3.17	3.70	4.23	4.76	109	
72		0.53	1.05	1.58	2.10	2.63	3.16	3.68	4.21	4.73	108	
73		0.52	1.05	1.57	2.09	2.62	3.14	3.66	4.18	4.71	107	
74		0.52	1.04	1.56	2.08	2.60	3.12	3.64	4.16	4.68	106	
76		0.52	1.03	1.55	2.06	2.58	3.09	3.61	4.12	4.64	104	
78		0.51	1.02	1.53	2.04	2.56	3.07	3.58	4.09	4.60	102	
80		0.51	1.02	1.52	2.03	2.54	3.05	3.55	4.06	4.57	100	
82		0.51	1.01	1.52	2.02	2.53	3.03	3.54	4.04	4.55	98	
84		0.50	1.01	1.51	2.01	2.52	3.02	3.52	4.02	4.53	96	
86		0.50	1.00	1.50	2.00	2.51	3.01	3.51	4.01	4.51	94	
90		0.50	1.00	1.50	2.00	2.50	3.00	3.50	4.00	4.50	90	

FINDING THE DISTANCE OF OBJECTS AT SEA

Owing to the Earth's curvature, the distance to the sea horizon is governed by the height of the observer's eye. The figure below illustrates this and also that, in conditions of clear visibility, the distance at which the top of an object first shows itself on the horizon depends upon its height as well as the height of eye.

In this example the distance of the horizon from the observer using the tables overleaf is 3.25 miles and the distance of the light from the horizon is 13.1 miles. The light will appear to the observer when it is 16.35 miles distant.

Range of lights

Luminous range is the maximum distance at which a light can be seen as determined by the intensity of the light and the meteorological visibility prevailing at the time; it takes no account of elevation, observer's height of eye or the curvature of the earth.

Nominal range is the luminous range when the meteorological visibility is 10 sea miles.

Geographical range is the maximum distance at which light from a light can theoretically reach an observer, as limited only by the curvature of the earth and the refraction of the atmosphere, and by the elevation of the light and the height of the observer. Geographical ranges are based on a height of eye of 15 ft (5 metres).

The range shown on modern charts for northern European waters is the nominal range.

All heights of lights are given above High Water. Allowance for the state of the tides should be made with lights of small elevation.

Tables I and II allow for the effect of normal atmospheric refraction but would be of no use when conditions are abnormal.

Glare from background lighting will reduce considerably the range at which lights are

sighted. A light of 100 000 candelas has a nominal range of about 20 miles; with minor background lighting as from a populated coastline this range will be reduced to about 14 miles, and with major background lighting as from a city or from harbour installations to about 9 miles.

Yachtsmen with a near horizon and utilising the powerful lights around the European coastline will probably be more concerned with the Geographical range of lights.

From the yachtsman's point of view it is useful to know when a charted light will become visible. For example a light with a charted range of 20 miles is 46 m high and the observer's eye is 2.1 m above sea level.

From Table 1 the light to horizon distance is 14.1 miles and observer to horizon is 3.04 miles, the light will therefore become visible when it is 17 miles distant.

To check whether or not a newly sighted light is actually on the horizon, if practicable, lower the eye immediately to find out if the light dips below the horizon again. In clear visibility and a heavy swell the light should alternately rise above and dip below the horizon with the ship's movement. The distance off from the light at this moment is often referred to as the "dipping range" or "dipping distance".

Table II will be found very useful for finding the dipping range of a light immediately by inspection.

Fix by dipping range and bearing: The light "X" has just appeared on the horizon in clear visibility and bearing 068°. If the height of eye is 3 m what is the ship's position?

The Visual Aids to Navigation Section gives the height of Light "X" as 40 m and the charted visibility as 17 miles. With height of eye 3 m at the top and 40 m at the side, Table II gives 16¾ miles.

The ship's position is, therefore, 18¾ miles 248° from Light "X".

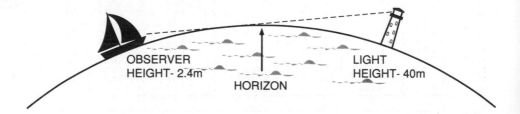

OBSERVER HEIGHT- 2.4m
LIGHT HEIGHT- 40m
HORIZON

TABLE I DISTANCE OF SEA HORIZON IN NAUTICAL MILES

Height in Metres	Height in Feet	Distance in Miles	Height in Metres	Height in Feet	Distance in Miles	Height in Metres	Height in Feet	Distance in Miles	Height in Metres	Height in Feet	Distance in Miles
0.3	1	1.15	4.3	14	4.30	12.2	40	7.27	55	180	15.4
0.6	2	1.62	4.9	16	4.60	12.8	42	7.44	61	200	16.2
0.9	3	1.99	5.5	18	4.87	13.4	44	7.62	73	240	17.8
1.2	4	2.30	6.1	20	5.14	14.0	46	7.79	85	280	19.2
1.5	5	2.57	6.7	22	5.39	14.6	48	7.96	98	320	20.5
1.8	6	2.81	7.3	24	5.62	15.2	50	8.1	110	360	21.8
2.1	7	3.04	7.9	26	5.86	18	60	8.9	122	400	23.0
2.4	8	3.25	8.5	28	6.08	20	70	9.6	137	450	24.3
2.7	9	3.45	9.1	30	6.30	24	80	10.3	152	500	25.7
3.0	10	3.63	9.8	32	6.50	27	90	10.9	183	600	28.1
3.4	11	3.81	10.4	34	6.70	30	100	11.5	213	700	30.4
3.7	12	3.98	11.0	36	6.90	40	130	13.1	244	800	32.5
4.0	13	4.14	11.6	38	7.09	46	150	14.1			

TABLE II TO FIND DISTANCE OF LIGHTS RISING OR DIPPING

Height of Light		HEIGHT OF EYE												
		Metres												
		1.5	3	4.6	6.1	7.6	9.1	10.7	12.2	13.7	15.2	16.8	18.3	19.8
		Feet												
		5	10	15	20	25	30	35	40	45	50	55	60	65
m	ft													
12	40	9¾	11	11¾	12½	13	13½	14	14½	15	15½	15¾	16¼	16½
15	50	10¾	11¾	12½	13¼	14	14½	15	15½	15¾	16¼	16¾	17	17½
18	60	11½	12½	13½	14	14¾	15¼	15¾	16¼	16½	17	17½	17¾	18¼
21	70	12¼	13¼	14	14¾	15½	16	16½	17	17¼	17¾	18	18½	19
24	80	13	14	14¾	15½	16	16½	17	17½	18	18½	18¾	19¼	19½
27	90	13½	14½	15½	16	16¾	17¼	17¾	18¼	18½	19	19½	19¾	20¼
30	100	14	15	16	16½	17¼	17¾	18¼	18¾	19¼	19½	20	20½	20¾
34	110	14½	15¾	16½	17¼	17¾	18¼	19	19¼	19¾	20¼	20½	21	21¼
37	120	15¼	16¼	17	17¾	18¼	19	19½	20	20¼	20¾	21	21½	22
40	130	15¾	16¾	17½	18¼	19	19½	20	20½	20¾	21¼	21½	22	22½
43	140	16¼	17¼	18	18¾	19½	20	20½	21	21¼	21¾	22	22½	23
46	150	16¾	17¾	18½	19¼	19¾	20½	21	21¼	21¾	22¼	22½	23	23¼
49	160	17	18¼	19	19¾	20¼	20¾	21½	21¾	22¼	22¾	23	23½	23¾
52	170	17½	18½	19½	20	20¾	21¼	21¾	22¼	22¾	23	23½	24	24¼
55	180	18	19	20	20½	21¼	21¾	22¼	22¾	23	23½	24	24¼	24¾
58	190	18½	19½	20¼	21	21½	22	22¾	23	23½	24	24½	24¾	25
61	200	18¾	20	20¾	21½	22	22½	23	23½	24	24½	24¾	25¼	25½
64	210	19¼	20¼	21	21¾	22½	23	23½	24	24½	24¾	25¼	25½	26
67	220	19½	20¾	21½	22¼	22¾	23¼	24	24¼	24¾	25¼	25½	26	26¼
70	230	20	21	22	22½	23¼	23¾	24¼	24¾	25	25½	26	26¼	26¾
73	240	20½	21½	22¼	23	23½	24	24½	25	25½	26	26¼	26¾	27
76	250	20¾	21¾	22½	23¼	24	24½	25	25½	26	26¼	26¾	27	27½
79	260	21	22¼	23	23¾	24¼	24¾	25¼	25¾	26¼	26¾	27	27½	27¾
82	270	21½	22½	23¼	24	24½	25¼	25¾	26¼	26½	27	27½	27¾	28¼
85	280	21¾	23	23¾	24½	25	25½	26	26½	27	27½	27¾	28	28½
88	290	22	23¼	24	24¾	25¼	26	26½	26¾	27¼	27¾	28	28½	28¾
91	300	22½	23½	24½	25	25¾	26¼	26¾	27¼	27½	28	28½	28¾	29¼
95	310	22¾	24	24¾	25½	26	26½	27	27½	28	28½	28¾	29	29½
98	320	23	24¼	25	25¾	26¼	27	27½	27¾	28¼	28¾	29	29½	29¾
100	330	23½	24½	25¼	26	26½	27¼	27¾	28	28½	29	29½	29¾	30
104	340	23¾	24¾	25¾	26¼	27	27½	28	28½	29	29¼	29¾	30	30½
107	350	24	25	26	26¾	27¼	27¾	28¼	28¾	29¼	29½	30	30½	30¾
122	400	25½	26½	27½	28	28¾	29¼	29¾	30¼	30¾	31	31½	32	32¼
137	450	27	28	28¾	29½	30	30¾	31¼	31¾	32	32½	33	33¼	33¾

TABLE FOR CONVERTING THE POWER OF A LIGHT INTO NOMINAL RANGE

Nominal Range Sea Miles	1	2	5	10	20	30
Luminous Intensity (candelas)	1	5	77	1,400	110,000	5,000,000

MEASURING SPEED

At a number of places on the coast marks have been erected which indicate specific measured distances (usually 1 mile) which can be used for checking the accuracy of speed indicating instruments.

The method is to travel at a constant speed between the two transits, ideally at slack water, noting the exact time elapsed. With only a single run allowance must be made for any tidal stream, in practice several runs should be made.

The downstream speed is found by dividing the distance by the downstream time and the upstream similarly and the vessels speed through the water will be half the total sum.

Example. Using a measured mile and the time and knot table ascertain the time taken on the measured mile in minutes and seconds and look up the table (minutes at the top and seconds at the side) to find the vessel's speed in knots.

Having covered the measured mile in 6 minutes 18 seconds, what is the speed? This will be found to be 9.524 knots.

For speeds lower than 5 knots simply halve the time taken and then halve the speed found, e.g., if the time taken on the mile is 17 minutes then look out under 8 min. 30 sec. The speed given is 7.059 which divided by 2 gives the speed of 3.529 knots (i.e., 3½ knots).

If the speed through the water determined by the Patent Log is required; record accurately the time taken to travel one mile; then read off the speed in knots from the table.

MEASURED MILE (TIME AND KNOT) TABLE

Secs.	2 min.	3 min.	4 min.	5 min.	6 min.	7 min.	8 min.	9 min.	10 min.	11 min.
0	30.000	20.000	15.000	12.000	10.000	8.571	7.500	6.667	6.000	5.455
1	29.752	19.890	14.938	11.960	9.972	8.551	7.484	6.654	5.990	5.446
2	29.508	19.780	14.876	11.921	9.945	8.531	7.469	6.642	5.980	5.438
3	29.268	19.672	14.815	11.881	9.917	8.511	7.453	6.630	5.970	5.430
4	29.032	19.565	14.754	11.842	9.890	8.491	7.438	6.618	5.960	5.422
5	28.800	19.459	14.694	11.803	9.863	8.471	7.423	6.606	5.950	5.414
6	28.571	19.355	14.634	11.765	9.836	8.451	7.407	6.593	5.941	5.405
7	28.346	19.251	14.575	11.726	9.809	8.431	7.392	6.581	5.931	5.397
8	28.125	19.149	14.516	11.688	9.783	8.411	7.377	6.569	5.921	5.389
9	27.907	19.048	14.458	11.650	9.756	8.392	7.362	6.557	5.911	5.381
10	27.692	18.947	14.400	11.613	9.730	8.372	7.347	6.545	5.902	5.373
11	27.481	18.848	14.343	11.576	9.704	8.353	7.332	6.534	5.892	5.365
12	27.273	18.750	14.286	11.538	9.677	8.333	7.317	6.522	5.882	5.357
13	27.068	18.653	14.229	11.502	9.651	8.314	7.302	6.510	5.873	5.349
14	26.866	18.557	14.173	11.465	9.626	8.295	7.287	6.498	5.863	5.341
15	26.667	18.461	14.118	11.429	9.600	8.276	7.273	6.486	5.854	5.333
16	26.471	18.367	14.062	11.392	9.574	8.257	7.258	6.475	5.844	5.325
17	26.277	18.274	14.008	11.356	9.549	8.238	7.243	6.463	5.835	5.318
18	26.087	18.182	13.953	11.321	9.524	8.219	7.229	6.452	5.825	5.310
19	25.899	18.090	13.900	11.285	9.499	8.200	7.214	6.440	5.816	5.302
20	25.714	18.000	13.846	11.250	9.474	8.182	7.200	6.429	5.806	5.294
21	25.532	17.910	13.793	11.215	9.449	8.163	7.186	6.417	5.797	5.286
22	25.352	17.822	13.740	11.180	9.424	8.145	7.171	6.406	5.788	5.279
23	25.175	17.734	13.688	11.146	9.399	8.126	7.157	6.394	5.778	5.271
24	25.000	17.647	13.636	11.111	9.375	8.108	7.143	6.383	5.769	5.263
25	24.828	17.561	13.585	11.077	9.351	8.090	7.129	6.372	5.760	5.255
26	24.658	17.476	13.534	11.043	9.326	8.072	7.115	6.360	5.751	5.248
27	24.490	17.391	13.483	11.009	9.302	8.054	7.101	6.349	5.742	5.240
28	24.324	17.308	13.433	10.976	9.278	8.036	7.087	6.338	5.732	5.233
29	24.161	17.225	13.383	10.942	9.254	8.018	7.073	6.327	5.723	5.225
30	24.000	17.143	13.333	10.909	9.231	8.000	7.059	6.316	5.714	5.217
31	23.841	17.062	13.284	10.876	9.207	7.982	7.045	6.305	5.705	5.210
32	23.684	16.981	13.235	10.843	9.184	7.965	7.031	6.294	5.696	5.202
33	23.529	16.901	13.187	10.811	9.160	7.947	7.018	6.283	5.687	5.195
34	23.377	16.822	13.139	10.778	9.137	7.930	7.004	6.272	5.678	5.187
35	23.226	16.744	13.091	10.746	9.114	7.912	6.990	6.261	5.669	5.180
36	23.077	16.667	13.043	10.714	9.091	7.895	6.977	6.250	5.660	5.172
37	22.930	16.590	12.996	10.682	9.068	7.877	6.963	6.239	5.651	5.165
38	22.785	16.514	12.950	10.651	9.045	7.860	6.950	6.228	5.643	5.158
39	22.642	16.438	12.903	10.619	9.023	7.843	6.936	6.218	5.634	5.150
40	22.500	16.364	12.857	10.588	9.000	7.826	6.923	6.207	5.625	5.143
41	22.360	16.290	12.811	10.557	8.978	7.809	6.910	6.196	5.616	5.136
42	22.222	16.216	12.766	10.526	8.955	7.792	6.897	6.186	5.607	5.128
43	22.086	16.143	12.721	10.496	8.933	7.775	6.883	6.175	5.599	5.121
44	21.951	16.071	12.676	10.465	8.911	7.759	6.870	6.164	5.590	5.114
45	21.818	16.000	12.632	10.435	8.889	7.742	6.857	6.154	5.581	5.106
46	21.687	15.929	12.587	10.405	8.867	7.725	6.844	6.143	5.573	5.099
47	21.557	15.859	12.544	10.375	8.845	7.709	6.831	6.133	5.564	5.092
48	21.429	15.789	12.500	10.345	8.824	7.692	6.818	6.122	5.556	5.085
49	21.302	15.721	12.457	10.315	8.802	7.676	6.805	6.112	5.547	5.078
50	21.176	15.652	12.414	10.286	8.780	7.660	6.792	6.102	5.538	5.070
51	21.053	15.584	12.371	10.256	8.759	7.643	6.780	6.091	5.530	5.063
52	20.930	15.517	12.329	10.227	8.738	7.627	6.767	6.081	5.521	5.056
53	20.809	15.451	12.287	10.198	8.717	7.611	6.754	6.071	5.513	5.049
54	20.690	15.385	12.245	10.169	8.696	7.595	6.742	6.061	5.505	5.042
55	20.571	15.319	12.203	10.141	8.675	7.579	6.729	6.050	5.496	5.035
56	20.455	15.254	12.162	10.112	8.654	7.563	6.716	6.040	5.488	5.028
57	20.339	15.190	12.121	10.084	8.633	7.547	6.704	6.030	5.479	5.021
58	20.225	15.126	12.081	10.056	8.612	7.531	6.691	6.020	5.471	5.014
59	20.112	15.063	12.040	10.028	8.592	7.516	6.679	6.010	5.463	5.007
Secs.	2 min.	3 min.	4 min.	5 min.	6 min.	7 min.	8 min.	9 min.	10 min.	11 min.

The above figures indicate the speed in knots according to a particular time in minutes and seconds

Section 13

TIME, SPEED and DISTANCE TABLE
for finding distance run in a given time at various Speeds, 2½ to 22 knots

							KNOTS							
Min	2½	3	3½	4	4½	5	5½	6	6½	7	7½	8	8½	Min
1	0.1	0.1	0.1	0.1	0.1	0.1	0.1	0.1	0.1	0.1	0.1	0.1	0.2	1
2	0.1	0.1	0.1	0.2	0.2	0.2	0.2	0.2	0.2	0.2	0.2	0.3	0.3	2
3	0.1	0.2	0.2	0.2	0.3	0.3	0.3	0.3	0.3	0.3	0.3	0.4	0.4	3
4	0.1	0.2	0.3	0.3	0.3	0.3	0.4	0.4	0.4	0.5	0.5	0.5	0.6	4
5	0.2	0.3	0.3	0.4	0.4	0.4	0.5	0.5	0.6	0.6	0.6	0.7	0.7	5
6	0.3	0.3	0.4	0.4	0.5	0.5	0.6	0.6	0.7	0.7	0.8	0.8	0.9	6
7	0.3	0.4	0.4	0.5	0.6	0.6	0.6	0.7	0.8	0.8	0.9	0.9	1.0	7
8	0.4	0.4	0.5	0.6	0.6	0.7	0.7	0.8	0.9	0.9	1.0	1.0	1.1	8
9	0.4	0.5	0.6	0.6	0.7	0.8	0.8	0.9	1.0	1.1	1.1	1.2	1.3	9
10	0.4	0.5	0.6	0.7	0.8	0.8	0.9	1.0	1.1	1.2	1.3	1.3	1.4	10
11	0.5	0.6	0.7	0.8	0.9	0.9	1.0	1.1	1.2	1.3	1.4	1.5	1.6	11
12	0.5	0.6	0.7	0.8	0.9	1.0	1.1	1.2	1.3	1.4	1.5	1.6	1.7	12
13	0.6	0.7	0.8	0.9	1.0	1.1	1.2	1.3	1.4	1.5	1.6	1.7	1.8	13
14	0.6	0.7	0.8	1.0	1.1	1.2	1.3	1.4	1.5	1.6	1.8	1.9	2.0	14
15	0.7	0.8	0.9	1.0	1.2	1.3	1.4	1.5	1.6	1.8	1.9	2.0	2.1	15
16	0.7	0.8	1.0	1.1	1.2	1.3	1.5	1.6	1.7	1.9	2.0	2.1	2.3	16
17	0.7	0.9	1.0	1.2	1.3	1.4	1.6	1.7	1.8	2.0	2.1	2.3	2.4	17
18	0.8	0.9	1.1	1.2	1.4	1.5	1.7	1.8	2.0	2.1	2.3	2.4	2.6	18
19	0.8	1.0	1.1	1.3	1.5	1.6	1.7	1.9	2.1	2.2	2.4	2.5	2.7	19
20	0.9	1.0	1.2	1.4	1.5	1.7	1.8	2.0	2.2	2.3	2.5	2.7	2.8	20
21	0.9	1.1	1.3	1.4	1.6	1.8	1.9	2.1	2.3	2.5	2.6	2.8	3.0	21
22	0.9	1.1	1.3	1.5	1.7	1.8	2.0	2.2	2.4	2.6	2.8	2.9	3.1	22
23	1.0	1.2	1.4	1.6	1.8	1.9	2.1	2.3	2.5	2.7	2.9	3.0	3.3	23
24	1.0	1.2	1.4	1.6	1.8	2.0	2.2	2.4	2.6	2.8	3.0	3.2	3.4	24
25	1.1	1.3	1.5	1.7	1.9	2.1	2.3	2.5	2.7	2.9	3.1	3.3	3.5	25
26	1.1	1.3	1.5	1.8	2.0	2.2	2.4	2.6	2.8	3.0	3.3	3.5	3.7	26
27	1.2	1.4	1.6	1.8	2.1	2.3	2.5	2.7	2.9	3.2	3.4	3.6	3.9	27
28	1.2	1.4	1.7	1.9	2.1	2.3	2.6	2.8	3.0	3.3	3.5	3.7	4.0	28
29	1.2	1.5	1.7	2.0	2.2	2.4	2.7	2.9	3.1	3.4	3.6	3.9	4.1	29
30	1.3	1.5	1.8	2.0	2.3	2.5	2.8	3.0	3.3	3.5	3.8	4.0	4.3	30
31	1.3	1.6	1.8	2.1	2.4	2.6	2.8	3.1	3.4	3.6	3.9	4.1	4.4	31
32	1.4	1.6	1.9	2.2	2.4	2.7	2.9	3.2	3.5	3.7	4.0	4.3	4.5	32
33	1.4	1.7	2.0	2.3	2.5	2.8	3.0	3.3	3.6	3.9	4.1	4.4	4.7	33
34	1.4	1.7	2.0	2.3	2.6	2.9	3.1	3.4	3.7	4.0	4.3	4.5	4.8	34
35	1.5	1.8	2.1	2.4	2.7	2.9	3.2	3.5	3.8	4.1	4.4	4.7	5.0	35
36	1.5	1.8	2.1	2.4	2.7	3.0	3.3	3.6	3.9	4.2	4.5	4.8	5.1	36
37	1.6	1.9	2.2	2.5	2.8	3.1	3.4	3.7	4.0	4.3	4.6	4.9	5.2	37
38	1.6	1.9	2.2	2.6	2.9	3.2	3.5	3.8	4.1	4.4	4.8	5.0	5.4	38
39	1.7	2.0	2.3	2.6	2.9	3.3	3.6	3.9	4.2	4.6	4.9	5.2	5.5	39
40	1.7	2.0	2.4	2.7	3.0	3.3	3.7	4.0	4.3	4.7	5.0	5.3	5.7	40
41	1.7	2.1	2.4	2.8	3.1	3.4	3.8	4.1	4.4	4.8	5.1	5.5	5.8	41
42	1.8	2.1	2.5	2.8	3.2	3.5	3.9	4.2	4.6	4.9	5.3	5.6	6.0	42
43	1.8	2.2	2.5	2.9	3.3	3.6	3.9	4.3	4.7	5.0	5.4	5.7	6.1	43
44	1.9	2.2	2.6	3.0	3.3	3.7	4.0	4.4	4.8	5.1	5.5	5.9	6.2	44
45	1.9	2.3	2.7	3.0	3.4	3.8	4.1	4.5	4.9	5.3	5.6	6.0	6.4	45
46	1.9	2.3	2.7	3.1	3.5	3.8	4.2	4.6	5.0	5.4	5.8	6.1	6.5	46
47	2.0	2.4	2.8	3.2	3.6	3.9	4.3	4.7	5.1	5.5	5.9	6.3	6.7	47
48	2.0	2.4	2.8	3.2	3.6	4.0	4.4	4.8	5.2	5.6	6.0	6.4	6.8	48
49	2.1	2.5	2.9	3.3	3.7	4.1	4.5	4.9	5.3	5.7	6.1	6.5	6.9	49
50	2.1	2.5	2.9	3.4	3.8	4.2	4.6	5.0	5.4	5.8	6.3	6.7	7.1	50
51	2.2	2.6	3.0	3.4	3.9	4.3	4.7	5.1	5.5	6.0	6.4	6.8	7.2	51
52	2.2	2.6	3.1	3.5	3.9	4.3	4.8	5.2	5.6	6.1	6.5	6.9	7.4	52
53	2.2	2.7	3.1	3.6	4.0	4.4	4.9	5.3	5.7	6.2	6.6	7.0	7.5	53
54	2.3	2.7	3.2	3.6	4.1	4.5	5.0	5.4	5.9	6.3	6.8	7.1	7.6	54
55	2.3	2.8	3.2	3.7	4.2	4.6	5.0	5.5	6.0	6.4	6.9	7.3	7.8	55
56	2.4	2.8	3.3	3.8	4.2	4.7	5.1	5.6	6.1	6.5	7.0	7.5	7.9	56
57	2.4	2.9	3.4	3.8	4.3	4.8	5.2	5.7	6.2	6.7	7.1	7.6	8.1	57
58	2.4	2.9	3.4	3.9	4.4	4.8	5.3	5.8	6.3	6.8	7.3	7.7	8.2	58
59	2.5	3.0	3.5	3.9	4.5	4.9	5.4	5.9	6.4	6.9	7.4	7.9	8.4	59
60	2.5	3.0	3.5	4.0	4.5	5.0	5.5	6.0	6.5	7.0	7.5	8.0	8.5	60
Min	2½	3	3½	4	4½	5	5½	6	6½	7	7½	8	8½	Min

Example 1. If steaming 7½ knots, what distance has been covered in 41 minutes?   Answer = 5.1 miles.

TIME, SPEED and DISTANCE TABLE

	KNOTS													
Min	9	9½	10	10½	11	11½	12	12½	13	13½	14	14½	15	Min
1	0.2	0.2	0.2	0.2	0.2	0.2	0.2	0.2	0.2	0.2	0.2	0.2	0.3	1
2	0.3	0.3	0.3	0.4	0.4	0.4	0.4	0.4	0.5	0.5	0.5	0.5	0.5	2
3	0.5	0.5	0.5	0.5	0.6	0.6	0.6	0.6	0.7	0.7	0.7	0.7	0.8	3
4	0.6	0.6	0.7	0.7	0.7	0.8	0.8	0.8	0.9	0.9	0.9	1.0	1.0	4
5	0.8	0.8	0.8	0.9	0.9	1.0	1.0	1.1	1.1	1.2	1.2	1.2	1.3	5
6	0.9	1.0	1.0	1.1	1.1	1.2	1.2	1.3	1.3	1.4	1.4	1.5	1.5	6
7	1.1	1.1	1.2	1.2	1.3	1.3	1.4	1.5	1.5	1.6	1.6	1.7	1.8	7
8	1.2	1.3	1.3	1.4	1.5	1.5	1.6	1.7	1.7	1.8	1.9	1.9	2.0	8
9	1.4	1.4	1.5	1.6	1.7	1.7	1.8	1.9	2.0	2.0	2.1	2.2	2.3	9
10	1.5	1.6	1.7	1.8	1.8	1.9	2.0	2.1	2.2	2.3	2.3	2.4	2.5	10
11	1.7	1.7	1.8	1.9	2.0	2.1	2.2	2.3	2.4	2.5	2.6	2.7	2.8	11
12	1.8	1.9	2.0	2.1	2.2	2.3	2.4	2.5	2.6	2.7	2.8	2.9	3.0	12
13	2.0	2.1	2.2	2.3	2.4	2.5	2.6	2.7	2.8	2.9	3.0	3.1	3.2	13
14	2.1	2.2	2.3	2.5	2.6	2.7	2.8	2.9	3.0	3.2	3.3	3.4	3.5	14
15	2.3	2.4	2.5	2.6	2.8	2.9	3.0	3.1	3.3	3.4	3.5	3.6	3.8	15
16	2.4	2.5	2.7	2.8	2.9	3.1	3.2	3.3	3.5	3.6	3.7	3.9	4.0	16
17	2.6	2.7	2.8	3.0	3.1	3.3	3.4	3.5	3.7	3.8	4.0	4.1	4.3	17
18	2.7	2.9	3.0	3.2	3.3	3.5	3.6	3.8	3.9	4.1	4.2	4.4	4.5	18
19	2.9	3.1	3.2	3.3	3.5	3.6	3.8	4.0	4.2	4.3	4.4	4.6	4.8	19
20	3.0	3.2	3.3	3.5	3.7	3.8	4.0	4.2	4.4	4.5	4.7	4.8	5.0	20
21	3.2	3.3	3.6	3.7	3.9	4.0	4.2	4.4	4.6	4.7	4.9	5.1	5.3	21
22	3.3	3.5	3.7	3.9	4.0	4.2	4.4	4.6	4.8	5.0	5.1	5.3	5.5	22
23	3.5	3.6	3.8	4.0	4.2	4.4	4.6	4.8	5.0	5.2	5.4	5.6	5.7	23
24	3.6	3.8	4.0	4.2	4.4	4.6	4.8	5.0	5.2	5.4	5.6	5.8	6.0	24
25	3.8	4.0	4.2	4.4	4.6	4.8	5.0	5.2	5.4	5.6	5.8	6.1	6.3	25
26	3.9	4.1	4.3	4.6	4.8	5.0	5.2	5.4	5.6	5.9	6.1	6.3	6.5	26
27	4.1	4.3	4.5	4.7	5.0	5.2	5.4	5.6	5.9	6.1	6.3	6.5	6.8	27
28	4.2	4.4	4.7	4.9	5.1	5.4	5.6	5.8	6.1	6.3	6.5	6.8	7.0	28
29	4.4	4.6	4.8	5.1	5.3	5.6	5.8	6.0	6.3	6.5	6.8	7.0	7.3	29
30	4.5	4.8	5.0	5.3	5.5	5.8	6.0	6.3	6.5	6.8	7.0	7.3	7.5	30
31	4.7	4.9	5.2	5.4	5.7	5.9	6.2	6.5	6.7	7.0	7.2	7.5	7.8	31
32	4.8	5.0	5.3	5.6	5.9	6.1	6.4	6.7	6.9	7.2	7.5	7.7	8.0	32
33	5.0	5.2	5.5	5.8	6.1	6.3	6.6	6.9	7.2	7.4	7.7	8.0	8.3	33
34	5.1	5.4	5.7	6.0	6.2	6.5	6.8	7.1	7.4	7.7	8.0	8.2	8.5	34
35	5.3	5.5	5.8	6.1	6.4	6.7	7.0	7.3	7.6	7.9	8.2	8.5	8.8	35
36	5.4	5.7	6.0	6.3	6.6	6.9	7.2	7.5	7.8	8.1	8.4	8.7	9.0	36
37	5.6	5.9	6.2	6.5	6.8	7.1	7.4	7.7	8.0	8.3	8.6	8.9	9.3	37
38	5.7	6.0	6.3	6.7	7.0	7.3	7.6	7.9	8.2	8.6	8.9	9.2	9.5	38
39	5.9	6.2	6.5	6.8	7.1	7.5	7.8	8.1	8.5	8.8	9.1	9.4	9.8	39
40	6.0	6.3	6.7	7.0	7.3	7.7	8.0	8.3	8.7	9.0	9.3	9.7	10.0	40
41	6.2	6.5	6.8	7.3	7.5	7.9	8.2	8.5	8.9	9.2	9.6	9.9	10.3	41
42	6.3	6.7	7.0	7.4	7.7	8.1	8.4	8.8	9.1	9.5	9.8	10.2	10.5	42
43	6.5	6.8	7.2	7.5	7.9	8.2	8.6	9.0	9.3	9.7	10.0	10.4	10.8	43
44	6.6	7.0	7.3	7.7	8.0	8.4	8.8	9.2	9.5	9.9	10.3	10.6	11.0	44
45	6.8	7.1	7.5	7.9	8.2	8.6	9.0	9.4	9.8	10.1	10.5	10.9	11.3	45
46	6.9	7.3	7.7	8.1	8.4	8.8	9.2	9.6	10.0	10.4	10.7	11.1	11.5	46
47	7.1	7.4	7.8	8.2	8.6	9.0	9.4	9.8	10.2	10.6	11.0	11.4	11.8	47
48	7.2	7.6	8.0	8.4	8.8	9.2	9.6	10.0	10.4	10.8	11.2	11.6	12.0	48
49	7.4	7.8	8.2	8.6	9.0	9.4	9.8	10.2	10.6	11.0	11.4	11.8	12.3	49
50	7.5	7.9	8.3	8.7	9.1	9.6	10.0	10.4	10.8	11.3	11.7	12.1	12.5	50
51	7.7	8.1	8.5	8.9	9.4	9.8	10.2	10.6	11.1	11.5	11.9	12.3	12.8	51
52	7.8	8.2	8.7	9.1	9.5	10.0	10.4	10.8	11.3	11.7	12.1	12.6	13.0	52
53	8.0	8.4	8.8	9.3	9.7	10.2	10.6	11.0	11.5	11.9	12.4	12.8	13.3	53
54	8.1	8.6	9.0	9.5	9.9	10.4	10.8	11.3	11.7	12.2	12.6	13.1	13.5	54
55	8.3	8.7	9.2	9.6	10.0	10.5	11.0	11.5	11.9	12.4	12.8	13.3	13.8	55
56	8.4	8.9	9.3	9.8	10.2	10.7	11.2	11.7	12.1	12.6	13.1	13.5	14.0	56
57	8.6	9.0	9.5	10.0	10.5	10.9	11.4	11.9	12.4	12.8	13.3	13.8	14.3	57
58	8.7	9.2	9.7	10.2	10.6	11.1	11.6	12.1	12.6	13.1	13.5	14.0	14.5	58
59	8.9	9.3	9.8	10.3	10.8	11.3	11.8	12.3	12.8	13.3	13.8	14.3	14.8	59
60	9.0	9.5	10.0	10.5	11.0	11.5	12.0	12.5	13.0	13.5	14.0	14.5	15.0	60
Min	9	9½	10	10½	11	11½	12	12½	13	13½	14	14½	15	Min

Example 2. How long will it take to steam 6.8 miles (when the course is to be altered)? Vessel's speed, 10½ knots. Answer = 39 minutes.

Section 13

TIME, SPEED and DISTANCE TABLE

Min	15½	16	16½	17	17½	18	18½	19	19½	20	20½	21	21½	22	Min
						KNOTS									
1	0.3	0.3	0.3	0.3	0.3	0.3	0.3	0.3	0.3	0.3	0.3	0.4	0.4	0.4	1
2	0.5	0.5	0.5	0.6	0.6	0.6	0.6	0.6	0.6	0.7	0.7	0.7	0.7	0.7	2
3	0.8	0.8	0.8	0.9	0.9	0.9	0.9	1.0	1.0	1.0	1.0	1.1	1.1	1.1	3
4	1.0	1.1	1.1	1.1	1.1	1.2	1.2	1.3	1.3	1.3	1.3	1.4	1.4	1.5	4
5	1.3	1.3	1.3	1.4	1.4	1.5	1.5	1.6	1.6	1.7	1.7	1.8	1.8	1.8	5
6	1.5	1.6	1.6	1.7	1.7	1.8	1.8	1.9	1.9	2.0	2.0	2.1	2.1	2.2	6
7	1.8	1.9	1.9	2.0	2.0	2.1	2.1	2.2	2.2	2.3	2.4	2.5	2.5	2.6	7
8	2.0	2.1	2.2	2.3	2.3	2.4	2.4	2.5	2.6	2.7	2.7	2.8	2.8	2.9	8
9	2.3	2.4	2.5	2.6	2.6	2.7	2.8	2.9	2.9	3.0	3.1	3.2	3.2	3.3	9
10	2.6	2.7	2.7	2.8	2.9	3.0	3.1	3.2	3.2	3.3	3.4	3.5	3.6	3.7	10
11	2.8	2.9	3.0	3.1	3.2	3.3	3.4	3.5	3.6	3.7	3.8	3.9	3.9	4.0	11
12	3.1	3.2	3.3	3.4	3.5	3.6	3.7	3.8	3.9	4.0	4.1	4.2	4.3	4.4	12
13	3.4	3.5	3.6	3.7	3.8	3.9	4.0	4.1	4.2	4.3	4.4	4.6	4.7	4.8	13
14	3.6	3.7	3.8	4.0	4.1	4.2	4.3	4.4	4.5	4.7	4.8	4.9	5.0	5.1	14
15	3.9	4.0	4.1	4.3	4.4	4.5	4.6	4.8	4.9	5.0	5.1	5.3	5.4	5.5	15
16	4.2	4.3	4.4	4.5	4.6	4.8	4.9	5.1	5.2	5.3	5.4	5.6	5.7	5.9	16
17	4.4	4.5	4.6	4.8	4.9	5.1	5.2	5.4	5.5	5.7	5.8	6.0	6.1	6.2	17
18	4.7	4.8	4.9	5.1	5.2	5.4	5.5	5.7	5.8	6.0	6.1	6.3	6.4	6.6	18
19	4.9	5.1	5.2	5.4	5.5	5.7	5.8	6.0	6.1	6.3	6.5	6.7	6.8	7.0	19
20	5.1	5.3	5.5	5.7	5.8	6.0	6.1	6.3	6.5	6.7	6.8	7.0	7.1	7.3	20
21	5.4	5.6	5.8	6.0	6.1	6.3	6.5	6.7	6.8	7.0	7.2	7.4	7.5	7.7	21
22	5.7	5.9	6.0	6.2	6.4	6.6	6.8	7.0	7.1	7.3	7.5	7.7	7.9	8.1	22
23	5.9	6.1	6.3	6.5	6.7	6.9	7.1	7.3	7.5	7.7	7.9	8.1	8.2	8.4	23
24	6.2	6.4	6.6	6.8	7.0	7.2	7.4	7.6	7.8	8.0	8.2	8.4	8.6	8.8	24
25	6.5	6.7	6.9	7.1	7.3	7.5	7.7	7.9	8.1	8.3	8.5	8.8	9.0	9.2	25
26	6.7	6.9	7.1	7.4	7.6	7.8	8.0	8.2	8.4	8.7	8.9	9.1	9.3	9.5	26
27	7.0	7.2	7.4	7.7	7.9	8.1	8.3	8.6	8.8	9.0	9.2	9.5	9.7	9.9	27
28	7.2	7.5	7.7	7.9	8.1	8.4	8.6	8.9	9.1	9.3	9.5	9.8	10.0	10.3	28
29	7.5	7.7	7.9	8.2	8.4	8.7	8.9	9.2	9.4	9.7	9.9	10.2	10.4	10.6	29
30	7.8	8.0	8.2	8.5	8.7	9.0	9.2	9.5	9.7	10.0	10.2	10.5	10.7	11.0	30
31	8.0	8.3	8.5	8.8	9.0	9.3	9.5	9.8	10.0	10.3	10.6	10.9	11.1	11.4	31
32	8.2	8.5	8.8	9.1	9.3	9.6	9.9	10.2	10.4	10.7	10.9	11.2	11.4	11.7	32
33	8.5	8.8	9.1	9.4	9.6	9.9	10.2	10.5	10.7	11.0	11.3	11.6	11.8	12.1	33
34	8.8	9.1	9.3	9.6	9.9	10.2	10.5	10.8	11.0	11.3	11.6	11.9	12.2	12.5	34
35	9.0	9.3	9.6	9.9	10.2	10.5	10.8	11.1	11.4	11.7	12.0	12.3	12.5	12.8	35
36	9.3	9.6	9.9	10.2	10.5	10.8	11.1	11.4	11.7	12.0	12.3	12.6	12.9	13.2	36
37	9.6	9.9	10.2	10.5	10.8	11.1	11.4	11.7	12.0	12.3	12.6	13.0	13.3	13.6	37
38	9.8	10.1	10.4	10.8	11.1	11.4	11.7	12.0	12.3	12.7	13.0	13.3	13.6	13.9	38
39	10.1	10.4	10.7	11.1	11.4	11.7	12.0	12.4	12.7	13.0	13.3	13.7	14.0	14.3	39
40	10.4	10.7	11.0	11.3	11.7	12.0	12.3	12.7	13.0	13.3	13.6	14.0	14.3	14.7	40
41	10.6	10.9	11.2	11.6	12.0	12.3	12.6	13.0	13.3	13.7	14.0	14.4	14.7	15.0	41
42	10.8	11.2	11.5	11.9	12.3	12.6	12.9	13.3	13.6	14.0	14.3	14.7	15.0	15.4	42
43	11.1	11.5	11.8	12.2	12.5	12.9	13.2	13.6	13.9	14.3	14.7	15.1	15.4	15.8	43
44	11.3	11.7	12.1	12.5	12.8	13.2	13.5	13.9	14.3	14.7	15.0	15.4	15.7	16.1	44
45	11.6	12.0	12.4	12.8	13.1	13.5	13.8	14.3	14.6	15.0	15.4	15.8	16.1	16.5	45
46	11.9	12.3	12.6	13.0	13.4	13.8	14.2	14.6	14.9	15.3	15.7	16.1	16.5	16.9	46
47	12.2	12.5	12.9	13.3	13.7	14.1	14.5	14.9	15.3	15.7	16.1	16.5	16.8	17.2	47
48	12.4	12.8	13.2	13.6	14.0	14.4	14.8	15.2	15.6	16.0	16.4	16.8	17.2	17.6	48
49	12.7	13.1	13.5	13.9	14.3	14.7	15.1	15.5	15.9	16.3	16.7	17.2	17.6	18.0	49
50	12.9	13.3	13.7	14.2	14.6	15.0	15.4	15.8	16.2	16.7	17.1	17.5	17.9	18.3	50
51	13.2	13.6	14.0	14.5	14.9	15.3	15.7	16.2	16.6	17.0	17.5	17.9	18.3	18.7	51
52	13.5	13.9	14.3	14.7	15.1	15.6	16.0	16.5	16.9	17.3	17.8	18.2	18.6	19.1	52
53	13.7	14.1	14.5	15.0	15.4	15.9	16.3	16.8	17.2	17.7	18.1	18.6	19.0	19.4	53
54	14.0	14.4	14.8	15.3	15.7	16.2	16.6	17.1	17.5	18.0	18.4	18.9	19.3	19.8	54
55	14.2	14.7	15.1	15.6	16.0	16.5	16.9	17.4	17.8	18.3	18.8	19.3	19.7	20.2	55
56	14.4	14.9	15.4	15.9	16.3	16.8	17.2	17.7	18.2	18.7	19.1	19.6	20.0	20.5	56
57	14.7	15.2	15.7	16.2	16.6	17.1	17.6	18.1	18.5	19.0	19.5	20.0	20.4	20.9	57
58	15.0	15.5	16.0	16.4	16.9	17.4	17.9	18.4	18.8	19.3	19.8	20.3	20.8	21.3	58
59	15.2	15.7	16.2	16.7	17.2	17.7	18.2	18.7	19.2	19.7	20.2	20.7	21.1	21.6	59
60	15.5	16.0	16.5	17.0	17.5	18.0	18.5	19.0	19.5	20.0	20.5	21.0	21.5	22.0	60
Min	15½	16	16½	17	17½	18	18½	19	19½	20	20½	21	21½	22	Min

Example 3. How far will a vessel steam at 17.5 knots in 25 minutes? Answer = 7.3 miles.

THE ELECTRONIC CALCULATOR IN COASTAL NAVIGATION

Coastal Navigation can be an almost continuous process and aids which can be utilised for rapid calculation should be seriously considered. It must always be understood, however, that the calculator is an aid – it is a piece of electronic equipment which is fallible, but useful for supplementing the basic skills of the navigator by enabling rapid checks to be carried out to calculations already made, and as confidence grows, of carrying out initial calculations. It would be most unwise to use a calculator without fully understanding the fundamental principles involved and being able to work out the problem in longhand. Trigonometrical tables should therefore always be carried on board.

Calculators can be divided into three main groups – the inexpensive arithmetical type with a decimal base, the scientific or slide rule calculator with algebraic, trigonometrical and logarithmic functions and a number of memories, and the most expensive calculators which can be programmed for repetition work either manually or by the insertion of magnetic cards and sometimes having printout facilities.

The middle range of scientific calculators with trigonometrical and logarithmic functions, square root, exponents and reciprocals, with two to three memories, would fulfil the needs of the average coastal navigator. The better the calculator the fewer the key sequences required. Key sequences and functions vary with different calculators and the maker's handbook should always first be studied.

The examples in this section have all been worked using sin, cos, tan and inverse (sometimes shown as ARC) keys together with the normal arithmetical functions, all of which are included on most scientific calculators.

BASIC TRIGONOMETRICAL FUNCTIONS

Before using these functions consider the method by which they are derived as this will assist in the solution of triangular problems. Given any right angle triangle ABC (Fig. 1) trigonometrical functions are:

$$\sin \text{ angle ABC} = \frac{\text{opposite}}{\text{hypotenuse}} = \frac{AC}{AB}$$

$$\cos \text{ angle ABC} = \frac{\text{adjacent}}{\text{hypotenuse}} = \frac{BC}{AB}$$

$$\tan \text{ angle} = \frac{\text{opposite}}{\text{adjacent}} = \frac{AC}{BC}$$

For example:

$$\sin \text{ angle BAC} = \frac{\text{opposite}}{\text{hypotenuse}} = \frac{BC}{AB}$$

These functions are the same for angle BAC except that adjacent and opposite sides are different.

Thus it will be seen that triangular problems can easily be solved if they can be reduced to right angle triangles.

SIMPLE NAVIGATIONAL PROBLEMS

Consider now the solution of one of the simplest navigational problems, finding the distance "off" from a fixed point. If using the "four points" rule or "doubling the angle" on the bow one has to wait for specific bearings to appear, i.e., 45° or 30° and 60°.

Using trigonometrical functions, however, the navigator can take the initial bearing at any suitable time. Consider the example in Fig. 2 where the vessel is on a course of 105° T and requires to know the distance off the headland when abeam.

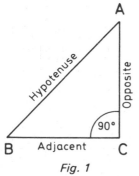

Fig. 1

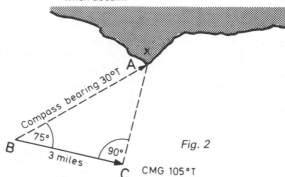

Fig. 2

In this example tidal set and leeway angle are ignored for the sake of simplicity.

Vessel's course = 105° T.

Compass bearing of A = 030° T.

∴ Relative Bearing (RB) = 75° (Angle ABC).

When the vessel is abeam of the fixed point A the relative bearing will be 90° and the log reads 3 miles.

From Fig. 1 it will be seen that:

$$\frac{AC}{BC} = \tan \text{ angle ABC}$$

∴ AC = BC × tan 75

AC = 3 × 3.732

   = 11.19 miles

Using the calculator to solve the problem the following steps are necessary:

Quantity	Entry	Reading
Clear calculator	C	0
Enter Relative Bearing (RB)	75	75
	tan	3.732
	×	3.732
Distance Run	3	3
Answer	=	11.19

Distance off = 11.19 miles

It will be appreciated that the distance run must be the distance over the ground and the log reading must therefore be adjusted for tidal set and leeway angle (read on for method of calculating this).

In many cases the navigator will wish to know his "distance off" before reaching the abeam position if for example there are outlying dangers as in the following example (Fig. 3).

The vessel is somewhere in vicinity of A on a course of 080° T and wishes to know if this will clear outlying danger.

At A first compass bearing is 050° T.
∴ first RB = 30°

Second compass bearing after 3 miles run is 035° T.
∴ second RB = 45°

Now consider the solution to obtain both a "fix" and a probable distance off using trigonometrical functions. (This working will be used to derive a formula which will considerably simplify later calculations.)

In Fig. 4 opposite the triangle ABD is completed by drawing BD at right angles to AX.

To find XC it is first necessary to evaluate BD and then BX

(1) To find DB referring again to Fig. 1 it will be seen that:

$$\sin 30° = \frac{DB}{AB} = \frac{DB}{3}$$

∴ 3 × 0.5 = 1.5 m

(2) To find XB angle DXB is first required. This is (45-30) = 15°

$$\sin 15° = \frac{DB}{XB} = 0.258$$

$$∴ XB = \frac{DB}{0.258} = \frac{1.5}{0.258} = 5.8 \text{ m.}$$

(3) To find XC

$$\sin 45° = \frac{XC}{5.8}$$

∴ XC = sin 45° × 5.8 = 4.1 m.

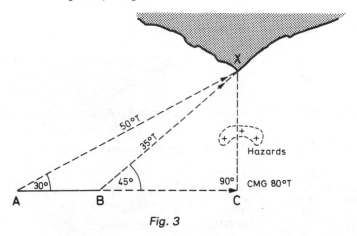

Fig. 3

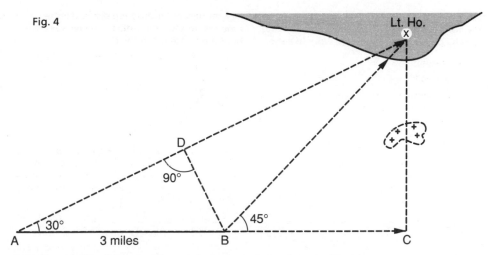

Fig. 4

Lt. Ho.

D

90°

30°   3 miles   B   45°

A   C

Referring to Fig. 4 the position at B can be established by describing a circle of radius 5.8 miles with centre at X and then drawing XB, the True bearing (*not* the relative bearing) and the point of intersection is the fix. Similarly with XC, giving the probable position when abeam.

Consider now the key sequences necessary on the calculator, first using the somewhat lengthy calculation shown earlier.

Quantity	Entry	Reading
Clear calculator	C	0
Enter first RB	30°	30°
	sin	0.5
	×	0.5
Enter Distance Run	3	3
	=	1.5
Store – Memory 1	M1+	1.5
Clear display	C	0
Enter angle DXB	15°	15°
	sin	0.2588
Store – Memory 2	M2+	0.2588
Clear display	C	0
Recall Memory 1	MR1	1.5
	÷	1.5
Recall Memory 2	MR2	0.2588
Answer	=	5.8

Distance off first bearing 5.8 miles

The key sequences for distance off when abeam will be:

Quantity	Entry	Reading
Clear calculator	C	0
Enter second RB	45°	45°
	sin	0.7071
	×	0.7071

Enter distance off at second RB   5.8   5.8
                                      =   4.1

Distance off when abeam = 4 miles

These somewhat lengthy calculations can be reduced and simplified to the following two formulae, thus obviating the necessity for any chartwork until the final fix is obtained.

Formula for Distance Off at 2nd Bearing

$D2$ = Distance off at 2nd Bearing.

R = Distance between 1st and 2nd Bearings.

RB1 = First Relative Bearing

RB2 = Second Relative Bearing

$$D2 = \frac{R \sin RB1}{\sin (RB2 - RB1)}$$

In the case above the calculations will therefore be:

$$\frac{3 \sin 30°}{\sin (45-30)} = \frac{3 \times 0.5}{0.258}$$

$$= 5.8 \text{ miles}$$

Formula for Distance Off when Abeam

$D2$ = Distance off at Second Bearing

RB2 = 2nd Relative Bearing

DA = Distance off when abeam

DA = $D2 \sin RB2$

= $5.8 \times \sin 45°$

= 4.1 miles.

From the calculations above it will be seen that the formula derived from the original rather lengthy calculations reduces the work to a short key sequence which is rapidly performed and requires no plotting until the navigator wishes to plot his position on the chart.

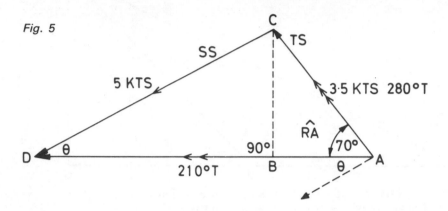

Fig. 5

Tide Correction Angle and Speed Made Good (Fig. 5)

Similarly a formula can be derived for calculating the tidal correction angle. Omitting the step by step calculation this formula is:

$$\sin \theta = \frac{TS \times \sin RA}{SS}$$

where θ = Tidal Correction Angle

TS = Tide Speed

RA = Relative angle between tide and course to be made good

SS = Ship's Speed

Example:

Tidal Stream 3.5 kts. 280° T
Ship's Speed 5 kts.
Course to be made good 210° T
∴ RA = 70°

$$CB = CA \times \sin 70°$$

$$\therefore \sin \theta = \frac{CA \times \sin 70°}{CD}$$

$$= \frac{3.5 \sin 70°}{5} = \frac{3.5 \times 0.94}{5} = 0.658$$

$$\theta = 41°$$

NOTE: To convert 0.658 use invert and sine keys. Method may vary with different types of calculator.

Speed made good = AD

= CD cos θ + AC cos 70°

in standard terms

= (Ship's speed × cos θ) + (Tide speed × cos RA)

= (5 × 0.754) + (3.5 × 0.342)

= 4.97 kts.

When R̂A is greater than 90° the complementary angle is used (e.g., R̂A = 150°, complementary angle = 180 − 150 = 30°) in both correction angle and speed calculations. The latter formula becomes SS cos θ − TS cos R̂A where R̂A is the complementary angle.

HORIZONTAL ANGLE FIX

A quick method of calculating the radius of the circle required in the horizontal angle fix omitting the step by step calculation is:

$$Radius = \frac{\frac{1}{2}AB}{\sin \theta}$$

Where AB is the horizontal distance between the two points and θ is the angle subtended at the vessel.

In the example opposite, if the distance AB = 7 miles and angle θ = 55°

$$Radius = \frac{AB}{2 \sin \theta} = \frac{7}{2 \times .819} = 4.27 \text{ m}$$

It will be appreciated that a position line cutting the circle will give a fix.

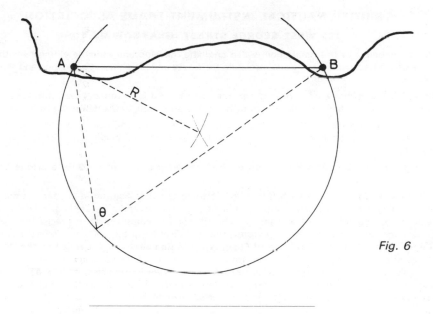

Fig. 6

BRITISH NAUTICAL INSTRUMENT TRADE ASSOCIATION

105 WEST GEORGE STREET, GLASGOW G2 1QP

The prime object of this Association is: "To originate, develop and promote all means within the scope of the trade for ensuring and increasing the safety and efficiency of navigation and shipping" – Rule 3D.

This short summary of efficient services promoted by members of the Association indicates the constant endeavour to fulfil their obligation to the Shipping Industry.

Magnetic Compasses – Advice on compass problems and the supply of the most suitable compasses for any requirements. Maintenance of an efficient and speedy repair service throughout the U.K.

Siting and Installation – Selection of the best magnetic position on the bridge and the supervision of installation.

Compass Adjusting – The services of a DoT Certified Compass Adjuster at any time of the day or night. It should be noted that proper adjustment of compasses and associated equipment including remote heading references, is a task which calls for the employment of precise and complex professional skills, and that the only professional qualification in the U.K. for full-time professional compass adjusters is the Certificate of Competency as Compass Adjuster issued by the DoT after examination following a period of practical training in making, repairing and adjusting compasses. The adjustment of compasses is not something that should be attempted by unqualified persons, and for a fully professional service only DoT Certificated Adjusters should be employed. Member firms who offer such facilities are marked * in the succeeding lists.

Charts – The supply of single charts of world outfits to special folio requirements from comprehensive stocks corrected up to the date of issue.

Chart Tracings – The supply of chart correction tracings supplementary to the Admiralty Notices to Mariners.

Chart Service – Examination and correction of charts at appropriate intervals by full-time qualified Chart Correctors, operating with the co-operation of the Hydrographic Department.

Nautical Publications – The latest "Pilot" or Hydrographic publication. It is almost certain that this Almanac was supplied by a member of the Association.

Chartroom Instruments – A range for Coastal, Home or World Trading voyages.

Sextants – The choice of a new sextant from a full range of instruments and a competent repair service in most Ports.

Binoculars and Telescopes – The cleaning, adjusting or repair of prismatic binoculars, or a wide variety of binoculars and telescopes from which a selection can be made for all needs.

Meteorological Instruments – Supply and repair of mercurial or aneroid barometers and barographs and associated instruments.

Sounding Machines – Stocks of complete sounding machine outfits and the supply of Sounding Tubes, refills and all accessories.

Ships Logs – Comprehensive range of Logs with all accessories, and full stock of manufacturers' spares for the maintenance of all models.

Clocks and Chronometers – The rating and cleaning of chronometers and the supply of clocks for all marine purposes.

Signalling Apparatus – Supply and repair of all signalling apparatus to DoT standards.

OVERSEAS MEMBERS

NOTE. Firms marked * employ DoT Certificated Adjusters. Other overseas firms listed employ Adjusters holding locally equivalent qualifications.

BELGIUM   *Bogerd Navtec NV, Oude Leeuwenrui 37, 2000 Antwerp.
                 *Martin & Co., Oude Leeuwenrui 37, 2000 Antwerp.
DENMARK   Iver C. Weilbach & Co., A/S, 35 Toldbodgade, Postbox 2051, DK-1253, Copenhagen K.

HOLLAND	*Datema Delfzijl BV, Oude Schans 11, 9934 Delfzijl.
HONG KONG	George Falconer (Nautical) Ltd., The Hong Kong Jewellery Building, 178-180 Queen's Road, Central.
	Hong Kong Ships' Supplies Co., Room 1614, Melbourne Plaza, 33 Queen's Road, Central.
NORWAY	A/S Navicharts Masteveien 3, N-1481 Hagan.
PORTUGAL	J. Garraio & Co. Lda., Avenida 24 de Julho, 2-1° D-1200, Lisbon.
SINGAPORE	Motion Smith, Marina House, 70 Shenton Way, 02-03 Singapore 0207.
SWEDEN	AB Ramantenn, Knipplagatan 12, S-414 74 Gothenburg.
URUGUAY	Marine Technical Services, Port of Montevideo, Florida 1562, 11100 Montevideo.

PORTS WHERE SHIPS' COMPASSES ARE ADJUSTED

Names of member firms. Those marked * have DoT Certificated Compass Adjusters available for Adjustment of Compasses day or night.

Port or District	Name and Address	Telephone
ABERDEEN	*Thomas Gunn Navigation Services,	
	62 Marischal Street, AB1 2AL.	0224 595045
AVONMOUTH	W.F. Price & Co., Ltd., 24 Gloucester Road, BS11 9AG.	0272 823888
	*Severnside Consultants, Imperial Chambers, 2nd Floor,	
	Gloucester Road, BS11 9AQ.	0272 827184
CARDIFF	*Blairs Nautical Supplies Ltd., Unit 3, 7-11 West Bute street, CF1 6EN.	0222 487746
	*T.J. Williams & Son, (Cardiff) Ltd., 19 & 19A West Bute Street,	
	The Docks, CF1 6EP.	0222 487676
FALMOUTH	*Marine Instruments, The Bosun's Locker, Upton Slip TR11 3DQ.	0326 312414
GLASGOW	Brown, Son & Ferguson Ltd.,	
	4-10 Darnley Street, G41 2SD.	041-429 1234
HULL	N. Carmichael, Shiptech Buildings, St. Andrews Dock.	0482 29916
	*B. Cooke & Son Limited, Kingston Observatory,	
	58/59 Market Place, HU1 1RH.	0482 223454
KENT	*S.I.R.S. Navigation Limited,	
	186a Milton Road, Swanscombe, DA10 0LX.	0322 843672
LIVERPOOL	Dubois-Philips & McCallum Ltd., Oriel Chambers,	
	Covent Garden L2 8UD.	051-236 2776
LONDON	Brown & Perring, Sestrel House, 36/44 Tabernacle Street EC2A 4DT.	071-253 4517
	*Kelvin Hughes Charts and Maritime Supplies,	
	New North Road, Hainault, Ilford, Essex IG6 2UR.	081-500 6166
	145 Minories, EC3N 1NH.	071-709 9076
	Thomas Reed Publications Ltd.,	
	Hazelbury Manor, Corsham, Wiltshire. SN14 9HX.	0225 812 013
	Silva (UK) Limited, 15 Bolney Way, Feltham, Middlesex TW13 6DB.	081-898 6901
	A.M. Smith (Marine) Ltd., 33 Epping Way, Chingford E4 7PB.	081-529 6988
LOWESTOFT	*Seath Instruments Ltd., Unit 30, Colville Road Works,	0502 573811
	Colville Road, NR33 9QS.	
NORTH SHIELDS	*John Lilley & Gillie (incorporating T.L. Ainsley Ltd.),	
	Clive Street NE29 6LF.	091-257 2217
PORTRUSH	Todd Chart Agency,	
	North Quay, The Harbour, Portrush, Co. Antrim BT56 8DF.	0265 824176
PORTSMOUTH	Robertson Autopilots U.K., Parklands Business Park,	
	Forest Road, Denmead, Waterlooville, Hampshire PO7 6XP.	0705 230885
SOUTHAMPTON	*R.J. Muir, 22 Seymour Close, Chandlers Ford, Eastleigh SO5 2JE.	0703 261042
	Frederick Ford, Esq., 15 Heath Road North, Locks Heath SO3 6PP.	048-95 84425
	Wessex Marine Equipment Ltd., 49-51 Millbrook Road East SO1 0HN.	0703 220735

Fast Boat Navigation

FAST BOAT NAVIGATION

The modern planing-hulled motorboat will often make short work of passagemaking around the British Isles and neighbouring countries. Cruising speeds of 20 knots or more bring flexibility over the choice of course and departure time, the relative effect of tidal streams will be much less and the risk of being caught by bad weather certainly reduced.

However, that is not to say that the fast boat navigator can completely turn his back on basic principles, or be encouraged to do less preparation before leaving the berth. In fact, the opposite is true, even if the methods of staying on a safe course are considerably different from the traditional divider and parallel rule approach.

UNDERSTANDING THE FAST BOAT AT SEA

To see why fast boat navigation techniques are essentially different from standard chart plotting, consider briefly the simplified case of two boats making an identical passage at the same time, one a fast planing-hulled design cruising at 24 knots, the other, a slow displacement craft running at 6 knots. Assuming the weather and other factors remain constant throughout, both boats will encounter the same number of waves, but the faster one will hit them four times faster. In doing so, it will accentuate the uneven pattern of the waves, something not noticed as much in a boat which stays in the water, rather than skims across it. Good hull design will cushion the ride, but the motion will nevertheless be lively in all but the calmest waters.

Other factors apply. Not every fast boat has the room, or the right layout, for a practical chart area, so the navigator has often to use a difficult working space made lively by the fast motion. In addition, on sportscruisers (open cockpit designs), this area will be relatively exposed, sheltered only from the 20 knot plus wind of the boat's high speed progress by a screen and possibly, a canopy.

Staying with our example, the fast boat moves towards navigation marks, conspicuous objects and potential hazards four times faster than its slower partner. At 24 knots, if the navigator dips his head for just one minute to check the details of the next buoy, as yet unseen, the boat will have covered nearly half-a-mile by the time he once again turns to search the sea. If the course-keeping is incorrect and the boat is approaching a sandbank which runs from deep water to 0.5m depth in 600m, the helmsman will only have 45 sec to detect the problem before running aground.

Fortunately, the answers to safe navigation at speed are quite simple — full preparation before departure and disciplined observation whilst at sea.

PREPARATION

There is a satisfying skill in putting together a good course and passage plan for a fast boat.

All of the basic chartwork skills described elsewhere in this almanac are still required, but the aim in this instance is to plot a full course before leaving.which anticipates as much as possible what will be encountered on the passage. A major advantage is the speed capability of the boat, which brings greater flexibility to planning if used wisely.

TIDE AND WIND

The fast boat navigator should look at tides with a different eye. Whilst the effect of cross-currents must still feature in calculations, the importance of 'catching' a tide to speed progress along a coast is less important than choosing the tide which is most favourable when considered with the wind direction. In this respect, advice in pilot books on suitable departure times for given passages, written with an eye to helping the sailing boat navigator, will often have to be ignored. A higher speed cruise into a foul stream with wind and tide together is often a far more efficient way of making progress than punching through choppy wind against tide waters riding a favourable stream.

Wind direction is also important in other ways. Planing-hulled boats have differing capabilities and courses should wherever possible be planned to give seas which are favourable for the craft concerned. At high speed, diversions from the most direct route are often not significant regarding the extra distance they entail and a good idea if calmer seas or a more favourable wave direction results. In some cases, given prevailing conditions, the decision may be taken to head for a harbour in an entirely different direction from that originally envisaged.

With a crosswind, some allowance should be made for leeway, especially on motor yachts with high superstructures.

PILOTAGE

A less direct course may also be appropriate to maximise the number of navigation marks encountered along the way.

Straightforward pilotage between buoys is a sensible approach to fast boat navigation, allowing quick and easy confirmation of current position, provided that positive identification is made. At high cruising speeds, navigation marks may not be seen until shortly before they are due to appear, although the higher vantage point of a flybridge helm position on a motor yacht is helpful in this respect.

RANGE AND DURATION

Fast motorboats use a lot of fuel and a 20% safety margin is the minimum when calculating range. This not only allows for unforeseen diversions, but avoids the bad practice of draining the bottom of the tank, where water and other contaminants might be lurking.

Head seas will tend to increase consumption. Also, for twin-engined boats with separate tanks and no switchover system, the range on one engine draining from one tank with the boat just off the plane may be less than with both motors working and must be taken into account in case of breakdown.

Fuel gauges should not be trusted; logging the consumption over a number of passages is a more accurate way of assessing maximum working range. Not every harbour has suitable fuelling facilities and a telephone call to check availability is often sensible.

A fast passage is exhilarating, but also tiring. The quick motion and often high noise levels promote fatigue, especially for inexperienced crew. Extended cruising should be planned accordingly.

HARBOURS

Just about all fast motorboats with inboard engines and even a good number with outdrives are not built to take the ground and non-drying harbours are essential. Access may be restricted by tides, and departure time planned accordingly. This should not only reflect the anticipated passage time, but incorporate a generous margin for slow speed manoeuvres at both ends and for a delay, or the need to set a slower cruising speed, en-route.

As with any navigation plan, suitable alternative harbours along the route should be considered

if these are available but for the faster boat, again the course can be shaped to make these quickly accessible as a safeguard against bad weather or breakdown.

CHARTWORK

With a broad idea of a plan, it is time to transfer to the chart. The first consideration before pencil hits paper is where will the chart be used?

Limited space and/or an exposed area should be considered. If paper charts are being used outside, these can be covered in transparent plastic, slipped inside proper covers manufactured for the purpose, or even encapsulated. If the working area is not satisfactory, or the chart is in danger of blowing away, it can be securely mounted to a suitable piece of board. For southern British and Northern French waters, the Stanford Allweather charts, printed on plastic, are durable enough to cope with the most extreme situations.

For the actual passage, it is easier to use a small scale chart. For planning, a larger scale is better and any important features not shown on the passage chart can be transferred over.

Wind, tide, pilotage and harbour considerations will already have given the gist of a basic course but this can be further tailored. A defensive approach is sensible, with generous allowance for anticipated cross tides and winds. Places where overfalls form are best avoided, as are areas where experience tells that fishing gear — lobster pot markers, drift nets and the like — might be found. A course through shallower water could represent the hazard of running aground, but will be clear of main shipping routes.

Ideally, courses should always be chosen which are easy to steer i.e. either ending in 0 or 5. Given a steady hand on the helm and an accurate compass, it is possible to achieve very good results at high speed under dead reckoning alone.

The chosen course, along with alternatives, should be marked very clearly, and major features ringed or highlighted. The navigator's concentration is constantly tested by the motion and noise of a fast boat, so any technique which makes the chart easier to read is sensible.

Section 14

PASSAGE PLAN

With a course to work from, a passage plan can be drawn up. This is another familiar part of any style of navigation but on the fast boat, the priority is on producing a precise account of what the navigator expects to see, when he expects to see it and what courses to steer — in effect, a navigation checklist. The more detail, the better.

Estimated time of arrival at each point can be shown either as real time if the departure hour is assured, or as elapsed time from departure. The stopwatch facility fitted to a number of electronic logs is useful on motorboats for the latter.

This vital piece of paper needs to be protected and secured so that it is readily available to those who will use it.

OUT AT SEA

The major deviation from conventional navigation on a fast boat is that accurate plotting on a paper chart is rarely possible, the reason for completing all of the paperwork before departure. Certain chart instruments, such as the Breton Plotter, are easier to use on a lively chart table but even with such devices, just a small jolt could throw a pencil position more than a mile or more out.

Instead, the chart is often only used for reference and a log account takes on greater importance. Because of the distances covered in a relatively short period, regular entries every half hour or even 20 minutes are common, rather than the customary hourly interval. If the boat's formal log book is not practical to use for this purpose, a rough version can be kept and written up later. Once again, this needs to be protected and secured.

A good grasp of basic navigation principles pays dividends at high speed. The fast boat navigator needs an ability to register all the information available to him — from the log, compass, depth sounder and what can be seen all around — and visualise that as a position on the chart. Cultivating an ability to accurately estimate distances off and understanding the optical illusions that the coastline can present to the observer are equally important.

In cases where doubt overcomes confidence — where a navigation mark fails to appear on schedule for instance — the navigator still has the ultimate safeguard; to request a slower speed or even to stop until the boat's position has been re-established.

ELECTRONIC NAVIGATION ON FAST BOATS

So far, we have concentrated on the ways in which traditional navigation techniques can be modified to suit high speed boating, But the appearance of a whole new generation of electronic instruments will bring about further changes as we move through the 1990s.

ELECTRONIC NAVIGATORS

Electronic navigators lie at the core of any modern set-up. The various land-based and satellite systems work on the same basic principal of an onboard receiver which provides a regularly-updated readout of position in latitude and longitude and at the next level, of assisting the navigator in steering between 'waypoints'. Waypoints are simply those turning points on a passage plan which we have already described above – navigation marks or other places where a course change is required to follow the desired track on the chart.

Electronic navigators vary greatly in complexity. The simplest types just give a lat/long position, the ability to store a single waypoint and enough steering information to find it. The most complex units can take 100 waypoints or more into a memory (which is retained after power is switched off). plus several routes (a string of waypoints or in effect, an electronic navigator's passage plan). The display can be changed to show the distance and direction of the next waypoint, cross track error (the distance from one side or the other of the straight track between the waypoint which has been passed and the one which lies ahead), speed over ground, satellite availability or strength of land-based transmitter signals, estimated accuracy and a host of other facts.

Three things are required for successful operation. The first is a basic grounding in traditional navigation techniques so that this plethora of information can be read, understood, appreciated and correctly interpreted. The second is to ensure good installation according to manufacturers' recommendations. Last but not least is a long evening or two spent making the acquaintance of any unfamiliar electronic navigator. Manuals vary widely in their ability to educate the potential user and delving through them is much easier if the unit itself is to hand. Indeed, it is often much less confusing to primarily explore the latter whilst keeping the former in reserve for reference.

With an electronic navigator fitted, it is common to express all waypoints on the passage plan in latitude and longitude form, along with an identification number or name. Before departure, these figures have to be accurately entered into the unit's memory and checked. The most common error in waters near the Greenwich meridian is to forget to change the longitude input from west to east or vice versa.

Once at sea, there are any number of ways in which the electronic navigator can be used by a fast boat navigator.

At its most basic level, it is possible to take a lat/long reading and check this against the chart. Another technique using the position information is to observe this in a defensive way. By noting that safe water lies above or below a certain latitude or to one side of a specified longitude (expressed in degrees and minutes only and allowing a good margin for error), it is possible to make a quick at-a-glance check that all is as it should be.

However, the waypoint facilities give far more accurate ways of using an electronic navigator to its best. Cross track error gives an instant indication of how far the boat is off course and what correction needs to be made, also showing the influence of cross tides and any leeway. This facility too can be used defensively; if it is known that a hazard lies to one side or other in the track, the helmsman can bias his steering accordingly.

THE CHANGING FACE OF FAST BOAT NAVIGATION.

The electronic navigator, used even in its most passive role, confirms the position of the boat in relation to what is calculated from conventional techniques. But advances in technology are making it possible for those roles to become reversed.

The helmsman may choose to steer using cross track error, rather than following the gyrations of an inadequately damped compass. A correctly-located electronic navigator display – either the unit itself, or a repeater by the helm – can actually be easier to interpret and provided allowances are made for potential errors in the system, bring about a far higher level of accuracy than conventional techniques could provide in similar circumstances.

AUTOPILOTS

Taking things one stage further, by interfacing (a compatible electronic connection) the electronic navigator to a compatible autopilot, course-keeping becomes an automatic function, leaving more time to monitor the equipment itself, other navigational factors and keep a better watch.

Modern autopilots designed for fast boats are simple to operate, with automatic trim controls and easy-to-understand helm functions. Whether or not used in conjunction with an electronic navigator, they are a real aid to safe navigation if used wisely.

PLOTTERS AND ELECTRONIC CHARTS

More equipment can be added. By interfacing a compatible plotter (which shows the track only according to other interfaced instruments) or more usefully, an electronic chart (which shows the same track but on an electronic representation of a chart), the navigator has a second reference source and a real time plot of perceived position.

Electronic chart units have undergone much refinement in the last five years. Most are based around bulky cathode ray displays and are of a similar size to a radar display unit, although flat LED screens are under development. But the main consideration when choosing a unit is the cartography on offer.

Software to produce the actual chart images on screen is usually supplied in the form of plug-in cartridges which contain microchips with the digitised information burnt into memory. Two Italian companies, C-Map and Navionics have established themselves as major suppliers of these cartridges, plus the necessary operating software and hardware. One or the other system is employed by most mainstream electronic chart manufacturers in their units but they are not compatible with each other.

At its meeting in Monaco during May 1992, the International Hydrographic Office furthered plans for an eventual single approved system for electronic chart cartography, but this is unlikely to emerge in the short term. However, IHO-approved electronic chart symbols are already beginning to feature in the latest software cartridges released by C-Map and Navionics.

OTHER ELECTRONICS

It is possible to extend the principal of interfacing boat instruments far beyond the trio of electronic navigator, autopilot and chart or plotter.

Basic instruments such as an electronic log, compass and depth sounder are now available as integrated systems or even single display units. These can be connected, for instance, to easily provide repeat information around the boat and a dead reckoned track (or estimated position if manually-entered tidal information can be entered) on the electronic chart display if no positional data is available from an electronic navigator.

Radar, if used correctly, will provide another independent source of information for the hard-pressed navigator. Additionally, an interfaced radar will be able to display repeat information from other instruments on screen.

Some units have a 'north-up' facility which, if connected with a compatible electronic compass, allows the display to show true north in the 12 o'clock position, rather than the boat's heading. Latest developments will allow the screen to alternate between the radar image and an electronic chart, or even to super-impose the two.

INTERFACING AND RELIABILITY

To make each individual instrument 'speak' to each other, it is important that they can send and receive data as a common electronic signal.

The industry standard has emerged around a set of 'languages' formulated by the National Marine Electronic Association (NMEA) in the United States of America. NMEA 0180 and NMEA 0183 are the most common standards, using a simple two wire interconnection.

In addition, especially for integrated instrument systems, individual manufacturers have developed their own languages and cabling systems. Mostly, these are incompatible with one another, although they additionally offer facilities for sending and receiving NMEA messages, but even within the NMEA protocol, there are some differences from company to company.

When planning any interfaced electronic system, from the simplest autopilot to electronic navigator arrangement, to the most complex array, it is important to seek the advice of manufacturers and specialist dealers before proceeding.

The same is true of installation and maintenance work.

Much of the argument against greater reliance on electronics for navigation at sea is to do with reliability, which is perceived as poor. Errors which are due to aberrations in satellite or land-based transmitter signals are well documented and can be allowed for. The biggest reason for breakdowns or misinformation is faulty installation and subsequently, failure to routinely check that all is in order.

It also makes good sense to plan any system so that there is a degree of redundancy – if the power supply to the radar fails, for instance, the rest of the instruments can still operate.

Distance Tables

$$\boxed{15}$$

USEFUL DISTANCES
from ports in the United Kingdom and Ireland

ABERDEEN to
Miles.

Antwerp	465
Ardrossan	485
Arendal	372
Belfast	464
Blyth	128
Boston	282
Bremerhaven	436
Burghead	91
Cardiff	740
Christiansand	355
Christiansund	479
Cromarty	110
Cuxhaven	428
Dover	415
Dublin	542
Dundee	61
Dunkirk	438
Emden	399
Flushing	415
Fredrikshaven	439
Glasgow	499
Gothenburg	458
Gravesend	408
Grimsby	249
Hamburg	480
Hartlepool	153
Harwich	360
Helgoland	387
Hook of Holland	374
Hull	260
Inverness	121
Kirkwall (Orkneys)	130
Leith	85
Lerwick (Shetlands)	186
Liverpool	597
Middlesbrough	161
Montrose	32
The Naze of Norway	303
Narvik	869
Ostende	415
Oslo	488
Rosyth	93
Rotterdam	391
Scapa	125
Sheerness	398
Sunderland	138
Stonehaven	14
Stromness (Orkneys)	127
Thorshaven (Faeroes)	328
Texel (The)	342
Tyne (The) (Ent.)	131
Whitby	185
Wick	101
Wilhelmshaven	420
Yarmouth (Gt.)	308
Ymuiden	363

BELFAST to
Miles.

Berehaven	328
Brest	416
Bristol (Avonmouth)	311
Campbeltown	53
Cardiff	297
Douglas	79
Dun Laoghaire	102
Fishguard	172
Galway	314
Greenock	90
Hamburg	959
Holyhead	102
Lamlash	60
Le Havre	520
Liverpool	137
Lundy Is.	246
Milford Haven	215
Ostende	639
Queenstown	256
Rosslare	169
Rothesay	79
Rotterdam	710
Sligo	186
Stornoway	236
Waterford	200

BEREHAVEN to

Brest	304
Bristol (Avonmouth)	288
Campbeltown	362
Cardiff	272
Cobh	82
Douglas	294
Dun Laoghaire	233
Fishguard	204
Galway	148
Greenock	390
Holyhead	251
Inishteraght	52
Inverary	410
Lamlash	363
Liverpool	315
Longships	188
Lundy Is.	211
Milford Haven	195
Portree	446
Rosslare	164
Rothesay	384
Shannon River (Tarbet Roads)	116
Sligo	243
Stornoway	458
Waterford	132

BLYTH to
Miles.

Aalesund	518
Aberdeen	128
Bergen	404
Boston	162
Bremerhaven	370
Cromarty	235
Cuxhaven	366
Dover	290
Dundee	102
Dunkirk	306
Ekersind	327
Emden	330
Flushing	302
Gravesend	297
Grimsby	125
Hartlepool	30
Harwich	246
Helgoland	331
Hook of Holland	279
Hull	141
Hungesund	350
Kirkwall	247
Leith	95
Lerwick	302
Middlesbrough	38
Montrose	105
Naze, The (Norway)	329
Ostende	286
Peterhead	145
Rosyth	105
Scapa	239
Sheerness	280
Stavanger	349
Sunderland	15
Texel (The)	255
Tyne (The) (Ent.)	8
Wick	218
Wilhelmshaven	360
Yarmouth (Gt.)	190
Ymuiden	270

BOSTON (Lincs.) to

Aberdeen	282
Bergen	484
Blyth	162
Bremerhaven	315
Cromarty	381
Cuxhaven	310
Dover	178
Dundee	261
Dunkirk	194
Emden	262
Flushing	181
Gravesend	180

USEFUL DISTANCES

from ports in the United Kingdom and Ireland

BOSTON (Lincs.) to

	Miles.
Grimsby	57
Hartlepool	134
Harwich	131
Helgoland	283
Hook of Holland	165
Hull	70
Hungesund	429
Kirkwall	404
Leith	258
Lerwick	442
Middlesbrough	142
Montrose	268
Naze, The (Norway)	380
Ostende	176
Peterhead	296
Rosyth	267
Scapa	394
Sheerness	165
Stavanger	425
Sunderland	150
Texel (The)	171
Tyne (The) (Ent.)	154
Wick	368
Yarmouth (Gt.)	78
Ymuiden	168

BRISTOL (Avonmouth) to

Ardrossan	363
Barrow	285
Barry	22
Belfast	311
Berehaven	288
Brest	276
Campbeltown	347
Cardiff	18
Cherbourg	322
Cobh	216
Dartmouth	258
Dublin	225
Dun Laoghaire	220
Douglas	274
Falmouth	198
Fishguard	156
Fort William	440
Galway	416
Greenock	378
Havre	395
Holyhead	228
Inishteraght	329
Inverary	398
Ilfracombe	58

BRISTOL (Avonmouth) to

	Miles.
Lamlash	347
Limerick	421
Liverpool	290
Loch Alsh (Balmacara)	478
Loch Broom (Ullapool)	540
Loch Nevis	465
Loch Ryan (Stranraer)	328
Longships	154
Lough Foyle (Moville)	374
Lough Swilly	406
Lundy Is.	83
Milford	99
Newport	10
Portland	288
Port Talbot	60
Rosslare	167
St. Malo	330
Swansea	55
St. Nazaire	416
Shannon River (Tarbert Roads)	389
Sligo	482
Troon	358
Waterford	176

CAMPBELTOWN to

Belfast	53
Berehaven	362
Bristol (Avonmouth)	347
Cardiff	332
Cobh	289
Douglas	106
Dun Laoghaire	136
Fastnet Rock	339
Fishguard	209
Fort William	125
Galway	302
Greenock	53
Holyhead	134
Inishteraght	330
Inishtrahull	71
Inverary	55
Lamlash	23
Liverpool	166
Loch Alsh (Balmacara)	166
Loch Broom (Ullapool)	228
Loch Nevis	151
Loch Ryan (Stranraer)	34
Longships	326
Lough Foyle (Moville)	66
Lough Swilly	98
Lundy Is.	379
Milford Haven	249

CAMPBELTOWN to

	Miles.
Rosslare	205
Rothesay	43
Shannon River (Tarbert Roads)	325
Sligo	173
Tobermory	115
Waterford	237

CARDIFF to

Avonmouth	18
Barry	9
Bristol	26
Belfast	297
Berehaven	272
Brest	260
Campbeltown	332
Cobh	205
Dublin	201
Douglas	254
Dun Laoghaire	204
Fastnet Rock	248
Fishguard	130
Fort William	425
Galway	405
Greenock	362
Glasgow	402
Holyhead	210
Inishteraght	313
Inverary	380
Lamlash	330
Liverpool	272
Loch Alsh (Balmacara)	460
Loch Broom (Ullapool)	523
Loch Nevis	451
Loch Ryan (Stranraer)	310
Longships	136
Lough Foyle (Moville)	358
Lough Swilly	391
Lundy Is.	67
Milford Haven	84
Newport	10
Plymouth	215
Port Talbot	38
Rosslare	145
Rothesay	350
Shannon River (Tarbert Roads)	378
Sligo	467
Stornoway	516
Sharpness	36
Swansea	40
Tobermory	412
Waterford	160

USEFUL DISTANCES
from ports in the United Kingdom and Ireland

COBH (Eire) to
Miles.

Ardrossan	316
Barrow	260
Belfast	256
Berehaven	82
Boulogne	435
Brest	267
Bristol (Avonmouth)	216
Campbeltown	289
Cardiff	205
Cherbourg	305
Douglas	220
Dieppe	405
Dublin	165
Dun Laoghaire	159
Falmouth	197
Fishguard	128
Fort William	381
Galway	225
Greenock	316
Havre	379
Holyhead	181
Inishteraght	124
Inverary	339
Lamlash	289
Liverpool	240
Loch Alsh (Balmacara)	419
Loch Broom (Ullapool)	482
Loch Nevis	409
Loch Ryan (Stranraer)	270
Longships	140
Lough Foyle (Moville)	316
Lough Swilly	348
Lundy Is.	144
Milford Haven	145
Rosslare	91
Rothesay	309
St. Nazaire	399
Shannon River (Tarbert Roads)	189
Sligo	314
Stornoway	474
Swansea	182
Tobermory	371
Waterford	60

DARTMOUTH to

Alderney (Braye)	64
Boulogne	200
Brest	149
Calais	215
Cherbourg	85
Dieppe	182
Dover	199
Dunkirk	230

DARTMOUTH to
Miles.

Falmouth	65
Folkestone	194
Havre	151
Longships	98
Newhaven	139
Penzance	89
Plymouth	36
Portland	51
Portsmouth	105
St. Helier	96
St. Malo	120
St. Mary's	117
Southampton	101
Torquay	11

DOUGLAS (Isle of Man) to

Bayonne	690
Belfast	79
Berehaven	294
Brest	378
Bristol (Avonmouth)	274
Campbeltown	106
Cardiff	254
Cobh	220
Dun Laoghaire	77
Fishguard	130
Fort William	200
Galway	371
Greenock	141
Holyhead	50
Inishteraght	330
Inishtrahull	145
Inverary	156
Lamlash	109
Liverpool	68
Loch Alsh (Balmacara)	340
Loch Broom (Ullapool)	302
Loch Nevis	227
Loch Ryan (Stranraer)	84
Longships	252
Lough Foyle (Moville)	136
Lough Swilly	168
Lundy Is.	204
Milford Haven	174
Rosslare	132
Rothesay	130
St. Nazaire	513
Sligo	244
Stornoway	295
Tobermory	195
Waterford	168

DOVER to
Miles.

Antwerp	137
Bergen	590
Boulogne	26
Brest	316
Bremerhaven	338
Calais	22
Cardiff	435
Cherbourg	150
Cromarty	504
Cuxhaven	334
Dieppe	72
Dunkirk	38
Dundee	390
Dublin	513
Emden	285
Falmouth	258
Flushing	87
Gravesend	70
Grimsby	190
Hamburg	391
Havre	120
Hartlepool	264
Harwich	64
Helgoland	309
Hook of Holland	116
Holyhead	504
Hull	203
Kirkwall (Orkneys)	526
Leith	390
Lerwick (Shetlands)	565
Limerick	609
Middlesbrough	270
Milford Haven	396
The Naze of Norway	454
Newcastle	296
Newhaven	59
Ostende	60
Penzance	281
Peterhead	419
Plymouth	225
Portland	159
Portsmouth	104
Rosyth	390
Rotterdam	135
St. Helier	200
St. Malo	229
Sheerness	53
Southampton	120
Texel (The)	168
Tyne (The) (Ent.)	286
Torquay	200
Waterford	430
Wick	491
Wilhelmshaven	330
Yarmouth (Gt.)	98
Ymuiden	158

4

USEFUL DISTANCES
from ports in the United Kingdom and Ireland

DUBLIN to

	Miles.
Ardrossan	156
Barrow	139
Barry	200
Belfast	112
Cherbourg	370
Douglas	86
Dun Laoghaire	7
Falmouth	250
Havre	452
Holyhead	63
Londonderry	194
Milford Haven	123
Swansea	172
Wicklow	28
Whitehaven	130

DUNDEE to

Aberdeen	61
Bergen	360
Blyth	102
Boston	261
Bremerhaven	444
Cromarty	172
Cuxhaven	433
Dover	390
Dunkirk	410
Emden	406
Flushing	406
Gravesend	395
Grimsby	228
Hartlepool	130
Harwich	344
Helgoland	390
Hook of Holland	369
Hull	240
Kirkwall	188
Leith	50
Lerwick	240
Middlesbrough	138
Naze, The (Norway)	343
Ostende	390
Peterhead	85
Rosyth	60
Scapa	183
Sheerness	378
Sunderland	116
Texel (The)	338
Tyne (The) (Ent.)	112
Wick	158
Wilhelmshaven	430
Yarmouth (Gt.)	295
Ymuiden	361

DUN LAOGHAIRE to

	Miles.
Bayonne	643
Belfast	102
Berehaven	233
Brest	321
Bristol (Avonmouth)	220
Campbeltown	136
Cardiff	204
Cobh	159
Douglas	77
Fishguard	89
Fort William	228
Galway (S. about)	365
Galway (N. about)	397
Greenock	166
Holyhead	56
Inishteraght	270
Inishtrahull	177
Inverary	184
Lamlash	136
Liverpool	113
Loch Alsh (Balmacara)	267
Loch Broom (Ullapool)	326
Loch Nevis	250
Loch Ryan (Stranraer)	114
Longships	199
Lough Foyle (Moville)	160
Lough Swilly	193
Lundy Is.	151
Milford Haven	122
Rosslare	68
Rothesay	155
St. Nazaire	460
Shannon River (Tarbert Roads)	334
Sligo	271
Stornoway	317
Tobermory	216
Waterford	107

FALMOUTH to

Boulogne	257
Brest	124
Calais	269
Cherbourg	137
Dartmouth	65
Dieppe	230
Dover	258
Dunkirk	291
Folkestone	254
Havre	200
Longships	40
Milford Haven	140
Newhaven	201
Penzance	33
Plymouth	38
Portland	112

FALMOUTH to

	Miles.
Portsmouth	165
St. Helier	131
St. Malo	149
Scilly Is. (St. Mary's)	60
Southampton	160
Torquay	73

FOLKESTONE to

Boulogne	26
Brest	312
Calais	25
Cherbourg	138
Dartmouth	194
Dieppe	68
Dover	6
Dunkirk	43
Falmouth	254
Havre	110
Longships	285
Newhaven	53
Penzance	275
Plymouth	224
Portland	151
Portsmouth	101
St. Helier	195
St. Malo	224
Scilly Is. (St. Mary's)	300
Southampton	117
Torquay	194

GRAVESEND to

Aberdeen	408
Bergen	594
Blyth	297
Boston	180
Bremerhaven	356
Cromarty	513
Dover	70
Dundee	395
Dunkirk	91
Emden	300
Flushing	128
Grimsby	197
Hartlepool	271
Harwich	65
Helgoland	328
Hook of Holland	149
Hull	209
Hungesund	540
Kirkwall	536
Leith	390
Lerwick	566
Middlesbrough	274
Naze, The (Norway)	469
Ostende	99

5

USEFUL DISTANCES
from ports in the United Kingdom and Ireland

GRAVESEND to

	Miles.
Peterhead	423
Rosyth	402
Sheerness	22
Sunderland	287
Texel (The)	187
Tyne (The) (Ent.)	293
Wick	497
Wilhelmshaven	347
Yarmouth (Gt.)	102
Ymuiden	174

GREENOCK to

Ardrossan	27
Barrow	159
Barry	372
Bayonne	794
Belfast	90
Berehaven	390
Brest	480
Bristol (Avonmouth)	378
Campbeltown	53
Cardiff	362
Cobh	316
Douglas	141
Dublin	173
Dun Laoghaire	166
Fishguard	240
Fort William	166
Galway	344
Glasgow	21
Holyhead	166
Inishteraght	374
Inishtrahull	118
Inverness	209
Inverary	62
Lamlash	31
Liverpool	200
Limerick	441
Londonderry	128
Loch Alsh (Balmacara)	206
Loch Broom (Ullapool)	268
Loch Nevis	198
Loch Ryan (Stranraer)	65
Longships	353
Lough Foyle (Moville)	110
Lough Swilly	144
Lundy Is.	305
Milford Haven	275
Port Patrick	93
Rothesay	14
Shannon River (Tarbert Roads)	370

GREENOCK to

	Miles.
Sligo	218
Stornoway	263
Stranraer	63
Tobermory	160
Troon	34
Waterford	268
Whitehaven	145

GRIMSBY to

Aberdeen	249
Bergen	454
Boston	57
Bremerhaven	324
Cromarty	353
Cuxhaven	320
Dover	190
Dundee	228
Dunkirk	209
Emden	271
Flushing	206
Gravesend	197
Hartlepool	101
Harwich	149
Helgoland	287
Hook of Holland	180
Hull	13
Hungesund	401
Kirkwall	370
Leith	228
Lerwick	412
Middlesbrough	104
Naze, The (Norway)	382
Ostende	191
Peterhead	264
Rosyth	235
Sheerness	184
Texel (The)	176
Tyne (The) (Ent.)	121
Wick	337
Wilhelmshaven	312
Yarmouth (Gt.)	96
Ymuiden	182

HARTLEPOOL to

Aberdeen	165
Antwerp	330
Bergen	402
Belfast	622
Blyth	30
Boston	134
Bremerhaven	362

HARTLEPOOL to

	Miles.
Cuxhaven	356
Dover	264
Dundee	130
Dunkirk	280
Emden	310
Flushing	280
Gravesend	271
Grimsby	101
Glasgow	663
Harwich	221
Hamburg	409
Helgoland	318
Hook of Holland	248
Hull	115
Hungesund	351
Kirkwall	280
Leith	124
Lerwick	330
Middlesbrough	11
Naze, The (Norway)	341
Ostende	267
Peterhead	174
Rotterdam	286
Rosyth	135
Sheerness	255
Texel (The)	235
Tyne (The) (Ent.)	22
Whitby	24
Wick	247
Wilhelmshaven	349
Yarmouth (Gt.)	171
Ymuiden	245

HARWICH to

Aberdeen	360
Antwerp	143
Bergen	542
Blyth	246
Boston	131
Bremerhaven	312
Cuxhaven	310
Dover	64
Dundee	344
Dunkirk	81
Emden	253
Flushing	93
Gravesend	65
Grimsby	149
Hamburg	361
Hartlepool	221
Helgoland	281
Hook of Holland	105
Hull	161

USEFUL DISTANCES
from ports in the United Kingdom and Ireland

HARWICH to
	Miles.
Hungesund	488
Kirkwall	489
Leith	340
Lerwick	516
Middlesbrough	221
Naze, The (Norway)	414
Ostende	79
Peterhead	376
Rosyth	350
Rotterdam	123
Sheerness	50
Sunderland	234
Texel (The)	141
Tyne (The) (Ent.)	241
Wick	446
Wilhelmshaven	300
Yarmouth (Gt.)	51
Ymuiden	127

HOLYHEAD to
Belfast	102
Berehaven	251
Brest	331
Bristol (Avonmouth)	228
Campbeltown	134
Cardiff	210
Cobh	181
Douglas	50
Dun Laoghaire	56
Fishguard	83
Fort William	227
Greenock	166
Inishteraght	290
Inishtrahull	171
Inverary	184
Lamlash	137
Liverpool	68
Loch Alsh (Balmacara)	267
Loch Broom (Ullapool)	230
Loch Nevis	254
Loch Ryan (Stranraer)	114
Longships	204
Lough Foyle (Moville)	164
Lough Swilly	192
Lundy Is.	159
Milford Haven	127
Rosslare	91
Rothesay	154
Shannon River (Tarbert Roads)	356
Sligo	273
Stornoway	318
Tobermory	216
Waterford	124

HULL to
	Miles.
Aberdeen	260
Antwerp	267
Bergen	472
Boston	70
Bremen	371
Bremerhaven	338
Bruges	209
Cuxhaven	329
Dover	203
Dundee	240
Dunkirk	222
Emden	280
Flushing	217
Fredrickstad	518
Gravesend	209
Grimsby	13
Ghent	250
Hartlepool	115
Harwich	161
Harlingen	319
Helgoland	298
Hook of Holland	193
Hungesund	417
Kirkwall	379
Leith	239
Lerwick	425
Middlesbrough	121
Naze, The (Norway)	374
Newcastle	136
Ostende	200
Peterhead	273
Rosyth	246
Rotterdam	210
Sheerness	195
Texel (The)	189
Tyne (The) (Ent.)	135
Whitby	87
Wick	349
Wilhelmshaven	325
Yarmouth (Gt.)	107
Ymuiden	193
Zeebrugge	199

KIRKWALL to
Aberdeen	130
Bergen	277
Blyth	247
Boston	404
Bremerhaven	510
Cromarty	100
Cuxhaven	496
Dover	526
Dundee	188
Dunkirk	543

KIRKWELL to
	Miles.
Emden	499
Flushing	520
Gravesend	536
Grimsby	370
Hartlepool	280
Harwich	489
Helgoland	464
Hook of Holland	490
Hull	379
Hungesund	253
Leith	212
Lerwick	98
Middlesbrough	280
Naze, The (Norway)	323
Ostende	521
Peterhead	102
Rosyth	220
Sheerness	520
Sunderland	260
Texel (The)	450
Tyne (The) (Ent.)	260
Wick	44
Wilhelmshaven	502
Yarmouth (Gt.)	433
Ymuiden	470

LEITH to
Aberdeen	85
Antwerp	454
Bergen	386
Berwick	52
Blyth	95
Bremerhaven	446
Cromarty	197
Dover	390
Dundee	50
Dunkirk	406
Emden	403
Flushing	404
Grangemouth	19
Gravesend	390
Grimsby	228
Hartlepool	124
Harwich	340
Hamburg	490
Helgoland	400
Hook of Holland	362
Hull	239
Hungesund	344
Inverness	203
Kirkwall	212
Lerwick	269
Middlesbrough	131
Naze, The (Norway)	356

7

USEFUL DISTANCES

from ports in the United Kingdom and Ireland

LEITH to
	Miles.
Newcastle	114
Ostende	386
Peterhead	106
Rotterdam	384
Rosyth	10
Sheerness	377
Sunderland	110
Texel (The)	335
Tyne (The) (Ent.)	103
Wick	181
Wilhelmshaven	431
Yarmouth (Gt.)	293
Ymuiden	354

LIVERPOOL (Landing Stage) to
Antwerp	698
Ardrossan	176
Barrow	48
Barry	264
Belfast	137
Berehaven	315
Brest	396
Bristol (Avonmouth)	290
Campbeltown	166
Cardiff	272
Cobh	240
Douglas	68
Dublin	126
Dunkirk	605
Dundee (N. about)	626
Dun Laoghaire	113
Falmouth	324
Fishguard	148
Fort William	260
Galway (N. about)	440
Galway (S. about)	445
Greenock	200
Havre	550
Holyhead	68
Inishteraght	356
Inishtrahull	200
Inverary	217
Lamlash	172
Limerick	468
London	698
Londonderry	215
Loch Alsh (Balmacara)	300
Loch Broom (Ullapool)	365
Loch Nevis	288
Loch Ryan (Stranraer)	146
Longships	269
Lough Foyle (Moville)	197
Lough Swilly	229
Lundy Is.	221

LIVERPOOL (Landing Stage) to
	Miles.
Manchester	40
Milford Haven	188
Newcastle (N. about)	736
Plymouth	353
Rosslare	154
Rothesay	190
Shields (N. about)	728
Stornoway	342
St. Nazaire	530
Swansea	242
Shannon River (N. about)	458
Shannon River (S. about)	414
Sligo	304
Tobermory	251
Waterford	192
Whitehaven	77

LONDON (Tower Bridge) to
Aberdeen	430
Antwerp	196
Ardrossan	721
Barrow	649
Belfast	665
Bergen	604
Blyth	303
Boulogne	97
Bremerhaven	381
Bristol	525
Bruges	143
Calais	96
Cuxhaven	382
Dover	91
Dublin	590
Dundee	416
Dunkirk	116
Flushing	146
Gravesend	23
Hamburg	422
Hartlepool	290
Harwich	87
Hull	228
Leith	431
Middlesbrough	296
Newcastle	316
Ostende	122
Rotterdam	187
Sheerness	45
Yarmouth (Gt.)	132
Zeebrugge	133

MIDDLESBROUGH to
	Miles.
Aberdeen	161
Bergen	416
Blyth	38
Boston	142
Bremerhaven	362
Cromarty	264
Cuxhaven	360
Dover	270
Dundee	138
Dunkirk	290
Emden	310
Flushing	286
Gravesend	274
Grimsby	104
Hartlepool	11
Harwich	221
Helgoland	325
Hook of Holland	256
Hull	120
Hungesund	361
Kirkwall	280
Leith	130
Lerwick	330
Naze, The (Norway)	340
Ostende	260
Peterhead	180
Rosyth	143
Sheerness	259
Sunderland	25
Texel (The)	235
Tyne (The) (Ent.)	32
Wick	255
Wilhelmshaven	351
Yarmouth (Gt.)	174
Ymuiden	249

MILFORD HAVEN to
Aberdeen	657
Ardrossan	267
Barrow	207
Barry Dock	86
Bideford	56
Boulogne	396
Brest	242
Calais	410
Cape Finisterre	564
Cherbourg	272
Dieppe	371
Dunkirk	432
Folkestone	391
Galway	337
Gravesend	466
Havre	336
Hull	600

USEFUL DISTANCES
from ports in the United Kingdom and Ireland

MILFORD HAVEN to

	Miles.
Inishtrahull	286
Leith	736
Limerick	338
Lowestoft	481
Newhaven	341
Newport	101
Ostende	455
Portishead	104
Portsmouth	298
St. Helier	262
Sheerness	449
Sligo	391
Southampton	296
Sunderland	676
Yarmouth (Gt.)	491

PETERHEAD to

Aberdeen	25
Bergen	286
Blyth	145
Boston	296
Bremerhaven	434
Cromarty	87
Cuxhaven	416
Dover	419
Dundee	85
Dunkirk	440
Emden	402
Flushing	418
Gravesend	423
Grimsby	264
Hartlepool	174
Harwich	376
Helgoland	381
Hook of Holland	391
Hull	273
Hungesund	248
Kirkwall	102
Leith	106
Lerwick	155
Middlesbrough	181
Naze, The (Norway)	286
Ostende	421
Rosyth	117
Sheerness	406
Sunderland	161
Texel (The)	350
Tyne (The) (Ent.)	156
Wick	73
Wilhelmshaven	420
Yarmouth (Gt.)	324
Ymuiden	370

PLYMOUTH to

	Miles.
Ardrossan	488
Barrow	352
Barry	208
Boulogne	227
Brest	138
Calais	242
Cherbourg	107
Dartmouth	36
Dieppe	212
Dover	225
Dunkirk	263
Falmouth	38
Folkestone	224
Galway	404
Greenock	446
Holyhead	280
Havre	175
Longships	72
Limerick	394
Milford Haven	192
Newport	230
Newhaven	165
Penzance	66
Portland	80
Portsmouth	134
St. Malo	135
St. Mary's	94
Southampton	135
Swansea	199
Torquay	41
Waterford	214
Whitehaven	360

PORTSMOUTH to

Aberdeen	521
Avonmouth	347
Berehaven	380
Bideford	283
Brixham	100
Caen	100
Calais	125
Cork	342
Devonport	136
Folkestone	99
Fowey	148
Hamble	16
Harwich	171
Havre	93
Honfleur	98
London	197
Ostende	165
Poole	37
Sheerness	159
Torquay	102

SHEERNESS to

	Miles.
Aberdeen	398
Bergen	573
Blyth	280
Boston	165
Bremerhaven	346
Chatham	8
Cromarty	490
Cuxhaven	341
Dover	53
Dundee	378
Dunkirk	74
Emden	285
Flushing	108
Gravesend	22
Grimsby	184
Hartlepool	255
Harwich	50
Helgoland	314
Hook of Holland	130
Hull	195
Hungesund	514
Kirkwall	520
Leith	377
Lerwick	550
Middlesbrough	259
Naze, The (Norway)	455
Ostende	85
Peterhead	406
Rosyth	386
Sunderland	277
Texel (The)	169
Tyne (The) (Ent.)	280
Wick	478
Wilhelmshaven	332
Yarmouth (Gt.)	86
Ymuiden	156

SHOREHAM to

Avonmouth	381
Boulogne	73
Caen	95
Calais	85
Dieppe	66
Dunkirk	106
Falmouth	191
Folkestone	67
Hamble	52
Havre	89
London	161
Portland	89
Portsmouth	41
Sheerness	123
St. Helier	136
St. Malo	161
Torquay	132
Waterford	359

USEFUL DISTANCES
from ports in the United Kingdom and Ireland

SOUTHAMPTON to
	Miles.
Boulogne	121
Brest	228
Calais	136
Cherbourg	90
Cowes	11
Dartmouth	101
Dieppe	118
Dover	120
Dunkirk	162
Falmouth	160
Folkestone	117
Guernsey	104
Havre	105
Longships	188
Newhaven	62
Penzance	184
Plymouth	135
Portland	55
Portsmouth	18
Ryde	13
St. Malo	166
St. Helier	128
St. Mary's	212
Torquay	97

SUNDERLAND to
Aberdeen	138
Antwerp	342
Bergen	400
Blyth	15
Boston (Lincs.)	150
Bremerhaven	368
Cromarty	243
Cuxhaven	360
Dover	280
Dundee	116
Dunkirk	300
Emden	320
Flushing	292
Gravesend	287
Grimsby	116
Hamburg	419
Hartlepool	17
Harwich	234
Helgoland	324
Hook of Holland	260
Hull	127
Hungesund	345
Kirkwall	260
Leith	110
Lerwick	314
London	284
Middlesbrough	25

SUNDERLAND to
	Miles.
Naze, The (Norway)	335
Newcastle	16
Ostende	279
Peterhead	161
Rosyth	120
Sheerness	277
Texel (The)	242
Tyne (The) (Ent.)	6½
Whitby	36
Wick	231
Wilhelmshaven	359
Yarmouth (Gt.)	186
Ymuiden	256

SWANSEA to
Avonmouth	62
Berehaven	238
Brest	254
Brixham	225
Cherbourg	457
Dartmouth	389
Douglas	223
Dublin	175
Falmouth	161
Hamble	305
Havre	349
Harwich	474
Liverpool	240
Penzance	134
St. Malo	290
Shoreham	345
Southampton	309

WATERFORD to
Belfast	200
Berehaven	132
Brest	258
Bristol (Avonmouth)	176
Campbeltown	237
Cardiff	160
Cobh	60
Douglas	168
Dun Laoghaire	107
Fishguard	75
Fort William	329
Galway	266
Greenock	268
Holyhead	124
Inishteraght	173
Inverary	287
Lamlash	238

WATERFORD to
	Miles.
Liverpool	192
Loch Alsh (Balmacara)	369
Loch Broom (Ullapool)	430
Loch Nevis	356
Loch Ryan (Stranraer)	216
Longships	132
Lough Foyle (Moville)	264
Lundy Is.	104
Milford Haven	75
Rosslare	39
Rothesay	256
St. Nazaire	394
Shannon River (Tarbert Roads)	238
Stornoway	423
Tobermory	321

YARMOUTH (GREAT) (Norfolk) to
Aberdeen	308
Bergen	494
Blyth	200
Boston (Lincs.)	78
Bremerhaven	275
Cromarty	410
Cuxhaven	273
Dover	98
Dundee	295
Dunkirk	116
Emden	218
Flushing	113
Gravesend	102
Grimsby	96
Hartlepool	171
Harwich	51
Helgoland	244
Hook of Holland	95
Hull	107
Hungesund	437
Kirkwall	433
Leith	293
Lerwick	476
Middlesbrough	174
Naze, The (Norway)	395
Ostende	100
Peterhead	326
Rosyth	303
Sheerness	86
Sunderland	186
Texel (The)	100
Tyne (The) (Ent.)	192
Wick	402
Wilhelmshaven	206
Ymuiden	114

ENGLISH CHANNEL DISTANCES

	Tower Bridge	Gravesend	Great Nore	Tongue Sand Towers	S. Goodwin Lt. F.	Dover	Dungeness	Royal Sovereign Lt.
Tower Bridge	–	23	43	60	84	91	109	131
Gravesend	23	–	23	38	63	68	86	108
Great Nore	43	19	–	19	43	48	67	90
Tongue Sand Towers	60	38	19	–	24	29	48	71
S. Goodwin Lt. F.	84	63	43	24	–	6	23	47
Dover	91	68	48	29	6	–	18	41
Dungeness	109	86	67	48	23	18	–	23
Royal Sovereign Lt.	131	108	90	71	47	41	23	–
Beachy Head	140	116	99	78	55	50	31	8
Newhaven	148	125	106	86	62	58	40	16
Owers Lanby	175	152	133	113	89	85	66	44
Portsmouth	194	171	152	133	108	104	86	62
Southampton	208	185	166	147	123	120	100	76
St. Catherines	199	176	158	137	114	110	91	69
Needles	214	191	173	154	130	125	106	84
Shambles Lt. By.	238	217	198	179	155	150	131	109
Portland Bill	242	222	203	182	160	155	135	114
Casquets	256	232	214	196	172	167	149	126
Dartmouth	287	264	245	226	202	196	178	154
Start Pt.	292	269	249	230	206	202	184	159
Prawle Pt.	295	272	252	233	209	205	187	162
Plymouth	318	295	276	257	233	229	210	187
Eddystone	314	292	272	253	230	225	207	183
Fowey	330	307	288	274	246	240	223	199
Dodman Pt.	336	313	294	277	252	246	229	204
Falmouth	345	321	304	286	261	255	238	213
Lizard	353	331	311	291	269	264	245	223
Penzance	370	347	328	308	285	280	261	239
Longships	378	355	336	316	293	287	268	247
Bishops Rk.	402	379	360	341	317	311	293	271

ENGLISH CHANNEL DISTANCES

	Beachy Head	Newhaven	Owers Lanby	Portsmouth	Southampton	St Catherines	Needles	Shambles Lt. By.
Tower Bridge	140	148	175	194	208	199	214	238
Gravesend	116	125	152	171	185	176	191	217
Great Nore	99	106	133	152	166	158	173	198
Tongue Sand Towers	78	86	113	133	147	137	154	179
S. Goodwin Lt. F. ...	55	62	89	108	123	114	130	155
Dover.....................	50	58	85	104	120	110	125	150
Dungeness	31	40	66	86	100	91	106	131
Royal Sovereign Lt..	8	16	44	62	76	69	84	109
Beachy Head	–	8	36	55	69	61	74	99
Newhaven	8	–	28	48	60	53	70	94
Owers Lanby	36	28	–	20	34	25	40	66
Portsmouth	55	48	20	–	14	21	21	51
Southampton	69	60	34	14	–	34	22	52
St. Catherines	61	53	25	21	34	–	13	40
Needles	74	70	40	21	22	13	–	30
Shambles Lt. By.	99	94	66	51	52	40	30	–
Portland Bill	104	99	71	55	56	46	34	5
Casquets	119	114	85	86	87	67	64	48
Dartmouth	147	141	113	101	102	86	79	48
Start Pt.	152	145	118	104	106	93	83	53
Prawle Pt.	155	149	121	108	109	95	86	57
Plymouth	179	172	144	132	133	120	110	80
Eddystone	176	169	141	129	130	117	106	78
Fowey	191	185	157	144	145	132	123	93
Dodman Pt.	196	191	163	150	151	138	129	99
Falmouth	206	200	172	159	160	147	138	108
Lizard	215	209	181	167	168	156	146	116
Penzance	231	225	197	183	184	172	161	132
Longships	239	233	205	191	192	180	170	140
Bishops Rk.	263	257	229	215	216	204	194	164

ENGLISH CHANNEL DISTANCES

	Portland Bill	Casquets	Dartmouth	Start Pt.	Prawle Pt.	Plymouth	Eddystone
Tower Bridge	242	256	287	292	295	318	314
Gravesend	222	232	264	269	272	295	292
Great Nore	203	214	245	249	252	276	272
Tongue Sand Towers	182	196	226	230	233	257	253
S. Goodwin Lt. F. ...	160	172	202	206	209	233	230
Dover	155	167	196	202	205	229	225
Dungeness	135	149	178	184	187	210	207
Royal Sovereign Lt..	114	126	154	159	162	187	183
Beachy Head	104	119	147	152	155	179	176
Newhaven	99	114	141	145	149	172	169
Owers Lanby	71	85	113	118	121	144	141
Portsmouth	55	86	101	104	108	132	129
Southampton	56	87	102	106	109	133	130
St. Catherines	46	67	86	93	95	120	117
Needles	34	64	79	83	86	110	106
Shambles Lt. By.	5	48	48	53	57	80	78
Portland Bill	–	48	44	49	52	75	72
Casquets	48	–	60	57	60	79	79
Dartmouth	44	60	–	9	12	36	33
Start Pt.	49	57	9	–	3	26	24
Prawle Pt.	52	60	12	3	–	23	22
Plymouth	75	79	36	26	23	–	11
Eddystone	72	79	33	24	22	11	–
Fowey	88	95	48	39	36	20	17
Dodman Pt.	93	99	55	46	42	27	21
Falmouth	103	106	63	55	51	38	30
Lizard	111	114	71	62	60	48	39
Penzance	127	127	88	79	76	64	55
Longships	135	134	96	87	84	72	62
Bishops Rk.	159	157	120	111	108	96	87

ENGLISH CHANNEL DISTANCES

	Fowey	Dodman Pt.	Falmouth	Lizard	Penzance	Longships	Bishop Rk.
Tower Bridge	330	336	345	353	370	378	402
Gravesend	307	313	321	331	347	355	379
Great Nore	288	294	304	311	328	336	360
Tongue Sand Towers	274	277	286	291	308	316	341
S. Goodwin Lt. F.	246	252	261	269	285	293	317
Dover	240	246	255	264	280	287	311
Dungeness	223	229	238	245	261	268	293
Royal Sovereign Lt.	199	204	213	223	239	247	271
Beachy Head	191	196	206	215	231	239	263
Newhaven	185	191	200	209	225	233	257
Owers Lanby	157	163	172	181	197	205	229
Portsmouth	144	150	159	167	183	191	215
Southampton	145	151	160	168	184	192	216
St. Catherines	132	138	147	156	172	180	204
Needles	123	129	138	146	161	170	194
Shambles Lt. By.	93	99	108	116	132	140	164
Portland Bill	88	93	103	111	127	135	159
Casquets	95	99	106	114	127	134	157
Dartmouth	48	55	63	71	88	96	120
Start Pt.	39	46	55	62	79	87	111
Prawle Pt.	36	42	51	60	76	84	108
Plymouth	20	27	38	48	64	72	96
Eddystone	17	21	30	39	55	62	87
Fowey	–	9	20	32	48	56	80
Dodman Pt.	9	–	11	22	39	47	71
Falmouth	20	11	–	15	32	40	64
Lizard	32	22	15	–	16	25	49
Penzance	48	39	32	16	–	15	42
Longships	56	47	40	25	15	–	31
Bishops Rk.	80	71	64	49	42	31	–

INTER-DISTANCES
between ports in the U.K / N. Europe / Baltic & White Sea

K via Kiel Canal	Aalborg	Aalsund	Aberdeen	Abo (Turku)	Antwerp	Archangel	Avonmouth	Bayonne
Aarhus	119	575	543	580	528K	1914	1034K	1196K
Amsterdam	479K	637	380	867K	148	1980	655	815
Antwerp	586K	790	450	974K	−	2040	631	791
Archangel	1855	1447	1745	2429	2040	−	2282	2719
Avonmouth	1089K	1020	754	1480K	631	2282	−	581
Bilbao	1250K	1375	1061	1638K	787	2714	604	60
Bordeaux	1237	1336	1026	1789	745	2646	556	205
Bremen	352K	603	460	740K	333	1881	873	1052
Brest	975K	1014	770	1363K	491	2313	308	318
Copenhagen	132	598	566	467	600K	1937	1106K	1268K
Dublin	945	822	542	1519	677	2084	220	627
Dunkirk	574K	674	418	962K	102	2016	529	701
Gydnia	419	922K	841K	384	737K	2315	1243K	1405K
Gibraltar	1808K	1947	1619	2196K	1345	3225	1158	978
Glasgow	902	597	499	1476	854	2032	373	804
Gothenburg	92	490	458	599	616K	1829	1063	1225
Hamburg	279K	601	473	667K	382	1917	893	1053
Havre	707	823	522	1098K	244	2104	438	593
Helsinki	681	1138	1106	108	1026K	2477	1532K	1694K
Hull	530	594	270	972K	265	1926	707	873
La Pallice	1162	1261	951	1714	670	2571	478	130
Lisbon	1570K	1695	1381	1958K	1107	2968	893	630
Liverpool	1000	848	597	1592K	698	2075	282	693
London	622	738	436	1015K	193	2061	586	747
Lulea	957	1389	1357	350	1273K	2728	1779K	1941K
Malmo	157	603	571	483	603K	1942	1109K	1271K
Newcastle	513	535	145	1015K	351	1804	789	954
Oslo	227	523	488	763	657	1836	1082	1445
Plymouth	824	949	638	1215K	366	2243	278	473
Reykjavik	1200	850	805	1755	1249	1883	1103	1369
Rotterdam	511K	673	391	899K	121	1950	632	794
St. Petersburg	868	1289	1257	268	1177K	2628	1683K	1845K
Southampton	746	845	535	1298	255	2155	345	536
Stockholm	559	1015	983	162	901K	2354	1407K	1569K
Szczecin	360	805K	724K	503	620K	2197	1126K	1288K

INTER-DISTANCES
between ports in the U.K / N. Europe / Baltic & White Sea

K via Kiel Canal	Bergen	Christiansand	Cork	Dundee	Emden	Flushing	Ghent	Gibraltar
Aarhus	432	217	1007K	528	324K	480K	509K	1750K
Amsterdam	502	360	628	374	166	100	124	1369
Antwerp	602	451	604	442	276	51	55	1345
Archangel	1443	1565	2555	1773	1878	1993	2023	3225
Avonmouth	935	1010	230	818	778	581	610	1158
Bilbao	1240	1142	577	1044	936	739	768	867
Bordeaux	1194	1102	547	1053	895	705	734	1011
Bremen	481	326	846	471	162	319	353	1606
Brest	944	851	281	753	645	448	477	973
Copenhagen	455	240	1079K	605	399K	552K	581K	1822K
Dublin	752	798	185	606	824	627	656	1204
Dunkirk	585	475	502	402	264	55	85	1255
Gydnia	833	618	1216K	840K	536K	689K	718K	1959K
Gibraltar	1798	1699	1131	1592	1494	1297	1326	—
Glasgow	700	755	338	563	868	804	833	1381
Gothenburg	356	132	1036	497	415K	517	546	1779
Hamburg	486	326	866	485	185	335	365	1607
Havre	702	600	411	505	396	197	227	1147
Helsinki	995	780	1505K	1145	825K	978K	1007K	2248K
Hull	474	407	680	240	279	218	248	1427
La Pallice	1119	1027	472	978	820	630	425	957
Lisbon	1560	1462	833	1364	1256	1059	1088	280
Liverpool	778	824	255	661	890	693	722	1270
London	613	514	559	420	318	146	176	1301
Lulea	1246	1031	1752K	1396	1072K	1225K	1474K	2495K
Malmo	460	245	1082K	610	402K	555K	584K	1825K
Newcastle	403	376	762	122	329	304	334	1508
Oslo	378	163	1077	536	449	607	637	1870
Plymouth	819	717	251	621	513	319	349	1036
Reykjavik	873	1025	979	864	1170	1199	1230	1930
Rotterdam	533	413	605	383	199	74	104	1348
St. Petersburg	1146	931	1656K	1296	976K	1129K	1158K	2399K
Southampton	703	610	340	510	405	200	232	1119
Stockholm	872	657	1380K	1022	700K	853K	882K	2123K
Szczecin	715	500	1099K	723K	419K	572K	601K	1842K

INTER-DISTANCES
between ports in the U.K / N. Europe / Baltic & White Sea

K via Kiel Canal	Glasgow	Gothenburg	Grangemouth	Hernosand	Ipswich	Kiel	Kotka	Larvik
Aarhus	961	118	606	696	513K	130	703	205
Amsterdam	865	464	384	951K	149	291	973K	448
Antwerp	854	616K	394	1058K	148	398	1080K	534
Archangel	2032	1829	1806	2053	1956	2037	2525	1647
Avonmouth	373	1063	839	1564	568	904	1586K	1055
Bilbao	827	1221	1057	1722K	718	1062	1744K	1219
Bordeaux	775	1178	1019	1902	684	1014	1899	1268
Bremen	926	382K	508	824K	366	164	846K	409
Brest	531	930	766	1447K	427	787	1469K	928
Copenhagen	984	134	629	580	585	202	830	220
Dublin	178	919	627	1593	614	950	1615	883
Dunkirk	752	553	414	1046K	90	386	1068K	572
Gydnia	1288	383	891K	509	722K	339	532	470
Gibraltar	1381	1779	1615	2280K	1276	1640	2302K	1777
Glasgow	–	876	584	1550	791	949	1572	840
Gothenburg	876	–	521	724	539	218	725	94
Hamburg	939	402	501	751K	370	91	773K	399
Havre	661	681	518	1182K	172	522	1204K	670
Helsinki	1524	657	1169	356	1011K	628	72	897
Hull	744	504	252	1024K	166	396	1078K	485
La Pallice	700	1103	944	1827	609	939	1824	1193
Lisbon	1116	1541	1377	2042K	1038	1382	2064K	1539
Liverpool	215	974	682	1648	680	1016	1670	938
London	809	596	432	1099K	83	439	1121K	608
Lulea	1775	866	1420	222	1258K	875	599	1019
Malmo	989	141	634	590	588K	205	587	233
Newcastle	649	487	131	1099K	264	439	1121K	468
Oslo	896	163	558	877	610	355	876	68
Plymouth	501	798	634	1299K	284	639	1321K	806
Reykjavik	854	1152	902	1867	1164	1252	1864	1115
Rotterdam	855	489	396	983K	131	323	1005K	494
St. Petersburg	1675	847	1320	507	1162K	779	108	919
Southampton	564	695	528	1410	193	522	1400	690
Stockholm	1401	512	1046	257	886K	503	279	645
Szczecin	1171K	390	774K	548	605K	222	621	488

INTER-DISTANCES
between ports in the U.K / N. Europe / Baltic & White Sea

K via Kiel Canal	Leith	Liverpool	London	Manchester	Murmansk	Narvik	Oporto	Oscarshamn
Aarhus	599	1084	569K	1124	1540	1045	1340K	386
Amsterdam	372	767	208	807	1517	1090	959	648K
Antwerp	453	698	193	738	1629	1211	935	755K
Archangel	1788	2075	2061	2115	473	986	2816	2179
Avonmouth	832	282	586	322	1969	1379	745	1261K
Bilbao	1042	716	743	756	2213	1778	436	1419K
Bordeaux	1000	672	702	712	2277	1790	580	1590
Bremen	475	985	409	1025	1492	1092	1196	521K
Brest	751	410	452	450	1959	1574	540	1144K
Copenhagen	822	1082	641	1122	1563	1068	1412K	217
Dublin	620	121	632	161	1771	1181	791	1269
Dunkirk	399	641	112	681	1646	1165	845	743K
Gydnia	838K	1460	970K	1500	1941	1446	1549K	218
Gibraltar	1600	1270	1301	1310	2977	2427	454	1977K
Glasgow	577	215	809	255	1719	1129	968	1226
Gothenburg	514	974	596	1014	1455	960	1369	422
Hamburg	486	1005	425	1045	1581	1081	1197	448K
Havre	503	550	205	590	1797	1304	737	879K
Helsinki	1127K	1622	1067K	1662	2103	1608	1838K	333
Hull	237	819	239	859	1566	1066	1017	753K
La Pallice	924	597	627	637	2202	1715	526	1515
Lisbon	1362	1005	1063	1045	2664	2164	176	1739K
Liverpool	675	–	698	40	1797	1207	857	1324
London	417	698	–	738	1715	1215	891	796K
Lulea	1413	1873	1314K	1703	2354	1859	2085K	561
Malmo	627	1087	644K	1127	1568	1073	1415K	291
Newcastle	116	747	325	787	1500	970	1098	796K
Oslo	538	969	666	1009	1450	976	1439	566
Plymouth	619	390	321	430	1928	1408	617	996K
Reykjavik	888	927	1231	967	1517	1096	1500	1555
Rotterdam	381	744	184	784	1628	1139	938	680K
St. Petersburg	1313	1773	1218K	1813	2254	1759	1989K	508
Southampton	508	461	211	501	1786	1299	714	1099
Stockholm	1039	1499	942K	1539	1980	1485	1713K	194
Szczecin	721K	1242K	661K	1282K	1823	1328	1432K	298

INTER-DISTANCES
between ports in the U.K / N. Europe / Baltic & White Sea

K via Kiel Canal	Oslo	Reykjavik	Riga	Rotterdam	Santander	Stockholm	Sunderland	Swansea
Aarhus	265	1235	570	453K	1169K	507	564	965K
Amsterdam	522	1462	846K	67	788	794K	268	547
Antwerp	630	1250	953K	121	764	901K	318	525
Archangel	1711	1883	2403	1950	2689	2354	1833	2241
Avonmouth	1163	1100	1459K	632	569	1407K	770	62
Bilbao	1292	1475	1617K	790	36	1585K	927	507
Bordeaux	1248	1755	1763	743	235	1716	890	828
Bremen	460	1236	719K	290	1025	667K	418	836
Brest	1001	1181	1342K	457	343	1290K	636	283
Copenhagen	272	1259	696	525K	1241K	409	587	1037K
Dublin	951	896	1493	678	615	1444	690	169
Dunkirk	617	1215	941K	104	674	889K	286	492
Gydnia	528	1521	309	662K	1378K	325	776K	1174K
Gibraltar	1850	1933	2175K	1348	835	2123K	1485	1121
Glasgow	908	855	1450	855	792	1401	647	345
Gothenburg	159	1152	586	489	1198	512	479	985
Hamburg	461	1234	646K	307	1026	594K	407	856
Havre	752	1305	1077K	250	566	1025K	392	401
Helsinki	948	1809	315	951K	1667K	230	1065K	1495K
Hull	559	1050	951K	211	846	899K	128	670
La Pallice	1173	1680	1688	668	200	1641	815	753
Lisbon	1612	2235	1937K	1110	557	1885K	1247	856
Liverpool	1006	927	1548	744	681	1499	882	236
London	668	1231	944K	184	720	942K	312	549
Lulea	1063	2047	629	1198K	1914K	443	1312K	1742K
Malmo	280	1266	456	528K	1244K	422	592	1040K
Newcastle	528	935	994K	285	927	942K	15	752
Oslo	—	1179	744	555	1253	694	521	1046
Plymouth	869	1150	1194K	367	446	1142K	500	241
Reykjavik	1179	—	1728	1182	1452	1681	936	1056
Rotterdam	554	1182	878K	—	767	826K	286	595
St. Petersburg	963	1950	504	1102K	1818K	386	1214K	1614K
Southampton	757	1265	1272	252	528	1225	400	309
Stockholm	819	1681	217	826K	1553K	—	940K	1370K
Szczecin	541	1638	495	545K	1272K	408	659K	1089K

DISTANCE TABLES
between ports in the U.K / N. Europe / Baltic & White Sea
and Mediterranean / Black Sea / Adriatic

	Aberdeen	Amsterdam	Antwerp	Archangel	Avonmouth	Belfast	Bergen	Bilbao
Alexandria	3449	3216	3181	5062	2981	3110	3620	2655
Algiers	2061	1828	1793	3695	1597	1725	2235	1270
Ancona	3187	2954	2919	4820	2698	2833	3360	2395
Barcelona	2176	1943	1908	3810	1674	1840	2350	1385
Beirut	3665	3430	3395	5310	3199	3340	3850	2885
Bourgas	3562	3329	3294	5195	3079	3225	3735	2770
Brindisi	2930	2697	2662	4565	2441	2595	3105	2140
Cagliari	2350	2115	2080	3995	1873	2025	2535	1570
Casablanca	1675	1445	1410	3306	1193	1327	1860	901
Constanza	3625	3392	3357	5257	3194	3287	3797	2832
Dubrovnik	3038	2781	2755	4655	2549	2681	3205	2256
Durres	3012	2780	2745	4660	2538	2690	3200	2235
Genoa	2506	2273	2238	4140	2035	2170	2680	1715
Gibraltar	1619	1369	1345	3225	1158	1292	1798	867
Haifa	3663	3430	3395	5310	3186	3340	3850	2885
Iskenderun	3688	3431	3405	5305	3199	3331	3855	2906
Istanbul	3433	3200	3165	5065	3001	3095	3605	2640
Izmir	3272	3039	3004	4905	2783	2935	3445	2480
Marseilles	2340	2107	2072	3975	1870	2005	2510	1550
Messina	2657	2424	2389	4290	2168	2320	2830	1865
Morphou Bay	3556	3323	3288	5190	3090	3220	3730	2765
Naples	2620	2387	2352	4253	2140	2283	2793	1828
Novorossisk	3873	3640	3605	5505	3384	3535	4045	3080
Odessa	3778	3545	3510	5420	3344	3440	3950	2985
Palermo	2547	2314	2279	4180	2058	2210	2720	1755
Piraeus	3157	2924	2889	4790	2680	2820	3330	2365
Port Said	3557	3324	3289	5175	3100	3220	3730	2765
Poti	4033	3800	3765	5660	3539	3690	4200	3235
Rijeka	3297	3001	2975	4875	2769	2901	3470	2505
Sfax	2654	2367	2332	4235	2165	2265	2775	1872
Syracuse	2674	2417	2391	4291	2185	2317	2841	1892
Taranto	2878	2621	2595	4495	2389	2521	3045	2140
Thessaloniki	3355	3120	3085	5000	2888	3030	3540	2575
Trieste	3333	3041	3015	4915	2809	2941	3505	2540
Tripoli (Libya)	2747	2514	2479	4380	2258	2410	2920	1955
Tunis	2425	2192	2157	4060	1977	2090	2600	1635
Valencia	2037	1804	1769	3670	1571	1700	2210	1245
Valetta	2631	2398	2363	4265	2165	2295	2805	1840
Venice	3324	3091	3056	4960	2819	2990	3500	2535
Zhdanov	3962	3730	3695	5605	3484	3635	4145	3180

DISTANCE TABLES
between ports in the U.K / N. Europe / Baltic & White Sea and Mediterranean / Black Sea / Adriatic

	Bordeaux	Bremen	Brest	Cherbourg	Copenhagen (via Kiel Canal)	Cork	Dublin	Dunkirk
Alexandria	2807	3428	2720	2905	3600	2898	3015	3083
Algiers	1419	2040	1335	1520	2215	1510	1630	1695
Ancona	2545	3166	2460	2645	3340	2636	2742	2821
Barcelona	1534	2155	1450	1635	2330	1625	1745	1810
Beirut	3023	3644	2950	3135	3830	3114	3245	3300
Bourgas	2920	3541	2835	3020	3715	3011	3130	3196
Brindisi	2288	2909	2205	2390	3085	2379	2500	2564
Cagliari	1708	2330	1635	1820	2515	1000	1030	1984
Casablanca	995	1668	980	1170	1824	1128	1225	1317
Constanza	2983	3604	2900	3082	3777	3074	3198	3259
Dubrovnik	2400	2996	2337	2488	3187	2487	2590	2655
Durres	2373	2995	2300	2485	3180	2465	2595	2650
Genoa	1864	2485	1780	1965	2660	1955	2075	2140
Gibraltar	1013	1606	973	1117	1822	1131	1204	1255
Haifa	3023	3645	2950	3135	3830	3115	3245	3275
Iskenderun	3083	3646	3010	3138	3837	3175	3240	3305
Istanbul	2791	3412	2705	2890	3585	2882	3000	3067
Izmir	2630	3251	2545	2730	3425	2721	2840	2906
Marseilles	1698	2319	1615	1800	2495	1789	1910	1974
Messina	2015	2636	1930	2115	2810	2106	2225	2291
Morphou Bay	2823	3535	2830	3015	3710	3005	3125	3290
Naples	1978	2599	1893	2078	2773	2069	2188	2254
Novorossisk	3231	3852	3202	3530	4025	3322	3440	3507
Odessa	3136	3757	3050	3235	3930	3227	3345	3412
Palermo	1905	2526	1820	2005	2700	1996	2115	2181
Piraeus	2515	3136	2430	2615	3310	2606	2725	2791
Port Said	2915	3536	2830	3015	3710	3006	3125	3191
Poti	3391	4012	3300	3485	4180	3482	3595	3667
Rijeka	2655	3216	2510	2755	3450	2746	2810	2875
Sfax	2016	2579	1953	2104	2803	2103	2206	2271
Syracuse	2036	2632	1973	2124	2823	2123	2226	2291
Taranto	2289	2836	2205	2328	3027	2327	2430	2495
Thessaloniki	2713	3335	2640	2825	3520	2805	2935	2990
Trieste	2691	3256	2605	2790	3485	2782	2850	2915
Tripoli (Libya)	2105	2726	2020	2205	2900	2196	2315	2381
Tunis	1783	2404	1700	1885	2580	1874	1995	2059
Valencia	1395	2016	1310	1495	2190	1486	1605	1671
Valetta	1989	2610	1905	2090	2785	2080	2200	2265
Venice	2682	3303	2600	2785	3480	2773	2895	2958
Zhdanov	3320	3940	3297	3430	4125	3410	3540	3595

DISTANCE TABLES
between ports in the U.K / N. Europe / Baltic & White Sea and Mediterranean / Black Sea / Adriatic

	Emden	Esbjerg	Finisterre	Flushing	Gdansk (via Kiel Canal)	Gibraltar	Gijon	Glasgow
Alexandria	3317	3400	2345	3115	3810	1800	2545	3198
Algiers	1933	2015	960	1730	2425	415	1160	1810
Ancona	3034	3140	2085	2855	3550	1540	2285	2936
Barcelona	2010	2130	1075	1845	2540	530	1275	1925
Beirut	3535	3630	2575	3345	4040	2030	2775	3430
Bourgas	3409	3515	2460	3230	3925	1915	2660	3311
Brindisi	2777	2885	1830	2600	3295	1285	2030	2679
Cagliari	2209	2315	1260	2030	2725	745	1460	2115
Casablanca	1556	1770	570	1359	2021	170	763	1420
Constanza	3530	3577	2522	3292	3987	2037	2722	3374
Dubrovnik	2959	3065	2010	2780	3475	1465	2210	2865
Durres	2874	2980	1925	2695	3390	1380	2125	2780
Genoa	2371	2477	1437	2174	2836	847	1632	2258
Gibraltar	1494	1600	560	1297	1959	–	755	1381
Haifa	3522	3630	2575	3345	4040	2000	2775	3430
Iskenderun	3651	3690	2635	3405	4100	2090	2835	3490
Istanbul	3337	3385	2330	3100	3795	1795	2530	3182
Izmir	3129	3225	2170	2940	3635	1685	2370	3021
Marseilles	2206	2295	1240	2010	2705	695	1440	2089
Messina	2504	2610	1555	2325	3020	1023	1755	2406
Morphou Bay	3426	3510	2455	3225	3930	1910	2655	3305
Naples	2476	2573	1518	2288	2983	973	1718	2369
Novorossisk	3720	3825	2770	3540	4235	2295	2970	3622
Odessa	3680	3730	2675	3445	4140	2186	2875	3527
Palermo	2394	2500	1445	2215	2910	900	1645	2296
Piraeus	3016	3110	2055	2825	3520	1520	2255	2906
Port Said	3436	3510	2455	3225	3920	1925	2655	3306
Poti	3875	3980	2925	3695	4390	2380	3125	3782
Rijeka	3159	3250	2195	2965	3660	1650	2395	3046
Sfax	2447	2555	1500	2270	2965	1055	1695	2349
Syracuse	2594	2700	1645	2415	3110	1100	1845	2500
Taranto	2801	2885	1830	2600	3295	1285	2030	2680
Thessaloniki	3224	3320	2265	3035	3730	1720	2465	3120
Trieste	3204	3285	2230	3000	3695	1685	2430	3082
Tripoli (Libya)	2594	2700	1645	2415	3110	1100	1845	2496
Tunis	2313	2380	1325	2095	2790	809	1525	2174
Valencia	1907	1990	935	1705	2400	390	1135	1786
Valetta	2501	2585	1530	2300	2995	985	1730	2380
Venice	3211	3280	2225	2995	3690	1700	2425	3073
Zhdanov	3820	3925	2870	3640	4335	2325	3070	3710

DISTANCE TABLES
between ports in the U.K / N. Europe / Baltic & White Sea and Mediterranean / Black Sea / Adriatic

	Gothenburg	Hamburg	Havre	Helsinki	Hernosand (via Kiel Canal)	Hull	Ipswich	Kiel (via Can
Alexandria	3600	3443	2985	4060	4115	3241	3099	3467
Algiers	2215	2055	1597	2675	2730	1853	1715	2079
Ancona	3340	3181	2723	3800	3865	2979	2815	3205
Barcelona	2330	2170	1712	2790	2845	1968	1792	2194
Beirut	3830	3660	3200	4290	4345	3457	3317	3683
Bourgas	3715	3556	3098	4175	4230	3354	3190	3580
Brindisi	3085	2924	2466	3545	3600	3733	2560	2948
Cagliari	2515	2345	1885	2975	3130	2142	1990	2383
Casablanca	1830	1669	1209	2310	2342	1489	1338	1702
Constanza	3777	3619	3161	4237	4292	3417	3252	3643
Dubrovnik	3265	3095	2635	3725	3780	2892	2740	3118
Durres	3180	3010	2550	3640	3695	2807	2655	3033
Genoa	2660	2500	2042	3120	3175	2298	2153	2524
Gibraltar	1779	1607	1147	2248	2280	1427	1276	1640
Haifa	3830	3660	3200	4290	4345	3457	3304	3683
Iskenderun	3890	3720	3260	4350	4405	3517	3433	3743
Istanbul	3585	3427	2969	4045	4100	3225	3119	3451
Izmir	3425	3266	2808	3885	3940	3064	2961	3290
Marseilles	2495	2334	1876	2955	3010	2132	1988	2358
Messina	2810	2651	2193	3270	3325	2449	2285	2675
Morphou Bay	3710	3550	3092	4170	4225	3348	3208	3574
Naples	2773	2614	2156	3233	3288	2412	2258	2638
Novorossisk	4025	3867	3409	4485	4540	3665	3500	3891
Odessa	3930	3772	3314	4390	4445	3570	3462	3796
Palermo	2700	2541	2083	3160	3215	2339	2175	2565
Piraeus	3310	3151	2693	3770	3825	2949	2798	3175
Port Said	3710	3551	3093	4170	4225	3349	3218	3567
Poti	4180	4027	3569	4640	4695	3825	3655	4051
Rijeka	3450	3291	2833	3910	3965	3089	2941	3315
Sfax	2755	2594	2136	3215	3270	2392	2230	2618
Syracuse	2900	2730	2270	3360	3415	2527	2375	2753
Taranto	3085	2925	2467	3545	3600	2723	2583	2949
Thessaloniki	3520	3350	2890	3980	4035	3147	3006	3373
Trieste	3485	3327	2869	3945	4000	3125	2986	3351
Tripoli (Libya)	2900	2741	2283	3360	3415	2539	2375	2765
Tunis	2580	2419	1961	3040	3095	2217	2095	2443
Valencia	2190	2031	1573	2650	2705	1829	1689	2055
Valetta	2785	2625	2167	3245	3300	2423	2283	2649
Venice	3480	3318	2860	3940	3995	3116	2993	3342
Zhdanov	4125	3956	3496	4585	4640	3752	3600	3980

DISTANCE TABLES

between ports in the U.K / N. Europe / Baltic & White Sea
and Mediterranean / Black Sea / Adriatic

	Klaipeda (via Kiel Canal)	Lands End	Leith	Leixoes	Lisbon	Liverpool	London	Lulea (via Kiel Canal)
Alexandria	3840	2822	3424	2277	2109	3079	3107	4277
Algiers	2455	1437	2036	893	721	1691	1719	2892
Ancona	3580	2562	3162	1994	1847	2817	2845	4017
Barcelona	2570	1552	2151	970	836	1806	1834	3007
Beirut	4070	3052	3640	2495	2330	3295	3320	4507
Bourgas	3955	2937	3537	2369	2222	3192	3220	4392
Brindisi	3325	2307	2905	1739	1590	2560	2588	3762
Cagliari	2755	1737	2325	1169	1010	1980	2005	3192
Casablanca	1682	1043	1662	479	324	1305	1363	2557
Constanza	4017	2999	3600	2490	2285	3255	3283	4454
Dubrovnik	3505	2487	3075	1919	1760	2730	2755	3942
Durres	3420	2402	2990	1834	1675	2645	2670	3857
Genoa	2900	1882	2481	1331	1166	2136	2164	3337
Gibraltar	2045	1022	1600	454	280	1270	1301	2495
Haifa	4070	3052	3640	2482	2325	3295	3320	4507
Iskenderun	4130	3112	3700	2544	2385	3335	3380	4567
Istanbul	3840	2817	3395	2249	2075	3065	3096	4262
Izmir	3665	2647	3247	2079	1932	2902	2930	4102
Marseilles	2740	1717	2295	1149	975	1965	1996	3172
Messina	3050	2032	2632	1464	1317	2287	2315	3487
Morphou Bay	3950	2932	3531	2364	2216	3186	3214	4387
Naples	3013	1995	2595	1436	1280	2250	2278	3450
Novorossisk	4265	3247	3848	2679	2533	3503	3531	4702
Odessa	4170	3152	3752	2640	2438	3408	3436	4607
Palermo	2940	1922	2522	1354	1207	2177	2205	3377
Piraeus	3550	2532	3132	1976	1817	2787	2815	3987
Port Said	3970	2957	3525	2389	2215	3205	3236	4387
Poti	4420	3402	4008	2834	2693	3663	3691	4857
Rijeka	3690	2672	3272	2119	1957	2927	2955	4127
Sfax	2995	1977	2575	1409	1260	2230	2258	3432
Syracuse	3140	2122	2710	1554	1395	2365	2390	3577
Taranto	3325	2307	2906	1739	1591	2561	2589	3762
Thessaloniki	3760	2472	3330	2184	2015	2985	3010	4197
Trieste	3725	2707	3308	2164	1993	2963	2991	4162
Tripoli (Libya)	3140	2122	2722	1554	1407	2377	2405	3577
Tunis	2820	1802	2400	1273	1085	2055	2083	3257
Valencia	2445	1422	2000	854	680	1670	1701	2867
Valetta	3025	2007	2606	1461	1291	2261	2289	3462
Venice	3720	2702	3299	2171	1984	2954	2982	4157
Zhdanov	4365	3347	3936	2779	2621	3591	3616	4802

DISTANCE TABLES
between ports in the U.K / N. Europe / Baltic & White Sea and Mediterranean / Black Sea / Adriatic

	Middlesbrough	Milford Haven	Murmansk	Narvik	Newcastle	Oslo	Rostock (via Kiel Canal)	Rotterdam
Alexandria	3306	2920	4620	4240	3306	3667	3537	3179
Algiers	1918	1535	3235	2855	1918	2282	2152	1791
Ancona	3044	2660	4360	3980	3044	3407	3277	2917
Barcelona	2033	1650	3350	2970	2033	2397	2267	1906
Beirut	3520	3150	4850	4470	3520	3897	3767	3395
Bourgas	3419	3035	4735	4355	3419	3782	3652	3292
Brindisi	2787	2405	4105	3725	2787	3152	3022	2660
Cagliari	2205	1835	3535	3155	2205	2502	2452	2080
Casablanca	1525	1132	3019	2464	1570	1912	1782	1410
Constanza	3482	3097	4797	4417	3482	3844	3714	3355
Dubrovnik	2955	2585	4285	3905	2955	3332	3202	2830
Durres	2870	2500	4200	3820	2870	3247	3117	2745
Genoa	2363	1980	3680	3300	2363	2727	2597	2236
Gibraltar	1504	1120	2977	2427	1508	1850	1720	1348
Haifa	3520	3150	4850	4470	3520	3897	3767	3395
Iskenderun	3580	3210	4910	4530	3580	3957	3827	3455
Istanbul	3290	2905	4605	4225	3290	3652	3522	3163
Izmir	3129	2745	4445	4065	3129	3492	3362	3002
Marseilles	2197	1815	3515	3135	2197	2562	2432	2070
Messina	2514	2130	3830	3450	2514	2877	2747	2387
Morphou Bay	3413	3030	4730	4350	3413	3777	3647	3286
Naples	2477	2093	3793	3413	2477	2840	2710	2350
Novorossisk	3730	3345	4045	4665	3730	4092	3962	3603
Odessa	3635	3250	4950	4570	3635	3997	3867	3508
Palermo	2404	2020	3720	3340	2404	2767	2637	2277
Piraeus	3014	2630	4330	3950	3014	3377	3247	2887
Port Said	3414	3030	4730	4350	3414	3777	3647	3287
Poti	3890	3500	5200	4820	3890	4247	4117	3763
Rijeka	3154	2770	4470	4090	3136	3517	3387	3027
Sfax	2457	2070	3775	3395	2457	2822	2692	2330
Syracuse	2590	2220	3920	3540	2590	2967	2837	2465
Taranto	2788	2405	4105	3725	2788	3152	3022	2661
Thessaloniki	3210	2840	4540	4160	3210	3587	3457	3085
Trieste	3190	2805	4505	4125	3190	3553	3422	3063
Tripoli (Libya)	2604	2220	3920	3540	2604	2967	2837	2477
Tunis	2282	1900	3600	3220	2282	2647	2517	2155
Valencia	1894	1510	3210	3830	1894	2257	2127	1748
Valetta	2488	2105	3805	3425	2488	2852	2722	2361
Venice	3181	2800	4500	4120	3181	3547	3417	3065
Zhdanov	3816	3445	5145	4765	3816	4192	4062	3691

DISTANCE TABLES
between ports in the U.K / N. Europe / Baltic & White Sea and Mediterranean / Black Sea / Adriatic

	St. Petersburg (via Kiel Canal)	Skaw	Southampton	Stockholm (via Kiel Canal)	Sunderland	Szczecin (via Kiel Canal)	Trondheim	Vasa (via Kiel Canal)
Alexandria	4220	3560	2996	3918	3316	3650	3887	4153
Algiers	2835	2175	1611	2533	1928	2265	2502	2768
Ancona	3960	3300	2736	3658	3054	3390	3627	3893
Barcelona	2950	2290	1726	2648	2043	2380	2617	2883
Beirut	4450	3790	3224	4148	3530	3880	4117	4383
Bourgas	4335	3675	3111	4033	3429	3765	4002	4268
Brindisi	3705	3045	2481	3403	2797	3135	3372	3638
Cagliari	3135	2475	1911	2833	2215	2565	2802	3068
Casablanca	2461	1795	1160	2185	1547	1904	2120	2380
Constanza	4397	3737	3173	4095	3492	3827	4064	4330
Dubrovnik	3885	3225	2661	3583	2965	3315	3552	3818
Durres	2800	3140	2576	3498	2880	3230	3467	3733
Genoa	3280	2620	2056	2978	2373	2710	2947	3213
Gibraltar	2399	1773	1119	2123	1485	1842	2099	2357
Haifa	4450	3790	3226	4148	3530	3880	4017	4383
Iskenderun	4510	3850	3286	4208	3590	3940	4177	4443
Istanbul	4194	3545	2981	3903	3300	3635	3872	4138
Izmir	4045	3385	2821	3743	3139	3475	3712	3978
Marseilles	3094	2455	1891	2813	2207	2545	2782	3048
Messina	3430	2770	2206	3128	2524	2860	3097	3363
Morphou Bay	4330	3670	3106	4028	3423	3760	3997	4263
Naples	3393	2733	2169	3091	2487	2823	3060	3326
Novorossisk	4645	3985	3421	4343	3740	4075	4312	4578
Odessa	4550	3890	3326	4248	3645	3980	4217	4483
Palermo	3320	2660	2096	3018	2414	2750	2987	3253
Piraeus	3930	3270	2706	3628	3024	3360	3597	3863
Port Said	4274	3670	3106	4028	3424	3760	3997	4263
Poti	4800	4140	3576	4498	3900	4230	4467	4733
Rijeka	4070	3410	2846	3768	3146	3500	3737	4003
Sfax	3375	2715	2151	3073	2467	2805	3042	3308
Syracuse	3520	2860	2296	3218	2600	2950	3187	3453
Taranto	3705	3045	2481	3403	2798	3135	3372	3638
Thessaloniki	4140	3480	2916	3838	3220	3570	3807	4073
Trieste	4105	3445	2881	3803	3200	3535	3772	4038
Tripoli (Libya)	3520	2860	2296	3218	2614	2950	3187	3453
Tunis	3200	2540	1976	2898	2292	2630	2861	3133
Valencia	2799	2173	1519	2523	1885	2242	2499	2757
Valetta	3405	2745	2181	3103	2498	2835	3072	3338
Venice	4100	3440	2836	3840	3202	3530	3767	4033
Zhdanov	4745	4085	3521	4443	3826	4175	4412	4678

BALTIC DISTANCES
S = via Sound

	Aarhus	Baltiysk	Kobnhavn	Gdansk	Gothenburg	Grimstad	Hanko	Helsinki
Aarhus	–	388S	113	379S	151	206	597S	663S
Baltiysk	388S	–	285	45	415	509S	339	402
Kobnhavn	113	285	–	274S	137	230	492S	555S
Gdansk	379S	45	274S	–	406S	496S	360	422
Gothenburg	151	415	137	406S	–	117	620S	687S
Grimstad	206	509S	230	496S	117	–	715S	780S
Hanko	597S	339	492S	360	620S	715S	–	82
Helsinki	663S	402	555S	422	687S	780S	82	–
Hernosand	721S	490	612S	518	745S	838S	291	365
Hudiksvall	671S	440	562S	468	695S	788S	241	315
Karlskrona	261S	180	156S	172	290S	380S	355	424
Kiel	133	343	162S	344	236	303S	570	631
Klaipeda	429S	88	323S	117	453S	547S	272	337
Kotka	716S	463	610S	486	741S	835S	141	87
Lindesnes	248	551S	272	538S	165	64	757S	822S
Oskarshamn	403S	220	302S	233	433S	526S	263	328
Oslo	260	549S	272	538S	163	139	755S	819S
Oulo	942S	705	833S	735	966S	1061S	507	582
Riga	586S	302	478S	322	609S	699S	251	316
Skaw	128	431S	152	418S	45	78	637S	702S
St. Petersburg	805S	546	699S	565	830S	921S	228	171
Stockholm	536S	318	427S	345	560S	652S	172	237
Szczecin	268S	243	163S	240	295S	389S	491	558
Tallin	640S	380	533S	406	665S	759S	62	48
Trelleborg	158	238	50	224	180S	273S	449	513
Turku	606S	363	497S	386	633S	725S	113	185
Uddevalla	181	460S	180	448S	71	135	667S	729S
Vaasa	791S	560	682S	588	815S	908S	361	435
Ventspils	466S	184	359	211	490S	583S	170	233
Vyborg	772S	511	666S	538	797S	889S	193	154

BALTIC DISTANCES
S=via Sound

	Hernosand	Hudiksvall	Karlskrona	Kiel	Klaipeda	Kotka	Lindesnes	Oskarshamn
Aarhus	721S	671S	261S	133	479S	716S	248	403S
Baltiysk	490	440	180	343	88	463	551S	220
Kobnhavn	612S	562S	156S	162S	323S	610S	272	302S
Gdansk...................	518	460	172	344	117	486	538S	233
Gothenburg.	745S	695S	290S	236	453S	741S	165	433S
Grimstad................	838S	788S	380S	303S	547S	835S	64	526S
Hanko	291	241	355	570	272	141	757S	263
Helsinki	365	315	424	631	337	87	822S	328
Hernosand	–	86	488	694	430	420	880S	381
Hudiksvall	86	–	438	644	380	370	830S	331
Karlskrona	488	438	–	237	203	478	422S	167
Kiel	694	644	237	–	397	690	345	381
Klaipeda	430	380	203	397	–	394	589S	202
Kotka	420	370	478	690	394	–	877S	387
Lindesnes	880S	830S	422S	345	589S	877S	–	568S
Oskarshamn	381	331	167	381	202	387	568S	–
Oslo	877S	827S	422S	355	579S	876S	194	566S
Oulo	262	331	705	909	653	638	1103S	598
Riga	423	373	350	550	236	373	741S	291
Skaw	760S	710S	302S	225	469S	757S	120	448S
St. Petersburg	508	458	568	778	478	106	963S	471
Stockholm	236	186	300	497	265	297	694S	196
Szczecin	615	566	179	221	294	611	431S	306
Tallin	343	293	400	610	316	99	801S	309
Trelleborg.	575	524	114	140	280	569	315S	260
Turku	290S	254	374	576	298	241	767S	270S
Uddevalla	788S	738S	332S	273	497S	785S	180	475S
Vaasa	113	174	558	558	500	490	950S	451
Ventspils	334	284	230	230	116	290	265S	190
Vyborg	469	419	530	530	450	63	931S	439

BALTIC DISTANCES
S=via Sound

	Oslo	Oulo	Riga	Skaw	St. Petersburg	Stockholm	Szczecin	Tallin
Aarhus	260	942S	586S	128	805S	536S	268S	640S
Baltiysk	549S	705	302	431S	546	318	243	380
Kobnhavn	272	833S	478S	152	699S	427S	163S	533S
Gdansk....................	538S	735	332	418S	565	345	240	406
Gothenburg.	163	966S	609S	45	830S	560	295S	665S
Grimstad................	139	1061S	699S	78	921S	652S	389S	759S
Hanko	755S	507	251	637S	228	172	491	62
Helsinki	819S	582	316	702S	171	237	558	48
Hernosand	877S	262	423	760S	508	236	615	343
Hudiksvall	827S	331	373	710S	458	186	566	293
Karlskrona	422S	705	350	302S	568	300	179	400
Kiel	355	909	550	225	778	497	221	610
Klaipeda	579S	653	236	469S	478	265	294	316
Kotka	876S	638	373	757S	106	297	611	99
Lindesnes	194	1103S	741S	120	963S	694S	431S	801S
Oskarshamn	566S	598	291	448S	471	196	306	309
Oslo	–	1096S	744S	132	965S	694S	429S	801S
Oulo	1096S	–	638	983S	721	450	838	565
Riga	744S	638	–	621S	457	266	476	291
Skaw	132	983S	621S	–	843S	574S	311S	681S
St. Petersburg	965S	721	457	843S	–	385	696	187
Stockholm	694S	450	266	574S	385	–	430	217
Szczecin	429S	838	476	311S	696	430	–	532
Tallin	801S	565	291	681S	187	217	522	–
Trelleborg.	315S	790	436	195S	654	388	129	490
Turku	763S	495	269	647S	330	164	509	160
Uddevalla	169	1010S	653S	61	873S	604S	340S	710S
Vaasa	948S	211	493	830S	578	306	685	413
Ventspils	623S	548	125	505S	376	179	359	210
Vyborg	929S	686	427	811S	88	366	664	147

Section 15

29

BALTIC DISTANCES
S=via Sound

	Trelleborg	Turku	Uddevalla	Vaasa	Ventspils	Vyborg
Aarhus	158	606S	181	791	466S	772S
Baltiysk	238	363	460S	560	184	511
Kobnhavn	50	497S	180	682S	359	666S
Gdansk...................	224	386	448S	588	211	538
Gothenburg.	180S	633S	71	815S	490S	797S
Grimstad................	273S	725S	135	908S	583S	889S
Hanko	449	113	667S	361	170	193
Helsinki	513	185	729S	435	233	154
Hernosand	575	290S	788S	113	334	469
Hudiksvall	524	254	738S	174	284	419
Karlskrona	114	374	332S	558	230	530
Kiel	140	576	273	558	230	530
Klaipeda	280	298	497S	500	116	450
Kotka	569	241	785S	490	290	63
Lindesnes	315S	767S	180S	950S	265S	931S
Oskarshamn	260	270S	475S	451	190	439
Oslo	315S	763S	169	948S	623S	929S
Oulo	790	495	1010S	211	548	686
Riga	436	269	653S	493	125	427
Skaw	195S	647S	61	830S	505S	811S
St. Petersburg	654	330	813S	578	376	88
Stockholm	388	164	604S	306	179	366
Szczecin	129	509	340S	685	359	664
Tallin	490	160	710S	413	210	147
Trelleborg.	–	459	228S	636	315	616
Turku	459	–	676S	360	194	287
Uddevalla	228S	676S	–	858S	534S	841S
Vaasa	636	360	858S	–	404	539
Ventspils	315	194	534S	404	–	344
Vyborg	616	287	841S	539	344	–

DISTANCES FROM USHANT TO EUROPA PT. (GIBRALTAR)
(Nautical Miles)

USHANT TO:

Gt. Nore	356
Dover	308
Dungeness	281
Beachy Head	255
Owers Lanby	222
St. Catherines Lt. Ho.	193
Anvil Pt.	180

USHANT TO:

Portland Bill	158
Start Point	119
Eddystone Lt. Ho.	110
Falmouth	108
Lizard	98
Longships	90
Casquets	135

USHANT TO EUROPA PT.

	Ushant	C. Finisterre	C. Roca	St. Vincent	Trafalgar	Tarifa	Europa Pt.
Ushant	–	390	638	746	898	922	937
C. Finisterre	390	–	248	356	508	532	547
C. Roca	638	248	–	108	284	308	323
St. Vincent	746	356	108	–	176	200	215
Trafalgar	898	508	284	176	–	24	39
Tarifa	922	532	308	200	24	–	15
Europa Pt.	937	547	323	215	39	15	–

USHANT TO ST. SEBASTIAN

	Ushant	Belle Ile	Ile d'Yeu	I'de Oléron	Arcachon	C. Breton	S. Sebastian
Ushant	–	110	160	216	311	367	393
Belle Ile	110	–	50	106	201	257	283
Ile d'Yeu	160	50	–	56	151	207	233
I'de Oléron	216	106	56	–	95	151	177
Arcachon	311	201	151	95	–	56	82
C. Breton	367	257	207	151	56	–	26
S. Sebastian	393	283	233	177	82	26	–

DISTANCES FROM USHANT TO EUROPA PT. (GIBRALTAR)
(Nautical Miles)

S. SEBASTIAN TO C. FINISTERRE

	S. Sebastian	Bilbao	Santander	C. de Peñas	Estaca Pt.	Coruña	C. Finisterre
S. Sebastian	–	50	95	195	277	327	392
Bilbao	50	–	45	145	227	277	342
Santander	95	45	–	100	182	232	297
C. de Peñas	195	145	100	–	82	132	197
Estaca Pt.	277	227	182	82	–	50	115
Coruña	327	277	232	132	50	–	65
C. Finisterre	392	342	297	197	115	65	–

C. FINISTERRE TO ST. VINCENT

	C. Finisterre	C. Silleiro	Rio Douro	Figueira	Berlenga Ile	C. Roca	St. Vincent
C. Finisterre	–	40	100	160	210	248	356
C. Silleiro	40	–	60	120	170	208	316
Rio Douro	100	60	–	60	110	148	256
Figueira	160	120	60	–	50	88	196
Berlenga Ile	210	170	110	50	–	38	146
C. Roca	248	208	148	88	38	–	108
St. Vincent	356	316	256	196	146	108	–

ST. VINCENT TO EUROPA PT.

	St. Vincent	C. Sta. Maria	Rio Guadiana	Cadiz	Trafalgar	Tarifa	Europa Pt.
St. Vincent	–	55	85	150	176	200	215
C. Sta. Maria	55	–	30	95	121	145	160
Rio Guadiana	85	30	–	65	91	115	130
Cadiz	150	95	65	–	26	50	65
Trafalgar	176	121	91	26	–	24	39
Tarifa	200	145	115	50	24	–	15
Europa Pt.	215	160	130	65	39	15	–

INTER-DISTANCES
between the Mediterranean and Black Sea Ports

	Algiers	Annaba	Batum	Beirut	Bourgas	Brindisi	Civitavecchia	Durres
Alexandria	1388	1164	1308	340	848	825	1126	856
Algiers	–	241	1970	1594	1516	874	525	905
Ancona	1139	921	1637	1266	1183	270	824	295
Banias	1607	1383	1391	85	931	1009	1322	1040
Barcelona	279	377	2055	1673	1595	934	439	965
Beirut	1594	1370	1396	–	942	1000	1314	1031
Cartagena	203	427	2163	1787	1703	1063	651	1094
Casablanca	599	826	2573	2191	2119	1469	1069	1500
Catania	644	420	1390	1018	930	277	348	308
Constanza	1580	1357	588	1006	126	982	1295	1013
Falconara	1145	927	1643	1272	1183	276	830	301
Genoa	528	450	1871	1500	1411	745	190	776
Gibraltar	412	639	2386	2004	1926	1282	882	1313
Iskenderun	1612	1388	1396	172	942	1014	1327	1044
Istanbul	1384	1161	586	810	126	786	1099	817
Lattakia	1592	1368	1376	100	916	994	1307	1025
Limassol	1477	1253	1278	132	818	885	1196	916
Marseilles	410	410	1964	1595	1510	838	312	869
Oran	202	437	2166	1790	1706	1070	700	1101
Patras	916	692	1192	821	732	239	606	270
Piraeus	1070	845	938	645	480	475	785	506
Port Said	1503	1280	1372	228	912	928	1233	959
Poti	1987	1764	31	1413	629	1389	1702	1420
Spezia	533	450	1835	1464	1375	709	154	740
Split	1080	862	1577	1207	1117	193	765	203
Trieste	1240	1022	1738	1367	1284	372	925	408
Tuapse	1875	1652	185	1301	518	1277	1590	1308
Tunis	384	161	1628	1252	1174	555	323	586
Venice	1256	1038	1755	1383	1295	387	941	418
Zhdanov	1947	1724	440	1373	492	1349	1662	1380

INTER-DISTANCES
between the Mediterranean and Black Sea Ports

	Famagusta	Galatz	Haifa	Marseilles	Melilla	Messina	Naples	Novorossisk
Alexandria	332	1042	292	1405	1689	826	1001	1178
Algiers	1544	1704	1589	410	304	615	579	1840
Ancona	1216	1371	1262	1103	1440	524	700	1507
Banias	96	1125	154	1601	1908	1022	1197	1261
Barcelona	1629	1789	1674	185	442	675	555	1925
Beirut	107	1130	72	1595	1895	1014	1189	1266
Cartagena	1737	1897	1782	458	166	802	753	2033
Casablanca	2141	2207	2187	877	324	1210	1166	2443
Catania	968	1124	1014	627	945	48	223	1260
Constanza	955	143	1012	1574	1881	995	1170	402
Falconara	1222	1377	1268	1109	1446	530	706	1513
Genoa	1449	1605	1496	201	787	486	334	1741
Gibraltar	1954	2120	2000	690	137	1023	979	2256
Iskenderun	140	1130	240	1606	1913	1027	1202	1266
Istanbul	759	320	816	1378	1685	799	974	456
Lattakia	92	1110	169	1586	1893	1007	1182	1246
Limassol	72	1012	144	1475	1778	896	1071	1148
Marseilles	1542	1698	1589	–	618	579	457	1834
Oran	1740	1900	1785	534	120	810	772	2036
Patras	770	926	817	885	1217	306	481	1062
Piraeus	590	670	640	1063	1370	485	660	806
Port Said	255	1106	169	1512	1804	933	1108	1242
Poti	1362	626	1419	1981	2288	1402	1577	227
Spezia	1413	1569	1460	228	803	450	298	1705
Split	1156	1311	1202	1044	1381	465	640	1447
Trieste	1317	1472	1363	1204	1541	625	800	1608
Tuapse	1250	488	1307	1869	2176	1290	1465	63
Tunis	1202	1362	1247	472	685	296	309	1498
Venice	1333	1489	1379	1220	1558	641	816	1625
Zhdanov	1322	533	1379	1941	2248	1362	1537	205

INTER-DISTANCES
between the Mediterranean and Black Sea Ports

	Odessa	Rijeka	Savona	Sfax	Sidon	Tarragona	Torrevieja	Valencia
Alexandria	1064	1151	1317	988	318	1507	1560	1554
Algiers	1726	1200	511	595	1586	270	192	226
Ancona	1393	110	1015	838	1258	1232	1304	1287
Banias	1147	1335	1513	1255	110	1726	1779	1773
Barcelona	1811	1260	338	691	1665	52	202	164
Beirut	1152	1327	1505	1235	27	1713	1766	1760
Cartagena	1919	1387	601	788	1779	249	43	155
Casablanca	2329	1795	1019	1192	2183	668	462	574
Catania	1146	603	539	317	1010	763	817	810
Constanza	173	1308	1486	1245	998	1699	1752	1746
Falconara	1399	114	1021	844	1264	1238	1310	1293
Genoa	1627	1071	22	652	1492	399	576	510
Gibraltar	2142	1608	832	1005	1996	481	275	387
Iskenderun	1152	1340	1518	1260	196	1731	1784	1778
Istanbul	342	1112	1290	1049	802	1503	1556	1550
Lattakia	1132	1320	1498	1240	119	1711	1764	1758
Limassol	1034	1210	1387	1116	132	1596	1649	1643
Marseilles	1720	1164	187	674	1587	232	423	345
Oran	1922	1396	670	791	1782	333	136	239
Patras	948	564	797	586	813	1014	1085	1069
Piraeus	692	798	975	734	633	1188	1241	1235
Port Said	1122	1254	1424	1115	204	1622	1675	1669
Poti	550	1715	1893	1652	1405	2106	2159	2153
Spezia	1591	1035	67	626	1456	426	603	537
Split	1333	165	956	778	1199	1173	1244	1228
Trieste	1494	110	1116	939	1359	1333	1402	1388
Tuapse	415	1603	1781	1540	1293	1994	2047	2041
Tunis	1384	881	472	252	1244	519	560	543
Venice	1511	129	1132	955	1375	1349	1421	1404
Zhdanov	450	1675	1853	1612	1365	2066	2119	2114

MEDITERRANEAN DISTANCES

ANTIBES to	
Anzio, Italy	278
Arbatax, Sardinia	267
Argostoli, Greece	765
Arzew, Algeria	583
Augusta, Sicily	582
Ayas, Turkey	1533
Ayia Marina, Greece	1095
Ayvalik, Turkey	1155
Bakar, Yugoslavia	1093
Bar, Yugoslavia	852
Barcelona, Spain	260
Bari, Italy	833
Barletta, Italy	861
Bastia, Corsica	127
Beirut, Lebanon	1532
Bengazi, Libya (via Bonifacio)	939
Beni Saf, Algeria	638
Benicarlo, Spain	360
Besike, Turkey	1158
Bisceglie, Italy	850
Bizerte, Tunisia	410
Bodrum, Turkey	1117
Bône, Algeria	404
Bonifacio, Corsica	166
Bougie, Algeria	422
Bozca ada, Turkey	1152
Brindisi, Italy	775
Brioni, Yugoslavia	1092
Budva, Yugoslavia	861
Burriana, Spain	396
Cagliari, Sardinia	335
Calvi, Corsica	94
Camogli, Italy	102
Canakkale, Turkey	1179
Cannes, France	11
Capraia, Italy	123
Capri, Italy	368
Carcúra, Libya	964
Carloforte, Sardinia	281
Cartegena, Spain	525
Castellammare del Golfo, Sicily	434
Castellammare di Stabia, Italy	375
Catania, Sicily	566
Catanzaro, Italy	615
Cavtat, Yugoslavia	880
Cefalù, Sicily (via Bonifacio)	468
Ceuta, Morocco	758
Cherchell, Algeria	477
Chioggia, Italy	1144
Cuidadela, Spain	268
Civitavecchia, Italy	224
Collo, Algeria	398
Corfu, Greece	780
Cres, Yugoslavia	1086
Crotone, Italy	644
Damietta (bocca di), Egypt	1419

ANTIBES to	
Daphni, Greece	1159
Dellys, Algeria	430
Denia, Spain	434
Derna, Libya	999
Djerba, Tunisia	660
Dubrovnik, Yugoslavia	883
Durrës, Albania	813
El-Aghéila, Libya	992
Enez, Turkey	1199
Es-Zuetina, Libya	994
Falconara Marittima, Italy	1044
Famagusta, Cyprus	1480
Favignana, Sicily	423
Fiumicino, Italy	252
Follonica, Italy	146
Gabès, Tunisia	688
Gaeta, Italy	330
Gallipoli, Italy	711
Gavriou, Greece	1021
Gaza, Egypt	1537
Gela, Sicily	534
Genova, Italy	96
Gibraltar	759
Giglio Marina, Italy	183
Gioia Tauro, Italy	511
Gji i Sarandë, Albania	771
Golfo Aranci, Sardinia	205
Gruž, Yugoslavia	887
Haifa, Israel	1528
Hermopoulis (Syros), Greece	1016
Hvar, Yugoslavia	936
Ibiza, Spain	389
Imperia, Italy	44
Iráklion, Crete	1016
Ischia, Porto d', Italy	352
Isthmia, Greece	1013
Izmir, Turkey	1157
Jablanac, Yugoslavia	1062
Jaffa, Israel	1536
Jelsa, Lesina, Yugoslavia	959
Jijelli, Algeria	412
Kalamata, Greece	864
Kalimnos, Greece	1095
Karlobag, Yugoslavia	1072
Karpathos, Greece	1120
Karystos, Greece	1019
Kaštel Novi, Yugoslavia	964
Kastelorizo, Greece	1220
Kastro (Lemnos), Greece	1139
Katakolon, Greece	802
Kavalla, Greece	1200
Khalkis, Greece	1056
Khanià, Crete	961
Khios, Greece	1094
Khithira, Greece	902
Khoms, Libya	749

MEDITERRANEAN DISTANCES

ANTIBES to

Komiža, Yugoslavia	937
Koper, Yugoslavia	1141
Korčula, Yugoslavia	913
Kos, Greece	1110
Kotor, Yugoslavia	882
Krk, Yugoslavia	1073
Kumkale, Turkey	1166
Kus-adasi, Turkey	1122
La Calle, Algeria	406
La Ciotat, France	86
La Goulette, Tunisia	451
La Maddalena, Sardinia	182
La Spezia, Italy	129
Lampedusa, Italy	563
Larnaca, Cyprus	1444
Latakia, Syria	1526
Levkas, Greece	779
Licata, Sicily	519
Limassol, Cyprus	1411
Limin Yithion, Greece	896
Lipari, Italy	484
Livorno, Italy	139
Luka Velji Lago, Yugoslavia	906
Mahon, Menorca	259
Makarska, Yugoslavia	945
Makri, Turkey	1195
Malaga, Spain	708
Manfredonia, Italy	885
Marbella, Spain	731
Marina di Carrara, Italy	131
Marmaris, Turkey	1167
Marsa Àin el-Gazala, Libya	1045
Marsa el-Auégia, Libya	925
Marsa el-Bréga, Libya	998
Marsa Matruh, Egypt	1231
Marsa Susa, Libya	967
Marsa Zliten, Libya	763
Marsala, Sicily	432
Marseille, France	106
Marzamemi, Sicily	590
Mazara del Vallo, Sicily	444
Melilla, Morocco	684
Mers-el-Kebir, Algeria	597
Mersin, Turkey	1483
Mesolongion, Greece	811
Messina, Sicily	518
Metković (Neretva), Yugoslavia	953
Milazzo, Sicily	497
Milos, Greece	972
Misurata Marina, Libya	781
Mitilini, Greece	1141
Molat, Yugoslavia	1025
Molfetta, Italy	846
Monastir, Tunisia	531
Monfalcone, Italy	1147
Monopoli, Italy	809

ANTIBES to

Monte Carlo, Monaco	16
Morphou, Cyprus	1382
Mostagenem, Algeria	570
Motril, Spain	665
Moudhrou (Lemnos), Greece	1141
Naples, Italy	368
Nauplia, Greece	979
Navarrino, Greece	826
Nemours, Algeria	664
Nice, France	10
Novi, Yugoslavia	1082
Olbia, Sardinia	210
Opuzen, Yugoslavia	948
Oran, Algeria	597
Orebić, Yugoslavia	912
Oristano, Sardinia	238
Ortona, Italy	965
Otranto, Italy	733
Pag, Yugoslavia	1079
Palamos, Spain	213
Palermo, Sicily	447
Palma, Mallorca	354
Pantelleria, Italy	474
Paros, Greece	1017
Porec, Yugoslavia	1113
Patrai, Greece	823
Pesaro, Italy	1073
Pescara, Italy	975
Philippeville, Algeria	403
Piombino, Italy	158
Piraeus, Greece	1002
Policastro, Italy	439
Pollensa, Mallorca	294
Ponza, Italy	315
Port-de-Bouc, France	116
Port-la-Nouvelle, France	194
Port Said, Egypt	1454
Port-Vendres, France	196
Portman, Spain	517
Porto Azzurro, Elba	163
Porto Bardia, Libya	1131
Porto Corsini, Italy	1113
Porto Empedocle, Sicily	497
Porto Ercole, Italy	197
Portolaki, Greece	1089
Porto Nikolo, Crete	1055
Porto Panagia, Greece	1194
Porto Pisteali, Greece	795
Porto Ponte Romano, Sardinia	296
Porto Quieto, Yugoslavia	1118
Porto San Nicolo (Kea), Greece	999
Porto Santo Stefano, Italy	188
Porto Sigri (Lesvos), Greece	1116
Porto Skala (Patmos), Greece	1082
Porto Skala (Stampalia), Greece	1063
Porto Torres, Sardinia	175

MEDITERRANEAN DISTANCES

ANTIBES to

Porto Vathi (Samos), Greece	1109
Porto Vecchio, Corsica	197
Portoferraio, Italy	151
Poseidonia, Greece	889
Pozzuoli, Italy	362
Prevesa, Greece	782
Primosten, Yugoslavia	967
Procida, Italy	353
Puerto de Los Alfaques, Spain	353
Pula, Yugoslavia	1092
Punta Penna, Italy	951
Rab, Yugoslavia	1057
Raša, Yugoslavia	1083
Reggio Calabria, Italy	523
Rethimnon, Greece	987
Rhodes, Greece	1155
Rijeka, Yugoslavia	1092
Rimini, Italy	1089
Riposto, Sicily	550
Rodi Garganico, Italy	896
Rogoznica, Yugoslavia	964
Rosas, Spain	199
Rosetta, Egypt	1354
Rovinj, Yugoslavia	1104
Sagunto, Spain	412
Saïda, Lebanon	1531
Saint-Louis-du-Rhône, France	119
Saint-Raphaël, France	24
Saint-Tropez, France	31
Salerno, Italy	392
Salina, Eolie, Italy	467
Salûm, Egypt	1145
San Benedetto del Tronto, Italy	1002
San Giovanni d'Acri, Israel	1529
San Remo, Italy	32
Santa Margherita Ligure, Italy	105
Santa Maria di Leuca, Italy	708
Savona, Italy	80
Sciacca, Sicily	472
Senj, Yugoslavia	1076
Sestri Levante, Italy	109
Sète, France	169
Sfax, Tunisia	655
Sibenik, Yugoslavia	979
Siracusa, Sicily	588
Sirte, Libya	877
Skyros, Greece	1079
Slano, Yugoslavia	894
Sorrento, Italy	372
Soúdha, Crete	979
Sour, Lebanon	1527
Sousse, Tunisia	530

ANTIBES to

Split, Yugoslavia	960
Starigrad, Yugoslavia	951
Stylis, Greece	1114
Sumartin (Brač), Yugoslavia	950
Supetar (Brač), Yugoslavia	960
Symi, Greece	1139
Taormina, Sicily	544
Taranto, Italy	727
Tarragona, Spain	305
Ténès, Algeria	503
Termini Imerese, Sicily	461
Termoli, Italy	936
Terracina, Italy	314
Thessaloniki, Greece	1208
Thira (Santorin), Greece	1014
Tivat, Yugoslavia	876
Tobruch, Libya	1078
Tocra, Libya (via Bonifacio)	938
Tolemeita, Libya	941
Torre Annunziata, Italy	374
Torre del Greco, Italy	370
Torrevieja, Spain	493
Tortosa, Spain	331
Toulon, France	72
Trani, Italy	854
Trapani, Sicily	425
Tremiti, Italy	915
Trieste, Italy	1145
Tripoli, Lebanon	1544
Tripoli, Libya (via Bonifacio)	715
Trogir, Yugoslavia	961
Trpanj, Yugoslavia	934
Ulcinj, Yugoslavia	843
Ustica, Italy	403
Vado, Italy	76
Valencia, Spain	424
Valletta, Malta	585
Varazze, Italy	83
Vasto, Italy	949
Velez de la Gomera, Morocco	738
Venice, Italy	1149
Viareggio, Italy	138
Vibo Valentia Marina, Italy	507
Vieste, Italy	881
Villefranche, France	11
Vis, Yugoslavia	939
Vlorë, Albania	775
Volos, Greece	1149
Zadar, Yugoslavia	1028
Zakyntos, Greece	786
Zuara, Libya	705

MARITIME BUOYAGE

16

IALA MARITIME BUOYAGE SYSTEM

LATERAL MARKS OF REGION A

(EUROPE, AFRICA, INDIA, AUSTRALIA, MOST OF ASIA)

PORT HAND
LIGHT: RED ANY RHYTHM

STARBOARD HAND
LIGHT: GREEN ANY RHYTHM

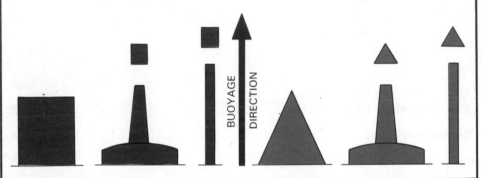

PREFERRED CHANNEL TO STARBOARD
LIGHT: COMPOSITE GROUP FLASHING
(2 + 1) RED

PREFERRED CHANNEL TO PORT
LIGHT: COMPOSITE GROUP FLASHING
(2 + 1) GREEN

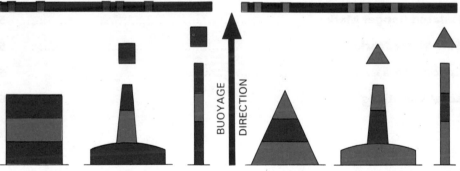

ISOLATED DANGER MARKS

LIGHT: WHITE GP. FL. (2)

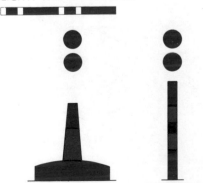

SAFE WATER MARKS
LIGHT: WHITE ISOPHASE, OCCULTING,
LONG FLASH EV. 10 S. OR MORSE A.

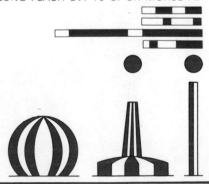

IALA MARITIME BUOYAGE SYSTEM 'A'

SPECIAL MARKS

LIGHT: YELLOW

SHAPE
OPTIONAL

CARDINAL MARKS

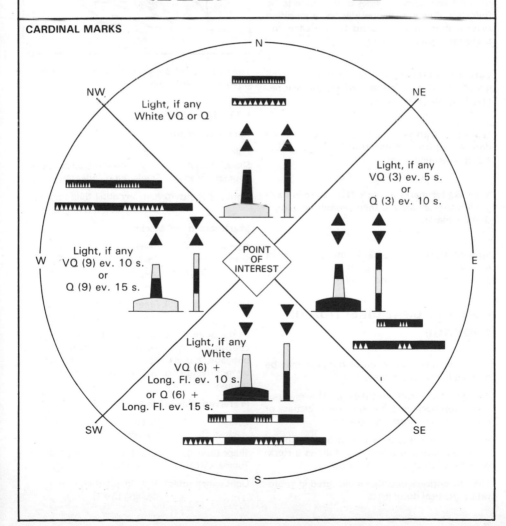

N

NW

NE

Light, if any
White VQ or Q

Light, if any
VQ (3) ev. 5 s.
or
Q (3) ev. 10 s.

W

POINT
OF
INTEREST

E

Light, if any
VQ (9) ev. 10 s.
or
Q (9) ev. 15 s.

Light, if any
White
VQ (6) +
Long. Fl. ev. 10 s.
or Q (6) +
Long. Fl. ev. 15 s.

SW

SE

S

IALA MARITIME BUOYAGE SYSTEM 'A'

THE SYSTEM

The system of buoyage provides the five types of marks described below which may be used in combination:

The significance of any mark depends upon one or more of the following features:

> By night — colour and rhythm of light.
> By day — colour, shape, topmark.

Lateral marks used in conjunction with a conventional direction of buoyage, generally used for well defined channels. These marks indicate the port and starboard sides of the route to be followed. Where a channel divides, a modified lateral mark may be used to indicate the preferred route.

Cardinal marks used in conjunction with the mariner's compass, indicate where the mariner may find navigable water.

Isolated Danger marks indicate isolated dangers of limited size that have navigable water all around them.

Safe Water marks indicate that there is navigable water all around their position, e.g. mid-channel marks.

Special marks not primarily intended to assist navigation but indicating an area or feature referred to in nautical documents.

CONVENTIONAL DIRECTION OF BUOYAGE

The conventional direction of buoyage may be defined in one of two ways:

The general direction taken by the mariner when approaching a harbour, river, estuary or other waterway from seaward, or

In other areas it is determined by the appropriate authority. In principle, it follows a clockwise direction around land masses.

The conventional direction is indicated in appropriate nautical documents.

CONVENTIONAL DIRECTION OF BUOYAGE AROUND THE UK

The Direction of Buoyage in rivers and estuaries is from seaward inward.

LATERAL MARKS

Port hand Marks

Colour:	Red
Shape (Buoys):	Cylindrical (can), pillar or spar
Topmark (if any):	Single red cylinder (can)

Light (when fitted): Red, any other than composite group flashing (2 + 1)

Starboard hand Marks

Colour:	Green
Shape (Buoys):	Conical, pillar or spar
Topmark (if any):	Single green cone, point upward

Light (when fitted): Green, any other than composite group flashing (2 + 1)

At the point where a channel divides, when proceeding in the conventional direction of buoyage, a preferred channel may be indicated by modifying Port or Starboard lateral marks as follows:

Preferred channel to Starboard:

Colour:	Red with one broad green horizontal band
Shape (Buoys):	Cylindrical (can), pillar or spar
Topmark (if any):	Single red cylinder (can)

Light (when fitted): Red, Composite group flashing (2 + 1)

Preferred channel to Port

Colour:	Green with one broad red horizontal band
Shape (Buoys):	Conical, pillar or spar
Topmark (if any):	Single green cone, point upwards
Light (when fitted):	Green, Composite group flashing (2 + 1)

CARDINAL MARKS

The four quadrants (North, East, South and West) are bounded by the true bearings NW-NE, NE-SE, SE-SW, SW-NW, taken from the point of interest. A cardinal mark is named after the quadrant in which it is placed. The name of a cardinal mark indicates that it should be passed to the named side of the mark. It may be used:

to indicate that the deepest water in that area is on the named side of the mark

to indicate the safe side on which to pass a danger

to draw attention to a feature in a channel such as a bend, a junction, a bifurcation, or the end of a shoal

NORTH CARDINAL MARK:

Topmark :	2 black cones, one above the other, points upward.
Colour :	Black above yellow.
Shape :	Pillar or spar.
Light (when fitted) :	White, V.Qk.Fl. or Qk.Fl.

EAST CARDINAL MARK:

Topmark :	2 black cones, one above the other, base to base.
Colour :	Black with a single broad horizontal yellow band.
Shape :	Pillar or spar.
Light (when fitted) :	White, V.Qk.Fl.(3) every 5s or Qk.Fl.(3) every 10s

SOUTH CARDINAL MARK:

Topmark :	2 black cones, one above the other, points downward.
Colour :	Yellow above black.
Shape :	Pillar or spar.
Light (when fitted) :	White, V.Qk.Fl.(6) + long flash every 10s or Qk.Fl.(6) + long flash every 15s

WEST CARDINAL MARK:

Topmark :	2 black cones, one above the other, point to point.
Colour :	Yellow with a single broad horizontal black band.
Shape :	Pillar or spar.
Light (when fitted) :	White, V.Qk.Fl.(9) every 10s or Qk.Fl.(9) every 15s

ISOLATED DANGER MARK

This is a mark over an isolated danger which has navigable water all around it.

Topmark :	2 black spheres, one above the other.
Colour :	Black with one or more broad horizontal red bands.
Shape :	Pillar or spar preferred
Light (when fitted) :	White, Gp.Fl.(2).

SAFE WATER MARKS

They indicate that there is navigable water all round the mark; these include centre line marks and mid-channel marks. Such a mark may also be used as an alternative to a cardinal or a lateral mark to indicate a landfall.

Colour :	Red and white vertical stripes.
Shape :	Spherical, pillar with spherical topmark or spar.
Topmark (if any) :	Single red sphere.
Light (when fitted) :	White, Isophase, occulting, one long flash every 10s or Morse A.

SPECIAL MARKS

Marks not primarily intended to assist navigation but which indicate a special area or feature referred to in appropriate nautical documents, e.g. Ocean Data Acquisition Systems (ODAS) marks; Traffic Separation marks where use of conventional channel marking may cause confusion; Spoil Ground marks; Military Exercise Zone marks; Cable or pipe line marks; Recreation Zone marks.

Colour :	Yellow
Shape :	Optional but not conflicting with navigational marks (e.g. a yellow can buoy will not be used in a 'starboard' situation in region A).
Topmark (if any) :	Single yellow 'X' shape.
Light (when fitted) :	Yellow

Section 16

5

NEW DANGERS

Used to describe newly discovered hazards not yet shown on charts, including naturally occurring obstructions such as sandbanks or rocks or man-made dangers such as wrecks.

New Dangers will be marked in accordance with these rules. In the case of an especially grave danger, one of the marks may be duplicated.

Any lighted mark used for this purpose shall have an appropriate cardinal or lateral V.Qk.Fl. or Qk.Fl. light character.

A duplicate mark will be identical to its partner in all respects. A duplicate mark may carry a racon, coded Morse D. The duplicate mark will be removed when the new danger has been sufficiently promulgated.

LOCAL VARIATIONS

German Frisian Islands

Channels are marked with withies:

Unbound (twig points up)
= porthand marks
bound (twig points down)
= starboard hand marks

Otherwise conventional direction of buoyage is always west to east.

Norway, Sweden and Finland

The buoyage system is IALA System 'A'. but the spar buoys are usually without topmarks. Go by the colour.

IALA SYSTEM 'B'

Lateral marks in the waters of North, Central and South America, Japan, Korea and the Philippines, use red to starboard, green to port. Otherwise the system uses similar marks to that of System 'A'.

ELECTRONIC AIDS TO NAVIGATION

17

ELECTRONIC AIDS TO NAVIGATION

Over the past few decades, electronic aids for yachtsmen have advanced dramatically in sophistication and ease of operation.

For years the most advanced aid for the navigation of small vessels was the RDF set, by means of which radio bearings were taken of fixed DF stations. This system is still in use but the advent of more accurate and advanced systems has led to declining importance from the yachtsman's point of view. Full information on its use, is still included for the benefit of those navigators who use the method.

Automatic position-fixing has been in use commercially for many years, using groups of shore stations. The advent of the microchip and miniaturisation generally, allowed the development to take place of very small, highly sophisticated units, which could easily be accommodated in small vessels. Thus Decca and Loran became practical possibilities for small craft. Omega, although having worldwide coverage, is of little interest to yachtsmen.

RADIO DIRECTION FINDING (RDF)

RDF bearings consist of two types:

(a) Bearings taken by the navigator of fixed stations.

(b) Bearings taken by a fixed station of a vessel which are then radioed to the vessel concerned, giving its position.

VHF EMERGENCY DF STATIONS

Certain Coastguard Stations will give a vessel its position using method (b) in an *emergency* not as a normal check on navigational problems.

On request from a vessel in an emergency, the station will transmit the bearing of the vessel FROM the DF antenna. Watch is kept on Ch.16. Vessel transmits on Ch.16 (distress only) or Ch.67 (UK), Ch.67 (Guernsey), Ch.82 (Jersey), Ch.11 (France), in order that the station can determine its bearing which is transmitted on the same frequency.

The bearing given is only accurate to ± 10°. No responsibility is accepted by H.M. Coastguard for any action taken by the master, based on information given.

Marine Directional Radiobeacons

Marine directional radiobeacons are designed and located mainly to enable vessels to enter a particular harbour in poor visibility or other adverse conditions. They are somewhat similar to air radio ranges, their special feature being that a bearing line is given as a line of approach (usually coinciding with the normal Leading Line). 'On beam' bearings and the terms 'to port' or 'to starboard' of the beam are given with reference to the ship steering towards the directional radiobeacon.

A central beam is signalled from the station and if the ship is 'on beam' (ie on the correct line of approach), usually a steady continuous note is heard (or in some harbours, a certain Morse letter or letters). If for example, the vessel is to port of the approach beam, she might hear the letter A (· −) being transmitted continuously, but if to starboard of the beam she would hear a succession of letter N's (− ·) Transmission of the A's and N's are so synchronised that when both are heard together on the central beam, they interlock, thus forming a continuous note. The same result is achieved at some stations by use of the letters E (·) and T (−) instead of A and N. Each station, of course, has different characteristics, and although Morse dots and dashes are used they are not necessarily given the normal Morse spacing. Station identification letters are usually non-directional. Most directional radiobeacons also transmit non-directional signals for use with ship's D/F. Directional signals can be used with an ordinary radio receiver or with a D/F set with the aerial turned to the position of maximum reception.

Range

The range of radiobeacons, where known, is shown in nautical miles, in some cases, however, only the output (in kilowatts) is known. Where this is the case the following table will act as an approximate guide for converting to nautical miles.

Output	Range	Output	Range
0.025	45	1.0	240
0.05	80	1.5	280
0.1	100	2.0	300
0.2	130	3.0	330
0.3	155	5.0	400
0.4	170	10.0	500
0.5	180		

In areas where radiobeacons are numerous, the power output at night is reduced. In these cases both day and night ranges are given, eg. 200/70.

MARINE AND AERO RADIOBEACONS

Marine Radiobeacons

The automatic DF sets used by the majority of merchant ships require an uninterrupted carrier wave from the beacon to enable the set to 'lock on' when using automatic control rather than the interruption which occurs when the carrier is switched. Continuous carrier wave emission was introduced primarily for this purpose, but it also has considerable advantages for the small hand-held DF set. Before the introduction of this type of emission the modulated carrier wave was switched so that nothing was radiated during the intervals between the Morse Code letters. With the A2A system the carrier wave is emitted continuously and the modulation is also switched on during the DF period. However, with aerobeacons the modulation is switched off during the DF period.

The following is a summary of radiobeacon emissions used by Marine and Aeronautical stations:

A1A — Unmodulated carrier frequency during DF period; on-off keying of unmodulated carrier frequency during identification.

A2A — Carrier frequency with modulating audio frequency during DF period; on-off keying of modulating audio frequency. Carrier frequency either continuous or keyed with audio frequency.

NON A2A — Unmodulated carrier frequency during DF period; continuous carrier frequency with on-off keying of modulating audio frequency during identification.

The composition of the Maritime Radiobeacon Characteristic Signal for Beacons situated North of Latitude 46°N has been standardised as follows:

1) Identification signal transmitted at least twice — 13s
2) Long dash lasting for — 47s

Total 60s

Certain marine radiobeacons emit an additional signal for the transmission of GPS differential corrections. See Section 10.

Aero Beacons

A glimpse at the list of aero beacons in the annual volume will show that these are few in number compared to Morse radiobeacons, bearing in mind that only those of use to surface vessels are included. These beacons, however, have the advantage that in general they are more powerful than the coastal marine beacons. The normal transmission consists of a long dash interrupted at approximately 15 second intervals with the call sign, although some may repeat the call sign continuously. The facility of being able to pick up a transmission at any moment without reference to a time sequence is often extremely useful, particularly when used in conjunction with a marine beacon.

The receiver should be used exactly as for marine beacons. However, in this case if the operator should forget to select DF/BFO position when he is taking his bearing, all he will hear is background noise. This once again illustrates the importance of developing an automatic procedure with respect to the operating controls of the particular set in use.

ERRORS AND CALIBRATION OF DF SETS

Quadrantal Error

The accuracy of an RDF set should not be relied upon until it has been checked for errors. The main error due to the vessel itself is quadrantal error which is caused by the re-radiation of radio waves from metal structures or rigging of the vessel. This re-radiated signal is picked up by the DF aerial and the set then indicates the resultant direction of the two waves. In the case of a sailing yacht the effect can be minimised by 'breaking' the closed loops of the rigging by inserting insulation but it is debatable whether this is really worth doing in most cases. It is much easier and more worthwhile to break the loops formed by steel life lines by using a rope seizing at one end of each line instead of a shackle. To calibrate for quadrantal error it is necessary to be within sight of a radiobeacon or in a known position so that the magnetic bearing of the beacon can be accurately determined. The visual (magnetic) and the DF bearings are compared at regular intervals, say 10°, while the vessel is rotated through 360°. A curve can then be plotted of the quadrantal error for each 10° of a relative bearing. Before plotting the curve it is important to remember to correct the compass bearings for deviation if any.

Night Effect

During the hours of darkness or more correctly between one hour before sunset to one hour after sunrise the radiobeacon signals are reflected back from the ionosphere and are picked up by the DF set slightly out of phase with the direct ground waves, resulting in a blurring of the null. The effect increases with distance from the beacon but close to the beacon, say within 15 miles, the effect is less noticeable. In areas where radiobeacons are numerous, it is found necessary to reduce the power output at night. In these cases the day and night ranges are both given, ie. 100/70. It is advisable to assume that MF beacons in general are not to be relied on at ranges of more than 70 miles in the presence of 'Night Effect', particularly around sunset and sunrise.

Coastal Refraction

Radio waves crossing a coastline at 90° are unaffected directionally but as the angle decreases refraction occurs, that is, the radio wave is bent in towards the land. The error, however, is really only significant when the angle is small and will always give a fix closer to the coastline than the actual position. Similarly, aerobeacons situated well inland may have the path of their ground waves seriously 'bent' due to the presence of high ground.

Remember

1. A beacon selected should not be beyond its official range and not more than 25 miles at night whatever its range otherwise bearings may be unreliable.

2. Try to ensure that the ship's head is kept on a steady bearing during the operation. This is essential with the loop type aerial as the ship's heading will be needed at the instant the beacon bearing is taken.

3. The DF set bearing is corrected for deviation and quadrantal error if appropriate.

4. When choosing the beacon make sure that the bearing does not make a small angle with the coastline, that high ground does not intervene between the beacon and the vessel and that bearings should be as widely divergent as possible. As with visual bearings, considerable reliance can be placed on three well spaced bearings producing a small cocked hat.

5. Other aerial circuits near a loop aerial should be disconnected from their sets.

6. Radiobeacons may be suspended from operation without notice due to defects, maintenance, etc., particularly beacons situated in light-vessels which may be removed from station for overhaul during the summer months.

SUPPRESSION OF ELECTRICAL APPARATUS

When any radio equipment is to be used on board it is important to ensure that any rotating electrical plant in the form of dynamos, alternators etc. is effectively suppressed. Normally, installations of this type are properly suppressed by the manufacturer, but if this has not been done or it has become defective it should be remedied if the best results are to be obtained from the radio equipment. It is incidentally worth bearing in mind that a very obtrusive static discharge can occur when the auxiliary of a sailing yacht is not in use but the propeller is allowed to rotate. A shaft brake should be fitted, alternatively a contact brush fitted on the shaft near the stern gland and suitably earthed will alleviate the trouble. All equipment should be earthed down to the engine bed plate and cathodic protection system.

NAVIGATION BY MEANS OF SHORE BASED STATIONS

There are three automatic position-fixing systems based on chains of shore stations transmitting on different wavelengths.

OMEGA

Omega is a long range hyperbolic fixing system operating in the very low frequency (VLF) band. Eight transmitting stations are sufficient to provide world-wide coverage.

Radio Frequency: The basic frequency is 10.2 kHz but signals of 11.33 kHz and 13.6 kHz are also transmitted. Each station transmits the same frequencies in turn, according to a schedule which repeats at 10 second intervals. The signals from individual stations are identified by the duration and sequence of the transmissions.

Principle: The phase of signals of pairs of stations from pairs of stations are compared (as in the Decca system) and a number of possible hyperbolic position lines are defined by an observed phase difference.

Accuracy: Observations of phase difference must be corrected for the phase variations which may be predicted according to the time of the day, season of the year and geographical location. When these corrections are applied, fixing accuracy may be expected to be of the order of ±1 nm by day and ± 2 nm by night (95 per cent probability).

OMEGA STATIONS

Ident Letter	Location	Lat.	Long.
A	Norway	66°25'N	13°09'E
B	Liberia	6°18'N	10°40'W
C	Hawaii	21°24'N	157°50'W
D	N. Dakota	46°22'N	98°20'W
E	La Réunion	20°58'S	55°17'E
F	Argentina	43°03'S	65°11'W
G	Australia	38°29'S	146°56'E
H	Japan	34°37'N	129°27E

LORAN C

Loran C is a development from the less successful Loran A. The radio Frequency is 100 kHz which is low enough to give a ground wave range of 800-1200 nm. Also sky waves may be used at longer ranges.

Principle: A Loran C chain consists of a master transmitting station and two to four slaves designated W,X,Y, and Z. The time interval between reception of signals from master and slave pairs is measured coarsely by comparing pulse envelopes and then finely by comparing the phase of the radio frequency cycles within the envelopes. The measured time difference defines the observer's position as on a hyperbola which can be identified on the appropriate Loran C lattice chart. Two master-slave pairs are needed to obtain a fix. Each chain is identified by a unique group repetition interval (GRI) at which the complete pattern of signals is repeated.

Range: The ground wave coverage of 800-1200 nm is increased to over 2000 nm by the use of sky waves but with reduced accuracy.

Accuracy: Within ground wave coverage the fixing accuracy is usually better than ± 500 metres (95 per cent probability).

ICELANDIC CHAIN

Sandur, Iceland	64 54 N	23 55 W	9980 (SS2)
Angissog, Greenland	59 59 N	45 10 W	9980-W
Ejde, Føroyar	62 18 N	07 04 W	9980-X

NORWEGIAN SEA CHAIN

Ejde, Føroyar	62 18 N	07 04 W	7970 (SL3)
Sylt, Germany	54 48 N	08 18 E	7970-W
Bø, Norway	68 38 N	14 28 E	7970-X
Sandur, Iceland	64 54 N	23 55 W	7970-Y
Jan Mayen	70 55 N	08 44 W	7970-Z

MEDITERRANEAN CHAIN

Sellia Marina, Italy	38 52 N	16 43 E	7990 (SL1)
Lampedusa, Italy	35 31 N	12 31 E	7990-X
Kargaburun, Turkey	40 58 N	27 52 E	7990-Y
Estartit, Spain	42 04 N	03 12 E	7990-Z

SAUDI ARABIAN NORTH CHAIN

Afif	23 49 N	42 51 E	8990
Salwa	24 50 N	50 34 E	8990-V
Ash Shaykh Humayd	28 09 N	34 46 E	8990-X
Al Lith	20 14 N	40 13 E	8990-Y
Al Muwassam	16 26 N	42 48 E	8990-Z

DECCA — COMMERCIAL SHIPPING

The Decca Navigator detects the radio position-line patterns laid down by a chain of Decca transmitting stations ashore. There are usually three such patterns, numbered and overprinted on standard marine charts in Red, Green and Purple colours.

The receiver drives three position-line indicators called Decometers which automatically and continuously display at any instant the numbers of the Decca position-lines passing through the vessel. To distinguish them the Lanes in each pattern are numbered differently: Red 0-23, Green 30-47, Purple 50-79. These numbers recur in groups, referred to as 'Zones', denoted by letters of the alphabet. Once the Decometers have been set up, the position can be read off without operating any controls.

During daylight periods ranges of 400 nautical miles or more are obtained, at night the ranges may be expected to be 250 nautical miles under good reception conditions, or only 200 nautical miles under adverse conditions.

Fixed and variable errors for the different chains are published in the Decca Marine Data Sheet Handbook.

Section 17

DECCA EQUIPMENT FOR SMALL CRAFT

Equipment manufactured for small craft does not utilise information received from the Decca chains in a similar manner to the so-called 'professional' receivers, resulting in differences in operation. The receivers give a direct reading of Latitude and Longitude, thus obviating the need for Lattice Charts and the updating occurs at 20 second intervals instead of continuously as in the commercial receiver. It is important to realise that the displayed latitude and longitude position is liable to fixed error and variable error. Fixed errors are caused by the bending of radio waves and are constant. Variable errors can arise from skywave effect, from self-generated interference and from thunderstorms. Whereas the sum of any errors offshore is unlikely to be important, IT IS VITAL FOR THE USER TO BE AWARE THAT THE DISPLAYED POSITION MUST BE REGARDED WITH CAUTION WHEN NAVIGATING IN NARROW CHANNELS OR CLOSE TO DANGERS. In short, this is not a substitute for established pilotage techniques.

DECCA CHAINS IN OPERATION

Station		Position	Frequency (kHz)
SOUTH-WEST BRITISH CHAIN (Chain 1 B)			
Bolberry Down	A	50°14'N	3°50'W	84.280
Jersey	B	49°15'N	2°05'W	112.373
St Mary's	C	49°56'N	6°18'W	126.420
Llancarfan	D	51°26'N	3°23'W	70.233
NORTH BRITISH CHAIN (Chain 3B)			
Kidsdale	A	54°42'N	4°25'W	84.645
Clanrolla	B	54°30'N	6°20'W	112.860
Neston	C	53°16'N	3°03'W	126.968
Stirling	D	56°04'N	4°03'W	70.538
HEBRIDEAN CHAIN (CHAIN 8E)			
Barra	A	56°59'N	7°25'W	85.635
Kendra Moss	B	56°45'N	5°49'W	114.180
Butt of Lewis	C	58°30'N	6°16'W	128.452
Dungloe	D	54°53'N	8°23'W	71.362
NORTH SCOTTISH CHAIN (CHAIN 6C)			
Kirkwall	A	59°04'N	3°15'W	85.185
Butt of Lewis	B	58°30'N	6°15'W	113.580
Lerwick	C	60°10'N	1°11'W	127.778
Peterhead	D	57°31'N	1°51'W	70.988

Station		Position		Frequency (kHz)
NORTHUMBRIAN CHAIN (Chain 2A)				
Allerdean Greens	A	55°42'N	2°02'W	84.455
Stirling	B	56°04'N	4°03'W	112.607
Peterhead	C	57°31'N	1°51'W	126.683
Burton Fleming	D	54°08'N	0°19'W	70.379
A142 ENGLISH CHAIN (Chain 5B)				
Puckeridge	A	51°55'N	0°00'E	85.00
Shotisham	B	52°33'N	1°20'E	113.33
East Hoathley	C	50°55'N	0°09'E	127.50
Wormleighton	D	52°12'N	1°22'W	70.83
IRISH CHAIN (Chain 7D)				
Galway	A	53°15'N	8°59'W	85.450
Ballydavid	B	52°12'N	10°22'W	113.933
Dungloe	C	54°53'N	8°23'W	128.175
Youghal	D	51°57'N	7°45'W	71.208
HOLLAND CHAIN (Chain 2E)				
Gilze-Rijen	A	51°37'N	4°56'E	85.450
Heiloo	B	52°35'N	4°45'E	112.733
Sas van Gent	C	51°13'N	3°52'E	126.825
Thorpeness	D	52°11'N	1°36'E	70.458
FRISIAN ISLANDS CHAIN (9B)				
Finsterwolde	A	53°12'N	7°06'E	85.720
Høyer	B	55°01'N	8°42'E	114.293
Heiloo	C	52°36'N	4°44'E	128.580
Zeven	D	53°17'N	9°16'E	71.433
DANISH CHAIN (Chain 7B)				
Samsø	A	55°57'N	10°35'E	85.365
Møen	B	54°57'N	12°28'E	113.820
Eøjer	C	55°01'N	8°42'E	128.047
Hjorring	D	57°27'N	10°03'W	71.138
SKAGERRAK CHAIN (Chain 10B)				
Fjällbacka	A	58°31'N	11°18'E	85.900
Jomfruland	B	58°52'N	9°36'E	114.533
Valda	C	57°29'N	11°57'E	128.850
Årjäng	D	59°21'N	12°11'E	71.583
SOUTH BALTIC CHAIN (Chain 0A)				
Holmsjö	A	56°27'N	15°40'E	84.100
Sandhammaren	B	57°02'N	18°15'E	112.133
Burgsvik	C	55°24'N	14°11'E	126.150
NORTH BALTIC CHAIN (Chain 4B)				
Nynashamn	A	58°57'N	17°57'E	84.825
Åland	B	60°07'N	19°49'E	113.100
Ar	C	57°55'N	18°57'E	127.238
Björkvik	D	58°51'N	16°34'E	70.688
GULF OF FINLAND CHAIN (Chain 6E)				
Mäntsälä	A	60°31'N	25°11'E	85.27
Padva	B	60°00'N	22°50'E	113.693
Sydänkylä	C	60°31'N	27°26'E	127.905

Station		Position	Frequency (kHz)
SOUTH BOTHNIAN CHAIN (Chain 8C)			
Njurunda	A	62°17'N 17°25'E	85.550
Skutskar	B	60°37'N 17°27'E	114.067
Jarnas	C	63°29'N 19°39'E	128.325
NORTH BOTHNIAN CHAIN (Chain 5F)			
Lovanger	A	64°21'N 21°21'E	85.095
Gamla Karleby	B	63°52'N 23°11'E	113.460
Kallax	C	65°32'N 22°04'E	127.6425
Jarnas	D	63°29'N 19°39'E	70.9125
VESTLANDET CHAIN (Chain 0E)			
Sotra	A	60°24'N 5°01'E	84.195
Statt	B	62°11'N 5°08'E	112.250
Shetland Is.	C	60°03'N 1°15'E	126.292
Jaren	D	58°47'N 5°33'E	70.162
TRØNDELAG CHAIN (Chain 4E)			
Skarsøy	A	63°20'N 8°27'E	84.915
Rørvik	B	64°55'N 11°10'E	113.220
Statt	C	62°12'N 5°08'E	127.373
Berkak	D	62°50'N 10°03'E	70.763
HELGELAND CHAIN (Chain 9E)			
Dønna	A	66°12'N 12°28'E	85.810
Røst	B	67°32'E 12°08'E	114.413
Rørvik	C	64°55'N 11°10'E	128.715
Mo i Rana	D	66°17'N 14°09'E	71.508
LOFOTEN CHAIN (Chain 3E)			
Andøya	A	69°09'N 16°02'E	84.735
Torsvag	B	70°15'N 19°30'E	112.980
Røst	C	67°32'N 12°09'E	127.103
Narvik	D	68°28'N 17°06'E	70.613
FINNMARK CHAIN (Chain 7E)			
Reksunnjarga	A	70°23'N 25°30'E	85.455
Virgasfjell	B	69°41'N 30°03'E	113.933
Fakken	C	70°06'N 20°07'E	128.175
Nordkapp	D	71°10'N 25°45'E	71.208
N.W. SPANISH CHAIN (Chain 4C)			
San Juan de Rio	A	42°24'N 7°18'W	84.830
Noya	B	42°44'N 8°55'W	113.107
Boal	C	43°27'N 6°49'W	127.245
Vitigudino	D	41°01'N 6°26'W	70.691
SOUTH SPANISH CHAIN (Chain 6A)			
Setenil	A	36°52'N 5°08'W	85.175
Padul	B	37°02'N 3°41'W	113.566
Los Barrios	C	36°11'N 5°29'W	127.762
Rociana	D	37°18'N 6°36'W	70.979

A *Master*
B *Red Slave*
C *Green Slave*
D *Purple SLave*

RADIO BEARINGS CORRECTION TABLE

Radio bearings of a ship (Q.T.G.s) which have been taken by a distant radio station are great circle bearings and they are represented on a Mercator chart by curved lines, except when they coincide with a meridian or the equator. As meridians are shown as parallel lines on a Mercator chart, these great circle curves will cut each meridian at a different angle.

Convergency is the difference in the angles formed by the intersection of a great circle with two meridians. Its value between any two points on the Earth can be found from the approximate formulae:

Convergency = difference of longitude x sin. mean latitude.

If two places on the chart are joined, first by a great circle and then by a straight line, the latter makes an angle with the great circle at each end. Each of these two angles may, for all practical purposes, be regarded as being equal to the **Half Convergency.**

It is important to remember that the straight line bearing on the Mercator chart always lies on the equatorial side of the great circle bearing.

D/F bearings are all great circle bearings and must, therefore, be corrected for Half Convergency before they can be plotted on a Mercator chart.

Rule for applying Half Convergency

It is usual for the ship to take a Radio D/F bearing of the shore station but in any case the following rule holds good even if the shore station has taken the bearings.

Always apply the Half Convergency TOWARDS THE EQUATOR.

A Half Convergency Correction table appears overleaf.

Section 17

HALF CONVERGENCY CORRECTION TABLE

Mean Lat	Longitude Difference between Radio Station and Ship												
	2°	4°	6°	8°	10°	12°	14°	16°	18°	20°	22°	24°	26°
3	0.1	0.1	0.2	0.2	0.3	0.3	0.4	0.4	0.5	0.5	0.6	0.6	0.7
6	0.1	0.2	0.3	0.4	0.5	0.6	0.7	0.8	0.9	1.0	1.1	1.2	1.3
9	0.2	0.3	0.5	0.6	0.9	0.9	1.1	1.2	1.4	1.5	1.7	1.8	2.0
12	0.2	0.4	0.6	0.8	1.1	1.2	1.5	1.6	1.9	2.0	2.3	2.5	2.7
15	0.3	0.5	0.8	1.0	1.3	1.6	1.9	2.0	2.3	2.5	2.8	3.1	3.3
18	0.3	0.6	1.0	1.2	1.6	1.9	2.2	2.4	2.8	3.0	3.4	3.7	4.0
21	0.3	0.7	1.1	1.4	1.9	2.2	2.5	2.8	3.2	3.5	3.9	4.3	4.6
24	0.4	0.8	1.2	1.6	2.1	2.5	2.9	3.2	3.6	4.0	4.4	4.8	5.2
27	0.4	0.9	1.3	1.8	2.3	2.8	3.2	3.6	4.0	4.5	5.0	5.4	5.9
30	0.5	1.0	1.4	2.0	2.5	3.0	3.5	4.0	4.5	5.0	5.5	6.0	6.5
33	0.5	1.1	1.5	2.2	2.7	3.3	3.8	4.4	4.9	5.4	6.0	6.5	7.1
36	0.6	1.2	1.7	2.4	2.9	3.5	4.1	4.7	5.3	5.9	6.5	7.0	7.6
39	0.6	1.3	1.8	2.6	3.1	3.8	4.4	5.0	5.6	6.3	7.0	7.5	8.1
42	0.7	1.4	1.9	2.8	3.3	4.0	4.7	5.3	6.0	6.7	7.5	8.0	8.7
45	0.7	1.5	2.0	2.9	3.5	4.2	5.0	5.6	6.3	7.1	7.9	8.5	9.2
48	0.7	1.5	2.1	3.0	3.7	4.5	5.3	5.9	6.7	7.4	8.2	8.9	9.6
51	0.8	1.6	2.3	3.2	3.9	4.7	5.5	6.2	7.0	7.8	8.5	9.3	10.0
54	0.8	1.6	2.4	3.4	4.1	4.9	5.7	6.5	7.3	8.1	8.9	9.7	10.5
57	0.8	1.7	2.5	3.5	4.3	5.1	5.9	6.8	7.6	8.4	9.2	10.0	10.9
60	0.9	1.8	2.6	3.6	4.4	5.2	6.1	7.0	7.9	8.7	9.5	10.3	11.2

Example: A vessel in Lat. 15°20'N,. Long. 50°20'W. obtains a Radio D/F bearing from a Station in Lat. 53°40'N., Long 5°10'W. True bearing signalled as 070°.

Enter the above table with the mean latitude (53°40' + 50°20' = 104°00' ÷ 2) = 52°00', and the Diff. Long. (15°20'– 5°10') = 10°10'W., and by inspection the approximate correction is found to be 4°. By the rule above this must be applied towards the Equator so 070° + 4° = 074°, which is the correct mercatorial bearing to lay off.

RADAR

Radar is probably the most useful of all the electronic navigation aids when coasting. It not only gives position but also indicates the dangers of collision or stranding.

Radar consists of four basic units: transmitter, aerial (scanner), receiver and display.

A very short pulse of powerful electromagnetic energy is transmitted from the aerial in a narrow, horizontal beam at the speed of light (300 million metres/sec.) at the same time a stream of electrons (the trace) is deflected from the centre of the cathode ray tube out towards the circumference of the tube face at a controlled rate, variable with the range scale in use. Only the outward trace is used.

Any object on the bearing of the transmitted pulse will re-radiate the energy in many directions and only a very small portion will return to the aerial.

REFLECTION

This signal once detected needs to be greatly amplified and changed to + D.C. voltage. The D.C. pulse allows an increase in the flow of electrons to make a bright mark on the screen to record the 'echo'. This sequence takes place many times each second (Pulse Repetition Frequency), the space between is to allow a returned echo to be detected and displayed before the next transmission. PRFs vary with range and/or make of set. Between 500-2000 per second. The aerial is set to rotate at about 20 revs. per minute and the trace rotation is synchronised with the direction of the rotating aerial (scanner) so the direction of every echo from the observer is shown on the display.

Even the smallest object will return several echoes before the beam moves on. This provides a storage effect of the returned energy to help display the weaker echoes.

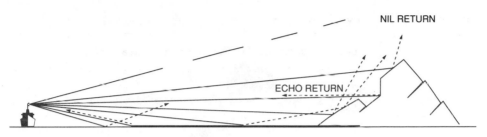

NIL RETURN

ECHO RETURN

SPECULAR REFLECTION

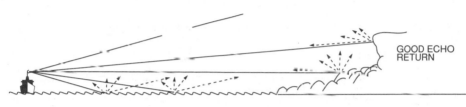

GOOD ECHO RETURN

SCATTERING

A most important point of reference is the Heading Marker. To enable the radar to give direction, a switch device is placed at the aerial unit. When the aerial is pointing ahead a pulse is sent from the aerial to the radar display which causes a line to show on the screen which represents the ship's head so that any echo displayed on the screen can be referred to the ship's head and the bearing of the echo obtained. If the Heading Marker switch is not pointing exactly ahead, relative bearings will be in error. A quick check is to head towards a small prominent visible object and see if the echo is under the Heading Marker, noting any difference.

The narrow horizontal beam is determined by the size of the aerial. The larger the scanner the smaller is the horizontal beam. The 6m. shore scanners have 0.5° beams. Merchant ships must have less than 2°. These large scanners are not practicable on small craft and the usual yacht scanner of about 0.5m. has a 6° beam.

To allow for the motion at sea the vertical beam is about 20°. The transmitted pulse has to contain sufficient energy to travel many miles and produce a detectable echo return. If a peak power of 1.5 kW. is transmitted for 0.5 millionths of a second (½ microsecond) this produces a pulse 150 m. long. The pulse is shorter on lower ranges (0.1 sec. = 30 m.)

This combined effect of pulse length and horizontal beam width will determine the picture resolution and ability to discriminate between objects close to each other. The beam distortion of echoes can be seen by apparently large echoes at the longer ranges, getting smaller as they near the centre. Small river or harbour entrances may not be detected, buoyed channels may close. Any objects within the beam at the same range will show on the radar at that bearing as a single echo.

The pulse length gives apparent length to an echo. Any two objects within the pulse appear as one. This is why the shortest pulse possible for detection is used on lower ranges.

The detection of objects is also determined by their shape, size aspect and material. Metal is a perfect reflector, while glass fibre is almost transparent to radar. This is why a metal reflector is a must for small glass fibre vessels (the metal reflectors may be set inside a fiberous material). Sea water is a very good re-radiator, most of the energy reflecting away but the scattered return from waves may give stronger echoes than objects within the waves. Sea clutter normally is more noticeable to windward, the backs of the lee waves giving less return to the aerial.

To remove this clutter around the centre of the display a special variable suppression is provided which works outward from the centre decreasing to nil at about 3 miles. This control, 'Sea Clutter', is regarded as the most dangerous control on the set, as 'wanted' real echoes may be removed without the observer realising the

Small objects, buoy (A) boat (B) small fishing vessel (C) in an area of rough sea.

extent of the 'hole' in the picture. This is worse for the small craft which may not be detected from a larger ship's radar display. 2(a) & 2(b)

Navigating Using Radar

Bearing in mind all the above limitations, radar is a most useful navigational aid. The presentation is a plan view of the locality which will relate to the chart in use. However, the picture will not be quite the same as the chart. Small insignificant objects may be enhanced while small prominent objects may not give a detectable return. Lower parts of the coast may be below the radar horizon and the coast on

the radar will be inland from the charted coast.

Bearings are quite difficult to take on a small craft radar. The heading must be read at the instant the bearing is read and converted to a true bearing and unless the object is identified the bearing may be laid off from the wrong place. Lighthouses are not usually at the exact point of land. The ends of land will be displaced by half beam width. The best position is obtained by taking a visual bearing of an isolated object and the best radar only position is by taking three or more radar ranges from the land. This will produce a 'cocked hat'. Take the closest to danger to be your position. In fog always 'stand off' to seaward of your intended track.

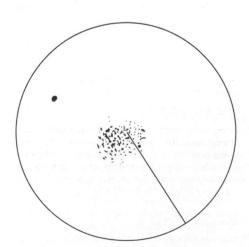

2(a)Sea Clutter masking echoes from A. B. and C.

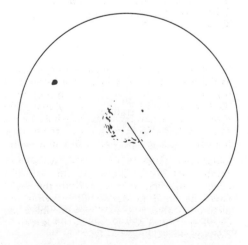

2(b) Sea Clutter Suppression applied echoes A, B. – not detected and C – just visible.

RADAR (HEAD UP)

6 MILE RANGE

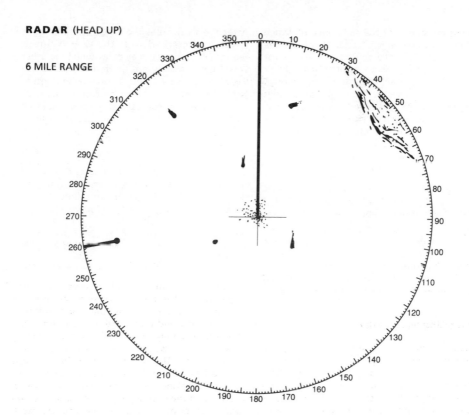

Course 240°T, Speed 8 knots. Land to starboard.
Racon 'Flash' marks structure to port.
5 echoes detected. Echoes at 340° and 130° visible beacons.
Echo at 240° vessel same course/speed.
Echo at 015° crossing clear.
Echo at 320° to be plotted.

Section 17

To aid radar navigation, important objects such as lightships or fairway buoys are fitted with responder beacons, 'Racons', which produce a 'flash' away from the racon, usually about two miles long. The racon searches the whole marine radar X band and may only strike your frequency once or twice each 100 or so seconds.

Radar presentations not yet widely available to small craft radars are North up, where a compass heading is introduced. As the vessel yaws the Heading Marker moves while the picture is stable. Also true motion, where the centre spot is set to move across the screen at own vessel's course and speed.

Plenty of clear weather practice is essential to build confidence in your own ability, or attend a

radar course where all these points will be amplified.

THE RADAR PLOT

In order to comply with the International Collision Regulations 'correct assessment' of a situation using radar can only be ascertained by carefully plotting the movement of an approaching vessel. Clear weather practice is essential before attempting radar navigation in fog.

The Relative Plot

The majority of small craft radars are only capable of a 'ship's head up' display. This is where the heading marker is always at zero and any movement of the craft will show as lateral rotating movement of the radar picture. When plotting in this mode it is better to convert the relative bearings into compass bearings for plotting — (no need to apply variation or deviation) — the vessel's course steered is drawn on the plotting diagram. Continuity of the plot after course alterations by your own vessel will be preserved as the only thing to be altered is the heading line. If the plot were to be made 'head up' all echoes will have to be transferred each time the course is changed. This is a frequent cause of mistakes.

The relative plot is a reproduction of the radar picture and on it a forecast of future movement of echoes can be made.

Bearings of echoes should be taken with the cursor through the centre of the echo and the range taken using the inner edge of the range marker through the inner edge. At the moment of bearing the heading should be noted along with the time. The accuracy of the plot is only as good as the accuracy with which the ship's head was noted. Without knowing the craft's heading at the moment of reading the bearing can be dangerous.

If our own vessel is stopped all ranges and bearings of echoes would produce a 'true motion picture'. All moving echoes would show their real direction while stationary objects would not move.

When your own vessel is moving, all stationary objects will show as movements in the opposite direction at your speed. The harbour entrance will 'come towards you' on the radar. All echoes which come from moving ships will move across the screen in a resultant direction of your own course and speed and the other's course and speed through the water. In order to decide upon a safe action, it is essential to know the other vessel's heading and speed. To do this we divide the movement into its known components to produce a triangle. By looking at the radar screen the afterglow from echo movements produces dim 'tails' behind the echo. This is only an indication of resultant movement, but useful in deciding which echoes may be closing.

To allow time to plot and assess which action to take the plot should start when the echo is some distance from the centre.

The triangle of motions is named in a standard form W.O. and A.A. series of three ranges and bearings are taken in a time interval of six minutes (1/10th hour)

The first position is named O and the time noted. On 3 minutes a check position is taken.

After the six minutes the range and bearing is taken and marked A. If the O → A line is reasonably straight it may be assumed the other vessel has probably not altered course during the plotting interval. This O → A line is projected past the centre to show the closest point of approach. A CPA of less than 1 mile should be considered potentially dangerous because of the small scale of the radar picture and the inaccuracy of radar bearings.

In the plotting interval of 6 minutes own vessel will have moved over a known course and distance (1/10th of the speed). This direction and distance is laid back from O and named W. W → O (Way of Own Ship). Join W to A. This represents the course and speed of the vessel. W → A (Way of Another). Use arrows on each line to indicate direction.

With this information avoiding action can now be planned. Whatever action is decided this may be applied to the plot to see the possible effect before the alteration is made. Alternatively a safe distance can be decided on and taken back to the plot (a new O/A line) to find the alteration needed to achieve this.

To aid visual appreciation of the situation, sketch in a boat shape at the centre of the plot in the direction of your own heading and another shape at A in the Direction W A, the other's heading.

With practice, and reasonable accuracy the radar plot gives a good general idea of the situation, assuming the other vessel has maintained course and speed. It is important to continue plotting an approaching echo until it is past and clear, especially after you have made an alteration, to see what effect has been made to the CPA.

The need for radar plotting became apparent soon after radar was introduced for use at sea in the 1940s. Many collisions in the early days were caused by misunderstanding of what was 'seen' on the screen. Since then technology and regulations have come a long way to improve the situation.

Very few of the modern developments extend to the small ship's radar and most are only able to present the original 'ships head up' display. The information may be filtered to the 'Rasterscan' type (television) display. Guard rings are available but the plotting and forecasting of subsequent movements are left to the observer.

RADAR PLOTTING SHEET

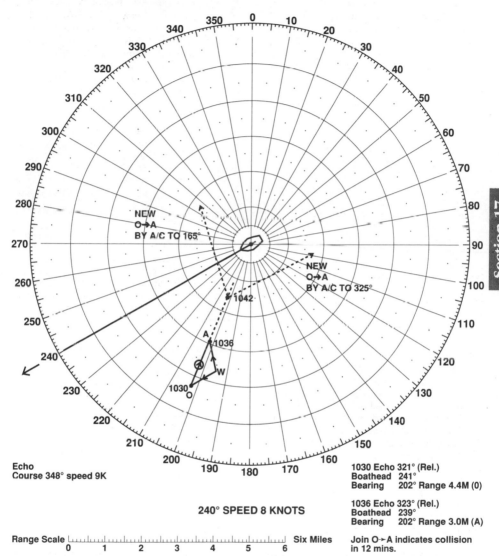

Echo
Course 348° speed 9K

240° SPEED 8 KNOTS

Range Scale |‌‌‌‌‌‌‌‌‌‌‌‌‌‌‌‌‌‌‌‌‌‌‌‌‌‌‌‌‌‌‌‌‌| Six Miles
0   1   2   3   4   5   6

1030 Echo 321° (Rel.)
Boathead 241°
Bearing 202° Range 4.4M (0)

1036 Echo 323° (Rel.)
Boathead 239°
Bearing 202° Range 3.0M (A)

Join O→A indicates collision
in 12 mins.

Assuming no significant changes in O ‣ A, Plot the forecast position say in 6 min. at 1042. From this position lay off tangents to the chosen pass distance (1 mile ring). Take this line back to A on the plot. Rotate W – O about W to touch this new O – A line at O₁. W ‣ O₁ is the new course. Repeat with the other O₁ – A line.

Note: From the plot an alteration to starboard will mean running on a near parallel course for a long time. An alteration to port is not recommended as the other vessel may be altering to starboard as we alter to port — most dangerous. In this situation stopping own vessel before 1042 will allow the other to pass well ahead. Remember the craft on your port quarter will now overtake you.

TIDES AND TIDAL STREAMS

18

TIDES AND TIDAL STREAMS

Tides have washed the northern and western coasts of Europe in a way that used to be shrouded in mystery, and even today that sense of mystery has not deserted us entirely.

The action of the tide can be very inconvenient at times, but with good forward planning it can often be used to advantage, especially the resultant tidal streams.

The following pages aim to dispel some of that uncertainty surrounding the subject, thereby enabling us to appreciate the value and accuracy of the data which we are given, and so to make the best use of it during our time afloat.

TIDAL DEFINITIONS AND EXPLANATIONS

The Lunar Tide: The result of the gravitational effect of the Moon only.

The effect of the Moon alone would be to cause the waters of the oceans to form an elliptical envelope around the Earth, with the major axis aligned with the Moon, thus:

under a deeper layer of water in the afternoon. This effect is known as the semi-diurnal (half daily) inequality.

It can also be seen that apart from the vertical changes, large horizontal forces are also present, and it is these which are more significant.

The distance between the Moon and the Earth varies, so causing the gravitational force to wax and wane. At **Perigee** the Moon is at its closest, and at **Apogee** it is at its furthest.

The Solar Tide: The result of the gravitational effect of the Sun.

The effect of the Sun alone would be to create an ellipse around the Earth with the major axis aligned with the Sun. One major difference is that the gravitational effect of the Sun is only half that of the Moon because it is so much further away.

The joint effect of these two major forces is to vary the shape of the ellipse according to whether the Sun and Moon are aligned and

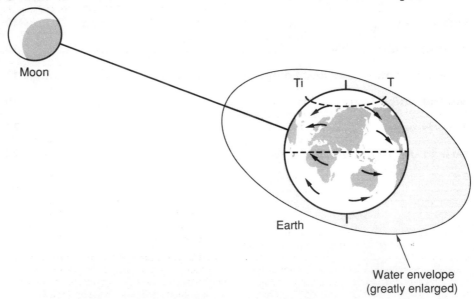

Moon

Ti | T

Earth

Water envelope
(greatly enlarged)

It can be seen that as the Moon changes in declination, so the axis of the ellipse will change. The effect of this is to make a considerable difference between the heights of the morning and afternoon tides. This is seen by noting that point 'T' on the Earth will be under one part of the envelope in (say) the morning, and as the Earth turns to lie at point T1, will be

therefore pulling together, or at right angles, so working against each other. In the normal way of events, this results in the variation between spring and neap tides, but where the Sun and Moon are aligned even more closely by declination as well as by longitude, the effect is to produce the **Equinoctial Tides,** when the highest tides are formed in March and

September and the opposite effect causing the **Solstice** Tides in June and December.

The distance between the Sun and the Earth varies, so causing the gravitational force to wax and wane. At **Perihelion** the Sun is at its closest, and at **Aphelion** it is at its furthest.

In fact there are many more astronomical and local features which affect the height of the tide, and some of these are discussed under Tide Predictions.

Spring and Neap Tides: When the Sun and Moon are lying at right angles to each other they are said to be in quadrature and form neap tides, and in conjunction they form spring tides. Because the variation between neaps and springs is caused by the position of the sun, the peak of these cycles occurs at much the same time of day. For example at London Bridge, spring tides always occur at 0330 and 1530 and neaps at 0930 and 2130. At Dover the times are three hours different from this but on the same day.

Lag: Because of the great mass of water lying around the Earth, the effects of the astronomical forces are not felt immediately, therefore spring tides tend to fall about 36 hours after new and full Moon rather than on the same day.

Chart Datum: The plane from which the depths of all features, either permanently or nearly permanently covered by the sea, are measured. It is also the plane from which the heights of all features, periodically covered and uncovered by the sea, are measured. The former are known as charted depths, and the latter, which are distinguished on the chart from charted depths by an underline, are known as Drying Heights. It is a fixed level below which all charted depths on a chart are given and above which all heights of the tide are given in the tide tables.

By international agreement chart datum is at a level below which the tide seldom falls. On British charts this plane has been, in the past, usually near or below Mean Low Water Springs in the locality, but these data are now adjusted to approximate to the level of the Lowest Astronomical Tide (L.A.T.)

The level of L.A.T. and other defined heights such as Mean High Water Springs are established after a study of the existing tidal patterns at the place. They are quoted as so many feet or metres below the national levelling datum. In the UK this is Ordnance Datum (Newlyn), and in the Netherlands it is called the Normaal

Amsterdams Piel and permits engineers and surveyors to relate the tidal levels exactly to their own projects along the coast.

The Height of the Tide is the vertical distance at any time between Chart Datum and the sea surface. It should not be confused with the rise of the tide or depth.

In an established port it is measured by reference to a tide board, the zero of which is aligned exactly with Chart Datum. Major ports such as London will have automatic recording gauges at many sites which describe the curve on a revolving graph and which radio the heights at one minute intervals to the navigation control centre, so keeping them perfectly aware of the state of the tide throughout its port and approaches.

A tide board should not be confused with a berth board which looks exactly the same, but where the zero of the board is set at the ground level of the berth and simply indicates the **depth** at the berth, not the height of tide.

The Rise of the Tide is the amount by which the tide has risen above the preceding low water. Similarly the **Fall of the Tide** is the amount by which the tide has fallen below the previous high water.

The Range of the Tide is the difference between the height of any high water and that of the preceding or following low water.

The Duration of the Tide is the time difference between any high water and the preceding or following low water.

Mean High Water Springs or Neaps are the mean levels of high water at spring or neap tides and are given above Chart Datum. All lights, bridge clearances and shore features are given in metres above MHWS. It is worth noting that a significant number of tides reach levels beyond these heights, not because of meteorological variations, but are properly predicted to do so.

Mean Low Water Springs or Neaps are the mean levels of low water springs and neaps. A percentage of the tides is predicted to reach levels less extreme than those defined by MHWN or MLWN.

Charted Depths show the depth of water below the level of Chart Datum. They are given in fathoms, feet or metres and tenths of a metre. When using an older chart it is wise to note whether chart datum is the same as at present. There are few such charts in use today, but they are at times studied out of interest

DIAGRAM OF SPECIFIC TIDAL HEIGHTS

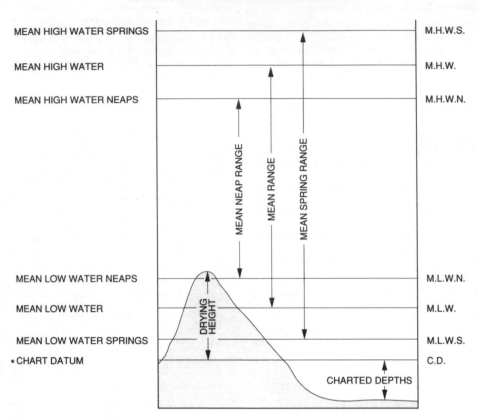

rather than necessity; indeed in older times the datum was set at mid-tide level, so giving the appearance of deeper water than today.

Drying Heights on a chart are the heights above Chart Datum which are periodically covered or uncovered by the sea (see diagram of specific tidal heights). They are distinguished on the chart from depths by an underline. They are never given in fathoms.

The Depth of Water is the sum at any moment of the charted depth and the height of tide. For this simple calculation the drying heights should be treated as minus figures., e.g.

Height of tide – drying height = depth

$$5.0\ m\ -\ \underline{2.0}\ m\ =\ 3.0\ m$$

NOTE THE DIFFERENCE BETWEEN HEIGHT, DEPTH AND RISE

TIDAL PREDICTIONS

Tidal predictions are based upon tides previously measured at the place of interest, they cannot be built up from an entirely theoretical base.

We have seen how the Sun and Moon cause the envelope of water around the Earth to be altered according to their disposition, but there are a large number of such factors affecting the height and time of tide at a place, some astronomical, others of a local nature such as shallow water effects. These are known as the *Harmonic Constants* of a place.

The change in sea levels in the deep oceans caused by the Sun and Moon are of the order of centimetres only, but such is the great mass of that water that the effect is greatly magnified when it reaches the continental shelf.

The sheer momentum of all that water rushing towards the shelf is not enough to create the tidal ranges we see at our coasts. Another essential ingredient is that the area should form a basin which, because of its depth and length, has a natural frequency which is attuned to the passage of the Sun or Moon past the meridian.

A good example of this is the North Sea which forms just such a basin, although open at one end. The tide (which after all is basically a wave) has a natural 'slop' frequency here in the same way that can be seen in a bath or a cup of tea. If a spoon is moved back and forth in a cup at a suitable frequency, the wave will build up and will perhaps go over the edge. If the spoon is moved at a frequency which is not a simple multiple of this figure, we merely get a disturbed surface. Or try pushing a child on a swing at an unnatural frequency.

The Mediterranean Sea has no great tides simply because its natural frequency does not match the passage of the tide raising forces. Even a totally enclosed sea will respond to tidal forces if its length and depth are suitable.

Some areas experience tides that are based purely on the momentum of the wave formed in an external basin. For example, the River Thames receives the wave from the North Sea and this pushes up the river at 15 to 20 knots, no longer influenced by the passage of the Moon, but by sheer received energy from the estuary. As it moves up-river, the front of the wave is running into shallower water all the time and it begins to slow down. This has the effect of raising the height of high and low waters and of changing the shape of the wave, so that by the time it reaches Richmond, the flood is of four hours duration and the ebb of over eight hours. It is only the wave which moves at this speed, not the water itself. The ultimate example of this can be seen in tsunamis, large waves caused by undersea earthquakes which begin life in deep water as only decimetres high but of great length These travel at several hundred knots until the leading edge begins to meet shallower water, where it slows down and allows the rest of the wave to catch up, so increasing its height enormously.

Bores. Bores occur when the depth of water in front of the incoming tide is insufficient to support the natural wave form, and as with a tsunami, the back begins to catch up with the front, and a very steep face is formed. Bores can vary in height from only 0.1 m high (around the back of Canvey Island on the Thames) to several

metres. They are generally predictable, therefore craft are not likely to be under way at its passing, but if a skipper should be caught out in this way, the procedure must be to batten down, stem the oncoming bore and apply full throttle as it arrives in order to maintain good steerage way. One rather alarming aspect of a bore is that right up to the foot the tide is ebbing, but as soon as the bore arrives, it is flooding and possibly carrying a large amount of floating branches and other wreckage in its wake.

Tide Prediction Tables. These are calculated as a result of the tidal pattern analysed at the place of interest. The best period of analysis is 18.6 years, since this allows for a complete cycle of astronomical events, but it is very cumbersome, and used only for research purposes. An analysis can be based on 25 hours observations, but its value is much reduced. Many of the tidal predictions around the UK and the world are based on analyses of only one month, but the standard ports are based upon a minimum of one year's data.

The accuracy of the predictions is remarkably high in long periods of settled weather, better than 0.1 m and 5 minutes, but the further away from deep open water one goes, the levels and times are more sensitive to weather. See 'The Effects of Meteorological Conditions on Tide Predictions' set out below. The times of high and low waters on tides of small range are difficult to predict because the turn of the tide is very much less well defined. There is some compensation in that on such tides, where any time error occurs, the resultant differences in height are very small.

Standard Ports. Standard ports are places at which the tide has been accurately measured for some time, and after due analysis can provide a good set of harmonic constants. From these constants the future behaviour of the tide can be predicted, and the results are printed as the Standard Port Predictions in Reed's Nautical Almanac.

Secondary Ports. These ports also have their harmonic constants, and from these, although often of lower precision, predicted tide curves can be calculated. The process is a long one without the aid of a computer or dedicated calculator, so we have to rely on Differences to determine the times and heights of high and low waters at these ports.

Differences. These are given for the times and heights of high and low waters. Since the differences given are average figures for the type of tides indicated, they will never be as accurate as the standard port data. The alternatives are to calculate on the basis of harmonic constants or to purchase a set of locally produced tables.

Co-Tidal Charts. Co-tidal charts are produced which show the time differences between high waters at the standard port (e.g Sheerness for the Thames Estuary) and the percentage change in range across the area. They enable the height of tide at points offshore to be calculated, but less accurately than with areas close inshore which are based on standard ports and differences. The construction of various platforms offshore has increased the quality of the data on these charts, but they should still be used with caution.

THE EFFECTS OF METEOROLOGICAL CONDITIONS ON TIDE PREDICTIONS

It has been shown that the major tidal forces are produced by the Sun and Moon, but the weather is very significant in some areas. It is not simply a local phenomenon, although of course these are important, but events a couple of hundred miles away can have a great influence. Good tidal predictions do try to take into account the features such as barometric pressure and prevailing seasonal winds, but there is a limit to what can be achieved in this way.

The Height of the Barometer. When local atmospheric pressure is increased, sea level is lowered simply by the greater pressure above it, and the opposite for low atmospheric pressure. Since the specific gravity of mercury is 13.6 it follows that a change of one inch or 34 millibars on the barometer will result in about 0.3 m of sea level. This is only a rough guide, and the effect is not immediate.

The mean barometric pressure in the South of England is 1016 mb and in Scotland 1011 mb.

The Direction of the Wind. In some areas the sea level is raised on the coast towards which the wind is blowing, and vice versa. It usually requires a steady wind over a period of several days to have any appreciable effect, and the local topography will have considerable influence on the result, for instance where the coast lies close to the open deep water, the effect will be less. The fetch of the wind will also be significant.

Rain or Melting Snow. In relatively small land-locked seas in high latitudes there is likely to be an appreciable rise in sea level following the melting of the snow. Generally speaking, rainfall will only affect the levels of the rivers themselves where the run-off is fairly rapid (where the hinterland is over rock or built-up areas) and where the river retains a narrow form. The River Thames for example has a very absorbent hinterland, so even in the most extreme rain conditions, the tide at London Bridge is raised by only 15 centimetres or so.

Storm Surges. The storm surges which occur in the North Sea when a particular set of conditions arise,are quite unpredictable, no more than a few hours ahead. When an area of low barometric pressure passes across the top of the North Sea, the southern part is subject to a strong southerly wind and this, combined with the fall in pressure in the northern half, causes water to pile up in the North. As the low moves eastwards, the wind becomes northerly and pressure increases, so pushing that excess water down South again, this time into a narrowing space. If the timing of the passage of the Low coincides with the natural frequency of the area, a giant excess wave is formed perhaps four metres high and four hours long which, if it arrives at the same time as normal high water, can cause the tide to reach flood levels. Negative surges can also occur, and radio warnings are promulgated when they are expected to exceed one metre.

INSTRUCTIONS IN THE USE OF TIDE TABLES

General Arrangement. Tides and tidal streams in Reed's Nautical Almanac are arranged so that all local information is given together. Therefore tidal predictions will be accompanied by tidal differences for secondary ports and tidal stream charts nearby where appropriate.

Additional tidal notes are given at the foot of standard port predictions. Full allowance is made in the Differences for changes in chart datum from one port to another. As far as possible the data for Differences are based upon the most suitable port.

Standard Ports. Twice daily predictions are given of the Time (to the nearest minute) and the Height (to the nearest decimal of a metre) throughout the year. Both High and Low Waters are given, except at Poole where only low waters are given.

Secondary Ports. Tidal information on these is given as Tidal Differences on Standard Ports. The differences for time and height should be applied to the standard port data to give the times and heights of high and low waters at secondary ports.

Notes. It is important to remember the difference between Height, Rise and Range of tide, and Depth.

All tidal information is approximate so allow a good safety margin, particularly during and after periods of unsettled weather.

The time of high water is approximately 50 minutes later each day.

Along the coast the normal interval between successive high waters is 12 hours 25 minutes and between successive high and low waters is 6 hours, 13 minutes.

As one goes further up a river or shorewards over large drying areas, the tide becomes distorted to give a shorter flood duration and a longer ebb duration. At London Bridge for example, the flood is of 5 hours and 55 minutes duration and the ebb is of 6 hours 31 minutes.

Tidal streams run faster at springs and slower at neaps.

To find the Time of High or Low Water.

Find the page of the required port from the Tidal Index at the back of the Almanac.

Standard Ports are followed by an (S) and the time can be read off alongside the date on the appropriate page.

Secondary Ports are listed without the (S) and the page given is based on the nearest or most suitable port. The time difference should be applied to the data given for the appropriate standard port, interpolating as necessary.

To find the Height of High or Low Water

Find the correct page from the Tidal Index.

Heights for Standard Ports are given on the appropriate page in metres and decimetres.

Heights for Secondary Ports are found by applying the differences to the Standard Port data, interpolating between spring and neap tides where necessary.

Example: Find the time and height of the afternoon H.W. and L.W. at List on 14th January.

The data for differences can be interpolated by the following graphic method or by the digital method shown on page 17. In the example the times and heights are shown on separate graphs, but by careful annotation of the graph lines, time and height can be drawn on the same sheet.

Note: The data used in this example do not refer to the year of these tables.

JANUARY

14 SA

	0143	2.2
	0808	0.2
	1355	2.6
	2045	0.2

HELGOLAND

PLACE	TIME DIFFERENCES				HEIGHT DIFFERENCES (Metres)			
	High	Water	Low	Water	MHWS	MHWN	MLWN	MLWS
HELGOLAND	0100 and 1300	0600 and 1800	0100 and 1300	0800 and 2000	2.7	2.3	0.4	0.0
LIST	+0256	+0246	+0207	+0213	−0.8	−0.6	−0.2	0.0

	Time		Height	
	HW	LW	HW	LW
Standard Port	1355	2045	2.6	0.2
Differences	+0254	+0212	−0.8	−0.1
Secondary Port	1649	2257	1.8	0.1

Section 18

7

Height

Choose a scale which will include the greatest differences shown (in this case from 0.0 to –0.8) and write the values along the top of the graph as appropriate.

Choose a scale which will include the level of MHWS and that of MLWS (in this case 2.7 to 0.0) and write the values along this side of the graph as appropriate.

Enter the data for the two high water points and join them with a straight line.

Do the same with the low water points

Read off the difference values associated with the day in question (in this case predicted HW at Helgoland was 2.6 m and LW was 0.2 m).

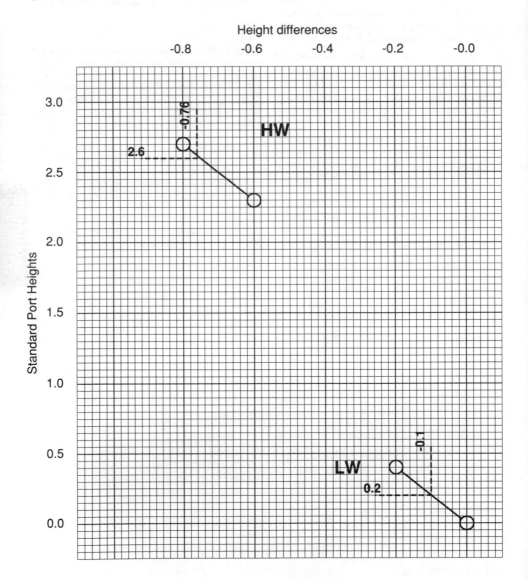

Time

Along the top of the graph choose a suitable scale and enter the values which will include the greatest range of differences shown, in this case from +0207 to +0256.

The right hand edge of the graph is for HW times.

Enter a set of times down the left hand edge which covers the predicted time of HW at the standard port and also the two times at which the time differences are known, in this case 1300 and 1800.

The difference at 1300 is +0256 and at 1800 is +0246. Note these two points on the graph and join them with a straight line.

Where the predicted time of HW at the standard port cuts the straight line, the time

difference can be read off the top of the graph at +0254 and applied:

```
 1355
+0254
 1649 = predicted time of HW at secondary
        port.
```

The left hand side is for LW times and the same process adopted for LW data.

Where there is a wide variation between the HW and LW time differences, the LW differences can be entered along the bottom of the graph in order to keep them separate.

In this example the HW and LW lines happen to be nearly parallel. This is quite by chance, and for another standard port may even cross if the data is so constructed. Where it appears to be too complex, plot HW and LW on different pieces of graph paper.

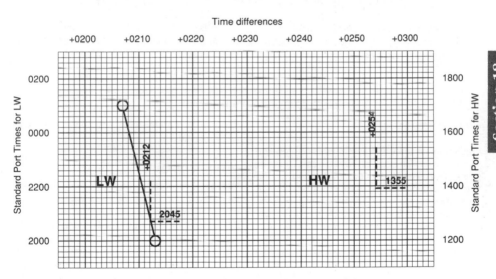

Time zones

The adjustment for the time zones into two parts, the zone of the standard port and that of the secondary ports.

(a). Standard ports. Where the zone is set at GMT there is no problem. Where the zone is set at –0100 one should subtract one hour from the printed times to arrive at GMT.

Example:

Cherbourg

Time zone – 0100		Adjusted for GMT		Adjusted for BST	
0235	4.9 m	0135	4.9 m	0235	4.9 m
1505	4.7 m	1405	4.7 m	1505	4.7 m

(b) Secondary Ports Where the standard and the secondary ports are both at the same time zone (in this case – 0100) the differences should be directly applied and the result will be in the same time bracket as both the standard and secondary ports.

Example:

| Omonville | Time zone | – 0100 |
| Standard port Cherbourg | Time zone | – 0100 |

Standard port	Difference	Secondary port
0235 local time	– 0015	0220 local Omonville time
0135 GMT		0120 GMT

Where the standard port is at GMT but the time difference is at –0100 the result will be in local **secondary port** time.

Example

| Corcubion (Spain) | Time zone – 0100 |
| Standard port Lisbon | Time zone GMT |

Standard port	Difference	Secondary Port
0820 GMT	+ 0055	0915 local Corcubion time
0820 GMT		0815 GMT

It follows that if the differences are applied exactly as they are printed the result will be in local time. 'Summer time' or 'daylight saving time' will require additional application.

It can be seen that secondary ports based on Lisbon are divided into GMT and – 0100 zones. Those in Portugal keep GMT and those in Spain keep to –0100.

Note: All calculations based on differences are less accurate than Standard Port predictions since the differences given are average values.

TIDE CURVES

Predictions of the times and heights of high and low waters have always been rather straightforward to use, but the period during the rise and fall is less easy to define for all ports. Curves are given for the standard ports, and every effort is made to relate the secondary ports to a suitable standard. However, the effect on the shape of the tide curve of the topography of the sea bed, particularly shallow water, is quite large at times. An extreme case is seen at Richmond, where the shape of the curve is very much altered from that of London Bridge on which it is based, the reason being the long stretch of shallow water, the bends in the river and the many bridges and other structures which all contribute to the distortion of the curve. On the other hand, along a coast with moderately deep open water close offshore, the distortion would be very slight.

A 'purer' tide curve will be formed the closer a port lies to such water. That is to say that it will not be influenced by local features which might otherwise distort it, and it more nearly takes up the form of a simple sine curve. In this case the simple Twelfths Rule can be used with

reasonable confidence to describe the rise and fall of the tide.

INTERPOLATION

Interpolation between Springs and Neaps can be carried out either by calculation or more simply and quickly by eye. For most applications the latter method is quite adequate, especially when one bears in mind the variations which can occur as a result of meteorological conditions. Readers can make their own assessment of 'by eye' interpolation by comparing the results achieved with a calculated answer.

TO FIND THE HEIGHT OF THE TIDE AT ANY TIME

A. The 'Twelfths' Rule

The following calculations are based on the assumption that the tide rises and falls in the same pattern and takes the form of a simple sine curve.

It follows that the answers to these calculations are approximate and should be treated with due caution.

Tidal Rise or Fall – The 'Twelfths' Rule

The level of the water does not rise or fall at a constant rate throughout the duration of a rising or falling tide, but the amount by which it will do so in a given time from HW or LW can be reckoned mentally by means of the following rough rule:

1st	hour's rise or fall	= $\frac{1}{12}$ of Range
2nd	hour's rise or fall	= $\frac{2}{12}$ of Range
3rd	hour's rise or fall	= $\frac{3}{12}$ of Range
4th	hour's rise or fall	= $\frac{3}{12}$ of Range
5th	hour's rise or fall	= $\frac{2}{12}$ of Range
6th	hour's rise or fall	= $\frac{1}{12}$ of Range

Aid to memory: = 1,2,3,–3,2,1

Example: If H.W. is 5.5 m. and the following L.W. is 0.7 m., how much will this tide fall below H.W. in 2 h. 20 min.:

Range = 5.5 m. – 0.7 m. = 4.8 m.

In 1st hour tide falls $\frac{1}{12}$ of 4.8 m.	= 0.4 m.
In 2nd hour tide falls $\frac{2}{12}$ of 4.8 m.	= 0.8 m.
In 20 min. of 3rd hour tide falls	
$\frac{1}{3}$ x $\frac{3}{12}$ of 4.8 m	= 0.4 m
Total	= 1.6 m.

The answer has to be applied to the predicted height of High Water or Low Water as appropriate. In the example, the fall was calculated, therefore the H.W. height has to be used.

B. Admiralty curves

Basic Entry. Using the left hand half of the graph.

(a) Mark the predicted height of High Water along the top line

(b) Mark the predicted height of Low Water along the bottom line.

(c) Join the two marks with a straight line

Using the right hand half of the graph

(d) Write in the predicted time of High Water in the H.W. box on the bottom line

(e) Write in the time values at one hour intervals as required along the bottom line

To Find the Height of Tide at a Given Time.

(f) Go to the required time along the bottom line

(g) Read vertically and note where it cuts the Spring or Neap curve, as appropriate

(h) Read horizontally from that point to where it cuts the sloping line which you have just drawn on the left

(i) Read vertically and note where it cuts on the top or bottom line

The result is in metres above Chart Datum.

For those tides falling between Spring and Neap, and where a significant difference in curves is seen, one should plot both and interpolate in the manner given under interpolation. Extrapolation is not permitted.

To Find the Time at Which the Tide Reaches a Certain Height

Carry out the instructions (a) to (e) above.

(j) Find the height required on the top or bottom line (left hand half)

(k) Read vertically to the sloping line

(l) Read horizontally from that point to the Neap or Spring curve, as appropriate

(m) Read vertically down to see the time given along the bottom line in the right hand half.

Interpolation between Neap and Springs can be made where the difference in curves is significant. Extrapolation is not permitted.

Section 18

Example A: To find the height of tide at Ullapool at 0400 h. on a given day

Predicted height of High Water 5.3 m Time 0745
Predicted Height of Low Water 0.8 m
             Range 4.5 m (a Spring tide)

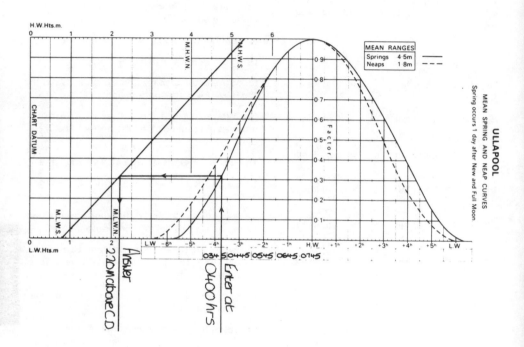

Answer: 2.20 m above Chart Datum
Note: The answer is for a full Spring tide.

Example B: To find the height of the tide at Ullapool at 0930 h. on a given day

Predicted height of High Water 3.9 m Time 1345
Predicted height of Low Water 2.1 m
            Range   1.8 m (a Neap tide)

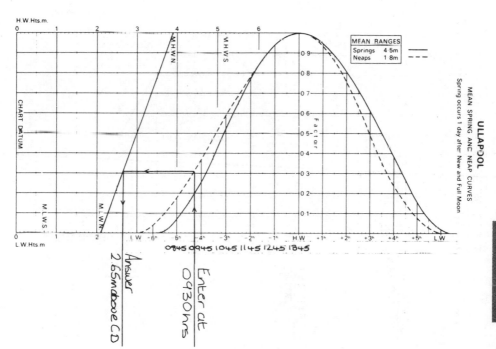

Answer: 2.65 m above Chart Datum
Note: The answer is for a Neap tide.

Example C: To find the time at which the tide at Ullapool will reach 2.2 m on a certain day

The exact reverse sequence used in example A is employed. The same basic data is used for ease of comparison.

Predicted height of High Water 5.3 m Time 0745
Predicted height of Low Water 0.8 m
                        Range 4.5 m (a Spring tide)

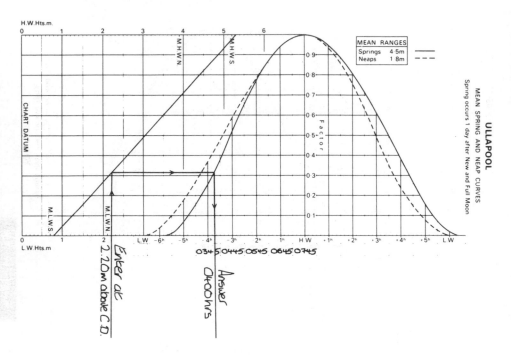

Answer: 0400 h.

Southampton and Swanage to Christchurch

Because of the complex nature of High Waters in the area, times are relative to Low Water. The procedure is otherwise identical.

Secondary Ports

Many secondary ports differ significantly from their standard port curve, therefore such curves should be used with great caution, particularly where the secondary port is not on the open coast.

On the left hand half of the graph the predicted heights of H.W. and L.W. at the secondary port should be plotted and the sloping line drawn. The choice of Spring or Neap curve and any

interpolation between should be based upon the standard port data..

Interpolation by Reed's Method

Interpolation is made between Spring and Neap tides and falls into three groups.

(a) When finding the height of tide predicted at a given time

(b) When finding the time at which a given height will be reach

(c) When applying time and height differences to calculate H.W. and L.W. at secondary ports.

The one format in the following examples will give an exact interpolation in all three cases. It may be used as an alternative to the system described on pages 7-10.

(a) To find the predicted height of the tide at Ullapool at 0700 on a given day

Predicted height of High Water   5.0 m Time 1045
Predicted height of Low Water   1.2 m
                    Range   3.8 m (between Spring and Neap)

The sloping line is drawn on the left of the graph, as earlier described and the data is transferred to the boxes below as entitled or by simple calculation.

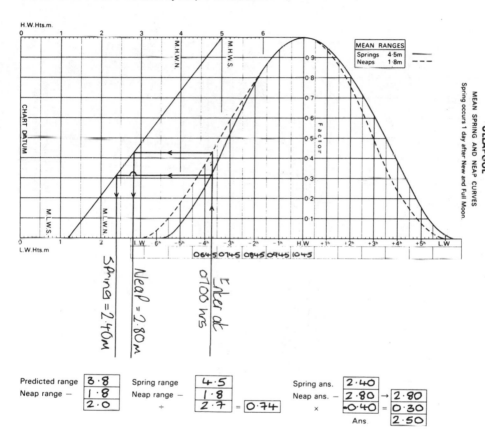

Predicted range	3·8	Spring range	4·5		Spring ans. —	2·40	
Neap range —	1·8	Neap range —	1·8		Neap ans. —	2·80 →	2·80
	2·0	÷	2·7 = 0·74		×	-0·40 =	0·30
					Ans.		2·50

Note that the final answer must lie between the Spring and Neap answer.

15

(b) To find the time at which the tide will reach 2.5 m at Ullapool.

Predicted height of High Water	5.0 m Time 1045
Predicted height of Low Water	1.2 m
Range	3.8 m (between Spring and Neap)

The sloping line is drawn on the left of the graph, as earlier described and the data is transferred to the boxes below, as entitled or by simple calculation.

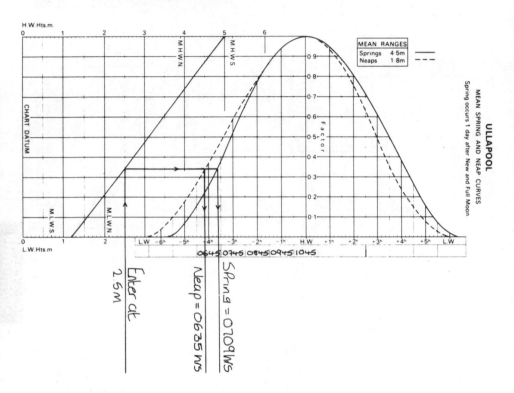

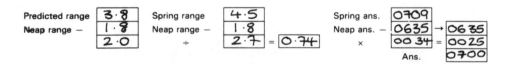

Predicted range	**3·8**	Spring range	**4·5**			Spring ans.	**0709**		
Neap range −	**1·8**	Neap range −	**1·8**			Neap ans. −	**0635**	→	**06 35**
	2·0	÷	**2·7**	=	**0·74**	×	**00 34**	=	**0025**
							Ans.		**0700**

Note that the final answer must lie between the Spring and Neap answer.

(c) To interpolate between the time differences given for High waters or Low water for a secondary port (digital Method).

This method is an alternative to the graphic system shown on Page 9. Its basis is that the left hand half of the format is designed to produce a factor or percentage. This shows how far

between the two time differences the required time lies. For instance, a factor of 0.5 will show that the required time is halfway between.

Example: To find the HW time difference at Portnancon (see differences on Ullapool) for a day when HW at Ullapool is predicted at 0300 hrs

Copy of heading of Differences High Water

	0100 and 1300	0700 and 1900
Portnancon	+0055	+0105

The required time of 0300 clearly lies between 0100 (the 'first time') and 0700 (the 'second time'), therefore the answer will lie between +0055 and +0105.

Enter the system of boxes thus:

Req'd time	0300	2nd time	0700			2nd time ans.	+0105		
1st time	0100	1st time	0100			1st time ans.	+0055	=	0065
	0200	–	0600	=	0·33	×	0010		0003
					(Factor)			Ans.	0058

It is suggested that users of Reed's Nautical Almanac draw up formats at a useful size and make photocopies for ready use.

C. Hand-Held Calculators and Computers.

There are two approaches to the use of hand-held calculators for the prediction of tide curves. One approach assumes that the curve is in the

form of a simple sine curve in the same way that the Twelfths Rule operates. A description of this method is given here and it can be applied to any scientific calculator.

Section 18

TO FIND THE DIFFERENCE IN HEIGHT OF TIDE AT A PARTICULAR TIME, USING A CALCULATOR

(Describing the simple tide curve)

Data required   Range of tide (in metres)

Duration (in hours and minutes)

Interval from nearest Low Water, before or after.

Algorithm $\text{DIFFERENCE} = (\text{Sin} \dfrac{90 \times \text{Interval}}{\text{Duration}})^2 \times \text{Range}$

Worked example   Note: Enter hours and minutes on your calculator as you would enter degrees and minutes.

Range   4.0 m
Duration 6 hr. 40 min.
Interval 5 hr. 20 min.

Quantity	Entry	Display
Interval from LW	5.20	5.20
Change to decimal	→H	5.33
	÷	5.33
Duration of tide	6.40	6.40
Change to decimal	→H	6.67
	X	0.80
	90	90
	=	72.00
	SIN	0.95
	X²	0.90
	X	0.90
Range	4	4
DIFFERENCE	=	3.62

THE DIFFERENCE MUST NOW BE ADDED TO THE PREDICTED HEIGHT OF LOW WATER.

If you have a programmable calculator, you may use one of the following programs.

Using algebraic logic Entry	Quantity	Using RPN logic Entry
Clear PGM		Clear PGM
RCL 1	Interval in hr. and min.	RCL 1
→H	Change to decimal	→H
÷		
RCL 2	Duration in Hr. and min.	RCL 2
→H	Change to decimal	→H
=		÷
X		90
90		X
=		Sin
Sin		X²
X²		
X		
RCL 3	Range	RCL 3
=		X
R/S		RTN

This is the simplest program approach. Further sophistication is possible.
The answer must be added to the predicted height of low water.

The other approach is to use the instrument to calculate the tide from the Tidal Constants given in the Admiralty Tide Tables, so providing a more accurate result. It is possible to write ones own program for this calculation or to purchase such a program, but the most straightforward way is to use a dedicated calculator, that is to say one which has this and other useful navigation programs permanently entered.

Programs are also available for IBM compatible PCs.

The Multiplication Table

The multiplication table given on the following pages may be used where a calculator is not available. The table was originally designed for use in the older Admiralty system of tidal curve prediction which used factors (which are still shown in the curves as they are now drawn) but is clearly useful for other purposes.

The table allows the multiplication of numbers between 1.0 and 13.0 in steps of 0.02.

Example:

5.8 (top line)
x 0.78 (left or right edge)

Ans   4.5

Where the precise number figures required for multiplication are not given, interpolation may be made between adjacent values.

Section 18

19

MULTIPLICATION TABLE

(RANGE)

FACTOR	1.00	1.4	1.8	2.2	2.6	3.0	3.4	3.8	4.2	4.6	5.0	5.4	5.8	6.2	6.6	7.0
.98	1.4	1.8	2.2	2.5	2.9	3.3	3.7	4.1	4.5	4.9	5.3	5.7	6.1	6.5	6.9
.96	1.3	1.7	2.1	2.5	2.9	3.3	3.6	4.0	4.4	4.8	5.2	5.6	6.0	6.3	6.7
.94	1.3	1.7	2.1	2.4	2.8	3.2	3.6	3.9	4.3	4.7	5.1	5.5	5.8	6.2	6.6
.92	1.3	1.7	2.0	2.4	2.8	3.1	3.5	3.9	4.2	4.6	5.0	5.3	5.7	6.1	6.4
.90	1.3	1.6	2.0	2.3	2.7	3.1	3.4	3.8	4.1	4.5	4.9	5.2	5.6	5.9	6.3
.88	1.2	1.6	1.9	2.3	2.6	3.0	3.3	3.7	4.0	4.4	4.8	5.1	5.5	5.8	6.2
.86	1.2	1.5	1.9	2.2	2.6	2.9	3.3	3.6	4.0	4.3	4.6	5.0	5.3	5.7	6.0
.84	1.2	1.5	1.8	2.2	2.5	2.9	3.2	3.5	3.9	4.2	4.5	4.9	5.2	5.5	5.9
.82	1.1	1.5	1.8	2.1	2.5	2.8	3.1	3.4	3.8	4.1	4.4	4.8	5.1	5.4	5.7
.80	1.1	1.4	1.8	2.1	2.4	2.7	3.0	3.4	3.7	4.0	4.3	4.6	5.0	5.3	5.6
.78	1.1	1.4	1.7	2.0	2.3	2.7	3.0	3.3	3.6	3.9	4.2	4.5	4.8	5.1	5.5
.76	1.1	1.4	1.7	2.0	2.3	2.6	2.9	3.2	3.5	3.8	4.1	4.4	4.7	5.0	5.3
.74	1.0	1.3	1.6	1.9	2.2	2.5	2.8	3.1	3.4	3.7	4.0	4.3	4.6	4.9	5.2
.72	1.0	1.3	1.6	1.9	2.2	2.4	2.7	3.0	3.3	3.6	3.9	4.2	4.5	4.8	5.0
.70	1.0	1.3	1.5	1.8	2.1	2.4	2.7	2.9	3.2	3.5	3.8	4.1	4.3	4.6	4.9
.68	1.0	1.2	1.5	1.8	2.0	2.3	2.6	2.9	3.1	3.4	3.7	3.9	4.2	4.5	4.8
.66	0.9	1.2	1.5	1.7	2.0	2.2	2.5	2.8	3.0	3.3	3.6	3.8	4.1	4.4	4.6
.64	0.9	1.1	1.4	1.7	1.9	2.2	2.4	2.7	2.9	3.2	3.5	3.7	4.0	4.2	4.5
.62	0.9	1.1	1.4	1.6	1.9	2.1	2.4	2.6	2.9	3.1	3.3	3.6	3.8	4.1	4.3
.60	0.8	1.1	1.3	1.6	1.8	2.0	2.3	2.5	2.8	3.0	3.2	3.5	3.7	4.0	4.2
.58	0.8	1.0	1.3	1.5	1.7	2.0	2.2	2.4	2.7	2.9	3.1	3.4	3.6	3.8	4.1
.56	0.8	1.0	1.2	1.5	1.7	1.9	2.1	2.4	2.6	2.8	3.0	3.2	3.5	3.7	3.9
.54	0.8	1.0	1.2	1.4	1.6	1.8	2.1	2.3	2.5	2.7	2.9	3.1	3.3	3.6	3.8
.52	0.7	0.9	1.1	1.4	1.6	1.8	2.0	2.2	2.4	2.6	2.8	3.0	3.2	3.4	3.6
.50	0.7	0.9	1.1	1.3	1.5	1.7	1.9	2.1	2.3	2.5	2.7	2.9	3.1	3.3	3.5
.48	0.7	0.9	1.1	1.2	1.4	1.6	1.8	2.0	2.2	2.4	2.6	2.8	3.0	3.2	3.4
.46	0.6	0.8	1.0	1.2	1.4	1.6	1.7	1.9	2.1	2.3	2.5	2.7	2.9	3.0	3.2
.44	0.6	0.8	1.0	1.1	1.3	1.5	1.7	1.8	2.0	2.2	2.4	2.6	2.7	2.9	3.1
.42	0.6	0.8	0.9	1.1	1.3	1.4	1.6	1.8	1.9	2.1	2.3	2.4	2.6	2.8	2.9
.40	0.6	0.7	0.9	1.0	1.2	1.4	1.5	1.7	1.8	2.0	2.2	2.3	2.5	2.6	2.8
.38	0.5	0.7	0.8	1.0	1.1	1.3	1.4	1.6	1.7	1.9	2.1	2.2	2.4	2.5	2.7
.36	0.5	0.6	0.8	0.9	1.1	1.2	1.4	1.5	1.7	1.8	1.9	2.1	2.2	2.4	2.5
.34	0.5	0.6	0.7	0.9	1.0	1.2	1.3	1.4	1.6	1.7	1.8	2.0	2.1	2.2	2.4
.32	0.4	0.6	0.7	0.8	1.0	1.1	1.2	1.3	1.5	1.6	1.7	1.9	2.0	2.1	2.2
.30	0.4	0.5	0.7	0.8	0.9	1.0	1.1	1.3	1.4	1.5	1.6	1.7	1.9	2.0	2.1
.28	0.4	0.5	0.6	0.7	0.8	1.0	1.1	1.2	1.3	1.4	1.5	1.6	1.7	1.8	2.0
.26	0.4	0.5	0.6	0.7	0.8	0.9	1.0	1.1	1.2	1.3	1.4	1.5	1.6	1.7	1.8
.24	0.3	0.4	0.5	0.6	0.7	0.8	0.9	1.0	1.1	1.2	1.3	1.4	1.5	1.6	1.7
.22	0.3	0.4	0.5	0.6	0.7	0.7	0.8	0.9	1.0	1.1	1.2	1.3	1.4	1.5	1.5
.20	0.3	0.4	0.4	0.5	0.6	0.7	0.8	0.8	0.9	1.0	1.1	1.2	1.2	1.3	1.4
.18	0.3	0.3	0.4	0.5	0.5	0.6	0.7	0.8	0.8	0.9	1.0	1.0	1.1	1.2	1.3
.16	0.2	0.3	0.4	0.4	0.5	0.5	0.6	0.7	0.7	0.8	0.9	0.9	1.0	1.1	1.1
.14	0.2	0.2	0.3	0.4	0.4	0.5	0.5	0.6	0.6	0.7	0.8	0.8	0.9	0.9	1.0
.12	0.2	0.2	0.3	0.3	0.4	0.4	0.5	0.5	0.6	0.6	0.6	0.7	0.7	0.8	0.8
.10	0.1	0.2	0.2	0.3	0.3	0.3	0.4	0.4	0.5	0.5	0.5	0.6	0.6	0.7	0.7
.08	0.1	0.1	0.2	0.2	0.2	0.3	0.3	0.3	0.4	0.4	0.4	0.5	0.5	0.5	0.6
.06	0.1	0.1	0.1	0.2	0.2	0.2	0.2	0.3	0.3	0.3	0.3	0.3	0.4	0.4	0.4
.04	0.1	0.1	0.1	0.1	0.1	0.1	0.2	0.2	0.2	0.2	0.2	0.2	0.2	0.3	0.3
.02	0.0	0.0	0.0	0.1	0.1	0.1	0.1	0.1	0.1	0.1	0.1	0.1	0.1	0.1	0.1

FACTOR

MULTIPLICATION TABLE

(RANGE)

	7.4	7.8	8.2	8.6	9.0	9.4	9.8	10.2	10.6	11.0	11.4	11.8	12.2	12.6	13.0	1.00
	7.3	7.6	8.0	8.4	8.8	9.2	9.6	10.0	10.4	10.8	11.2	11.6	12.0	12.4	12.7	.98
	7.1	7.5	7.9	8.3	8.6	9.0	9.4	9.8	10.2	10.6	10.9	11.3	11.7	12.1	12.5	.96
	7.0	7.3	7.7	8.1	8.5	8.8	9.2	9.6	10.0	10.3	10.7	11.1	11.5	11.8	12.2	.94
	6.8	7.2	7.5	7.9	8.3	8.6	9.0	9.4	9.8	10.1	10.5	10.9	11.2	11.6	12.0	.92
	6.7	7.0	7.4	7.7	8.1	8.5	8.8	9.2	9.6	9.9	10.3	10.6	11.0	11.3	11.7	.90
	6.5	6.9	7.2	7.6	7.9	8.3	8.6	9.0	9.3	9.7	10.0	10.4	10.7	11.1	11.4	.88
	6.4	6.7	7.1	7.4	7.7	8.1	8.4	8.8	9.1	9.5	9.8	10.1	10.5	10.8	11.2	.86
	6.2	6.6	6.9	7.2	7.6	7.9	8.2	8.6	8.9	9.2	9.6	9.9	10.3	10.6	10.9	.84
	6.1	6.4	6.7	7.1	7.4	7.7	8.0	8.4	8.7	9.0	9.3	9.7	10.0	10.3	10.7	.82
	5.9	6.2	6.6	6.9	7.2	7.5	7.8	8.2	8.5	8.8	9.1	9.4	9.8	10.1	10.4	.80
	5.8	6.1	6.4	6.7	7.0	7.3	7.6	8.0	8.3	8.6	8.9	9.2	9.5	9.8	10.1	.78
	5.6	5.9	6.2	6.5	6.8	7.1	7.4	7.8	8.1	8.4	8.7	9.0	9.3	9.6	9.9	.76
	5.5	5.8	6.1	6.4	6.8	7.0	7.3	7.5	7.8	8.1	8.4	8.7	9.0	9.3	9.6	.74
	5.3	5.6	5.9	6.2	6.5	6.8	7.1	7.3	7.6	7.9	8.2	8.5	8.8	9.1	9.4	.72
	5.2	5.5	5.7	6.0	6.3	6.6	6.9	7.1	7.4	7.7	8.0	8.3	8.5	8.8	9.1	.70
	5.0	5.3	5.6	5.8	6.1	6.4	6.7	6.9	7.2	7.5	7.8	8.0	8.3	8.6	8.8	.68
	4.9	5.1	5.4	5.7	5.9	6.2	6.5	6.7	7.0	7.3	7.5	7.8	8.1	8.3	8.6	.66
	4.7	5.0	5.2	5.5	5.8	6.0	6.3	6.5	6.8	7.0	7.3	7.6	7.8	8.1	8.3	.64
	4.6	4.8	5.1	5.3	5.6	5.8	6.1	6.3	6.6	6.8	7.1	7.3	7.6	7.8	8.1	.62
	4.4	4.7	4.9	5.2	5.4	5.6	5.9	6.1	6.4	6.6	6.8	7.1	7.3	7.6	7.8	.60
	4.3	4.5	4.8	5.0	5.2	5.5	5.7	5.9	6.1	6.4	6.6	6.8	7.1	7.3	7.5	.58
	4.1	4.4	4.6	4.8	5.0	5.3	5.5	5.7	5.9	6.2	6.4	6.6	6.8	7.1	7.3	.56
	4.0	4.2	4.4	4.6	4.9	5.1	5.3	5.5	5.7	5.9	6.2	6.4	6.6	6.8	7.0	.54
	3.8	4.1	4.3	4.5	4.7	4.9	5.1	5.3	5.5	5.7	5.9	6.1	6.3	6.6	6.8	.52
	3.7	3.9	4.1	4.3	4.5	4.7	4.9	5.1	5.3	5.5	5.7	5.9	6.1	6.3	6.5	.50
	3.6	3.7	3.9	4.1	4.3	4.5	4.7	4.9	5.1	5.3	5.5	5.7	5.9	6.1	6.2	.48
	3.4	3.6	3.8	4.0	4.1	4.3	4.5	4.7	4.9	5.1	5.2	5.4	5.6	5.8	6.0	.46
	3.3	3.4	3.6	3.8	4.0	4.1	4.3	4.5	4.7	4.8	5.0	5.2	5.4	5.5	5.7	.44
	3.1	3.3	3.4	3.6	3.8	3.9	4.1	4.3	4.5	4.6	4.8	5.0	5.1	5.3	5.5	.42
	3.0	3.1	3.3	3.4	3.6	3.8	3.9	4.1	4.2	4.4	4.6	4.7	4.9	5.0	5.2	.40
	2.8	3.0	3.1	3.3	3.4	3.6	3.7	3.9	4.0	4.2	4.3	4.5	4.6	4.8	4.9	.38
	2.7	2.8	3.0	3.1	3.2	3.4	3.5	3.7	3.8	4.0	4.1	4.2	4.4	4.5	4.7	.36
	2.5	2.7	2.8	2.9	3.1	3.2	3.3	3.5	3.6	3.7	3.9	4.0	4.2	4.3	4.4	.34
	2.4	2.5	2.6	2.8	2.9	3.0	3.1	3.3	3.4	3.5	3.6	3.8	3.9	4.0	4.2	.32
	2.2	2.3	2.5	2.6	2.7	2.8	2.9	3.1	3.2	3.3	3.4	3.5	3.7	3.8	3.9	.30
	2.1	2.2	2.3	2.4	2.5	2.6	2.7	2.9	3.0	3.1	3.2	3.3	3.4	3.5	3.6	.28
	1.9	2.0	2.1	2.2	2.3	2.4	2.5	2.7	2.8	2.9	3.0	3.1	3.2	3.3	3.4	.26
	1.8	1.9	2.0	2.1	2.2	2.3	2.4	2.4	2.5	2.6	2.7	2.8	2.9	3.0	3.1	.24
	1.6	1.7	1.8	1.9	2.0	2.1	2.2	2.2	2.3	2.4	2.5	2.6	2.7	2.8	2.9	.22
	1.5	1.6	1.6	1.7	1.8	1.9	2.0	2.0	2.1	2.2	2.3	2.4	2.4	2.5	2.6	.20
	1.3	1.4	1.5	1.5	1.6	1.7	1.8	1.8	1.9	2.0	2.1	2.1	2.2	2.3	2.3	.18
	1.2	1.2	1.3	1.4	1.4	1.5	1.6	1.6	1.7	1.8	1.8	1.9	2.0	2.0	2.1	.16
	1.0	1.1	1.1	1.2	1.2	1.3	1.4	1.4	1.5	1.5	1.6	1.7	1.7	1.8	1.8	.14
	0.9	1.0	1.0	1.0	1.1	1.1	1.2	1.2	1.3	1.3	1.4	1.4	1.5	1.5	1.6	.12
	0.7	0.8	0.8	0.9	0.9	0.9	1.0	1.0	1.1	1.1	1.1	1.2	1.2	1.3	1.3	.10
	0.6	0.6	0.7	0.7	0.7	0.8	0.8	0.8	0.8	0.9	0.9	0.9	1.0	1.0	1.0	.08
	0.4	0.5	0.5	0.5	0.5	0.6	0.6	0.6	0.6	0.7	0.7	0.7	0.7	0.8	0.8	.06
	0.3	0.3	0.3	0.3	0.4	0.4	0.4	0.4	0.4	0.4	0.5	0.5	0.5	0.5	0.5	.04
	0.1	0.2	0.2	0.2	0.2	0.2	0.2	0.2	0.2	0.2	0.2	0.2	0.2	0.3	0.3	.02

FACTOR (left)   FACTOR (right)

Section 18

TIDAL STREAMS

Tidal streams are the horizontal movements of the water, occurring in response to the same forces as the vertical movements. In European waters, although not invariably the rule in other parts of the world, the tidal streams vary in magnitude with changing astronomical conditions in the same proportions as the range of the tide, so that the strongest streams occur at Spring tides and the weakest at Neap tides. In these circumstances the directions and rates of the tidal streams may be predicted by reference to the times of high water and the ranges of the tide at some suitable Standard Port.

All the tidal stream charts are referred to the time of high water at Dover and some are also referred to a local standard port. The European edition of Reed's Nautical Almanac includes more than 100 tidal stream chartlets.

Tidal streams are a horizontal oscillation of particles of water. In narrow channels and straits each particle travels in a more or less straight line, in the general direction of the channel; and then returns along the same path. There is no onward movement, simply an oscillation to and fro along the same track. The distance travelled in both directions varying from day to day with changes in the range of the tide.

The stream is said to be Slack at that instant when its direction of travel is reversed; but usually the expression is used to cover that period around the instant of reversal when the rate of the stream is a quarter of a knot or less. The tidal stream at most places attains its greatest rate roughly midway between successive occurrences of slack water. In rivers and estuaries, however, the greatest rate may be attained fairly soon after the stream has commenced to run in a particular direction.

In open waters and estuaries the particles of water do not oscillate to and fro in a straight line, but travel in an ellipse. There is then no true slack water but a falling off in rate when the stream is running in directions at about right angles to those in which it flows at its greatest rates. The ellipse in which a particle travels will be largest at springs and smallest at neaps.

In the past the expression "Flood" and "Ebb" were loosely employed to describe either the rising tide or the ingoing tidal stream and either the falling tide or the outgoing tidal stream. Such expressions can only legitimately be employed where the ingoing stream runs from low water to high water, and the outgoing stream from high water to low water. This is more or less what occurs in rivers, but in open waters it is exceptional. The streams may be running at their greatest rates at the times of high and low water and in the old days seamen described such streams as "tide and a half" indicating that the stream which they described as the flood ran from three hours before to three hours after high water, and that described as the ebb from three hours before to three hours after low water. The streams are invariably described by the directions in which they are running, such as "ingoing", "outgoing", "eastgoing", "westgoing", etc.

Current is an onward horizontal movement of water, arising mainly from meteorological effects. The rate of movement is not affected by astronomical changes but it may vary in direction and rate with meteorological conditions.

The horizontal movement of particles of water is the resultant of both tidal streams and current; this is described as "flow". Owing to the influence of the current the distance travelled by a particle in one direction will be greater than in the other, the duration and rate of flow will be increased in the former and correspondingly decreased in the latter. If the current is as strong as the tidal stream, then the flow will be constantly in one direction, varying from a maximum rate, when the tidal stream is running at its greatest rate, in the direction of the current, to zero when the tidal stream is running at its greatest rate in the opposite direction to the current. Generally the tidal streams around the British Isles are considerably stronger than the current, but in the eastern approaches to Dover Strait, at neap tides, during and after gales, the current may be strong enough to equalise the tidal streams, depending on meteorological conditions.

The tidal streams are described by their directions and rates at hourly intervals as measured at a depth of one metre. Below this level the speed and direction of the water can alter considerably, even to the point of complete reversal, i.e. flood on the surface and ebb close to the sea bed. This is not likely to cause a problem to yachtsmen and to vessels of only two or three metres draught. The causes of this change down through the profile are often due to differences in the density of water at the surface and lower down. On the River Thames for example there is a net flow of water **inward** on the bed due to the pressure of denser sea water pushing up underneath as the ebb eases above.

Jetty heads are constructed to lie in the same direction as the current which is likely to be felt by the ships using it, perhaps ten or fifteen metres in draught, so a smaller vessel coming alongside may experience a strong set on or off the face.

STRENGTH OF THE TIDAL STREAM

The coasts of Western Europe, with its large volume of shipping, prevalence of fog and Tidal Streams, are amongst the most difficult in the world to navigate. Although the average strength of the Tidal Streams is only one to three knots, in many places they run three to five knots, and in Pentland Firth and the Race of Alderney up to nine and ten knots during the height of the tidal stream.

Such streams cannot be ignored but with intelligence may be made use of and danger avoided.

The golden rule in low powered vessels is "Work Your Tidal Streams" – that is, use them to your advantage.

THE REQUIREMENTS OF THE NAVIGATOR

The Navigator requires to know at any hour which way the tidal stream is running, how long it will continue in that direction, and when it will turn and run in another direction, also when it is at maximum and when at minimum or Slack, so he can decide in advance if any allowance must be made to the Course to be steered.

Although the Sailing Directions contain much specialised information on local peculiarities, a greater understanding of the Streams generally can be obtained from a close study of the Tidal Stream Charts.

The scale of these chartlets cannot show the movements of the Tidal Streams close to the coast, and it should be noted that at times the Streams close inshore turn one or two hours earlier than the main channel streams.

INSET WARNING

Many strandings occur during foggy weather, and can frequently be attributed to the vessel having experienced an unusual inset.

Strong tidal insets are frequently overlooked because they are unsuspected. It should be remembered however, that the stream will always set into a bay and thus towards the land.

We strongly recommend that, in addition to allowances for Variation and Deviation of the Compass and Leeway, that an allowance for Inset should be carefully considered.

SET AND DRIFT

The effect of tidal streams upon a ship over a period of time is described by the "set" or direction in which they have carried the ship; and by the "drift" or distance to which they have carried the ship.

The seaman says, e.g., that during the previous 24 hours the Set and Drift has been 067° 12 miles, meaning the vessel has been set 12 miles in an 067° direction. This is the exact opposite way in which we refer to the wind; as we speak of "a SW gale" meaning that it is coming from that direction.

TIDAL STREAM DIAMONDS – ADMIRALTY CHARTS

The rate and direction of the tidal stream are given at a number of points on Admiralty charts. At the selected point a diamond enclosing a letter, thus ◇ is printed. This is the point at which the measurements were taken in the first place in normal weather conditions.

At a suitable place elsewhere on the chart the tidal stream data for that point is given in the form shown overleaf:

It can be seen that the rate and direction for springs and neaps is given at each hour either side of high water at a standard port (in this case at Flushing). The latitude and longitude are also given.

As an example, at Point 'C' the tidal stream at two hours before predicted high water (Flushing) will be running in the direction 075° true at 1.8 kn (springs) and 1.2 kn (neaps).

As with all tidal data, it should be used with caution, especially in periods of bad weather. It should also be remembered that a significant number of tides are beyond the range of spring or neap tides, and the rates shown should be extrapolated accordingly.

23

Tidal Streams referred to H.W. at FLUSHING

	Hours	Dir.ⁿ	Sp.	Np.	Dir.ⁿ	Sp.	Np.
		A 51°16'6N. 2°54'9E.			B 51°22'5N. 3°01'5E.		
			Rate (*kn*)			Rate (*kn*)	
Before H.W. Flushing	6	225°	1.8	1.2	235°	1.6	1.1
	5	238°	1.3	1.1	215°	1.5	1.0
	4	225°	0.9	0.6	197°	1.1	0.7
	3	160°	0.7	0.2	169°	0.7	0.4
	2	060°	1.9	0.8	101°	0.9	0.6
	1	050°	2.2	1.1	077°	1.3	0.9
H.W.		054°	2.0	1.1	062°	1.6	1.1
After H.W. Flushing	1	053°	1.7	0.6	040°	1.2	0.8
	2	105°	0.8	0.2	023°	0.9	0.6
	3	242°	0.4	0.4	348°	0.8	0.5
	4	236°	1.1	0.9	299°	0.8	0.5
	5	235°	1.6	1.4	262°	1.3	0.9
	6	225°	1.8	1.3	244°	1.7	1.1
		C 51°23'2N. 3°14'5E.			D 51°24'5N. 3°23'3E.		
			Rate (kn)			Rate (kn)	
	Hours	Dir.ⁿ	Sp.	Np.	Dir.ⁿ	Sp.	Np.
Before H.W. Flushing	6	251°	2.0	1.3	252°	1.9	1.1
	5	240°	1.3	0.8	247°	0.6	0.3
	4	190°	0.7	0.4		Slack	
	3	090°	0.9	0.6	084°	1.1	0.7
	2	075°	1.8	1.2	076°	2.4	1.5
	1	075°	2.4	1.6	080°	3.5	2.1
H.W.		074°	2.0	1.4	078°	2.5	1.5
After H.W. Flushing	1	070°	1.4	1.0	070°	1.4	0.9
	2	046°	0.7	0.5		Slack	
	3	305°	0.7	0.5	263°	1.9	1.1
	4	260°	1.8	1.2	258°	3.1	1.8
	5	252°	2.4	1.6	254°	3.1	1.9
	6	252°	2.2	1.5	253°	2.3	1.4

CURRENTS OF THE WORLD

The great variety in the pattern of tides seen off Western Europe can be experienced in many parts of the world when one is relatively close inshore, but away into deeper water the more extensive ocean currents are found. These, too, can run at appreciable velocities, the Gulf Stream for example reaching two or three knots in places. The ocean currents are driven by a variety of forces in the same way as inshore currents, but meteorology plays the greatest part. Thinking again of the Gulf Stream, it is the prevailing wind which provides the major force. Details of these currents are given on Ocean Charts, in Sailing Directions and in Ocean Passages for the World.

RACES

A Race is caused generally when a headland protrudes into a fast moving tidal stream. A number of such Races exist on the coasts of Western Europe such as Portland, St. Catherine's, St. Albans, and Alderney. Races become more dangerous at Spring Tides and in rough weather, so use every endeavour to avoid them in these conditions.

OVERFALLS

Where the Tidal Stream crosses quickly shoaling water an Overfall occurs. This is really a "tumbling over" of the waters. In small boats keep clear of them or at least approach with caution.

Unfortunately a typical example can be found over the sand bars which lie at the entrance to a number of ports, and so perhaps cannot be avoided. In such waters there is a great danger of broaching to or gybing, or indeed of becoming swamped by a breaking wave over the stern.

HOW TO USE THE TIDAL STREAM CHARTS

The chartlets show the average direction of the main Tidal Streams at High Water Dover and at each hour before or after H.W. Dover (or the nearest Standard Port).

They enable the mariner to estimate the Set and Drift likely to be experienced over any period of time. Where two figures are given against the arrows, the smaller is the rate at neaps and the larger the rate at springs. Where no figures are given the rate generally will be less than 1 knot. Rates are either in knots or tenths of a knot as indicated, e.g. English & Bristol Channels Tidal Streams. Figures against arrows give mean neap and spring rates in tenths of a knot, thus 11.19 indicates a mean neap rate of 1.1 knots and a mean spring rate of 1.9 knots.

These charts give a general idea of the tidal streams but, owing to their small scale the inshore streams and detailed information of eddies and cross sets in the smaller channels and harbour entrances cannot be shown. The largest scale Chart or the Sailing Directions should always be consulted with regard to the tidal streams, when making harbour or when navigating in restricted waters.

If it is required to know how the Tidal Stream is setting at any time, first find the time of H.W. Dover (remember this is given in G.M.T.); then calculate how many hours before or after H.W. Dover the required time will be. On the corresponding chart will be shown the main direction of the stream in the desired locality.

Strong winds may prolong or retard Tidal Streams for even an hour or more.

Example:

Required to know the set of the Tidal Stream and its Rate of Drift when leaving Poole to cross to Cherbourg at a certain time and date.

H.W. Dover is found to be three hours before this, therefore the Tidal Stream chartlets (H.W. Dover + 3 hours) should be consulted. These show the Tidal Stream setting down Channel about 260° (T) at 1½-3 knots (Neaps – Springs). Note how the height of tide is on your chosen day and decide whether this is a Neap or Spring tide or whereabouts in between and interpolate between the 1½-3 knots accordingly.

Two hours later the stream is slackening and probably does not exceed one knot, but the chart shows that there is still up to two knots three quarters of the way across. As the French Coast is approached, the Channel Islands Tidal Stream Charts should be consulted and the estimated stream allowed for as the land is approached.

METEOROLOGY

Page

MARINE METEOROLOGY

Meteorology is the science of the atmosphere, embracing both weather and climate.

Marine meteorology deals with the cause and effect of changes in atmospheric conditions over the oceans.

It is important that the Navigator of a small craft should have some idea of what weather he may expect on a certain passage. On this will depend firstly, whether it is prudent to undertake such a voyage and, secondly, what course to take, but this course may have to be amended during the voyage, on a further forecast of the weather being obtained.

Generally speaking, it is imprudent to be badly "caught out" at sea when coasting – but if it is unavoidable, then a proper realisation of the likely weather will enable the vessel to be snugged down in plenty of time, and a proper offing obtained from any lee shore.

If it is decided to seek shelter of a harbour or some good anchorage, than an early recognition of the probable weather will enable this decision to be carried out in safety and before a shift of wind makes it an impossibility.

Weather is a most fascinating study , and happy is the man who makes wise use of the official forecast. To lie in a snug anchorage and hear the wind blowing, after having made a decision to seek shelter because of your information, is to have a feeling of mastery over the elements, and members of the crew – whether amateur or professional – will have renewed confidence in the Owner or Master, without which confidence there can never be a "happy ship".

It therefore behoves any Navigator who is unable to pick up the forecasts, to do his best to anticipate the probable weather for himself. He should keep a watch on the movement of the barometer; note any tendency to significant variations in the direction and force of the wind and, perhaps most important of all, keep a very wary eye open for changes in the appearance of the sky. Should he be able to take dry and wet bulb temperature readings, so much the better, as the information gained about the humidity of the air might be a useful guide to any impending change in visibility. The hints given in the following pages, used in conjunction with the observations made, should give some indication as to the kind of weather to expect in the next few hours but it is unlikely that the mariner, with only these means at his disposal, will become a "forecaster": this is a highly specialised job. Listen when possible to the official forecasts, and be guided by them.

SINGLE OBSERVER FORECASTING

The observer in temperate latitudes, who is unable to obtain an official forecast, should not expect much success with his own forecasts for periods longer than six hours. It is generally quite impossible from observations at a single place to say today what the weather will be like tomorrow.

Barometer and Barograph. The onset of a gale is often heralded by a fall of the barometer and by a backing of the wind, but sometimes it is associated with a rapidly rising barometer and veering wind. Both the barometer and the wind usually give significant indications of the change to come an appreciable time before the actual gale begins, but the time interval may vary widely. The rate at which the barometer falls depends to some extent on the locality. Extremely rapid falls 10 mb. (0.3 in) in three hours occasionally occur in the extreme north and west of the British Isles, but in the south and east they are very rare. Falls of 5 mb. (0.15 in) in three hours may occur half a dozen times a month in stormy winters, but on the other hand a whole winter month may pass without such a fall.

A rapid rise or fall does not always bring a gale; in fact the wind will probably not actually reach gale force more than once out of every three occasions of rapid rise or fall. It is, however, not safe to conclude because a gale has not come with a rapidly falling barometer, that it will not come at all. Some of the worst gales come after the barometer has ceased falling or even when it has started rising. Another point worth remembering is that gales with a rapidly rising barometer are generally more squally than gales with a falling barometer. As the barograph may not give a long warning of an approaching gale, it should be looked at frequently.

In the southern districts of England and in the Irish Sea easterly gales often come on without much fall of barometer; so with a moderate easterly wind a slight fall of barometer should be looked on with suspicion, especially in late winter and early spring. In NE Scotland and Orkney and Shetland the same is true of southerly or south-easterly gales. As regards the direction from which a gale will come the barograph gives only a rough general indication, viz., S'ly gales are most likely with a falling barometer and NW'ly gales with a rising barometer. If the wind has been W'ly with alternations of good and bad weather and signs of an approaching gale are observed with a falling barometer, it is very probable that the gale will be from S or SW at first, veering to W or NW suddenly with the worst squalls as the cold front passes.

Charts of average pressure over the E Atlantic show two semi-permanent features which largely control the region's weather: these are the "Icelandic Low" and the "Azores High". The Icelandic Low is the region of lowest average pressure in the N Atlantic and, in most months of the year, is centred near Iceland. It is most fully developed in winter, when the centre lies to the SW of Iceland and when the circulation is large enough to embrace all the coasts of NW Europe.

In summer the Icelandic Low is weaker and the Azores High becomes more dominant. Although the centre of this pressure system remains to the S or SW of the Azores throughout the year, and the central pressure is slightly higher in July (1025 mb) than in January (1023 mb), pressure on its N flank rises considerably in summer as the Icelandic Low fills. The average pressure pattern in summer gives a ridge of high pressure extending NE from the Azores across France to N Germany.

A third feature of average pressure is the "Siberian High", that is, the high pressure system centred over Siberia with a ridge extending W to the Alps; it occurs only in winter. While in most years the winter conditions on the North Sea coasts are controlled by the Icelandic Low, they are influenced from time to time by the W extension of the Siberian High, which involves the formation of a centre of high pressure over S Scandinavia. Then, E winds and very low temperatures are experienced in marked contrast to the mild SW weather.

A barometer rise with N winds, after a depression has passed away E, is not a sure indication of settled fair weather on the coast, even if there is a temporary improvement, for secondary disturbances may soon reach the North Sea from regions further N and cause very unsettled weather for several days, with periods of snow in winter and spring, and sometimes NW and N gales.

When fresh to strong E winds prevail over the North Sea, no reliance can be placed on a barometer rise as a sign of the wind moderating. Many E gales have begun with a rising barometer, although few SW gales have done so.

Whereas a rapidly falling barometer will give warning of a developing gale in the NE Atlantic,

there are occasions when a vessel close to the Norwegian coast will have little warning from the barometer. This is because, especially in winter, pressure tends to remain relatively high over the coast of Norway between Lindesnes and Oslo, even when large falls in pressure are occurring over the open sea.

Apart from the large pressure changes due to travelling or developing systems, there is also a small regular diurnal variation of pressure with maxima at 1000 and 2200 and minima at 0400 and 1600. The variation is 0.5 mb. from minimum to maximum. This small variation should be borne in mind when interpreting barometer readings, although it is normally masked by the much bigger changes due to movement and development of pressure systems.

When pressure becomes high over N Russia and Scandinavia, E winds usually blow over the whole area and especially between October and May, are apt to be very persistent, sometimes lasting for a week or two. There is no part of the area where the barometer is a reliable guide to changes in the strength of the wind when it blows from this quarter.

Anticyclones which develop over Scandinavia are sometimes persistent and may cause a spell of strong E or SE winds or gales over much of the area. These conditions are most likely to occur between mid-December and early April.

In the Baltic Sea the actual distribution over short periods varies a great deal especially in winter. In some years when the 'Siberian High' extends W in mid-winter, the mean for February is 1028 mb but if the "Icelandic Low" dominates the NE Atlantic, the mean for February is about 1000 mb. The normal for each month at coastal stations shows little seasonal change. Extremes of pressure variation are most likely in winter with values of up to 1040 mb occurring near the centre of a large anticyclone and down to 980 mb with the passage of a deep depression. In winter, spells of anticyclonic weather alternating with a more changeable pattern, may persist for several weeks at a time.

During April and May in most years, a ridge of high pressure extends NE from the "Azores High" and the "Icelandic Low" is then less dominant. This process causes a gradual veer of the prevailing SW wind to become mainly W. During June to August the pressure distribution is more regular, but in late September and October it becomes changeable and the weather then more disturbed.

The position of the centres of high and low pressure and the resulting flow of the airstream is more relevant to the weather pattern than the barometer reading at a particular location.

In the Southern Baltic atmospheric pressure at mean sea level decreases from an average 1014 mb in the winter to 1012 mb in the summer; in the N half of Gulf of Bothnia, the mean annual value is about 1010 mb.

The mean seasonal isobars indicate a moderate gradient for winds from between S and W in winter.The summer pattern on the other hand gives a slack pressure distribution with mainly light and variable winds.

The variations in the mean values from year to year are small, but occasional large differences occur, ranging from 1000 mb to 1035 mb. The main factor in such cases is the intensity, persistence and W extension of the *Siberian High.*

Changes in the daily values are also greater in winter with readings of about 960 mb at the centre of a depression and rising to 1050 mb or more in an intense anticyclone.

In addition to its usefulness in giving warning of approaching bad weather, the barograph is also of use in foretelling whether a quiet interval will last. If the pressure is above 1020 mb. (30.12 in.) and steady or rising, quiet weather is likely to last for at least 24 hours. Strong winds may occur with a high barometer, but as they come gradually this increase acts as its own warning. In unsettled weather a rapid rise of barometer is often quickly followed by a fall, but if the rise reaches a comparatively high level, and improvement in the general conditions may be expected. The single observer has no means of foretelling whether the strongest winds will occur before or after the passage of a front. Generally the wind is strongest in the warm sector and decreases on passage of the cold front. On occasions however, the wind rises to a maximum shortly before or actually as the cold front passes, and continues for several hours to blow harder than it did in the warm sector.

The speed of the wind tends to increase near headlands and straits and the direction of the wind under these circumstances tends to follow the run of the coast.

Cloud. The single observer forecaster will probably derive more assistance from studying the trend of cloud development, than he will from any other single element on its own. Of all the cloud types, Ci and Cs are especially to be watched, as these often afford the first indications of the presence – possibly 500-600 miles away – of an advancing warm front or occlusion, with which bad weather is commonly associated. If fine cirrus is approaching from NW, increasing and thickening into a sheet and showing a halo, then it is fairly certain that bad weather will follow before long, especially if the barometer continues to fall and the wind backs and freshens. With these signs to guide him, the prudent mariner will take any necessary precautions to safeguard his craft.

The speed of the forerunning cirrus is not a good guide to the speed of approach of a depression, although slow moving cirrus is not usually found before a rapidly advancing depression. Upper clouds moving rapidly are not infrequently a sign of unsettled conditions.

Small or medium sized cumulus is a fair weather cloud forming over the land soon after sunrise and disappearing about sunset. Towering cumulus show that there is a large lapse-rate and so showers and squalls should be expected. Any clouds of Cu type observed over land at dawn are more likely to be Sc than true cumulus. At sea, as opposed to over the land, large active cumulus may be found by night as well as by day, there being no appreciable diurnal range of temperature at the sea surface.

The increasing and thickening of high and medium cloud does not invariably indicate the approach of frontal weather, as it is not uncommon for the upper cloud associated with Cumulonimbus to spread over in advance of the main cloud mass. At times the undersurface of this type of cloud presents a rippled or mammillated appearance. neither the barometer, which is often unsteady, nor the wind can provide any useful indication of future trends in these conditions, but is well to be prepared for showers and squalls and possibly thunder. The squalls may be quite severe and come from a direction quite different from that of the wind previously experienced.

In the summer, the appearance in the sky of ragged looking Altocumulus or Ac. of the castellated variety is an almost certain indication that thunderstorms, more widespread than local, will follow before many hours have passed. This is especially the case in the English Channel area and the southern North Sea, as it is an indication that thundery troughs will move up from France, bringing storms which may be severe and possibly prolonged. If the sky clears after the passage of a cold front and the wind veers to NW, an interval of 6 - 12 hours of fair weather should follow. A close watch should however be kept on the barometer and wind. if the former begins to fall and the wind backs towards SW, with increasing upper cloud, renewed bad weather may be expected within a few hours.

The sun setting behind a bank of clouds may well mean the cloud of an advancing front. On the other hand a "low" sunset shows that there is no frontal cloud within many hours run. A "high" dawn may be due to the end of frontal cloud, but a "low" dawn has no special significance.

A heavy dew or hoar frost shows that the sky was clear during the night, but this, on its own, is not necessarily an indication of continued good weather throughout the day. A lot of haze in the lower layers shows the presence of an inversion at no great height, probably caused by subsidence in an anticyclone, and so is a sign of good weather. Unfortunately this prognostic is only valid in dry summer weather when it is already obviously fine. Clouds becoming lower indicate the approach of bad weather.

The popular prognostics of red sunrises and sunsets probably refer to the colour of clouds when the horizon is clear. Minute dust particles in the atmosphere, not amounting to haze, are responsible for the red colour. The tendency seems to be for a red sunrise to precede bad weather and a red sunset good weather, but the type of clouds should be studied in conjunction with the colour. If the redness in the morning is caused by high or medium clouds spreading from the west, but not quite extending to the eastern horizon the warning is emphasised. The season of the year is important as a sunset in winter reddening the south-western sky may be misleading, since the bad weather, if it comes, may come from the north; or again stray clouds in the north-west may be tinged with red at a summer sunset while the southern horizon is clouding over due to a depression moving up from south. Cirrus dissolving indicates fine weather.

Temperature and Humidity of the Air. The temperature and humidity of the surface air over the land are not of great assistance to the single observer forecaster as they are so subject to local effects; but if full consideration is given to all existing circumstances the variation of temperature and humidity from the normal, at the place of observation, for the season and time of day may provide a clue to forthcoming changes in the weather. When the wind sets in from some cold or warm region the temperature does not generally reach its minimum or maximum respectively for a day or two.

Temperature of the Sea. Since it is only the surface of the sea which is in contact with the air, the temperature of the surface is of particular importance in meteorology. A comparison of sea and air temperatures is a useful guide in recognising the type of air stream, air colder than sea meaning polar air and air warmer than sea tropical air. In a flat calm the actual surface of the sea may be several degrees warmer than the water at a depth of a couple of feet. This is particularly the case when the temperature is rising. Care therefore should be taken to collect water from as near the surface as possible when taking the sea temperature. At times the temperature is uniform from the surface downwards to a variable depth. This is particularly the case when there is interior mixing caused by waves or by tidal currents or when the temperature is falling, as at the end of the day or the end of the summer; cooling occurs by conduction to the air or radiation to the sky, and the surface water becomes denser and sinks .

The water used for taking the sea surface temperature should be drawn in a canvas or special rubber bucket from over the ship's side. The temperature of this water is taken by an ordinary thermometer. Some sea water thermometers have a small reservoir round the bulb so that if it is necessary to remove the thermometer from the bucket to read it, the bulb will remain immersed in water. The temperature should be read as soon as possible after the water has been drawn; many thermometers need to be in the water, provided that it is well stirred, for only about 30 seconds to read correctly.

Cold water from the depths, brought to the surface by shoals may cause a deterioration of visibility.

A long line of foam is often caused by the meeting of two currents, one of which sinks below the other. There is generally a difference in the temperature of the water on the two sides of the line.

Fog. Fog is forecast at sea whenever the temperature of the sea is equal to or below the dew-point of the air. This condition is most often found with a southerly or south-westerly wind. If the air is full of salt particles, fog may form before the air is cooled to its dew-point.

Occasionally fog is experienced with a westerly or north-westerly wind in the Channel Approaches. This is generally due to the existence of an anti-cyclone to the westward, round which a flow of tropical air reaches the British Isles after passing further north than usual. 'Hazy" steaming lights often give a warning of the formation of fog.

A change in tidal stream or an ocean current often brings colder water to the surface and this may cool the air sufficiently to form fog.

An alteration in wind direction or speed may cause the fog to thin or thicken.

If the sky above a fog is free from cloud during the day, a clearance is more likely than if the sky is cloudy.

The clearance of a shallow fog has sometimes been successfully forecast when the top of the fog is observed to start breaking up into wisps. The periodical appearance of the masthead of a nearby ship can be a useful guide in these circumstances.

When sea fog clears, especially at night, it is often difficult to say whether the ship has run out of it or the fog has dispersed or blown away.

In general, fog in the open sea will not finally clear until the arrival of a cold front, though any increase in the sea temperature has a tendency to lift the fog.

Sea and Swell. Swell is often followed by strong winds or a gale from the direction of the swell, but it is far from being an infallible sign, as the depression causing the strong winds which are the cause of the swell may alter course or slow down and fill up. The most profitable use of swell is in showing the existence and rough position of a tropical revolving storm.

A heavy swell may be caused by strong winds at some distance or by moderate winds closer at hand, but a wave-period of ten seconds or a wave-length of 500 feet in the open sea shows that the wind producing the swell must at least have been of gale force.

TABLE OF SEA STATES

1) Swell Waves – Length

	metres
Short	0-100
Average	100-200
Long	over 200

(2) Swell Waves – Height

	metres
Low	0-2
Moderate	2-4
Heavy	over 4

(3) Sea Waves – Height

Code		metres*
0	Calm – glassy	0
1	Calm – rippled	0-0.1
2	Smooth wavelets	0.1-0.5
3	Slight	0.5-1.25
4	Moderate	1.25-2.5
5	Rough	2.5-4
6	Very Rough	4-6
7	High	6-9
8	Very High	9-14
9	Phenomenal	over 14

Note: In each case the exact boundary of length or height is included in the lower category, e.g., a sea of four metres is described as "Rough".

* Average wave height.

Change in Wave Height in Opposing or Following Currents.

Following current with a velocity of $\frac{1}{4}$ that of waves – wave height reduced by 25%.
Opposing current with a velocity of $\frac{1}{10}$ that of waves – wave height increased by 21%.
Opposing current with a velocity of $\frac{1}{4}$ that of waves – wave height increased by 300%.

WEATHER FORECASTS FROM DAILY OBSERVATIONS

Sunrise

A low dawn (day breaking on or near the horizon) means FAIR WEATHER.

A high dawn (day breaking above a cloud bank) means WIND.

A purple sky at dawn means BAD WEATHER (much wind or rain – stormy).

A red sunrise with clouds towering later means RAIN.

TEMPERATURE CONVERSIONS

C°	F°	C°	F°	C°	F°	C°	F°	C°	F°
00	32.0								
01	33.8	21	69.8	41	105.8	61	141.8	81	177.8
02	35.6	22	71.6	42	107.6	62	143.6	82	179.6
03	37.4	23	73.4	43	109.4	63	145.4	83	181.4
04	39.2	24	75.2	44	111.2	64	147.2	84	183.2
05	41.0	25	77.0	45	113.0	65	149.0	85	185.0
06	42.8	26	78.8	46	114.8	66	150.8	86	186.8
07	44.6	27	80.6	47	116.6	67	152.6	87	188.6
08	46.4	28	82.4	48	118.4	68	154.4	88	190.4
09	48.2	29	84.2	49	120.2	69	156.2	89	192.2
10	50.0	30	86.0	50	122.0	70	158.0	90	194.0
11	51.8	31	87.8	51	123.8	71	159.8	91	195.8
12	53.6	32	89.6	52	125.6	72	161.6	92	197.6
13	55.4	33	91.4	53	127.4	73	163.4	93	199.4
14	57.2	34	93.2	54	129.2	74	165.2	94	201.2
15	59.0	35	95.0	55	131.0	75	167.0	95	203.0
16	60.8	36	96.8	56	132.8	76	168..8	96	204.8
17	62.6	37	98.6	57	134.6	77	170.6	97	206.6
18	64.4	38	100.4	58	136.4	78	172.4	98	208.4
19	66.2	39	102.2	59	138.2	79	174.2	99	210.2
20	68.0	40	104.0	60	140.0	80	176.0	100	212.0

CONVERTING BAROMETER READINGS - INCHES TO MILLIBARS

In.	Mill.	In.	Mill.	In.	Mill.	In.	Mill.
27.00	914.3						
27.05	916.0	28.05	949.9	29.05	983.8	30.05	1017.7
27.10	917.7	28.10	951.6	29.10	985.5	30.10	1019.4
27.15	919.4	28.15	953.2	29.15	987.2	30.15	1021.0
27.20	921.1	28.20	954.9	29.20	988.9	30.20	1022.7
27.25	922.8	28.25	956.6	29.25	990.6	30.25	1024.4
27.30	924.5	28.30	958.3	29.30	992.3	30.30	1026.1
27.35	926.2	28.35	960.0	29.35	994.0	30.35	1027.8
27.40	927.8	28.40	961.7	29.40	995.6	30.40	1029.5
27.45	929.5	28.45	963.4	29.45	997.3	30.45	1031.2
27.50	931.2	28.50	965.1	29.50	999.0	30.50	1032.9
27.55	932.9	28.55	966.8	29.55	1000.7	30.55	1034.6
27.60	934.6	28.60	968.5	29.60	1002.4	30.60	1036.3
27.65	936.3	28.65	970.2	29.65	1004.1	30.65	1038.0
27.70	938.0	28.70	971.9	29.70	1005.8	30.70	1039.7
27.75	939.7	28.75	973.6	29.75	1007.5	30.75	1041.4
27.80	941.4	28.80	975.3	29.80	1009.2	30.80	1043.1
27.85	943.1	28.85	977.0	29.85	1010.9	30.85	1044.8
27.90	944.8	28.90	978.6	29.90	1012.6	30.90	1046.4
27.95	946.5	28.95	980.3	29.95	1014.3	30.95	1048.1
28.00	948.2	29.00	982.1	30.00	1016.0	31.00	1049.8

BAROMETER INDICATIONS

Certain fundamental principles may be helpful to remember concerning weather, generally:

(a) **Low Pressure** shows unstable and changing conditions.
(b) **High Pressure** shows stable and continuing good conditions.
(c) **Steady Rise** shows good weather approaching.
(d) **Steady Fall** shows bad weather approaching.
(e) **Rapid Rise** shows better weather may not last.
(f) **Rapid Fall** shows stormy weather approaching rapidly.

Section 19

7

Sunset

A rosy sky at sunset (whether cloudy or clear) means FAIR WEATHER.

A greenish–grey (or pale yellow) sky means RAIN.

A dark red or purple sky means RAIN.

A bright yellow (or copper coloured) sky means WIND.

A sickly looking grey or greenish orange (or copper sky) means WIND and RAIN.

Moon

A full Moon, rising clear foretells FAIR WEATHER

A Full Moon rising pale yellow brings RAIN.

In the wane of the moon a cloudy morning brings a FAIR afternoon.

A large ring around the Moon and high clouds foretells RAIN in several days.

A red Moon means WIND.

Halo (a large circle)

A Halo round the Sun or Moon – the larger the Halo the sooner the RAIN. The open side of the Halo tells the quarter from which the rain will come.

A Halo round the Sun or Moon after fine weather means STORMY WEATHER (wind or rain).

Corona (a small circle)

A Corona round the Sun or Moon and growing larger indicates FAIR WEATHER.

A Corona round the Sun or Moon and growing smaller means RAIN.

Rainbow

A Rainbow in the evening means FAIR WEATHER. A secondary bow – with colours reversed – may be seen frequently about 10° outside the main Rainbow.

WELL PROVED INDICATION FOR FORECASTING THE WEATHER

Fair weather. Barometer steady (near 1,012.5 mb or 29.90 in.) or RISING at a steady rate. Mares Tail Clouds at great height or Cumulus clouds.

Rain. Barometer falling slowly (about 0.14 mb. or 0.004 inches per hour). Strange hues of clouds with hard defined outlines. White distant watery looking clouds which increase and are followed by an overcast murky vapour that becomes cloudy –this is a certain sign of rain.

Wind. Barometer falling gradually (0.37 mb. or 0.011 inches per hour)
Hard edges on oily looking clouds.
High upper clouds crossing a different direction from that of the lower clouds or surface wind. This, when visible, is a useful sign and foretells change of wind towards their direction. Generally the harder the clouds look the stronger the wind will be.

Wind and Rain together Barometer falling moderately (say 0.51 mb. or 0.015 inches per hour).

Strong coloured clouds at low heights.

Stormy Weather; Strong Winds (perhaps rain) Barometer falling or rising rapidly (say 1.35 mb. or 0.04 inches per hour).

If oily looking clouds overcast there will be Wind, but if watery looking clouds overcast there will be Rain

Unusual hues of cloud with hard outlines. Green and black clouds foretell lightning and storm.

SEAMEN'S RHYMES

These rhymes, which are familiar to all seamen, summarise rather neatly, and in a form which is easily remembered, a number of rules for the amateur weather forecaster. Experience has shown there to be a considerable degree of truth in them and on that account they are included here. It should be borne in mind, however, that the rhymes are neither infallible nor always true, and they should be accepted with caution.

The Barometer

Long foretold, long last,
Short notice, soon past,
Quick rise after low,
Sure sign of stronger blow.

When the glass falls low,
Prepare for a blow;
When it slowly rises high,
Lofty canvas you may fly

At sea with low and falling glass
Soundly sleeps a careless ass,
Only when it's high and rising
Truly rests a careful wise one.

Wind and Weather

A red sky at night is a sailor's delight,
A red sky in the morning is a sailorman's
warning.

The evening red and morning grey
Are sure signs of a fine day,
But the evening grey and the morning red,
Makes the sailor shake his head.

Mackerel sky and mare's tails,
Make lofty ships carry low sails.

When the wind shifts against the sun,
Trust it not, for back it will run.

When rain comes before the wind,
Halyards, sheets and braces mind,
But when wind comes before rain
Soon you may make sail again.

If clouds are gathering thick and fast,
Keep sharp look out for sail and mast,
But if they slowly onward crawl,
Shoot your lines, nets and trawl.

FORECASTING INSTRUMENTS

The BAROMETER and – to a much lesser extent –
the THERMOMETER are the two most used
instruments for forecasting the weather. In any
vessel large enough to house it a BAROGRAPH –
which is simply a recording barometer – is of the
utmost value as the movements of the record –
whether up or down on the scale – can be seen
over any period of several days at a glance
without any written recordings being necessary.

Many large vessels, and all meteorological
voluntary recording vessels carry a Mercurial
Barometer which houses a column of mercury
and very accurate readings may be made by this
standard barometer from which all other
barometers may be set for comparison.

In any small vessel (and of course this is also
used in larger vessels too) the Aneroid type
barometer is always used. The word "ANEROID"
means "no fluid" and relies for its movement on
the pressure of the atmosphere and is therefore
quite unlike the Mercurial Barometer. The
Aneroid Barometer should occasionally be
compared at sea level with the mercurial type
and if the Aneroid requires adjusting this is
done very simply by carefully turning the screw
at the back of the instrument (using a thin
ended screwdriver) thus turning the indicators
on the face of the Aneroid to a higher or lower
reading as required.

FORECASTING FACTORS

The essential factors in forecasting the weather
at sea are the following in their relationship one
to the other:

(a) The direction and force of the wind.

(b) The pressure of the atmosphere
(i.e. Barometer readings) and its heat
(i.e. thermometer readings).

(c) The formation and movement of cloud.

Expected weather cannot be forecast simply by
reading the barometer and thermometer at any
given time or place. It is very necessary that a
record should be kept of their movements and
in practice this means that the barometer and
thermometer readings, direction and force of
the wind and cloud appearance should be
entered continually in the Log Book so that a
more or less constant record may be available.

On a passage in a vessel of any size watches
must be kept and the watch on deck can find
from the Log Book these observations made by
previous watch keepers without rousing them
from their sleep to ask them questions.

The Mercury Barometer. For purposes of
comparison of different barometric readings,
any variation from standard gravity has to be
corrected by using a formula giving the gravity
at the station in terms of the latitude and the
height above sea level. Corrections must also be
applied for any difference between the
temperature of the instrument and the standard
temperature, for the height above m.s.l.* (as it
affects the height of atmosphere above the
instrument) and for the instrumental errors
given on the certificate which accompanies the
barometer. When the three corrections for
gravity, temperature and height of instrument
above sea level have been made the resultant
value can be directly compared with that of any
other barometer similarly corrected. These
corrections may be simply and rapidly applied
by the use of the Gold slide. When reading a
barometer the eye should be exactly on a level
with the top of the mercury column, thus
eliminating parallax.

* m.s.l. = mean sea level. Allowances for change
of barometric pressure due to height of tide are
negligible as the atmospheric pressure near the
surface decreases approximately one millibar for
every 28 feet ascent.

Section 19

DEWPOINT(°C) TABLE

Dry Bulb °C	0°	0.2°	0.4°	0.6°	0.8°	1.0°	2.0°	2.5°	3.0°	3.5°	4.0°	4.5°	5.0°	5.5°	6.0°	6.5°	7.0°	7.5	Dry Bulb °C
									Depression of Wet Bulb										
40	40	40	40	39	39	39	38	37	36	36	35	34	34	33	32	32	31	30	40
39	39	39	39	38	38	38	37	36	35	35	34	33	33	32	31	31	30	29	39
38	38	38	38	37	37	37	35	35	34	34	33	32	32	31	30	29	29	28	38
37	37	37	37	36	36	36	34	34	33	32	32	31	30	30	29	28	28	27	37
36	36	36	35	35	35	35	33	33	32	31	31	30	29	29	28	27	26	26	36
35	35	35	34	34	34	34	32	32	31	30	30	29	28	28	27	26	25	24	35
34	34	34	33	33	33	33	31	31	30	29	29	28	27	26	26	25	24	23	34
33	33	33	32	32	32	32	30	30	29	28	28	27	26	25	25	24	23	22	33
32	32	32	31	31	31	31	29	29	28	27	26	26	25	24	23	23	22	21	32
31	31	31	30	30	30	30	28	28	27	26	25	25	24	23	22	21	21	20	31
30	30	30	29	29	29	29	27	27	26	25	24	24	23	22	21	20	19	18	30
29	29	29	28	28	28	28	26	25	25	24	23	22	22	21	20	19	18	17	29
28	28	28	27	27	27	27	25	24	24	23	22	21	20	20	19	18	17	16	28
27	27	27	26	26	26	26	24	23	23	22	21	20	19	18	18	17	16	15	27
26	26	26	25	25	25	25	23	22	22	21	20	19	18	17	16	15	14	13	26
25	25	25	24	24	24	24	22	21	20	20	19	18	17	16	15	14	13	12	25
24	24	24	23	23	23	23	21	20	19	19	18	17	16	15	14	13	12	11	24
23	23	23	22	22	22	21	20	19	18	17	17	16	15	14	13	12	10	9	23
22	22	22	21	21	21	20	19	18	17	16	15	14	13	12	11	10	9	8	22
21	21	21	20	20	20	19	18	17	16	15	14	13	12	11	10	9	8	6	21
20	20	20	19	19	19	18	17	16	15	14	13	12	11	10	9	7	6	5	20
19	19	19	18	18	18	17	16	15	14	13	12	11	10	9	7	6	4	3	19
18	18	18	17	17	17	16	15	14	13	12	11	10	8	7	6	4	3	1	18
17	17	17	16	16	16	15	14	13	12	11	9	8	7	6	4	3	1	-0	17
16	16	16	15	15	15	14	12	11	10	9	8	7	6	4	3	1	0	-2	16
15	15	15	14	14	14	13	11	10	9	8	7	6	4	3	1	0	-2	-5	15
14	14	14	13	13	13	12	10	9	8	7	6	4	3	1	0	-2	-4	-7	14
13	13	13	12	12	11	11	9	8	7	6	4	3	1	0	-2	-4	-7	-9	13
12	12	12	11	11	10	10	8	7	6	4	3	1	0	-2	-4	-6	-9	-12	12
11	11	11	10	10	9	9	7	6	4	3	1	0	2	-4	-6	-8	-12	-15	11
10	10	10	9	9	8	8	6	4	3	2	0	-2	-3	-6	-8	-11	-15	-19	10
9	9	9	8	8	7	7	4	3	2	0	-1	-3	-5	-8	-10	-14	-18		9
8	8	8	7	7	6	6	3	2	0	-1	-3	-5	-7	-10	-13	-17			8
7	7	7	6	6	5	5	2	1	-1	-3	-4	-7	-9	-12	-16				7
6	6	6	5	5	4	4	1	-0	-2	-4	-6	-9	-11	-15					6
5	5	5	4	4	3	2	0	-2	-4	-6	-8	-10	-14	-15					5
4	4	4	3	2	2	1	-1	-3	-5	-7	-10	-11	-14	-18					4
3	3	3	2	1	1	0	-3	-5	-7	-8	-11	-14	-17						3
2	2	2	1	0	0	-1	-4	-5	-8	-10	-13	-16							2
1	1	1	0	-1	-1	-2	-5	-7	-9	-12	-15	-19							1
0	0	-1	-1	-2	-2	-3	-7	-9	-11	-14	-18								0

In the table lines are ruled to draw attention to the fact that above the line evaporation is going on from a water surface, while below the line it is going on from ice surface. Owing to this, interpolation must not be made between figures on different sides of the lines.

The Aneroid Barometer. Also registers atmospheric pressure and consists fundamentally of a shallow box, made of thin corrugated metal, from which almost all the air has been removed. The pressure exerted by the atmosphere, on the outside of the box, is very great, while that inside is very small, and were it not for the presence of a spring placed between the faces of the box, the latter would be crushed. However, the spring allows a certain degree of controlled "collapse" to occur and the small relative movements of the faces due to the changes of pressure acting on the outside are magnified by a series of levers and made to actuate a pointer on a dial. For increased sensitivity a number of boxes are linked together. The aneroid needs no correction for temperature or for gravity – only for height above m.s.l.*

To guard against any loss of accuracy of reading, it should be checked fairly often against the corrected readings of a mercury barometer.

Barometer Readings. Seldom does a single reading have important indications, it is the rate of change that counts, but directly we have two or more readings, separated by time or distance, or both, the observer is in a somewhat better position to deduce probable changes in weather conditions. How accurate these deductions will be depends on the correct interpretation of other factors and the intelligent application of known meteorological facts.

THE HYGROMETER

Water Vapour. The atmosphere at all times has a certain amount of water vapour in it. When it holds the maximum quantity possible at any given temperature, the air is said to be saturated, and any fall in temperature will then cause the excess vapour to be condensed. As it is important to know what this water vapour content actually is, a hygrometer is used to measure it. This usually consists of two thermometers. One, known as the dry-bulb thermometer, indicates the temperature of the air. The other has its bulb wrapped in muslin, and is kept moist by being connected by a cotton wick to a small container of distilled water and is known as the wet-bulb thermometer. When evaporation takes place from the surface of the wet-bulb heat is abstracted from the bulb of the thermometer and its reading is less than that of the dry-bulb thermometer by an amount which indicates the

humidity, or dampness of the air. When the air becomes saturated this so-called depression of the wet-bulb decreases to nothing because no evaporation is occurring at the wet-bulb. Hygrometer observations are important, as by means of a Dewpoint Table it is possible to find what fall in temperature will cause the formation of mist or fog in the local area. The lowest temperature to which air can be cooled without condensation is called the dew point.

The two common types of instruments for measuring humidity are: (a) Mason's hygrometer, consisting of the wet and dry bulb thermometer side by side in a louvred screen – exposed on the weather side of the ship. (b) The "aspirated" psychrometer, in which a steady current of air is drawn past the two thermometers by means of a small electric, clockwork or hand operated fan.

CLOUDS

Clouds are aggregates of minute water drops or ice crystals or both held in suspension in the atmosphere. Cloud Atlases are available illustrating the many varieties of cloud forms. For practical purposes a classification into ten main types is adopted. This classification is as follows:

(1) *High Clouds*

Cirrus (Ci)
Cirro-cumulus (Cc)
Cirro-stratus (Cs)

(2) *Middle Clouds*
Alto-cumulus (Ac)
Alto-stratus (As)
Nimbo-stratus (Ns)

(3) *Low Clouds*
Strato-cumulus (Sc)
Stratus (St)

(4) *Low Clouds of marked vertical extent*
Cumulo-nimbus (Cb)
Cumulus (Cu)

Brief descriptions of the different cloud types are given below

Cirrus (Ci). Detached clouds composed of ice crystals, of delicate and fibrous appearance, without shading, generally white in colour, often of silky appearance. Tufted cirrus clouds are popularly known as "Mares' Tails."

Cirro-cumulus (Cc). A cirriform layer or patch composed of small white flakes or of very small globular masses, without shadows, arranged in groups or lines, or more often in ripples resembling those of sand on the sea shore.

Cirro-stratus (Cs). A transparent whitish veil of fibrous or smooth appearance, composed of ice crystals, which totally or partially covers the sky and usually produces halo phenomena.

Alto-cumulus (Ac). A layer, or patches, composed of laminae or rather flattened globular masses, the smallest elements of the regularly arranged layer being fairly small and thin, with or without shading.

Alto-stratus (As). A striated or fibrous veil, more or less grey or bluish in colour. It does not give rise to halo phenomena.

Strato-cumulus (Sc). A layer, or patches, composed of globular masses or rolls; the smallest of the regularly arranged elements are fairly large; they are soft and grey with darker parts.

Stratus (St). A uniform layer of cloud, like fog, but not resting on the ground.

Nimbo-stratus (Ns). A low, amorphous, and rainy layer, of a dark-grey colour and nearly uniform.

Cumulus (Cu). Thick clouds with vertical development; the upper surface is dome shaped and exhibits protuberances, while the base is nearly horizontal.

Cumulo-nimbus (Cb). Heavy masses of cloud with great vertical development, whose cumuliform summits rise in the form of mountains or towers, the upper parts having fibrous texture and often spreading out in the shape of an anvil.

The degree of cloudiness is normally expressed on a scale from 0 to 8, in which 0 represents a sky quite free from cloud and 8 an entirely overcast sky in which no patches of blue are visible. The estimation is one of "eighths of sky covered" (oktas).

The height of base cloud is a factor of great importance to aviation. During the daytime it may be measured by timing the ascent of a small balloon rising at a fixed rate. At night a ceiling light projector (cloud searchlight) may be used on large ships. As the use of balloons and searchlights is impracticable in most ships, cloud height is normally estimated at sea.

Approximate Heights of Cloud Bases

High clouds above 18,000 ft; Middle clouds 8,000 to 18,000 ft; Low clouds below 8,000 ft.

These limits tend to be higher in low latitudes, and lower, especially for high clouds, in high latitudes.

HIGH CLOUD

Photo by R. K. Pilsbury.

(1) CIRRUS (Ci)(Mares' Tails).Cirrus increasing and thickening is a sign of unsettled weather.

HIGH CLOUD

Photo by R. K. Pilsbury.

(2) CIRROCUMULUS (Cc) (Mackerel Sky)
When the above clouds move rapidly and become Cirrostratus unsettled weather is approaching.

HIGH CLOUD

Photo by R. K. Pilsbury.

(3) CIRROSTRATUS (Cs).A covering of this cloud with a Halo, as shown, is a sure sign of deteriorating weather approaching.

Section 19

MIDDLE CLOUD

Photo by R. K. Pilsbury.

(4) ALTOCUMULUS (Ac) Similar to a Mackerel sky but with larger globules of cloud, often packed in tight lines. If these tend to join and become Altostratus, rain is on the way. Altocumulus in lines with castellated tops, like the battlements on a castle wall, indicate thundery conditions.

MIDDLE CLOUD

Photo by R. K. Pilsbury.

(5) ALTOSTRATUS (As) A continuous layer of grey cloud from which rain will soon fall. It is then known as Nimbostratus (Ns) and its base may fall to only a few hundred feet above MSL.

LOW CLOUD

Photo by R. K. Pilsbury.

(6) CUMULONIMBUS (Cb) The Thunderstorm Cloud, often accompanied by sudden squalls and rapidly changing winds

LOW CLOUD

Section 19

Photo by R. K. Pilsbury.

(7) CUMULUS (Cu). Small Cumulus not increasing means fine weather, however if growing upwards like a 'Cauliflower' showers are likely.

LOW CLOUD

Photo by R. K. Pilsbury.

(8) STRATOCUMULUS (Sc). More frequent in the colder months especially near windward coasts.
STRATUS (St) (not illustrated) a grey featureless low cloud often shrouding cliff and hill tops on windward coasts. When broken by turbulence it is called FRACTOSTRATUS (FrSt)

STATE OF SEA PHOTOGRAPHS FOR ESTIMATING WIND SPEEDS

The following photographs illustrate the appearance of the sea corresponding to the Beaufort wind scale. Their purpose is to assist observers in estimating the wind speed when making weather reports. The description of the sea is according to the SEA CRITERION laid down by the World Meteorological Organisation.

The appearance of the sea may be affected also by fetch (the distance which the wind has travelled over a water surface in nearly the same direction), depth of water, swell, heavy rain, tidal streams and the lag affect between the wind getting up and the sea increasing.

Probable wave heights and probable maximum wave heights have been added only as a rough guide to show what may be expected in sea areas remote from land. In enclosed waters, or when near land with an off-shore wind, wave heights will be smaller and the waves steeper.

Aboard a moving vessel it is essential to know the time, wind force and direction and the Beaufort scale provides the best method of making this important observation. The line of sight at right angles to the wave's line of advance indicates the true direction of the wind.

It is difficult at night to estimate wind force by the sea criterion.

Photo by R. R. Baxter (Crown Copyright).

FORCE 0 (CALM) Wind speed less than one knot
(Sea like a mirror)

Photo by R. R. Baxter (Crown Copyright).

FORCE 1 (LIGHT AIR) Wind speed 1-3 knots; mean, 2 knots
(Ripples with the appearance of scales are formed, but without foam crests). Probable wave height, ½ foot.

Photo by R. R. Baxter (Crown Copyright).

FORCE 2 (LIGHT BREEZE) Wind speed 4-6 knots; mean, 5 knots
(Small wavelets, still short but more pronounced – Crests have a glassy appearance and do not break. Probable wave height ½ foot - 1 foot maximum.

Photo by R. Palmer

FORCE 3 (GENTLE BREEZE) Wind speed 7-10 knots; mean ,9 knots
(Large wavelets. Crests begin to break. Foam of glassy appearance . Perhaps scattered white horses). Probable wave height 2 feet – maximum, 3 ft.

Photo by P. J. Weaver

FORCE 4 (MODERATE BREEZE) Wind speed 11-16 knots; mean, 13 knots
(Small waves, becoming longer; fairly frequent white horses). Probable wave height
3½ feet – maximum, 5 feet.

Photo by R. R. Baxter (Crown Copyright).

Section 19

FORCE 5 (FRESH BREEZE) Wind speed 17-21 knots; mean 19 knots
(Moderate waves, taking a more pronounced long form; many white horses are
formed. Chance of some spray). Probable wave height 6 feet – maximum, 8½ feet.

Photo by R. R. Baxter (Crown Copyright).

FORCE 6 (STRONG BREEZE) Wind speed 22-27 knots; mean, 24 knots
(Large waves begin to form; the white foam crests are more extensive everywhere. Probably some spray). Probable wave height 9½ feet – maximum, 13 feet.

Photo by R. R. Baxter (Crown Copyright).

FORCE 7 (NEAR GALE)   Wind speed 28-33 knots; mean, 30 knots
(Sea heaps up and white foam from breaking waves begins to be blown in streaks along the direction of the wind). Probable wave height 13½ feet – maximum, 19 feet.

Photo by R. P. Baxter (Crown Copyright).

FORCE 8 (GALE) Wind speed 34-40 knots; mean, 37 knots
(Moderately high waves of greater length; edges of crests begin to break into spindrift. The foam is blown in well marked streaks along the direction of the wind). Probable wave height 18 feet – maximum, 25 feet.

Photo by O. R. Bates

FORCE 9 (STRONG GALE) Wind speed 41-47 knots; mean, 44 knots
(High waves. Dense streaks of foam along the direction of the wind. Crests of waves begin to topple, tumble and roll over. Spray may affect visibility). Probable wave height 23 feet – maximum, 32 feet.

Section 19

Photo by J. Hodkinson.

FORCE 10 (STORM) Wind speed 48-55 knots; mean, 52 knots

Viewed at right angles to the trough. (Very high waves with long overhanging crests. The resulting foam, in great patches, is blown in dense white streaks along the direction of the wind. On the whole, the surface of the sea takes a white appearance. The tumbling of the sea becomes heavy and shock-like. Visibility affected). Probable wave height 29 feet – maximum, 41 feet.

Photo (Crown Copyright).

FORCE 11 (VIOLENT STORM) Wind speed 56-63 knots; mean, 60 knots

(Exceptionally high waves. Small and medium-sized ships might be for a time lost to view behind the waves. The sea is completely covered with long white patches of foam lying along the direction of the wind. Everywhere the edges of the wave crests are blown into froth. Visibility affected). Probable wave height 37 feet – maximum, 52 feet.

Photo (Crown Copyright).

FORCE 12 (HURRICANE) Wind speed greater than 63 knots
(The air is filled with foam and spray. Sea completely white with driving spray; visibility very seriously affected). Probable wave height 45 feet.
The Beaufort Scale actually extends to force 17 (up to 118 knots), but Force 12 is the highest which can be identified from the appearance of the sea.

WIND

Wind is the movement of air across the surface of the earth and basically it is caused by differences of temperature between one large area and another. This in turn gives rise to the pressure differences which are the direct cause of the air movements. The pressure difference over a unit distance is known as the pressure gradient and the steeper the gradient the stronger is the wind. (Air also moves upwards and downwards in the atmosphere and these movements are very largely responsible for the formation or dispersal of cloud; the occurrence of precipitation, thunderstorms, etc.

Buys Ballot's Law A useful rule for the observer in the northern hemisphere to remember is, that when he faces the wind, the region of lowest barometric pressure will lie towards his right side and the highest towards his left. The reverse holds good in the southern hemisphere.

Permanent winds which blow in approximately the same direction throughout the year over large parts of the ocean are called "trade winds." Regular winds whose directions depend greatly on the sun's declination are termed "seasonal winds." To this group belong the well-known monsoons of the Indian Ocean and China Sea. Similar periodic winds occur in many other localities, and in nearly all areas on the earth the "prevailing wind" depends more or less on the season and consequent pressure distribution.

Rotational Effect of the Earth. When considering the motion of air over the earth's surface it is necessary to take into account the effect of the earth's rotation, which deflects moving air to the right in the Northern Hemisphere and to the left in the Southern Hemisphere. Near the surface of the earth the effect of friction is important and the air does not move exactly along the isobar but is inclined to it at an angle, inwards towards the low pressure.

Section 19

23

BEAUFORT WIND SCALE

Beaufort Number	Mean Velocity		Descriptive Term	Deep Sea Criterion	Probable Height of Waves in metres*
	knots	m/s			
0	Less than 1	0-0.2	Calm	Sea like a mirror	
1	1-3	0.3-1.5	Light breeze	Ripples with the appearance of scales are formed but without foam crests.	0.1 (0.1)
2	4-6	1.6-3.3	Light breeze	Small wavelets, still short but more pronounced. Crests have a glassy appearance	0.2 (0.3)
3	7-10	3.4-5.4	Gentle breeze	Large wavelets. Crests begin to break. Foam of glassy appearance. Perhaps scattered white horses	0.6 (1)
4	11-16	5.5-7.9	Mod. breeze	Small waves, becoming longer: fairly frequent horses.	1 (1.5)
5	17-21	8.0-10.7	Fresh breeze	Moderate waves, taking a more pronounced long form; many white horses are formed. (Chance of some spray)	2 (2.5)
6	22-27	10.8-13.8	Strong breeze	Large waves begin to form, the white foam crests are more extensive everywhere. (Probably some spray).	3 (4)
7	28-33	13.9-17.1	Near gale	Sea heaps up and white foam from breaking waves begins to be blown in streaks along the direction of the wind.	4 (5.5)
8	34-40	17.2-20.7	Gale	Moderately high waves of greater length; edges of crests begin to break into spindrift. The foam is blown in well-marked streaks along the direction of the wind.	5.5 (7.5)
9	41-47	20.8-24.4	Strong Gale	High waves. Dense streaks of foam along the direction of the wind. Crests of waves begin to topple, tumble and roll over. Spray may affect visibility.	7 (10)
10	48-55	24.5-28.4	Storm	Very high waves with long overhanging crests. The resulting foam in great patches is blown in dense white streaks along the direction of the wind. On the whole the surface of the sea takes a white appearance. The tumbling of the sea becomes heavy and shocklike. Visibility affected.	9 (12.5)
11	56-63	28.5-32.6	Violent storm	Exceptionally high waves. (Small and medium-sized ships might be for a time lost to view behind the waves). The sea is completely covered with long white patches of foam lying along the direction of the wind. Everywhere the edges of the wave crests are blown into froth. Visibility affected.	11.5 (16)
12	64+	32.7+	Hurri-cane	The air is filled with foam and spray. Sea completely white with driving spray; visibility very seriously affected	14 (–)

Notes

(1) It must be realised that it will be difficult at night to estimate wind force by the sea criterion.
(2) The lag effect between increase of wind and increase of sea should be borne in mind.
(3) Fetch, depth, swell, heavy rain and tide effects should be considered when estimating the wind force from the appearance of the sea.

*This table is intended only as a guide to show roughly what may be expected in the open sea, remote from land. In enclosed waters, or when near land with an off-shore wind, wave heights will be smaller, and the waves steeper. Figures in brackets indicate probable max. height of waves.

WARNING: FOR A GIVEN WIND FORCE, SEA CONDITIONS CAN BE MORE DANGEROUS NEAR LAND THAN IN THE OPEN SEA, IN MANY TIDAL WATERS WAVE HEIGHTS ARE LIABLE TO INCREASE CONSIDERABLY IN A MATTER OF MINUTES.

THE WEATHER MAP

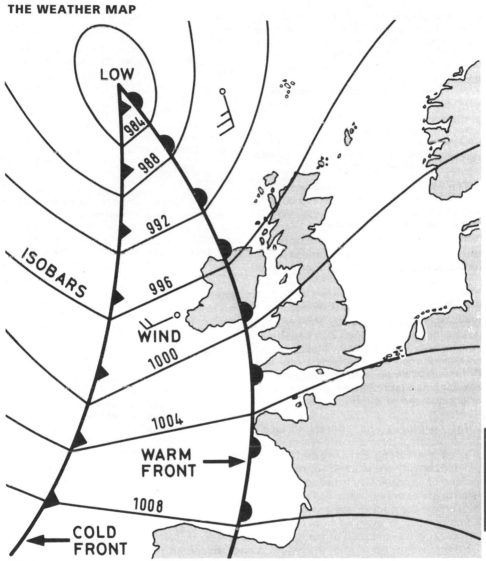

Wind
1) Blows along the isobars, anti-clockwise round a low pressure area (a depression).
2) The closer the isobars the stronger the wind.
3) Shifts of wind and squalls are most likely to occur at fronts, particularly at cold fronts.

Rain
Most likely to occur at fronts:
a) prolonged rain at warm fronts – defined rounded modules
b) showers at cold fronts – defined by triangular modules.

Temperature and Humidity
Air flowing from, say, the SW across the British Isles will be warm and wet Air flowing from, say, Scandinavia in winter across the British Isles will be cold and dry.

Future Movement of Low. The "Low" will probably move in the direction of the isobars in the warm sector, i.e., the isobars between the warm and cold fronts.

Wind Direction and Speed. The direction of a wind is the true bearing of the point from which it blows. Wind force is estimated in the Beaufort Scale. For use in synoptic weather messages, Beaufort force is converted into knots. It is generally estimated by the experienced observer with fairly reasonable accuracy, but only practice and careful observation can lead to proficiency in this. In modern, large, fast vessels the tendency is probably for an inexperienced observer to overestimate slightly the force of light winds and to underestimate the strong ones.

When determining wind direction, care should always be taken to eliminate the effect of the ship's speed and direction from the force and direction of the wind as observed. Tables are available for this purpose.

The effect of wind is always manifested on the surface of the sea. The probable appearance of waves in the open sea remote from land, which will be raised by different wind strengths is given in the table of Beaufort Wind Scale

WHEN INTERPRETING WEATHER FORECASTS and deciding whether it is more prudent to remain (or seek shelter) in harbour until conditions moderate, be sure to consult the Beaufort Wind Scale and give careful consideration to the notes and WARNING at the bottom of the Table.

CONVERSION TABLE FOR WIND SPEED

knots	metres per sec
2	1
5	2.6
10	5.1
15	7.7
20	10.3
25	12.9
30	15.4
40	20.6
50	25.7
60	30.9

1 knot = 0.514 metres per sec.
1 metre per sec. = 1.943 knots.

LOCAL WINDS

Bise

A cold dry wind which blows from the north-east, north or north-west in southern France during winter. The cold north-west wind, unlike the Mistral, is accompanied by heavy cloud.

Bora

A cold, often dry, north-easterly to easterly wind which blows down the slopes of the Dalmatian Mountains and off the eastern shores of the Adriatic. It is partly katabatic, strongest and most frequent in winter, and sometimes attains gale force when the pressure distribution is favourable and the pressure gradient strong. Often dangerous when it arrives suddenly with little warning, in the form of violent gusts.

Etesians

This is the Greek name for the winds which blow, at times, from a direction between north-east and north-west in the Aegean Sea from May to October. The weather is usually fine and clear. These seasonal winds temper the summer heat. They are called the *Meltemi* by the Turks.

Föhn

A warm dry wind blowing down the leeward slopes of a mountain range. When moist air ascends the weather slopes to heights well above the condensation level, much of its original moisture may become trapped on the high ground, or deposited there by precipitation. Thus the air descending the lee slopes has a much lower moisture content; evaporation commences at a higher level than that at which condensation began. Below the "evaporation level", warming takes place at the dry adiabatic lapse rate (1°C per 100 metres) and the air finishes its descent relatively warm and dry. The Föhn is a local name which originated in the Swiss Alps, but the effect is experienced anywhere where the conditions are suitable. A notable example is the "Chinook".

Gregale

A strong NE wind experienced in the central and western Mediterranean. It is capable of raising heavy seas which affect harbours having a northerly aspect at Malta and the east coast of Sicily. Occurs mainly in winter when pressure is high to the north or north-west and low to the south. Usually lasts for one or two days and occasionally for five days.

Harmattan

A dry and comparatively cool easterly wind which blows over north-west Africa during the dry season (November to March). It carries with it much dust from the Sahara, and reduces visibility for many miles to seaward. The period of the Harmattan decreases southwards.

Khamsin

A hot dry, dust-laden southerly wind in the eastern Mediterranean or North Africa. They are most frequent from February to June. Gales in the Red Sea from south or south-west are also called Khamsin.

Leste

A hot dry southerly wind occurring between Madeira and Gibraltar and along the north African coast in front of an advancing depression.

Levanter

An easterly wind in the Straits of Gibraltar, bringing excessive moisture, local cloud, heavy dews, poor or bad visibility, and sometimes rain. It can occur at any time of the year, but is most frequent in March and July to October. The Levanter is generally associated with high pressure over western Europe and low pressure to the south-west of Gibraltar or to the south over Morocco. It is usually light or moderate in force, and a banner cloud extends for a mile or so to leeward of the Rock. On occasions, when it blows fresh or strong, dangerous eddies are formed in the lee of the Rock.

Llevantades

Gales from between north-north east and east-north-east are the most important gales of the east coast of Spain. They are known locally as llevantades, and are an intense form of the llevante or levante, i.e. north-easterly winds of long fetch, as opposed to diurnal coastal breezes. These gales are most frequent and dangerous in spring and autumn (February to May and October to December), and are generally associated with slow-moving depressions crossing the Mediterranean between France and Algeria.

Leveche

A hot, dry, sand-and-dust-laden southerly wind which blows on the south-east coast of Spain. It occurs in front of an advancing depression, and its approach is often heralded by a belt of brownish cloud moving up from the south. (See also Scirocco.)

Libeccio

The predominating westerly or south-westerly wind in north Corsica. It often causes high seas and may be accompanied by violent squalls. It is most persistent during summer months. In winter it alternates with winds from the north or north-east (see Tramontana).

Maestro

A fresh north-westerly wind which blows in the Adriatic in summer it is accompanied by fine weather.

Marin

A strong south-easterly wind in the Gulf of Lyons. It is associated with depressions moving north east or east from northern Spain or southern France. Usually it brings warm cloudy weather with rain.

Meltemi (Etesians)

During the summer in the Aegean Sea, the prevailing winds of the main circulation are due chiefly to the deep continental depression centred over the north-west of India. These winds are known as Meltemi by the Turks and Etesians by the Greeks. They blow from a direction which may be anywhere between north-east and north-west according to the character of the country surrounding the region concerned; Meltemi weather is ordinarily fine and clear, the northerly winds tempering the fierce summer heat of the region.

Mistral

A cold dry, strong N or NW wind blowing over the northwest coasts of the Mediterranean. It occurs usually when there is high pressure to the north-west, over France, and low to the south-east. It often attains gale force, especially in winter, when the flow of air over the Gulf of Lyons is reinforced by katabatic drainage from the French Maritime Alps and also from the funnelling of the Rhone Valley.

Scirocco

The local name for a southerly wind in the Mediterranean. Originating in the desert regions of North Africa, it crosses the African coast as a hot, dry wind and often carries much dust. Blowing over the relatively cool water surface, it picks up moisture and tends to

Section 19

become stable; thus it reaches the northern coast as a warm, unpleasantly humid wind, often with fog or low stratus.

Solano

An easterly or south-easterly wind which brings rain to the Straits of Gibraltar and the south-east coast of Spain.

Tramontana

This is a local name for a north-easterly or northerly wind which in winter is prominent on the west coast of Italy and fairly prevalent off the north of Corsica. It is a fresh wind of the fine-weather Mistral type, and does not often reach gale force. It is associated with a depression over the Adriatic simultaneously with an anticyclone further west.

Vendavales

Strong SW winds off the east coast of Spain, and in the Straits of Gibraltar. Associated with advancing depressions from late autumn to early spring. Often accompanied by violent squalls, heavy rain and thunderstorms.

VISIBILITY SCALE
(SPECIFICATION FOR USE AT SEA)

The numbers 90 - 99 shown below are those used for reporting visibility observations in coded radio weather messages.

*90 – Visibility less than 55 yards.
*91 – Visibility 55-220 yards.
*92 – Visibility 220-550 yards.
*93 – Visibility 550-1,100 yards.
94 – Visibility 1,100-2,200 yards.
95 – Visibility 2,200-2.2 nautical miles.
96 – Visibility 2.2-5.4 nautical miles.
97 – Visibility 5.4-10.8 nautical miles.
98 – Visibility 10.8-27 nautical miles
99 – Visibility 27 nautical miles or more.
(*Fog.)

Note: In a large vessel, the occasions on which the lowest numbers in the visibility scale 90 and 91 are appropriate, can be determined by noting the distance at which objects on board become invisible in the fog.

If there is any obscurity or abnormal refraction the visible horizon may be very misleading as a means of judging distance, particularly when the height of the eye is great as in the case of an observer on the bridge of a large liner.

Visibility of less than 1,100 yards, however caused, is classed as fog (code figures 90-93 used). As a rough guide, poor visibility, but over 1,100 yards is called mist if the humidity is 95% or higher, and haze if the humidity is less than 95%, i.e. the difference between mist and haze is simply one of damp air.

In the Beaufort notation describing weather, fog is represented by f, mist by m and haze by z. At night it is difficult to judge the density of fog with accuracy and the practice is to use the diffracted blur around the masthead light as a criterion.

Letters to indicate the state of the weather (Beaufort Notation)

"Beaufort Notation," a system of notation devised by Admiral Beaufort, consisting as a rule of the initial letter of the phenomenon to be indicated, has been in use for many years. It affords a simple and concise means of indicating by a group of letters either the actual state of the weather at the hour of observation, "present weather"; or a general summary of the conditions over the interval since the last observation was made, "past weather"

b	=	blue sky (0 - 2/8 clouded).
bc	=	sky partly clouded (3 - 5/8 clouded).
c	=	cloudy (6 --8/8 clouded).
d	=	drizzle.
e	=	wet air (without precipitation).
f	=	fog.
g	=	gale.
h	=	hail.
jp	=	precipitation in sight of ship or station.
kq	=	line squall.
ks	=	storm of drifting snow.
kz	=	sandstorm or dust storm.
l	=	lightning.
m	=	mist.
o	=	overcast sky (the sky completely covered with a uniform layer of thick or heavy cloud.)
q	=	squally weather.
r	=	rain.
rs	=	sleet (rain and snow together).
s	=	snow.
t	=	thunder.

tlr = thunderstorm with rain.
tls = thunderstorm with snow.
u = ugly, threatening sky.
v = unusual visibility
w = dew
x = hoar frost.
y' = dry air
z = haze

p, formerly used as a Beaufort letter, to denote "passing showers", is now only to be used as a prefix, denoting "passing showers of e.g., ph, passing showers of hail; phr passing showers of mixed hail and rain.

The times of commencement and ending of heavy showers should be noted.

Capital letters indicate "intense"' the suffix$_0$ indicates "slight"; repetition of letters denotes continuity. The prefix i indicates "intermittent." Thus R, indicates heavy rain; r$_0$ slight rain; rr, continuous rain; ir$_0$ intermittent slight rain.

g is used to indicate that a wind of at least Beaufort force 8 has persisted for not less than 10 minutes. If the wind in 10 minutes has not fallen below force 10, the capital letter G is used.

d, drizzle, is to be used for precipitation in which the drops are very small. If the drops are of appreciable size, although the rain is small in amount, r$_0$ is used.

Depressions

The cyclonic systems of temperate latitudes are now usually referred to as depressions or "lows" to distinguish them from the tropical revolving storms which are often called cyclones or tropical cyclones.

The depression is a normal feature of temperature latitudes and is an integral part of the general circulation of the atmosphere, forming an essential link in the interchange of air between polar and equatorial regions.

Depressions in general move in both hemispheres in a more or less easterly direction, though considerable variations occur, including sometimes a reversal of direction for a time. More or less stationary and permanent areas of high pressure are to be found in the oceans between latitudes 20° and 40° N and S. In the North Atlantic, North and South Pacific and South Indian Oceans the tropical revolving storms progress round the equatorial sides of these areas and up their western sides in a poleward direction. Occasionally a tropical

revolving storm will continue into temperate latitudes, gradually changing its character and becoming a depression.

The concept of the "frontal surface" is vital to the theory of the formation and development of depressions. Warm air masses of tropical origin meet the colder masses of polar origin along a sloping surface of discontinuity, the colder and therefore heavier air lying beneath the warmer lighter air in the form of a wedge of small angle. The sloping surface of discontinuity is called a "frontal surface." the depression is then envisaged as an unstable wave on the surface of discontinuity. Pictured in terms of development at the surface the cold air replaces the warm tropical air along the "cold front" while the warm air replaces the cold air at the "warm front." The movement of the depression as a whole is in the direction of the isobars in its warm sector. The cold front moves faster than the warm front and the warm sector becomes progressively more narrow. Eventually the cold front overtakes the warm front, at first near the centre of the depression but progressively further and further away from the centre, the warm air being lifted from the surface. This lifting of the warmer air is known as "occlusion." The depression is said to be "occluding", the line at the surface which now takes the place of the warm and cold fronts known as an "occlusion." Much of the bad weather in the temperate zones is associated with the fronts of depression. It is this fact which gives the "frontal theory" of depressions its great value as a forecasting tool.

GLOSSARY OF TERMS USED IN MARINE METEOROLOGY

Air Mass. A mass of air which is largely homogeneous in a horizontal direction. Its physical properties are determined by the nature of the surface over which it forms and may be subsequently modified when the air mass moves over a different type of surface. Air masses are often separated from each other by frontal surfaces, which form discontinuities.

Anemometer. An instrument for measuring the speed of the wind.

Angle of Indraft. The angle between an isobar and the direction of the wind, near the earth's surface.

Anticyclone. A region characterised in the barometric pressure field by a system of closed isobars, with the highest pressure on the inside.

Aurora.. Bright streamers of light, ascending from the horizon towards the zenith, or luminous arcs, which are manifestations of electrical energy in the upper atmosphere. The aurora is seen in both hemispheres, in high and sometimes in medium or low latitudes. In the northern hemisphere it is known as Aurora Borealis, the southern as Aurora Australis.

Backing. A change in the direction of the wind, in an anti-clockwise direction.

Blizzard. A high wind accompanied by great cold and drifting or falling snow.

Col. The saddle-backed region occurring between two anticyclones and two depressions, arranged alternately.

Cold front. The boundary line between the advancing cold air at the rear of a depression and the warm sector. Line squalls may occur at the passage of this front, which was formerly called the squall line.

Cold Sector. The part of a depression associated with relatively cold air on the earth's surface.

Convection. In convection, heat is carried from one place to another by the bodily transfer of the matter containing it. In particular, this is the method by which heat raises the temperature of a fluid mass. The part in close contact with the heat rises, and the surrounding fluid moves in to take its place. This action in the atmosphere gives rise to convectional currents, which may produce cumulus or cumulonibus cloud.

Convergence. Consider an area on the earth's surface. On the sides which face the wind, air will flow into the area, while on the other sides air will flow out. If, however, the wind is not uniform, more air may flow in than flows out, and the amount of air in the area will tend to increase. The air cannot, however, go on accumulating, and the excess will have to flow out over the top, thus leading to a rising air current, and perhaps to clouds and rain. The contrary case, when more air flows out of the area than flows into it is called **Divergence.** In this case there is a deficit of air, which is balanced by a descent of the upper air layers above the area. This descent is called **Subsidence.** The subsiding air warms up, its relative humidity falls, and fine weather is the usual accompaniment of subsidence, though fog may occur under certain conditions.

Corona(ae). A series of coloured rings round the sun or moon caused by diffraction of its light by water-drops, chiefly in alto-clouds.

Corposants. Luminous brush discharges of electricity, sometimes observed at the mastheads, and on projecting parts of ships during electrical storms. Also known as **St. Elmo's Fire.** Due to atmospheric electricity.

Cyclone. A name given to the tropical revolving storms of the Bay of Bengal and the Arabian Sea. Sometimes used as a general term for tropical revolving storms of all oceans, or in the form "Tropical Cyclone."

Cyclonic. Refers to wind circulating anti-clockwise round a low pressure area surrounded by an area of higher pressure in North latitudes – clockwise in South latitudes.

Dangerous Quadrant. The forward quadrant of the dangerous semi-circle of a cyclone, which before recurvature is nearer the pole (in both hemispheres).

Depression. A region characterised in the barometric pressure field by a system of closed isobars, having lowest pressure on the inside.

Dew. Water drops deposited by condensation of water vapour from the air, mainly on the horizontal surfaces cooled by nocturnal radiation.

Dew Point. The lowest temperature to which air can be cooled without causing condensation.

Diurnal Variation. This term is used to indicate the changes in the course of an average day, in the magnitude of a meteorological element. The most striking example of this is the diurnal variation of barometric pressure in the tropics, the chief component of which was a 12-hourly period. The maxima of this variation are about 10 a.m. and 10 p.m., the minima about 4 a.m. and 4 p.m. local time.

Doldrums. The equatorial oceanic regions of calms and light variable winds, accompanied by heavy rains, thunderstorms and squalls. These belts are variable in position and extent, and as a whole move north and south with the annual changes of the sun's declination.

Eye of Storm. The calm central area of a tropical cyclone. The most noticeable feature of this area is the sudden drop in wind from hurricane force to light unsteady breezes or even to a complete calm, with more or less cloudless sky and absence of rain. The sea in this area is, however, often very high and confused.

Front. The line of separation at or above the earth's surface between cold and warm air masses.

Frontogenesis. The development or marked intensification of a front.

Frontolysis. The disappearance or marked weakening of a front. Subsidence is the most important factor in causing frontolysis.

Gust. A comparatively rapid fluctuation in the strength of the wind, characteristic of winds near the surface of the earth. Gusts are mainly due to the turbulence or eddy motion arising from the friction offered by the ground to the flow of the current of air. (See **Squall**).

Hail. Hard pellets of ice, of various shapes and sizes, and more or less transparent, which fall from cumulonimbus clouds and are often associated with thunderstorms.

Halo. Halo phenomena constitute a large group of phenomena produced by the refraction or reflection of the light of the sun or moon by the ice crystals composing cirrus or cirrostratus cloud.

Hurricane. A name given to the tropical revolving storm of the West Indian region. Also applied to force 12 in the Beaufort Scale, whatever its cause.

Inversion. An abbreviation for "inversion of temperature Gradient." The temperature or the air generally decreases with increasing height, but occasionally the reverse is the case; when the temperature thus increases with height there is said to be an inversion. When an inversion exists at the surface, fog often occurs.

Isallobars. Isallobars are lines drawn upon a chart through places at which equal changes of pressure have occurred in some places at the same period of time. Lines of equal change, or isallobars, are drawn to enclose regions of rising or of falling pressure.

Isobars. Lines drawn through positions having the same barometric pressure, when reduced to sea level.

Isotherms. Lines drawn through positions having the same temperatures.

Katabatic Wind. A wind that flows down slopes, usually at night. The air at the top of the slope is cooled to a greater amount by radiation than the air lower down, become heavier, and flows down the slope under the influence of gravity. The opposite of katabatic is **anabatic,** applied to a wind blowing up a slope, if it is caused by the convection of heated air.

Land and Sea Breezes. These are caused by the unequal heating and cooling of land and water under the influence of solar radiation by day and radiation to the sky at night, which produce a gradient of pressure near the coast. During the daytime the land is warmer than the sea and a breeze, the sea breeze, blows onshore; at night and in the early morning the land is cooler than the sea and the land breeze blows offshore. Land breeze is usually less developed than sea breeze.

Line Squall. A more or less violent squall, accompanying the passage of the cold front of a depression, distinguished by a sudden or rapid rise of wind strength, a change of wind direction, a rapid rise of the barometer and a fall of temperature. There is usually heavy rain or hail, sometimes a thunderstorm, or snow. The accompanying low black cloud forms a line or arch.

Local Winds. Winds prevalent in particular areas at particular times with special features, eg, the **Bora, Pampero, Mistral, Levanter, Sumatra.**

Mirage. The appearance of one or more images of a terrestrial object in the sky; also all forms of distortion of objects, due to abnormal refraction.

Occlusion, Occluded Depression. When the whole of the warm sector of a depression has been "pushed up" from the earth's surface by the advance of the cold front behind it, this is known as occlusion, and the depression in which it occurs is called an occluded depression.

Orographic Rain. Rain caused by the interference of rising land in the path of moisture laden air. A horizontal air current striking a mountain slope is deflected upwards, and the consequent dynamical cooling associated with the expansion of the air produces cloud and rain, if the air contains sufficient aqueous vapour.

Polar Front. The line of discontinuity, which is developed in suitable conditions between air originating in polar regions and air from low latitudes, and on which the majority of the depressions of temperate latitudes develop. It can sometimes be traced as a continuous wavy line thousands of miles in length, but it is interrupted when polar air breaks through to feed the trade winds, and is often replaced by a very complex series of fronts, or by a more gradual change of temperature.

Section 19

Precipitation. Any aqueous deposit, in liquid or solid form, derived from the atmosphere. The precipitation at a given station during a given period includes not only the rainfall but also dew and the water equivalent of any solid deposits (snow, hail, or hoar frost) received in the rain gauge.

Recurvature of Storm. This expression refers to the recurvature of the track of a tropical cyclone. In the northern hemisphere a tropical cyclone, after proceeding in a more or less westerly direction, recurves and normally takes a north-easterly direction; in the southern hemisphere the final direction is normally south-easterly.

Ridge. An extension of an anticyclone or high pressure area shown on a pressure chart, corresponding to a ridge running out from the side of a mountain.

Roaring Forties. A nautical expression for the region of westerly winds in south temperate latitudes, which reach their greatest development south of 40°S. A general term for the prevailing westerly winds in the temperate latitudes of both hemispheres is Brave West Winds.

Scud. A word used by sailors to describe ragged fragments of cloud drifting rapidly in a strong wind, often underneath rain clouds. The meteorological term is fractostratus.

Secondary Depression or "Secondary." The isobars around a depression are frequently not quite symmetrical, they sometimes show bulges or distortions, which are accompanied by marked deflections in the general circulation of the wind in the depression; such distortions are called secondaries; they may appear merely as sinuosities in the isobars, but at other times they enclose separate centres of low pressure and show separate wind circulations from that of the parent depression.

Shower. In describing present or past weather, the following distinction is made between the use of the terms "showers" and "occasional precipitation." In general, showers are of short duration, and the fair periods between them are usually characterised by definite clearance of the sky. The clouds which give the showers are, therefore, isolated. The precipitation does not usually last more than fifteen minutes, though it may occasionally last for half an hour or more. Occasional precipitation, on the other hand, usually lasts for a longer time than the

showers, and the sky in the periods between the precipitation is usually cloudy or overcast. Sleet. Precipitation of snow and rain together, or of melting snow and rain.

Snow. Precipitation of ice crystals of feathery or needlelike structure.

Squall. A strong wind that increases suddenly, lasts for some minutes, and decreases again comparatively rapidly. It is frequently, but not necessarily, associated with a temporary change of direction. (See **Gust**)

Stratosphere. The region of the atmosphere immediately above the troposphere (q.v.). In the lower stratosphere temperature may continue to decrease with increase of height (but more slowly than in the troposphere) or may remain practically constant, or may increase with height. The transition from troposphere to stratosphere, judged by change of temperature with height is not always abrupt.

There are other regions, at greater heights, with special characteristics, e.g.:
(a) The ozonosphere, where the concentration of ozone gas is greatest, centred at a height of about 20 miles.
(b) The ionosphere, the highly electrically conducting region of ionised gases, extending upwards from the height of 50 or 60 miles. This region plays an important part in radio propagation. The main subdivisions of this region in order of increasing height are usually referred to as the D,E (or Kennelly-Heaviside), F (or Appleton) regions or layers.

Synoptic. An adjective derived from the noun "synopsis," a brief or condensed statement presenting a combined or general view of something. Thus a synoptic chart shows the weather conditions over a large area at a given instant of time.

Tendency of the Barometer. The amount of change in barometric pressure in the 3 hours preceding the time of observation. The characteristic of the tendency is the type of change during the same period, e.g. "rising," "falling at first then rising," "steady".

Thunder. The noise made by an electric discharge (lightning) from charged raindrops in a cloud to another cloud (or another part of the same cloud) or to the earth, or to the air surrounding the charged cloud. Sound travels 1 mile in about 5 seconds, while the lightning flash is seen as soon as it occurs, hence the interval of time between the two will give the distance from the observer.

Tornado. A violent and destructive whirl accompanying a thunderstorm.

Trade Winds. The name given to the winds which blow from the tropical high pressure belts towards the equatorial region of low pressure, from the N.E in the northern hemisphere and from the S.E. in the southern hemisphere.

Troposphere. The lower region of the atmosphere, throughout which temperature in general decreases as height increases, and within which occur practically all clouds and the various other phenomena normally styled "weather." The upper boundary of the region is known as the tropopause. The height of the tropopause varies with latitude from an average of about 5½ miles in our polar regions to about 11 miles at the equator, but the height also varies from summer to winter and with the general meteorological situation. (See **Stratosphere**).

Trough. The trough line of a circular depression is the line, through the centre, perpendicular to the line of advance of the centre. During the passage of a depression over any given place the pressure at first falls and later rises; the trough line passes over the place during the period of transition from the falling to the rising barometer. The word trough is also used in a more general sense for any

"valley" of low pressure, and is thus the opposite of a "ridge" of high pressure.

Typhoon. A name given to the tropical revolving storms of the China Sea and the west of the North Pacific Ocean.

Veering. A change in the direction of the wind, in a clockwise direction.

Vertex. The westernmost point in the track of a tropical revolving storm.

Vortex. Centre of tropical revolving storm, where barometric pressure is least.

Warm Sector, Warm Front. Most depressions in their earlier stages have an area of warm air on the side nearest the equator, known as the warm sector. The warm front is the boundary between the front of the warm sector, as the depression advances, and the colder air in front of it.

Waterspout. An air whirl, normally with a funnel shaped cloud projecting downwards from a cumulonimbus cloud, accompanied by an agitation of the sea surface beneath it, and the formation of a cloud of sprays. The waterspout is formed when the funnel shaped cloud has descended to join up with the cloud of spray; the spout then assumes the appearance of a column of water.

Wedge. An area of high pressure bounded by wedge shaped isobars. It is the converse of a V-shaped depression.

Section 19

Ocean Navigation

OCEAN NAVIGATION

THE MODERN SCENE

Top venture on an ocean passage is the ambition or dream of nearly every yachtsman. Only a few years ago he was able to call upon very little in the way of navigational aids to enable him to fix his position. Nowadays there is no such lack; and the advent of reasonably priced GPS receivers means that nearly all yachts heading for blue waters will carry equipment which will give a constant readout of position anywhere in the world – with an accuracy of 100 metres. A description of the various radio navigational aids which are available to yachtsmen can be found in Section 10.

It is helpful if the modern yachtsman understands the principles behind his electronic gear, and obviously he must master the 'procedures' which will enable him to get the best out of his particular set. Will this equipment and this knowledge therefore allow him to embark on his passage with complete confidence that he will always be able to answer the question, "Where am I?" The answer must be no.

PITFALLS

There are three ways in which electronic navigational aids may be disabled: firstly, the set itself is as vulnerable to breakdown as other items of electrical equipment on board; secondly, it may be deprived of the electrical power necessary to run it; thirdly, lightning strike will cause serious damage. The chances of these mishaps occurring may be small but they must be recognised by the prudent mariner.

SEXTANT NAVIGATION

We advocate therefore that the ocean navigator should carry a sextant, should practise how to use it effectively and should have at his fingertips a method of doing the associated arithmetic, i.e. sight reduction. There is the added stimulus that the art of astro-navigation gives a great deal of pleasure and satisfaction, and that is surely why the yachtsman goes to sea.

REED'S POLICY

We, at Reed's, have made the deliberate decision that we will continue to provide the ocean-going yachtsman with the data necessary for him to perform all the necessary astro-navigation tasks so that the partnership of the yachts-man, his sextant and his almanac will keep him out of trouble when the going gets tough. To this end we have retained, with some small revision, the descriptions, explanations, examples and tables which have appeared in Reed's for many years. Moreover, we have not been tempted to 'update' the elegant prose style of much of the original material, which came from the pen of Captain O. M. Watts himself.

SIGHT REDUCTION

Getting good sextant altitudes is the most difficult part of astro-navigation, and this can only be achieved by practice. The business of manipulating figures in order to perform the sight reduction is merely a matter of arithmetic. Not so long ago this was an onerous task, bedevilled by potential error. Nowadays it can be done relatively easily by a number of different methods, using tables, calculators or computers. Essentially, these are all ways of solving the spherical triangle by trigonometry, using long established formulae.

Some calculators and computers carry all or part of the ephemeris in their memories, thus appearing to make redundant the same data that we print. Whilst not decrying this obvious use of computer power, it is our view that no sensible navigator would go to sea without carrying his ephemeris in (indestructible) book form. If this is accepted, the need for also carrying the data in an electronic memory is debatable.

One further point; those navigators who use tabular methods of sight reduction usually require the ephemeris to be presented in degrees and minutes of arc; those who use calculators or computers may prefer the presentation in degrees and decimal parts of a degree. We have decided to continue with the former, traditional, method. Our reason is that users of calculators almost always have a quick and simple means of making the conversion, whereas the same is not true for users of tabular methods.

REED'S METHODS

Reed's offers well tried and inexpensive methods of doing the arithmetic. *Firstly,* we provide the data and the guidance for doing the work, without going outside the almanac, using the versine method and ABC tables. This method is still used by many navigators all over the world, and we regard it as an essential 'fall-back' feature of the almanac. *Secondly,* we show, in the text, how to do the job using a simple scientific calculator.

THE ALMANAC – NEW FORMAT

Reed's is now divided into two parts, all the data which is unchanging (or changes seldom) in the Companion, and the material which changes annually in a separate edition. However, there is an important exception to this general rule; we have arranged things so that the sight reduction process, whichever method the navigator uses, can be accomplished by using the annual volume alone. This is because we believed it would be inefficient for him to switch from book to book during his work. In order to ensure coherence, there is some data which is carried in both books.

AN INVITATION

We hope these new arrangements will be approved by ocean navigators, actual and putative, and also by those who are engaged in teaching the art. As ever, we are open to any suggestions aimed at improving our content or presentation.

NAVIGATION

THE ART OF NAVIGATION

The Art of Navigation is the means by which vessels of any size are sailed from one safe place to another. The art is the same essentially, whether the vessel is large or small or under sail or power. Larger vessels carry more responsibilities; but smaller vessels, where conditions are much more difficult – owing to space and motion – call for the same art of navigation; but it is carried out in a different manner.

The knowledge required may conveniently be split up into two parts – the practice of navigation in sight of (or close to) the land, generally termed Coastal navigation; whilst the practice of navigation out of sight of land over the boundless ocean is termed Celestial, Ocean, Deep Sea or Astro (Astronomical) navigation, or frequently and perhaps more correctly, just navigation.

Pilotage is generally defined as the art of navigating a vessel in enclosed waters or in harbours and estuaries.

As it is obvious that Coastal navigation cannot be carried out without a knowledge of pilotage – one must enter harbour sometimes – it is equally clear that Ocean navigation cannot be carried out without a knowledge of Coastal navigation – as one must leave and arrive from some coastline.

Where countries or islands are adjacent, or separated by short distances, then the two types of navigation mentioned overlap somewhat and short voyages can be carried out without the instruments required for longer voyages. Conversely the instruments or knowledge required essentially for long voyages can be employed usefully on the coast.

It is essential also that anyone who wishes to navigate anywhere must acquire the art of seamanship. Each art is really dependent on the other. One may be able to navigate successfully in all weathers; but if for example the navigator cannot handle his ship – then there probably will not be any ship left to navigate.

ASTRO NAVIGATION

Astro navigation has two main functions:

1) To determine the azimuth (bearing) of the sun (star, planet, moon) and thereby establish the compass error and

2) To determine a position line when coastal methods of fixing are not available.

(**Note**, two or more position lines are necessary to fix the observer's position.)

Astro navigation has the advantage that it is cheap – all you need is Reed's Almanac, a sextant and a watch accurate to the nearest second or so, and you have a system that can be used anywhere at any time, provided the cloud is not too dense.

Beginners to Astro navigation must not let the theory or the threat of massive calculations deter them. The theory can be largely ignored if simple routines are adopted and the calculations considerably reduced by a variety of ways, many of which are indicated on the following pages.

The beginner should start by finding the latitude from the sun and pole star.

Section 20

THE NAVIGATIONAL TRIANGLE

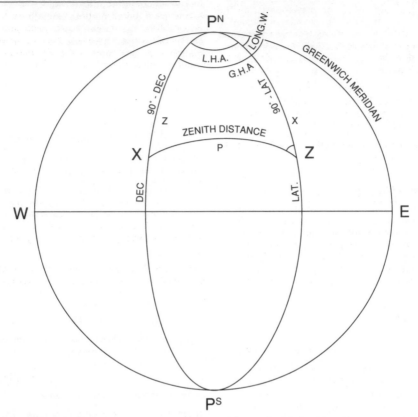

A GLOSSARY OF TERMS used in astro navigation is given later in this section.

PRINCIPLES OF ASTRO POSITION LINE NAVIGATION

To obtain a position line from a celestial body the following principles are involved.

The actual distance of the heavenly bodies from the earth are disregarded (as only angular measurements from the earth's centre are involved), and all bodies are assumed to be on the surface of an imaginary sphere, "the Celestial Sphere", with the centre of the earth at the centre. Angular measurements on the celestial sphere correspond to those on the earth, i.e., the celestial equator is on the same plane as the terrestrial equator and north or south latitude (called (Declination on the Celestial Sphere) correspond. Longitude on the celestial sphere, or hour angle, is the angle at the pole measured from the meridian of Greenwich westward from 0° to 360°.

The Navigational Triangle

Thus, as shown in the diagram above, it can be seen that obtaining a "Position Line" from a celestial observation requires resolving a spherical triangle PZX, the "Navigational Triangle". All calculations for celestial observations are related to this PZX triangle as will be readily appreciated throughout the following examples.

In the triangle, the angle ZPX is the angle at the nearest Pole (N or S) between the observer's meridian (longitude) and the meridian of the body at the time of observation. It is therefore the Local Hour Angle (LHA) of the body and is found (as shown in the annual volume) for the sun.

Z is the position of the observer, the Observer's Zenith; X is the position of the observed body.

PZ is the arc of the observer's meridian between

the Pole and the Observer's Zenith and is therefore the Observer's Latitude subtracted from 90°. (Co-latitude.)

PX is the arc of the body's meridian between the Pole and the observed body and is therefore the body's Declination subtracted from 90° (Polar Distance).

ZX is the Zenith Distance, or the arc of a great circle contained between the Observer's Zenith and the observed body. It is therefore the altitude of the body subtracted from 90°.

The angle PZX is the Azimuth or True Bearing of the observed body.

THE ASTRO POSITION LINE

The corrected sextant altitude subtracted from 90 does therefore give you the distance in nautical miles (as 1' of arc = 1 nautical mile) from the point on the earth's surface directly beneath the body observed (*i.e.*, the geographical position).

In practice this zenith distance is too large to plot so the observer compares his actual distance (True Zenith Distance) with the distance he has calculated from some assumed position (Calculated Zenith Distance). This comparison tells the observer that he is so many miles nearer or further away from the body than he had assumed.

i.e. True Zenith Distance   –   40 10
    Calc   „   „   =   <u>40   5</u>

                  Intercept 5 miles away

that is the observer is five miles further away from the G.P. than he had assumed.

As the radius of the position circle is so large the small section the observer is concerned with, can be drawn as a straight line at right angles to the Azimuth.

Note. The easiest position line to obtain is when the body lies due north or south. In this case the

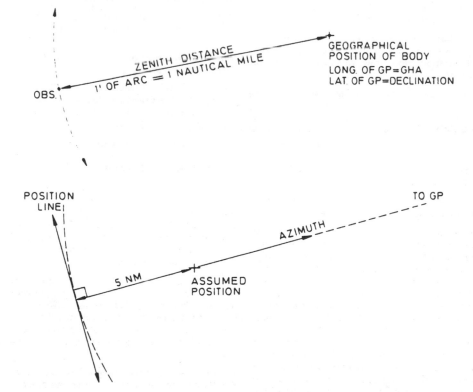

OBS.

ZENITH DISTANCE
1' OF ARC = 1 NAUTICAL MILE

GEOGRAPHICAL
POSITION OF BODY
LONG. OF GP=GHA
LAT. OF GP=DECLINATION

POSITION LINE

TO GP

AZIMUTH

5 NM

ASSUMED POSITION

Section 20

5

calculation is minimal and the position line obtained can be assumed to be the latitude.

See annual volume.

AMPLITUDES

The bearing of the sun when rising or setting is known as its Amplitude.

It is the quickest and easiest method of obtaining the compass error as "Time" does not enter nto the problem at all. Also the Amplitude is the only astronomical sight that can be made accurately without the aid of any instrument (other than the compass), Nature's own instrument – the horizon being used.

All that is required is to know the approximate latitude from the chart, and the approximate declination from this Almanac, see annual volume.

With these quantities a simple inspection of the table on following pages will give the True Bearing of the Sun at Sunrise or Sunset in any part of the world up to Latitude 66°; which, when compared with the compass bearing at sunrise or sunset will give the error of the compass. The Deviation can then be found immediately.

To take the observation

The "Theoretical Sunrise" is considered to take place at the moment when its centre is on the edge of the horizon to the westward.

In consequence of refraction (i.e., the bending of rays of light when passing through the atmosphere) the sun appears higher than it actually is and it must therefore be remembered that it apparently rises before it is actually above the horizon, and it is actually set when you can still see a small portion of the limb.

Amplitudes should therefore be taken, both at rising and setting, when the sun's lower limb is about half the sun's diameter above the horizon, as it is then that the centre of the sun may be taken as being on the horizon.

This table can also be used for true bearing at rising and setting of any celestial body other than the moon, within these declinations.

Example – On November 18th, in latitude 18°N. declination 19°S. the sun rose bearing by compass N88°E (or 088°). The Variation from the chart was 24°E. Find the deviation.

Draw diagrams as shown at foot of page to help in naming the error (D) and deviation (C).

Further Examples of the Use of the Table on following pages

1. In latitude 20°N. and declination 10°N. what is the sun's true bearing at sunrise? On examination it will be seen to be 79.4, which by the footnote is N 79.4°E.

2. In latitude 29°S. and declination 19°S., what is the sun's true bearing at sunset? The table shows it to be 68.2, which by the footnote is S 68.2°W.

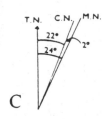

Sun's True Bearing (by table)	S 70°E. (110)
" Observed " (by compass)	N88°E. (88)
Error	22°E.
Variation	24°E.
Deviation	2°W.

C

To name the deviation.

To name the error

SUN'S TRUE BEARING AT SUNRISE AND SUNSET

LATITUDES 0° to 66°   DECLINATIONS 0° to 11°

LAT.	DECLINATION											
	0°	1°	2°	3°	4°	5°	6°	7°	8°	9°	10°	11°
0° to 5°	90	89	88	87	86	85	84	83	82	81	80	79
6°	90	89	88	87	86	85	84	83	82	81	79.9	78.9
7°	90	89	88	87	86	85	84	83	81.9	80.9	79.9	78.9
8°	90	89	88	87	86	85	84	82.9	81.9	80.9	79.9	78.9
9°	90	89	88	87	86	85	83.9	82.9	81.9	80.9	79.8	78.9
10°	90	89	88	87	86	84.9	83.9	82.9	81.9	80.9	79.8	78.8
11°	90	89	88	87	86	84.9	83.9	82.9	81.9	80.8	79.8	78.8
12°	90	89	88	87	85.9	84.9	83.9	82.9	81.8	80.8	79.8	78.8
13°	90	89	88	86.9	85.9	84.9	83.8	82.8	81.8	80.8	79.7	78.7
14°	90	89	88	86.9	85.9	84.8	83.8	82.8	81.8	80.7	79.7	78.7
15°	90	89	88	86.9	85.9	84.8	83.8	82.8	81.7	80.7	79.6	78.6
16°	90	89	87.9	86.9	85.8	84.8	83.8	82.7	81.7	80.6	79.6	78.6
17°	90	89	87.9	86.9	85.8	84.8	83.7	82.7	81.6	80.6	79.5	78.5
18°	90	89	87.9	86.9	85.8	84.8	83.7	82.6	81.6	80.5	79.5	78.4
19°	90	89	87.9	86.8	85.8	84.7	83.7	82.6	81.5	80.5	79.4	78.4
20°	90	88.9	87.9	86.8	85.8	84.7	83.6	82.6	81.5	80.4	79.4	78.3
21°	90	88.9	87.9	86.8	85.7	84.7	83.6	82.5	81.4	80.4	79.3	78.2
22°	90	88.9	87.9	86.8	85.7	84.6	83.5	82.5	81.4	80.3	79.2	78.1
23°	90	88.9	87.9	86.7	85.7	84.6	83.5	82.4	81.3	80.2	79.1	78.0
24°	90	88.9	87.8	86.7	85.6	84.5	83.4	82.3	81.2	80.1	79.0	78.0
25°	90	88.9	87.8	86.7	85.6	84.5	83.4	82.3	81.2	80.1	79.0	77.9
26°	90	88.9	87.8	86.7	85.6	84.4	83.3	82.2	81.1	80.0	78.9	77.8
27°	90	88.9	87.8	86.6	85.5	84.4	83.3	82.1	81.0	79.9	78.8	77.6
28°	90	88.9	87.8	86.6	85.5	84.4	83.2	82.1	80.9	79.8	78.7	77.5
29°	90	88.9	87.8	86.6	85.5	84.3	83.1	82.0	80.9	79.7	78.6	77.4
30°	90	88.9	87.7	86.5	85.4	84.2	83.1	81.9	80.8	79.6	78.5	77.3
31°	90	88.9	87.7	86.5	85.4	84.2	83.0	81.8	80.7	79.5	78.3	77.1
32°	90	88.9	87.7	86.5	85.3	84.1	82.9	81.7	80.6	79.4	78.2	77.0
33°	90	88.8	87.7	86.4	85.3	84.0	82.8	81.7	80.5	79.3	78.0	76.9
34°	90	88.8	87.6	86.4	85.2	84.0	82.7	81.5	80.3	79.1	77.9	76.7
35°	90	88.8	87.5	86.3	85.1	83.9	82.7	81.4	80.2	79.0	77.8	76.5
36°	90	88.8	87.5	86.3	85.0	83.8	82.6	81.3	80.1	78.8	77.6	76.3
37°	90	88.7	87.5	86.2	85.0	83.7	82.5	81.2	80.0	78.7	77.4	76.2
38°	90	88.7	87.5	86.2	84.9	83.6	82.4	81.1	79.8	78.5	77.3	76.0
39°	90	88.7	87.4	86.1	84.8	83.6	82.3	81.0	79.7	78.4	77.1	75.8
40°	90	88.7	87.4	86.1	84.8	83.5	82.1	80.8	79.5	78.2	76.9	75.6
41°	90	88.7	87.3	86.0	84.7	83.4	82.0	80.7	79.4	78.0	76.7	75.3
42°	90	88.6	87.3	86.0	84.6	83.3	81.9	80.6	79.2	77.8	76.5	75.1
43°	90	88.6	87.3	85.9	84.5	83.1	81.8	80.4	79.0	77.6	76.4	74.9
44°	90	88.6	87.2	85.8	84.4	83.0	81.6	80.2	78.8	77.4	76.0	74.6
45°	90	88.6	87.2	85.7	84.3	82.9	81.5	80.1	78.6	77.2	75.8	74.3
46°	90	88.6	87.1	85.7	84.2	82.8	81.3	79.9	78.4	77.0	75.5	74.0
47°	90	88.5	87.1	85.6	84.1	82.6	81.2	79.7	78.2	76.7	75.2	73.7
48°	90	88.5	87.0	85.5	84.0	82.5	81.0	79.5	78.0	76.5	75.0	73.4
49°	90	88.5	86.9	85.4	83.9	82.4	80.8	79.3	77.7	76.2	74.6	73.1
50°	90	88.4	86.9	85.3	83.8	82.2	80.7	79.1	77.5	75.9	74.3	72.7
51°	90	88.4	86.8	85.2	83.6	82.0	80.4	78.8	77.2	75.6	74.0	72.3
52°	90	88.4	86.7	85.1	83.5	81.9	80.2	78.6	76.9	75.3	73.6	71.9
53°	90	88.3	86.7	85.0	83.3	81.7	80.0	78.3	76.6	74.9	73.2	71.5
54°	90	88.3	86.6	84.9	83.2	81.5	79.7	78.0	76.3	74.6	72.8	71.0
55°	90	88.2	86.5	84.8	83.0	81.3	79.5	77.7	75.9	74.2	72.4	70.6
56°	90	88.2	86.4	84.6	82.8	81.0	79.2	77.4	75.6	73.7	71.9	70.0
57°	90	88.2	86.3	84.5	82.6	80.8	78.9	77.1	75.2	73.3	71.4	69.5
58°	90	88.1	86.2	84.3	82.4	80.5	78.6	76.7	74.8	72.8	70.9	68.9
59°	90	88.0	86.1	84.2	82.2	80.2	78.3	76.3	74.3	72.3	70.3	68.2
60°	90	88.0	86.0	84.0	82.0	80.0	77.9	75.9	73.8	71.8	69.7	67.6
61°	90	87.9	85.9	83.8	81.7	79.6	77.5	75.4	73.2	71.2	69.0	66.8
62°	90	87.9	85.7	83.6	81.4	79.3	77.1	74.9	72.7	70.5	68.3	66.0
63°	90	87.8	85.6	83.4	81.2	78.9	76.7	74.4	72.1	69.8	67.5	65.1
64°	90	87.7	85.4	83.1	80.8	78.5	76.2	73.9	71.5	69.1	66.7	64.2
65°	90	87.6	85.3	82.9	80.5	78.1	75.7	73.2	70.8	68.3	65.7	63.2
66°	90	87.5	85.1	82.6	80.1	77.6	75.1	72.6	70.0	67.4	64.7	62.0

Name the Bearing the same as the Declination NORTH or SOUTH and EAST if rising, WEST if setting. For example of use of this Table see previous page.

Section 20

SUN'S TRUE BEARING AT SUNRISE AND SUNSET

LATITUDES 0° to 66°   DECLINATIONS 12° to 23°

LAT.	12°	13°	14°	15°	16°	17°	18°	19°	20°	21°	22°	23°
	°	°	°	°	°	°	°	°	°	°	°	°
0° to 5°	77.9	76.9	75.9	74.9	73.9	72.9	71.9	70.9	69.9	68.8	67.9	66.9
6°	77.9	76.9	75.9	74.9	73.9	72.9	71.9	70.9	69.9	68.8	67.9	66.9
7°	77.9	76.9	75.9	74.9	73.9	72.9	71.9	70.8	69.8	68.8	67.8	66.8
8°	77.9	76.9	75.9	74.8	73.8	72.8	71.8	70.8	69.8	68.8	67.8	66.8
9°	77.8	76.8	75.8	74.8	73.8	72.8	71.8	70.7	69.7	68.7	67.7	66.7
10°	77.8	76.8	75.8	74.8	73.7	72.7	71.7	70.7	69.7	68.7	67.6	66.6
11°	77.8	76.8	75.7	74.7	73.7	72.7	71.6	70.6	69.6	68.6	67.6	66.5
12°	77.7	76.7	75.7	74.6	73.6	72.6	71.6	70.6	69.5	68.5	67.5	66.4
13°	77.7	76.6	75.6	74.6	73.6	72.5	71.5	70.5	69.4	68.4	67.4	66.4
14°	77.6	76.6	75.6	74.5	73.5	72.5	71.4	70.4	69.4	68.3	67.3	66.2
15°	77.6	76.5	75.5	74.4	73.4	72.4	71.3	70.3	69.3	68.2	67.2	66.1
16°	77.5	76.5	75.4	74.4	73.3	72.3	71.2	70.2	69.1	68.1	67.1	66.0
17°	77.4	76.4	75.3	74.3	73.3	72.2	71.1	70.1	69.0	68.0	66.9	65.9
18°	77.4	76.3	75.3	74.2	73.2	72.1	71.0	70.0	68.9	67.9	66.8	65.7
19°	77.4	76.2	75.2	74.1	73.0	72.0	70.9	69.9	68.8	67.7	66.7	65.6
20°	77.2	76.1	75.1	74.0	72.9	71.9	70.8	69.7	68.6	67.6	66.5	65.4
21°	77.1	76.0	75.0	73.9	72.8	71.7	70.7	69.6	68.5	67.4	66.3	65.2
22°	77.0	76.0	74.9	73.8	72.7	71.6	70.5	69.4	68.3	67.3	66.2	65.1
23°	76.9	75.9	74.8	73.7	72.6	71.5	70.4	69.3	68.2	67.1	66.0	64.9
24°	76.8	75.7	74.6	73.5	72.5	71.3	70.2	69.1	68.0	66.9	65.8	64.7
25°	76.7	75.6	74.5	73.4	72.3	71.2	70.1	68.9	67.8	66.7	65.6	64.5
26°	76.6	75.5	74.4	73.3	72.1	71.0	69.9	68.8	67.6	66.5	65.4	64.2
27°	76.5	75.4	74.3	73.1	72.0	70.8	69.7	68.6	67.4	66.3	65.1	64.0
28°	76.4	75.2	74.1	73.0	71.8	70.7	69.5	68.4	67.2	66.1	64.9	63.8
29°	76.2	75.1	73.9	72.8	71.6	70.5	69.3	68.2	67.0	65.8	64.6	63.5
30°	76.1	75.0	73.8	72.6	71.4	70.3	69.1	67.9	66.7	65.5	64.4	63.2
31°	76.0	74.8	73.6	72.4	71.2	70.0	68.9	67.6	66.5	65.3	64.1	62.9
32°	75.8	74.6	73.4	72.2	71.0	69.8	68.6	67.4	66.2	65.0	63.8	62.6
33°	75.7	74.4	73.2	72.0	70.8	69.6	68.4	67.1	65.9	64.7	63.5	62.2
34°	75.5	74.2	73.0	71.8	70.6	69.3	68.1	66.9	65.6	64.4	63.1	61.9
35°	75.3	74.1	72.8	71.6	70.3	69.1	67.8	66.6	65.3	64.0	62.8	61.5
36°	75.1	73.8	72.6	71.3	70.1	68.8	67.5	66.3	65.0	63.7	62.4	61.1
37°	74.9	73.6	72.4	71.1	69.8	68.5	67.2	65.9	64.6	63.3	62.0	60.7
38°	74.7	73.4	72.1	70.8	69.5	68.2	66.9	65.6	64.3	62.9	61.6	60.3
39°	74.5	73.2	71.9	70.5	69.2	67.9	66.6	65.2	63.9	62.5	61.2	59.8
40°	74.2	72.9	71.6	70.2	68.9	67.6	66.2	64.8	63.5	62.1	60.7	59.3
41°	74.0	72.7	71.3	70.0	68.6	67.2	65.8	64.4	63.0	61.6	60.2	58.8
42°	73.7	72.4	71.0	69.6	68.2	66.8	65.4	64.0	62.6	61.2	59.7	58.3
43°	73.5	72.1	70.7	69.3	67.9	66.4	65.0	63.6	62.1	60.7	59.2	57.7
44°	73.2	71.8	70.3	68.9	67.5	66.0	64.6	63.1	61.6	60.1	58.6	57.1
45°	72.9	71.4	70.0	68.5	67.0	65.6	64.1	62.6	61.1	59.5	58.0	56.4
46°	72.6	71.1	69.6	68.1	66.6	65.1	63.6	62.1	60.5	58.9	57.4	55.8
47°	72.2	70.7	69.2	67.7	66.2	64.6	63.0	61.5	59.9	58.3	56.7	55.0
48°	71.9	70.3	68.8	67.2	65.7	64.1	62.5	60.9	59.3	57.6	55.9	54.3
49°	71.5	69.9	68.4	66.8	65.1	63.5	61.9	60.2	58.6	56.9	55.2	53.4
50°	71.1	69.5	67.9	66.2	64.6	63.0	61.3	59.6	57.8	56.1	54.3	52.6
51°	70.7	69.0	67.4	65.7	64.0	62.3	60.6	58.8	57.1	55.3	53.5	51.6
52°	70.3	68.6	66.9	65.1	63.4	61.6	59.9	58.1	56.2	54.4	52.5	50.6
53°	69.8	68.0	66.3	64.5	62.7	60.9	59.1	57.2	55.4	53.4	51.5	49.5
54°	69.3	67.5	65.7	63.9	62.0	60.2	58.3	56.4	54.4	52.4	50.4	48.3
55°	68.7	67.9	65.0	63.2	61.3	59.3	57.4	55.4	53.4	51.3	49.2	47.1
56°	68.2	66.3	64.4	62.4	60.5	58.5	56.4	54.4	52.3	50.1	47.9	45.7
57°	67.6	65.6	63.6	61.6	59.6	57.5	55.4	53.3	51.1	48.8	46.5	44.2
58°	66.9	64.9	62.8	60.8	58.6	56.5	54.3	52.1	49.8	47.4	45.0	42.5
59°	66.2	64.1	62.0	59.8	57.6	55.4	53.1	50.8	48.4	45.9	43.3	40.6
60°	65.4	63.3	61.1	58.8	56.5	54.2	51.8	49.4	46.8	44.2	41.5	38.6
61°	64.6	62.3	60.1	57.7	55.3	52.9	50.4	47.8	45.1	42.3	39.4	36.3
62°	63.7	61.4	59.0	56.5	54.0	51.5	48.8	46.1	43.2	40.2	37.1	33.7
63°	62.7	60.3	57.8	55.2	52.6	49.9	47.1	44.2	41.1	37.9	34.4	30.6
64°	61.7	59.1	56.5	53.8	51.0	48.2	45.2	42.0	38.7	35.2	31.3	27.0
65°	60.5	57.8	55.1	52.2	49.3	46.2	43.0	39.6	36.0	32.0	27.6	22.4
66°	59.2	56.4	53.5	50.5	47.3	44.0	40.5	36.8	32.8	28.2	22.9	16.1

**Name the Bearing the same as the Declination NORTH or SOUTH
and EAST if rising, WEST if setting.**

CELESTIAL SIGNS AND ABBREVIATIONS

SIGNS OF THE PLANETS

⊙ The Sun.   ⊕ The Earth.   ♄ Saturn.
☾ The Moon.   ♂ Mars.   ♅ Uranus.
☿ Mercury.   ♃ Jupiter.   ♆ Neptune.
♀ Venus.

SIGNS OF THE ZODIAC

The Zodiac is the belt or zone extending 8° on either side of the Ecliptic, which contains the apparent paths of the Sun, Moon and the principal planets. It is divided into twelve angular portions of 30° (equalling the circle of 360°), each portion containing one constellation or sign, termed collectively The Signs of the Zodiac.

The seasons associated with these signs are given below, however, owing to the precession of the equinoxes the vernal equinox now actually occurs during Pisces instead of marking the First Point of Aries.

Northern Signs

Spring Signs	1. ♈ Aries	0°
	2. ♉ Taurus	30°
	3. ♊ Gemini	60°
Summer Signs	4. ♋ Cancer	90°
	5. ♌ Leo	120°
	6. ♍ Virgo	150°

Southern Signs

Autumn Signs	7. ♎ Libra	180°
	8. ♏ Scorpio	210°
	9. ♐ Sagittarius	240°
Winter Signs	10. ♑ Capricornus	270°
	11. ♒ Aquarius	300°
	12. ♓ Pisces	330°

ASPECTS

☌	Conjunction, or having the same Longitude or Right Ascension.
□	Quadrature, or differing ±90° in Longitude or Right Ascension.
☍	Opposition, or differing 180° in Longitude or Right Ascension.

ABBREVIATIONS

☊	Ascending Node
☋	Descending Node
N	North
S	South
E	East
W	West
°	Degrees
'	Minutes of Arc
"	Seconds of Arc
h	Hours
m	Minutes of Time
s	Seconds of Time

GREEK ALPHABET

Letter	Name	Letter	Name	Letter	Name
α	Alpha	ι	Iota	ρ	Rho
β	Beta	κ	Kappa	σ	Sigma
γ	Gamma	λ	Lambda	τ	Tau
δ	Delta	μ	Mu	υ	Upsilon
ε	Epsilon	ν	Nu	φ	Phi
ζ	Zeta	ξ	Xi	χ	Chi
η	Eta	ο	Omicron	ψ	Psi
θ	Theta	π	Pi	ω	Omega

A SHORT GLOSSARY OF TERMS
USED IN NAUTICAL ASTRONOMY
AND ASTRO NAVIGATION

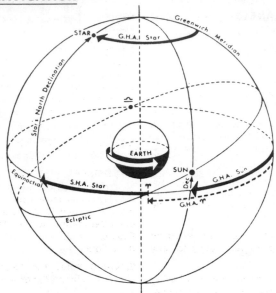

The Celestial Sphere

The Celestial Sphere (also termed the Celestial Concave — or the Heavens) illustrated above, is really the "Space" around the Earth into which we gaze at the Stars. Although it has no defined outline, being so far away it is assumed for practical purposes to be a hollow Sphere, of very large radius, having the Earth at its centre, and all heavenly bodies located on its surface.

Owing to the Earth's radius being so small in comparison, the observer's eye may be assumed to be at the centre of the Earth. Positions on the Earth's surface may be projected from the centre outwards on to the celestial sphere, also Parallels of Latitude and Meridians of Longitude.

Altitude. The Observed Altitude is the angular height of an object above the visible horizon, measured on a Vertical Circle (which is a great Circle perpendicular to the horizon) by a Sextant. After correcting this Observed Altitude for Dip, Refraction, Semi-Diameter and Parallax (all embodied in a Total Correction Table in this Almanac) the True Altitude is obtained.

Amplitude. The bearing of a heavenly body when rising or setting measured from the east or west points of the observer's horizon.

Apogee. The position in the orbit of the Moon which is farthest from the Earth. Opposite to Perigee.

Aphelion. When the Earth or other Planet is at the farthest point (in its orbit) from the Sun, opposite to Perihelion.

Apparent Time. Time measured by the Apparent Sun.

Apparent Sun, The, is the "True" and actually visible Sun of which observations can be taken.

An Apparent Solar Day is the interval between two consecutive transits of the Apparent Sun over an observer's meridian.

Apparent Noon at a place is the time when the Apparent Sun is on the Meridian of that place.

Ship Apparent Time (S.A.T.) **or Local Apparent Time** at any instant is the L.H.A. of the True (or actual) Sun ± 12h., S.A.T. is reckoned Westwards (0h. to 24h.) from the antimeridian of the place.

The measurement of Apparent Solar Time at any place is simply the measurement of the Apparent Sun's angular distance from the antimeridian of that place. As the Apparent Sun does not move uniformly, it is of no use as a standard time-keeper so another unit is adopted, called Mean Time (q.v.)

Arc. A part of the circumference of any circle.

Aries. One of the constellations of the Zodiac (see First Point of Aries).

Ascension (Right). See Right Ascension.

Astronomical Day, The. is composed of 24 mean solar hours, and begins at midnight on the civil day. It is reckoned from 0h. to 24h.

Autumnal Equinox. The time of the year — September 23rd — when the Sun crosses the Equator from North to South declinations.

Azimuth of a body is the arc of the horizon contained between the observer's meridian and a vertical circle through the centre of the body. It is simply the bearing of a Heavenly Body measured from the North or South points of the horizon.

Azimuth Tables. A set of Tables to determine the true bearing of a Heavenly Body for any Latitude and time.

Calendar Month. The ordinary month having 30, 31 or 28 (and in a leap year 29) days in gen eral use.

Celestial Poles, The. are the N. and S. poles of the Earth projected from the Earth's centre on to the Celestial Sphere.

Circumpolar Stars. Stars which never set below the horizon at the place of observation and to get this phenomenon the Latitude of the place must be more than the Polar distance of such Stars. Hence, there are no circumpolar stars at the Terrestrial Equator; but at the Terrestrial Poles all the Stars visible are circumpolar.

Civil Time is composed of 24 mean solar hours divided into two equal portions, the first marked A.M., from midnight to noon, the second marked P.M., from noon to midnight.

The civil year is 365 days (366 to every 4 years — Leap Year).

Conjunction. When two Celestial bodies are in the same direction from the Earth they are said to be in conjunction.

Constellations. The groups into which the stars are divided for identification purposes; the ancients gave these groups names of a fish, bird or figure which they were thought to resemble.

Culmination. The time of a Heavenly body reaching its highest altitude in the Heavens, when it crosses the observer's meridian or "culminates".

Cycle. The period of time between some celestial phenomena and its repetition.

Day. See Apparent Time, Mean Day and Sidereal Day.

Declination. The Declination (Dec.) of a body is its angular distance North (N) or South (S) of the Celestial Equator. Declination on the Celestial Sphere corresponds to Latitude on the Earth. North is sometimes written as + (plus) and South as – (minus), but this form of notation is not in general use.

Eclipse. The period when one Celestial body passes through the shadow of another.

The Ecliptic is the Great circle on the Celestial Sphere in which the Sun appears to move during its annual movement round the Earth. Its plane is inclined $23° 27'$ (which is the Sun's maximum Declination) to the plane of the Celestial Equator, which angle is called the Obliquity of the Ecliptic.

Elevated Pole. The Celestial Pole which is above the observer's horizon.

Ephemeris (Ephemerides). The special calendar showing the predicted timetable of the moving Celestial Bodies.

Ephemeris Time (E.T.). A conception of time for presentation of Ephemerides of the Sun, Moon and Planets.

Equation of Time (Eq.T.). The excess of Mean Solar Time over Apparent Solar Time. When Apparent Time is greater than Mean Time the equation of time is a negative quantity and is prefixed with a minus sign.

Equinoctial (or Celestial Equator). The Equinoctial is a Great Circle dividing the Celestial Sphere into two equal parts. It is in the same plane as the Earth's Equator.

Equinox. See Autumnal Equinox, also Vernal Equinox.

First Point of Libra. The Autumnal Equinoctial Point; the point where the Sun's centre crosses the Equinoctial as it moves along the Ecliptic and changes its Declination from North to South on the 23rd of September each year. It is diametrically opposite to the First point of Aries.

First Point of Aries. The starting point for measuring right ascensions. The point where the Sun's centre crosses the Celestial Equator (Equinoctial) when moving along the Ecliptic and changing from South to North Declination on March 21st. It is called the Vernal (or Spring) Equinox.

At this time the lengths of the day and night are equal throughout the world. See also Transit of Aries.

Full Moon. When the Moon is in "opposition" to the Sun, or on the Sun's antimeridian; i.e., when it is on the Meridian about midnight — 12 hours different from the Sun.

Geographical Position. The. of a Heavenly body is the point on the Earth's surface directly underneath that object (i.e., the object is in this position's Zenith). Its actual position is found by its Declination (i.e., Latitude) and its G.H.A. (i.e., Longitude).

G.H.A. in the Heavens corresponds to the Longitude (measured 0° to 360° westwards from the Prime Meridian) of the Geographical Position of the body.

Gibbous Moon. The phases of the Moon when the Moon's disc is more than half illuminated; i.e., between First Quarter and Full Moon and also between Full Moon and Last Quarter.

Greenwich Mean Time (G.M.T.) is the Time at Greenwich by the Mean Sun and is the standard to which all observations can be referred.

Greenwich Hour Angle, The. is the angle at the pole between the Meridian at Greenwich and the Meridian or hour circle through the body. As can be seen clearly from the figure p.10: it may also be measured Westward from 0° to 360° along the Celestial Equator from the Celestial Meridian of Greenwich.

Greenwich Sidereal Time (G.S.T.) is the same as G.H.A. Aries.

Harvest Moon. The Full Moon nearest the Autumnal Equinox (Sept. 23rd).

Hemisphere. Half of the Sphere. A plane (Equator) passing through the centre of a Sphere (the Earth) divides it into two equal parts (the Northern and Southern Hemispheres).

Horizontal Parallax (H.P.). Any Heavenly body on an observer's horizon would have no altitude, but if observed from the Earth's centre there would be an altitude as it would be above the horizon from the different viewpoint. The angle between these two positions is termed the Horizontal Parallax.

Hour Angle (of the Heavenly Bodies). The Hour Angle of a heavenly body is the angle at the Pole between the observer's meridian and

the meridian through the Body. It is purely a system of measurement, but because it often expresses "time" it is termed the Hour Angle, and when it is measured Westward from the Meridian (0° to 360° in arc or 0 to 24 hours in time) it is called "Local Hour Angle" (L.H.A.); but if measured Eastwards from the Meridian it is called "Easterly Hour Angle" and labelled E.H.A.

As the earth is rotating slowly unceasingly, the hour angle of any body that is fixed in the celestial concave will increase constantly during the 24 hours. When the body is on the observer's meridian the Hour Angle is 0 hours; and it is 24 hours later when it again returns to the observer's meridian.

The Local Hour Angle (L.H.A.) of the True (or actual) Sun is denoted by L.H.A.T.S. and that of the Mean Sun by L.H.A.M.S. (See also under Greenwich Hour Angle above.)

The L.H.A. of a Heavenly Body is also the sum of the L.H.A. of the First Point of Aries (i.e., the local Sidereal time) and the Sidereal Hour Angle (S.H.A.) of the body.

Hunter's Moon. The Full Moon nearest October 21st; but it is not so pronounced as the phenomenon of the Harvest Moon.

Inferior Planet. A Planet whose orbit round the Sun is between the Earth and the Sun. Only Mercury and Venus are Inferior Planets.

Latitude. (Terrestrial). The angular distance of a place on the Earth's surface North or South of the Equator.

Latitude. (Celestial). The angular distance of a Celestial Body North or South of the Ecliptic.

Leap Year. The year really consists of 365¼ days; but as the Civil year consists of 365 days, the extra 6 hours (¼ day) is added at the end of the fourth year as an extra day in February to give Leap Year.

Limb. The edge (Upper or Lower) of the Sun, Moon or Planet's disc.

Line, The. The Seaman's name for the Equator. When a vessel moves from South to North Latitude or vice versa she is said to "Cross the Line".

Local Hour Angle (L.H.A.) (or the Hour Angle at the ship), is the difference between the Longitude of the Geographical Position of the body and the Longitude of the Observer. It is measured WESTWARDS (0° to 360°) from the Observer's Meridian.

The modern Navigator who determines his

position by celestial observation and "position lines" is first and foremost concerned with obtaining his Local Hour Angle (L.H.A.).

Local Mean Time. The mean time at any place on the Earth's surface (see Ship Mean Time).

Local Sidereal Time (or Sidereal time of a place at any instant) is the L.H.A. of the First Point of Aries at that instant reckoned (0-24 hours) Westward from the meridian of the place. It is also the angular distance of the meridian Eastward from the First Point of Aries of the Right Ascension of the meridian (R.A.M.).

Longitude. The angular distance between the Greenwich Meridian and the meridian passing through any place, measured along the Equator, and named E or W of Greenwich from 0° to 180°.

Longitude of Time is the difference between S.M.T. and G.M.T. and the difference of longitude between two places is the difference between the local mean times of the places. From which statements we get the rhyme — Longitude East, Greenwich Time Least, Longitude West, Greenwich Time best — which gives the rule for turning Ship Time into Greenwich Time (and vice-versa). As the Mean Sun moves westwards through 360° of longitude in 24 hours, the difference in time between the two places 15° of longitude apart is 1h. and so on in proportion. In other words time can be converted into arc at the rate of 15° to 1h., 1° to 4min., or 1' to 4 sec. (See annual volume.) As the earth rotates from West to East, Easterly meridians will pass under the Mean Sun before that of Greenwich; hence the time for a place East of Greenwich is in advance of Greenwich time, i.e., S.M.T. is for any instant greater than G.M.T. for the same instant.

Lunar Distance. The angular distance of the Moon from other Heavenly Bodies.

Lunar — of the Moon. (A Lunar Day is the time between two successive transits of the Moon over the same meridian.)

Magnitude. Relative brightness of a Star or Planet.

Mean Time. The Mean Solar Day, which is the average of all the Apparent solar days throughout a large number of years, may also be defined as the interval of time between two consecutive transits of the Mean Sun over an observer's meridian. This Mean Sun is an imaginary celestial body supposed to move along the celestial equator with a uniform speed equal to the average speed of the true Sun in the ecliptic.

Meridian. An imaginary great circle extending from North to South Pole. Any heavenly body reaching the highest point of its arc is said to be "on the Meridian" of any observer.

Meridian Altitude. The highest altitude above the horizon of a heavenly body when "on the Meridian".

Meridian, Prime. The Meridian of Greenwich (England) — Longitude 0°.

Moon's Age. The Moon's Age is the number of days that have passed since the previous New Moon.

Nadir. The point opposite to the Zenith, i.e., the point of the heavens directly below the observer.

New Moon. When the Sun and Moon are on the same celestial longitude, i.e., are in conjunction, it is called "New Moon". Is often incorrectly applied to the time when the Moon is first visible as a crescent in the West after Sunset.

Noon (Apparent). When the centre of the actual Sun is on the observer's meridian.

Obliquity of the Ecliptic. See Ecliptic.

Occultation. When one heavenly body eclipses another.

Opposition. When a heavenly body is 180° of Longitude from another. At Full Moon the Moon is in opposition to the Sun.

Orbit. The elliptical path of one heavenly body round another body.

Parallax. The apparent movement of an object when viewed from two different positions.

Perigee. The position in the Moon's orbit nearest to the Earth, opposite to Apogee.

Perihelion. The point in the orbit of the Earth or other Planet when it is nearest to the Sun, opposite to Aphelion.

Phase. The particular aspects of a heavenly body as Phases of the Moon, etc.

Polar Distance. the angular distance of a heavenly body from the nearer celestial Pole.

Prime Meridian. See Meridian, Prime.

Prime Vertical. Vertical Circle of the celestial sphere passing through East and West points of the horizon. a heavenly body is on the "Prime Vertical" when it bears East or West (true).

Quadrature. When the positions of the heavenly bodies differ by 90° of longitude. At First Quarter and Last Quarter the Moon is in Quadrature.

Quarter, First and Last. At "Half Moon", when the Sun and Moon are 90° apart — the Phases of the Moon when the body is half illuminated.

Right Ascension. The Right Ascension (R.A.) of a heavenly body is the angular distance Eastward from the First Point of Aries, to the point where the Great Circle through the Pole and the body cuts the Equator, always expressed in hours 0-24.

Rising. The appearance of a heavenly body above the horizon of the observer. Owing to refraction, the object appears above the horizon when it is really still below it.

Seasons. The variation in the length of day and night is due to the inclining of the Earth's axis to the plane of its orbit.

Semi-Diameter (S.D.). Half the angular diameter of a heavenly body. The S.D. of the Sun and Moon is roughly 16'.

Sun's Semi-Diameter. The Sun has a perceptible disc and so its centre cannot be observed. The part of the circumference actually observed is called the Limb. If the lower limb be observed in an altitude, the semi-diameter must be added to get the altitude of the centre; but from an altitude of the upper limb, the semi-diameter must be subtracted.

Ship Mean Time (S.M.T.) or **Local Mean Time** at any instant is the H.A. of the Mean Sun ± 12h. S.M.T. is reckoned Westward (0h. to 24h.) from the antimeridian of the ship.

Sidereal. In relation to the Stars. Time is an element of the highest importance in all observations of heavenly bodies. One unit of time is provided by the rotation of the earth on its axis from West to East.

Thus:

A Sidereal Day is the time occupied in one complete rotation of the Earth upon its axis, or more particularly it is the interval between two successive transits of the First Point of Aries over an observer's meridian. (See First Point of Aries.) Sidereal Time is used by astronomers.

Sidereal Hour Angle (The) S.H.A. of a star, is the angle at the pole measured (from 0° to 360°) from the meridian of Aries to the meridian of the Star in a WESTERLY direction.

Signs of the Zodiac. The twelve constellations through which the Ecliptic runs.

Solstices. When the Sun is farthest from the Celestial Equator (i.e., Declination 23½° North or South) June 21st, December 22nd, the "longest" and "shortest" days, respectively, in northern latitudes.

Superior Planets. Those Planets whose orbits are outside that of the Earth, and farthest from the Sun. That is all Planets except Mercury and Venus.

Time. See Apparent, Mean, Sidereal.

Transit. The passage of a heavenly body across the observer's Meridian.

Transit of Aries. The Transit of the First Point of Aries and of the fixed Stars occurs approximately 4 minutes earlier on each successive day; so that every month the Transit occurs 2 hours (approx.) earlier and thus 24 hours per year in completing the cycle.

Twilight. The periods of the day when, although the Sun is below the visible horizon, the observer does not experience complete darkness because indirect light is received from the Sun through reflection and scattering by the upper atmosphere. Complete darkness occurs when the Sun's centre is 18° below the horizon. Civil Twilight begins or ends when the Sun is 6° below the horizon, at which time the sea horizon is clear and the brightest stars are visible — the most favourable time for stellar observations.

Universal Time (U.T.). Another name for G.M.T. (Greenwich Mean Time).

Vernal Equinox. Also called the Spring Equinox, when the Sun crosses the Equinoctial from South to North (about March 21st). See First Point of Aries.

Waxing and waning. The Moon is said to be waxing between New Moon and Full Moon when its light increases and waning when its light decreases between Full Moon and New Moon.

Zenith, Zenith Distance is the angular distance of an object from the observer's Zenith (the point vertically overhead in the celestial sphere). It is the complement of the Altitude, i.e., 90° minus the Altitude. Zenith is opposite to Nadir.

Zodiac. An imaginary belt of sky along the Ecliptic, in which the Sun, Moon and larger Planets perform their revolutions.

THE FIXED STARS

These are called "fixed" as their position in relation to one another changes but a fraction. All stars appear to move across the sky from East to West, and across the meridian about four minutes earlier each day. They do not move about the heavens at random as the Moon and the Planets appear to do. The Stars are at an immense distance from the Earth and, unlike the Moon and Planets, which shine with the reflected light of the Sun, shine with their own light.

At first sight there appears to be an immense number of Stars in the heavens; but on due examination it will be seen that there are relatively few bright Stars and only some hundreds of smaller ones, which latter, of course, are of no use for Navigational purposes.

STELLAR MAGNITUDES

The stars are classified according to the amount of light which is received from them on Earth. The magnitude of a star is a measure of its relative brilliance; the actual grading being based on the definition that "a star of magnitude 1 is one from which the Earth receives 100 times as much light as it receives from a star of magnitude 6". Thus a star of magnitude 2 is 100 times brighter than a star of magnitude 7; a star of magnitude 3 is 100 times brighter than a star of magnitude 8. It follows therefore that a star of magnitude 0 is 100 times brighter than a star of magnitude 5, and a star which is 100 times brighter than a star of magnitude 4 must have a magnitude of –1. Sirius, the brightest star in the heavens, has a magnitude of –1.6.

In practice, the terms "stars of the first magnitude" (of which there are 12 only) refers to all those whose magnitude is less than 1.0.

Note: A sixth-magnitude star is only just visible to the naked eye.

The Planets Venus and Jupiter have variable minus magnitudes in the nature of –3.5 and –2.0, respectively. An interesting comparison also is that of the Sun and the Full Moon which have magnitudes of –26.7 and –12.5 respectively.

CONSTELLATIONS

From ancient times Stars have been divided into groups called Constellations; and as it would be impossible to name each Star with a proper name the Stars were named according to their Constellation. The brightest Star in a constellation is prefixed with the Greek Letter α (alpha), the second brightest Star is prefixed β (Beta); and so on in order of their brightness as, for example, α Andromedae and β Andromedae. Proper Names have also been given to the brightest of the Fixed Stars — especially in the Northern Hemisphere — as, for example, Alpheratz (α Andromedae); Mirach (β Andromedae); Vega (Alpha Lyrae); Altair (Alpha Aquiliae); Canopus (Alpha * Carinae); and Denebola (Beta Leionis), etc.

It is frequently of advantage to be able to judge the angular distance between heavenly bodies, and this can be done by comparing the distance with the known angular distance between specified stars or arcs.

The following examples of varying sized angles may be useful to serve as a guide to the estimation of apparent distances in the sky when using Star Charts.

360° All round the horizon.
180° East to West along the horizon or through Zenith.
90° Horizon to Zenith.
60° Dubhe (Great Bear) to Caph (β Cassiopeiae).
30° Polaris to Caph (β Cassiopeiae).
23° Vega to Deneb.
20° Betelguese to Rigel (Orion).
5° Merak to Dubhe (Pointers to the Plough).
4° Castor to Pollux.
*Formerly Argus

HOW TO FIND THE PRINCIPAL FIXED STARS LISTED IN REED'S NAUTICAL ALMANAC

The Navigator will usually find a Star Map or Atlas of great benefit, especially if he is not able to take Star Sights often; but as many Star Maps are still graduated in Right Ascension, for the purposes of identification, we give the R.A. of each Star as well as its S.H.A.

Generally, of course, the brighter Planets and Stars are used to take observations and Azimuths, so the annual edition of Reed's Almanac has tabulated each month the position, i.e., Declination and G.H.A., etc. of 60 Principal Stars. Each of these Stars is numbered as follows, and to assist the beginner especially, we give the following notes on how to find every one of these navigational Stars in the same numerical order as in the Almanac.

Pronunciations are also given for some of the Stars. Always accent the syllable marked.

(1) Alpheratz. A line from the Pole Star through β Cassiopeiae (Caph) and produced the same distance beyond leads to Alpheratz (α Andromedae), which together with the Stars Markab, Algenib and Scheat form the Square of Pegasus with Markab at the south-west corner. These are all bright Stars, and make almost an exact square which is easily found.

(2) Ankaa. (α Phoenicis). A second magnitude Star situated just east of a line from Achernar to Fomalhaut.

(3) Schedar. The brightest Star in Cassiopeiae. This constellation is on the opposite side of the Pole to the Plough and about the same distance away. It is in the shape of a 'W' and is known as Cassiopeiae's Chair.

When the Great Bear (or Plough) is on the meridian above the Pole, Cassiopeiae is on the meridian below the Pole, and the two constellations appear to revolve round the Pole Star at equi-distances. A line drawn from Aldebaran through Algol will intersect Schedar.

(4) Diphda. A Star of second magnitude which lies by itself about half way between the Square of Pegasus and Achernar.

(5) Achernar. (Ak'-er-nar). The brightest Star in the constellation Eridanus in the Southern Hemisphere. Lies about 70° west of Canopus just off a line between Canopus and Fomalhaut.

(6) POLARIS (or POLE STAR). See diagram of the Great Bear and description on page 20.

(7) Hamal. The brightest Star in the constellation Aries. A line from Betelgeuse through Aldebaran leads to Hamal which lies midway between Aldebaran and the Great Square of Pegasus.

(8) Acamar. A third magnitude Star situated about 20° N.E. of Achernar.

(9) Menkar. A second magnitude Star which lies S.W. of Aldebaran and forms the apex of a triangle (upside down) with Aldebaran and Hamal. A line from Sirius through Rigel about the same distance beyond points to Menkar (α Ceti).

(10) Mirfak. Lies North of Algol and on a line from Capella to Cassiopeiae.

(11) Aldebaran (Al-deb'-ar-an). See the diagram of the constellation of Orion on p. 20. This very bright red Star lies to the North of Orion just a little off the line of the Belt. It lies at the top of one of the arms of a V-shaped cluster of small Stars — the Hyades. The Pleiades, a well defined cluster of Stars (The Seven Sisters) lie close to the Hyades, and form a valuable sky-mark.

(12) Rigel (Ri'-jel). See diagram of the constellation of Orion on p. 20.

(13) Capella (Ca-pel'-la). A line drawn from the Pole Star away from the Great Bear but perpendicular to the Pointers leads to Capella. It will readily be recognised as a bright yellow Star.

A line from Polaris to Rigel nearly intersects Capella, which is 45° from the Pole Star and 55° from Rigel. It may be recognised also from being in a line from Menkar through the Pleiades about 30° N.E. of that cluster of Stars.

(14) Bellatrix (Bel'-la-trix). See the diagram of the constellation of Orion on p. 20.

(15) Elnath (Nath). The second brightest Star to Aldebaran in the constellation Taurus, and lies about halfway along a line between Orion's Belt and Capella.

(16) Alnilam. The middle Star of the three bright Stars in the centre of Orion forming the Belt.

(17) Betelgeuse (Bet'-el-joox). See the diagram of the constellation of Orion. Betelgeuse has a reddish appearance rather like Aldebaran.

(18) Canopus (Can-o'-pus). α Carinae (formerly Argus). The second brightest Star in the sky, but situated in 52° South declination. A line drawn from Bellatrix through the northern star in Orion's Belt passes to Canopus. It is almost due South from Sirius and a pale blue colour.

(19) Sirius (Sir'-e-us). The Dog Star — is magnificent — in that he is the brightest Star in the sky (surpassing in brilliance the Planets, Mars and Saturn), and has a gorgeous pale blue colour. The three Stars in the Belt of Orion lead directly away from Aldebaran to Sirius which lies S.E. of Orion.

A fine heavenly curve is formed by Capella, Castor, Pollux, Procyon and Sirius. See diagram of the constellation of Orion.

(20) Adhara. This is a first magnitude star which lies about 10° South of Sirius.

(21) Castor and Pollux (Kas'-ter and Pol'-lux). Known as the Twins — these two Stars lie nearly halfway between the Plough and Orion. A line from Rigel through the centre Star in Orion's Belt points to Castor. Pollux (the brighter Star of the two) will be found 4½° to the southward.

(22) Procyon (Pro'-se-on). A line drawn from Castor and Pollux to Sirius passes almost through Procyon, the little Dog Star.

(23) Pollux. (See No. 21.)

(24) Avior. This first magnitude Star lies far South (60° declination) about 30° S.E. of Canopus and a little to the East of a line joining Canopus to Miaplacidus.

(25) Suhail (υ Velorum). A second magnitude Star South of Alphard and E.N.E. of Canopus.

(26) Miaplacidus (β Carinae formerly Argus). A far southerly first magnitude Star, situated about halfway between Canopus and Acrux, but about 10° S.W. of a line joining them.

(27) Alphard. This second magnitude Star lies on a line drawn from the Great Bear Star Alioth through Regulus and about 20° beyond to the S.S.W. Its name means "the solitary one" because there is no other bright star near it.

(28) Regulus (Reg'-u-lus). A line from the Pole Star through the Pointers of the Plough, and continued about 45° leads close to Regulus. This Star may be found easily, as it is situated at the end of the "handle" of the "Sickle" (which shape the constellation Leo takes), and is the brightest Star in the group.

(29) Dubhe. The northern and brightest of the two Pointers of the Great Bear.

(30) Denebola (De-neb'-o-la). The second brightest Star in the constellation of Leo. Lies about halfway along a line from Arcturus to Regulus.

(31) Gienah (γ Corvi). A second magnitude Star situated S.W. of Spica.

(32) Acrux. The brightest and most southerly Star in the Southern Cross or Crux. Together with the bright Stars, α and β Centauri, the Southern Cross, or Crux, forms the most remarkable constellation in the Southern Hemisphere. It is unfortunately not visible far North, and only shows up over the horizon when sailing South and the Latitude 20's are reached.

(33) Gacrux (γ Crucis) is nearly as bright as Mimosa (β Crux) and is situated at the top (North) of the Cross.

(34) Mimosa. (γ Crucis). Is the second brightest Star in the Crux and lies at the eastern arm of the Cross.

(35) Alioth. On of the Stars in the Tail of the Great Bear.

(36) Spica (Spi'-ka). When the curve of the three Stars in the Tail of the Great Bear is continued through Arcturus, and about 30° beyond it passes through Spica, a first magnitude Star. Just South-West of Spica are four Stars which look exactly like a Spanker sail, and are known as Spica's Spanker, the gaff of which always points to Spica.

(37) Alkaid (Benetnasch). A first magnitude Star situated at the extreme Tail of the Great Bear.

(38) Hadar (β Centauri). The two Stars β and α Centauri lie close Eastward of the Southern Cross, and are called the Southern Cross Pointers. β Centauri is the nearer of the two to Crux.

(39) Menkent (θ Centauri). A second magnitude Star situated about halfway between Spica and β Centauri and slightly east of a direct line.

(40) Arcturus (Ark-tu-rus). If the Great Bear is followed southwards away from the Pole Star for the same distance as the length of the Plough itself, it will lead to Arcturus (a yellow Star). There are three small Stars just to the Westward of Arcturus which form a small triangle. Arcturus is the second brightest Star in the Northern heavens.

(41) Rigil Kent (α Centauri). See No. 38 above. α Centauri is the nearest fixed Star to the Earth.

(42) Zuben'ubi (α Librae). A second magnitude Star situated on a line about halfway between Spica and Antares.

(43) Kochab. A second magnitude Star in Ursa Minor.

(44) Alphecca. A second magnitude Star in the constellation Corona Borealis but the brightest in the heavenly jewel, the Northern Crown. A line drawn from Megrez through Alkaid (the last Star in the tail of the Great Bear) leads to Alphecca in the Northern Crown — an almost perfect semi-circular group of small Stars. It lies a third of the distance from Arcturus to Vega about 20° E.N.E. of Arcturus.

(45) Antares (An'-ta-rez). A line from Regulus through Spica the same distance beyond leads to Antares — a bright red Star. It lies about 45° S.W. of Altair.

(46) Atria (α Trianguli Australis). A first magnitude Star and the brightest of the three Stars lying at the S.E. apex of the Southern Triangle, which lies S.E. of Centaurus and about 45° due South of Antares.

(47) Sabik (η Ophiuchi). A second magnitude

Star situated N.E. of Antares about a quarter of the way towards Altair.

(48) Shaula. A first magnitude Star lying 15° S.E. of Antares about a quarter of the way on a line drawn from Antares to Peacock (α Pavonis).

(49) Rasalhague. A second magnitude Star lying about 25° W.N.W. of Altair. It lies also on a line between Vega and Antares. It forms a triangle with Altair and Vega.

(50) Eltanin. A second magnitude Star lying about 10° N.N.W. of Vega on a line from Altair through Vega.

(51) Kaus Australis. A second magnitude Star lying with the many Stars of the constellation of Sagittarius. It is difficult to identify and lies about 25° E.S.E. of Antares, but East of a line from Antares to Peacock (No. 55).

(52) Vega (Ve'-ga). A line curving through Dubhe, Megrez, Alioth and Mizar (see diagram of the Great Bear (on p.20) and following to the west for about thirty five degrees leads close to Vega — the brightest and most beautiful Star in the Northern heavens, and of a fine pale blue colour. Vega may also be found by a line from Arcturus through the Northern Crown Star (Alphecca) and extending about 40° beyond.

(53) Nunki. A second magnitude Star lying amongst many others of the constellation Sagittarius about 35° due East of Antares.

(54) Altair (Al-tair'). Is easily recognised as a bright Star lying between two smaller Stars which are close in line and point in the direction of Vega. A line from the Pole Star between Vega and Deneb and extended the same distance beyond leads to Altair.

(55) Peacock. This second magnitude Star lies alone in 57° South declination about halfway between Achernar and Centauri on the same parallel of latitude (West from Achernar). It lies S.E. of Antares and S.W. of Fomalhaut and about 65° due South of Altair.

(56) Deneb (Den'-eb). This first magnitude Star lies E.N.E. of Vega and is the brightest Star in the constellation of Cygnus (the Swan). A line drawn from Castor and Pollux through the Pole Star and extended the same distance beyond passes through Deneb, which is readily found as it is at the top of a "Cross" of Stars (very similar to the Southern Cross). The constellation is usually known as the "Kite" — it is exactly this shape. It lies about 25° Eastward of Vega.

(57) Enif (ε Pegasi). A second magnitude Star situated about halfway between Altair and Markab (Square of Pegasus).

(58) Al Na'ir (α Gruis). This second magnitude Star lies West of β Gruis and is situated on a line about halfway between Fomalhaut and Peacock.

(59) Fomalhaut (Fom'-al-haut). A line drawn from Scheat through Markab (which Stars form one side of the Great Square of Pegasus) passes through Fomalhaut, which may be found readily as it has a small square of Stars near it. Situated about 45° South of Markab.

(60) Markab. Is in the S.W. Corner of the Square of Pegasus. A line from Altair N.E. through the Dolphin 50° from Altair will lead to Scheat. It lies about 45° to the east of Altair and about 45° North of Fomalhaut.

ALPHABETICAL INDEX OF PRINCIPAL STARS with their approximate places

PROPER NAME	Constellation Name	Mag.	R.A.	Dec.	S.H.A.	No.
			h. m.	°	°	
Acamar	θ Eridani	3.1	2 58	S 40	315	8
Achernar	α Eridani	0.6	1 37	S 57	336	5
Acrux	α Crucis	1.1	12 26	S 63	173	32
Adhara	ε Canis Majoris	1.6	6 58	S 29	255	20
Aldebaran	α Tauri	1.1	4 36	N 16	291	11
Alioth	ε Ursae Majoris	1.7	12 54	N 56	167	35
Alkaid	η Ursae Majoris	1.9	13 47	N 49	153	37
Al Na'ir	α Gruis	2.2	22 08	S 47	28	58
Alnilam	ε Orionis	1.8	5 36	S 1	276	16
Alphard	α Hydrae	2.2	9 27	S 9	218	27
Alphecca	α Coronae Bor	2.3	15 34	N 27	126	44
Alpheratz	α Andromedae	2.2	0 08	N 29	358	1
Altair	α Aquilae	0.9	19 51	N 9	62	54
Ankaa	α Phoenicis	2.4	0 26	S 42	354	2
Antares	α Scorpii	1.2	16 29	S 26	113	45
Arcturus	α Bootis	0.2	14 15	N 19	146	40
Atria	α Triang Aust	1.9	16 48	S 69	108	46
Avior	ε Carinae	1.7	8 22	S 59	234	24
Bellatrix	γ Orionis	1.7	5 25	N 6	279	14
Betelgeuse	α Orionis	0.1-1.2	5 55	N 7	271	17
Canopus	α Carinae	-0.9	6 24	S 53	264	18
Capella	α Aurgae	0.2	5 16	N 46	281	13
Castor	α Geminorum	1.6	7 34	N 32	246	21
Deneb	α Cygni	1.3	20 41	N 45	50	56
Denebola	β Leonis	2.2	11 49	N 15	183	30
Diphda	β Ceti	2.2	0 43	S 18	349	4
Dubhe	α Ursae Majoris	2.0	11 03	N 62	194	29
Elnath	β Tauri	1.8	5 26	N 29	279	15
Eltanin	γ Draconis	2.4	17 56	N 51	91	50
Enif	ε Pegasi	2.5	21 44	N 10	34	57
Fomalhaut	α Piscis Aust.	1.3	22 57	S 30	16	59
Gacrux	γ Crucis	1.6	12 31	S 57	172	33
Gienah	λ Corvi	2.8	12 15	S 18	176	31
Hadar	β Centauri	0.9	14 03	S 60	149	38
Hamal	α Arietis	2.2	2 07	N 23	328	7
Kaus Aust.	ε Sagittarii	2.0	18 24	S 34	84	51
Kochab	β Ursae Minoris	2.2	14 51	N 74	137	43
Markab	α Pegasi	2.6	23 04	N 15	14	60
Menkar	α Ceti	2.8	3 02	N 4	315	9
Menkent	θ Centauri	2.3	14 06	S 36	148	39
Miaplacidus	β Carinae	1.8	9 13	S 70	222	26
Mimosa	β Crucis	1.5	12 47	S 60	168	34
Mirfak	α Persei	1.9	3 24	N 50	309	10
Nunki	σ Sagittarii	2.1	18 55	S 26	76	53
Peacock	α Pavonis	2.1	20 25	S 57	54	55
POLARIS	α Ursae Minoris	2.1	2 25	N 89	324	6
Pollux	β Geminorum	1.2	7 45	N 28	244	23
Procyon	α Canis Minoris	0.5	7 39	N 5	245	22
Rasalhague	α Ophiuchi	2.1	17 35	N 13	96	49
Regulus	α Leonis	1.3	10 08	N 12	208	28
Rigel	β Orionis	0.3	5 14	S 8	281	12
Rigil Kent	α Centauri	0.1	14 39	S 61	140	41
Sabik	η Ophiuchi	2.6	17 10	S 16	102	47
Schedar	α Cassiopaiae	2.5	0 40	N 56	350	3
Shaula	λ Scorpii	1.7	17 33	S 37	97	48
Sirius	α Canis Majoris	-1.6	6 45	S 17	259	19
Spica	α Virginis	1.2	13 25	S 11	159	36
Suhail	λ Velorum	2.2	9 08	S 43	223	25
Vega	α Lyrae	0.1	18 37	N 39	81	52
Zuben'ubi	α Librae	2.9	14 51	S 16	137	42

The last column refers to the number given to the Star in the annual volume of this Almanac. The Star's exact position may be found according to this number on the monthly pages.

AUXILIARY STAR CHARTS

POLE–PLOUGH–DUBHE–BENETNASCH–KOCHAB

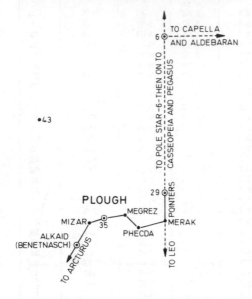

No. 6. POLARIS

No. 29. DUBHE.

No. 35. ALIOTH.

No. 43. KOCHAB.

No. 11. ALDEBARAN.

No. 13. CAPELLA.

Polaris—the Pole Star—familiar in the Northern Hemisphere is always seen in the same part of the heavens, over the Pole of the Earth. It is the brightest star in the Little Bear (Ursa Minor). The position of Polaris in the Little Bear corresponds to the position of Alkaid (Benetnasch) 37, in the Great Bear. The Plough or Great Bear (Ursa Major) is the easiest recognisable constellation in the northern heavens, a straight line through Merak and Dubhe—the Pointers—leads to the Pole Star.

CAPELLA–POLLUX–SIRIUS–ORION–ALDEBARAN

No. 11. ALDEBARAN.

No. 12. RIGEL.

No. 13. CAPELLA.

No. 14. BELLATRIX.

No. 17. BETELGEUSE.

No. 19. SIRIUS.

No. 21. CASTOR.

No. 22. PROCYON.

No. 23. POLLUX.

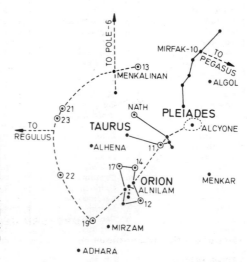

Orion is the finest constellation visible in the Northern Hemisphere, is easily recognised, and the many fine stars around it make it invaluable. The three bright stars in line form Orion's belt with Alnilam at the centre and the sword hanging down below the belt. Four bright stars surround Orion—Betelgeuse, Bellatrix, Rigel and Saiph. Orion is near the meridian at midnight late in the year, and therefore is only visible in northern latitudes in winter and early spring.

Further instructions will be found on pages 16 —18   under star numbers.

STAR CHART NO. 1

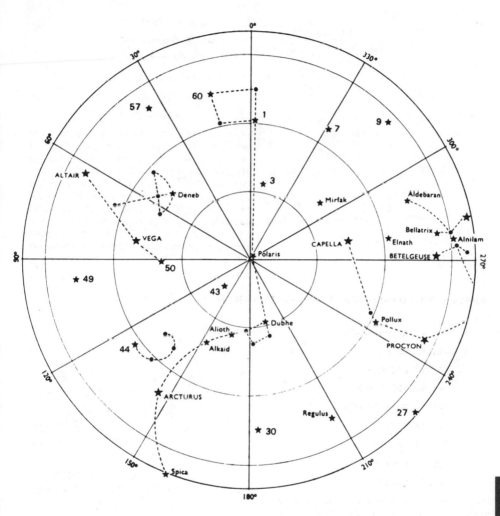

NORTHERN HEMISPHERE

*Stars of the first magnitude
 (capital leters)

• **Stars of magnitude 2.0 to 1.0**
  (small letters)

Key to numbered stars

1 Alpheratz	27 Alphard	49 Rasalhague
3 Schedar	30 Denebola	50 Eltanin
7 Hamal	43 Kochab	57 Enif
9 Menkar	44 Alphecca	60 Markab

Section 20

21

STAR CHART NO.2

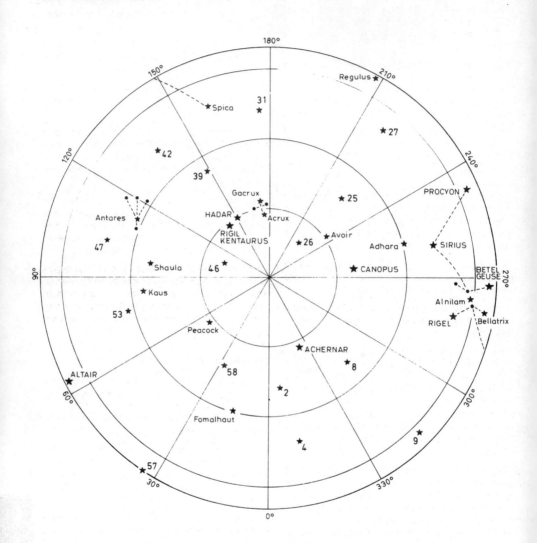

SOUTHERN HEMISPHERE

*Stars which are less bright than mag. 2.0 but are listed and numbered as Selected Stars.

• Stars of lesser magnitude, included to help identification of some constellations.

Key to numbered stars

2 Ankaa	26 Miaplacidus	46 Atria
4 Diphda	27 Alphard	47 Sabik
8 Acamar	31 Gienah	53 Nunki
9 Menkar	39 Menkent	57 Enif
25 Suhail	42 Zuben'ubi	58 Al Na'ir

HOW TO RECOGNISE THE PLANETS

The principal planets are Mercury (☿), Venus (♀), the Earth (⊕ or ♁), Mars (♂), Jupiter (♃), Saturn (♄), Uranus (♅) and Neptune (♆).

Planets are heavenly bodies of which our Earth is an example—which revolve round the Sun in their own particular orbits (or paths). These planets are situated at varying distances from the Sun and thus have entirely different periods of revolution.They are all, however, situated in a belt of the celestial sphere about 8° on either side of the Ecliptic called the Zodiac.

The planets, like the Earth's satellite—the Moon—(and the Comets when visible), all receive their light from the reflected rays of the Sun. Those between the Earth and the Sun are Mercury and Venus and are called Inferior plants, the others are outside the Earth's Orbit and are called Superior planets.

On account of their position varying so much in comparison with the fixed stars, the planets are often termed "wandering stars."

None of the visible planets ever twinkle like the Stars so they may readily be recognised in consequence.

Mercury is very close to the Sun and being seldom seen is of little use to the Navigator. Uranus on the other hand, is not visible, except perhaps with a telescope, so is of no service either. The remainder of the planets are never visible to the naked eye, except Venus, Jupiter, Mars and Saturn, which are all four of great importance and assistance to the practical Navigator.

Venus is only visible for a short time after sunset and before sunrise, because its orbit is between the Earth and the Sun, and it appears to cross and recross the Sun continually. In practice, the time of the meridian passage of Venus is constantly changing from about 9 a.m. to 3 p.m. As Venus is so bright, she can, at all times, during clear weather and when not too near the Sun, be observed during the daytime, even though not visible to the naked eye. Many Navigators get a splendid position during the day by taking Venus on the meridian crossed with a Sun position line.

Venus has a bluish light and with the exception of the Sun and Moon, is by far the brightest object in the heavens. She is outstanding for easy navigation and may readily be observed during twilight.

Jupiter, whilst not so bright as Venus, is nevertheless brighter than any fixed star and may be used for a daytime fix with a powerful sextant telescope.

Mars' distance from the Earth varies and in consequence is sometimes very bright and at others very faint. Mars has a reddish colour.

Saturn is the least bright of the four planets and shines at the equivalent of a first magnitude star. Saturn has a yellowish colour.

The diameter of Jupiter is quite appreciable and is about three times that of Saturn. As their semi-diameters vary, it is customary to observe the centre of the planet to avoid any correction for semi-diameter.

The notes on monthly Planet pages in the annual volume show whether the Planet is a Morning or Evening Planet and whether it is too close to the Sun for observation and give an indication of its position in the heavens.

When the meridian passage (given daily) occurs at midnight the body is in Opposition to the Sun and is visible all night so may be observed in both morning and evening twilights; it bears to the east of the meridian before meridian passage.

THE MOON'S PHASES

The time required for the Moon to make one orbit using the Sun as a reference point, i.e., the interval between two successive New Moons, is approximately 29½ days and is called a Synodical Month or a Lunation.

A Sidereal Month is the time taken for one complete orbit with reference to a fixed star. It is the time interval from Perigee to Perigee or Apogee to Apogee, and is approximately 27 days.

A Lunar Day is the time interval between two successive transits of the Moon over the same meridian. It averages about 24 hours and 50 minutes. The minutes in excess of 24 hours vary from 38 to 66 minutes due to the irregular speed of the Moon along its orbit.

Because the Moon crosses the meridian later each day, there is always a day in each synodical month in which there is no meridian passage, another in which there is no moonrise and another with no moonset. For example, if Moonrise occurs at, say, 2330 on a Monday, the following Moonrise may not occur until 0020 on Wednesday.

AN EXPLANATION OF THE MOON'S PHASES

The Moon's Phases are changes in the appearance of the Moon's disc due to variations in its position with reference to the Earth and Sun. Some knowledge of this is of good practical use to the seaman because, at a single glance at the Moon he will know without reference to books or tables, its phase, rough time of meridian passage and the state of the tides in regard to Springs and Neaps.

Spring Tides do not occur in European waters until about 2 days after the New and Full Moon. Similarly Neaps occur about 2 days after the Moon's Quarters.

The Sun is so far away from us that, for all practical purposes, its light is considered to reach the whole of the Earth-Moon system in parallel rays.

Figure 1 – looking down onto the North pole of the Earth—shows 8 successive positions of the Moon as it orbits the Earth in an anticlockwise direction. It also shows how at all times one hemisphere of the Moon is illuminated by the Sun's rays whilst the opposite hemisphere is in total darkness. The 8 positions are numbered consecutively commencing at the New Moon, Position 1.

Figure 2 illustrates the appearance of the Moon's disc corresponding to each of the positions, numbered 1 to 8, in Figure 1. This shows how the Moon looks to an observer in, say, the British Isles or in any latitude from which the Moon bears South at its meridian passage.

When comparing Figures 1 and 2, remember that an observer looks from the Earth towards the Moon. Thus if Figure 1 is turned upside down to look at the Moon in Position 7, its corresponding appearance in Figure 2 (not upside down) is obvious.

Figure 2, when turned upside down, shows the appearance of the Moon at each phase (keeping the same numbers as before) when seen from latitudes in which it passes North of the observer at meridian passage.

PHASES OF THE MOON

Referring again to Figures 1 and 2:

Position No.	Moon's Phase	Age	Time of Mer. Pass (Approx)	Remarks
		Days	Hrs.	
1	New Moon	0	1200	Sun and Moon "in conjunction". Moon not visible because only the dark hemisphere faces the Earth.
2	Between New Moon and First Quarter	3-4	1500	Visible as a crescent with its bow towards the West. Waxing.
3	First Quarter	7	1800	Moon 90° East of Sun (in East Quadrature). Visible as a half-disc with its bow towards the West. Waxing.
4	Between First Quarter and Full Moon	11-12	2100	Three quarters of the disc visible (called a Gibbous Moon), the more rounded side towards the West. Waxing.
5	Full Moon	15	2400	Moon on Sun's antimeridian, i.e., "in opposition". The whole of the illuminated hemisphere is visible.
6	Between Full Moon and Last Quarter	18-19	0300	Three quarters of the disc visible (called a Gibbous Moon), the more rounded side towards the East. Waning.
7	Last Quarter	22	0600	Moon 90° West of the Sun (in West Quadrature). Visible as a half-disc with its bow towards the East. Waning.
8	Between Last Quarter and New Moon	25-26	0900	Visible as a crescent with its bow towards the East. Waning.

In low latitudes, Moonrise and Moonset occur a few minutes more than 6 hours before and after mer. pass., respectively. In high latitudes the times vary with changes in the Moon's Declination.

THE MOON'S PHASES

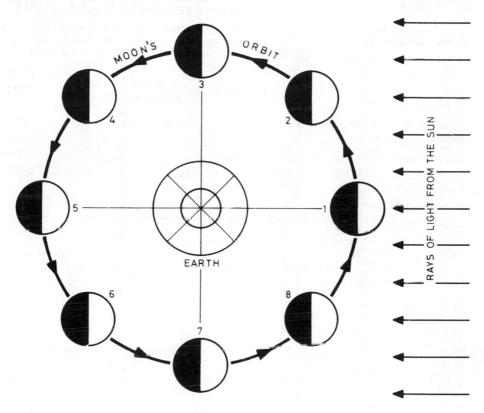

Figure 1

Successive positions (1 to 8) of the Moon along its orbit round the Earth.

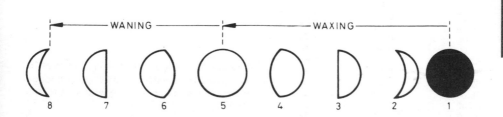

Figure 2

Phases of the Moon as viewed from the Earth's surface.

Section 20

DEPARTURE INTO D. LONG AND VICE VERSA

Dep=D. Long Cos. Mean Lat.
D. Long. = Dep. Sec. Lat.

MEAN LAT	COS. LAT	SEC. LAT
0.00	1.00	1.00
5.00	1.00	1.00
10.00	0.98	1.02
12.00	0.98	1.02
14.00	0.97	1.03
15.00	0.97	1.04
16.00	0.96	1.04
17.00	0.96	1.05
18.00	0.95	1.05
19.00	0.95	1.06
20.00	0.94	1.06
21.00	0.93	1.07
22.00	0.93	1.08
23.00	0.92	1.09
24.00	0.91	1.09
25.00	0.91	1.10
26.00	0.90	1.11
27.00	0.89	1.12
28.00	0.88	1.13
29.00	0.87	1.14
30.00	0.87	1.15
31.00	0.86	1.17
32.00	0.85	1.18
33.00	0.84	1.19
34.00	0.83	1.21
35.00	0.82	1.22
36.00	0.81	1.24
37.00	0.80	1.25
38.00	0.79	1.27
39.00	0.78	1.29
40.00	0.77	1.31
41.00	0.75	1.33
42.00	0.74	1.35
43.00	0.73	1.37
44.00	0.72	1.39
45.00	0.71	1.41
46.00	0.69	1.44
47.00	0.68	1.47
48.00	0.67	1.49
49.00	0.66	1.52
50.00	0.64	1.56
51.00	0.63	1.59
52.00	0.62	1.62
53.00	0.60	1.66
54.00	0.59	1.70
55.00	0.57	1.74
56.00	0.56	1.79
57.00	0.54	1.84
58.00	0.53	1.89
59.00	0.52	1.94
60.00	0.50	2.00
61.00	0.48	2.06
62.00	0.47	2.13
63.00	0.45	2.20
64.00	0.44	2.28
65.00	0.42	2.37

Therefore to find the departure simply multiply the cos. Mean Latitude by the D. Long e.g. Mean Lat 27, D. Long 247, Dep=247x0.89=219.8.

To convert departure into D. Long multiply the departure by the secant of the Latitude, e.g. Mean Lat 51, Dep 150, D. Long=150x1.59= 238.5.

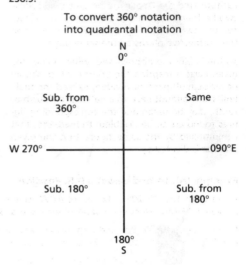

To convert 360° notation into quadrantal notation

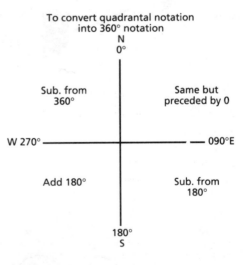

To convert quadrantal notation into 360° notation

Example: 320°→N 40°W 220°→S 40°W 140°→S 40°E. Note with values from 0°–90° although numerically the same they are written as N 40 E or 040°.

TRAVERSE TABLES

For those with scientific calculators see page 32.

These Tables have many uses but briefly it may be said that if the values for any two of the four things, viz. the Course, Distance, Difference of Latitude and the Departure be given, and these two be found together in the Tables, the values for the two remaining parts will be found in their respective places on the same page.

As the Tables are abbreviated, when any of the given parts (excepting the Course, which should never be multiplied or divided) exceed the table limits, any aliquot part, as a half, third, fourth or tenth, may be taken and the corresponding figures found are to be doubled, trebled, etc., that is multiplied by the same figure that the given number is divided by.

The Tables will be found useful for the run between sights where a large scale chart is not available—also to find the vessel's D.R. position at any time, or to find the Course to steer and distance to run over Short Navigation Distances of a few hundred miles or less.

The Tables are entered by using the Mean Latitude between any two positions, the Difference of Latitude (D. Lat.) in minutes of arc; and the Departure (Dep.) in nautical miles. Departure is the Distance made good in an east/west direction in nautical miles.

Departure may be changed into difference of longitude by using the table opposite.

Example (A). To find vessel's D.R. Position

A vessel in Lat. 17°20'N., Long. 38°41'W. steers 320°. Distance 54 miles. What position has she arrived at? From example on page 26 we see that 320°=N 40°W.

So we require the D. Lat. and Dep. for 40° and 54 miles; It is easier to divide the distance by 2 (and multiply the figures found by 2) so on page 30 we find:

Under 40° and 27' D. Lat. = 20.7 × 2=41.4 and Dep. 17.4 × 2=34.8.

Now Lat. from=	17°20'N	Mean Lat. is therefore 18° by	Now. Long. from=	38°41'W
D. Lat...	41'.4N	the table on page 26 against Lat. 18 the Secant = 1.05	D. Long..	36'.5W
Lat. in...	18°01'.4N	D. Long=34.8 x1.05=36.5	Long. in..	39°17'.5W

Hence the vessel's position is Lat. 18°01'.4N., Long. 39°17'.5W. (approx.)

Example (B). To find the Course and Distance

What is the True Course and Distance to steer from Lat. 49°57'N., Long. 6°00'W to Lat. 43°04'N., Long. 9°38'W.? Mean Lat. is about 46°.

Lat. from	49°57'N.		Long. from	6°00'W.
Lat. to	43°04'N.		Long. to	9°38'W
D. Lat =	6°53'S. x 60 = 413'S.		D. Long. =	3°38'W x 60 = 218'W

Using Mean Lat. 46° we find that cos 46 is 0.69. Therefore the Dep. = 218 x 0.69 = 150. So we search the Traverse Table to find D. Lat. 4.13 and Dep. 1.5 (both divided by 100). We find them adjacent on page 28 on the line of Course 20° and half way between Distance columns 4' and 5', i.e., 4.4 x 100 = 440.

So the Course is S20°W. and the Distance 440 miles.

Practice with interpolation will give greater accuracy, but the table—abbreviated as it is—will give quite close results with care.

TRAVERSE TABLES

COURSE	1′ D.Lat	1′ Dep	2′ D.Lat	2′ Dep	3′ D.Lat	3′ Dep	4′ D.Lat	4′ Dep	5′ D.Lat	5′ Dep	6′ D.Lat	6′ Dep	7′ D.Lat	7′ Dep	8′ D.Lat	8′ Dep	9′ D.Lat	9′ Dep	10′ D.Lat	10′ Dep	11′ D.Lat	11′ Dep	COURSE
0	1.0	0.0	2.0	0.0	3.0	0.0	4.0	0.0	5.0	0.0	6.0	0.0	7.0	0.0	8.0	0.0	9.0	0.0	10.0	0.0	11.0	0.0	90
1	1.0	0.0	2.0	0.0	3.0	0.1	4.0	0.1	5.0	0.1	6.0	0.1	7.0	0.1	8.0	0.1	9.0	0.2	10.0	0.2	11.0	0.2	89
2	1.0	0.0	2.0	0.1	3.0	0.1	4.0	0.1	5.0	0.2	6.0	0.2	7.0	0.2	8.0	0.3	9.0	0.3	10.0	0.3	11.0	0.4	88
3	1.0	0.1	2.0	0.1	3.0	0.2	4.0	0.2	5.0	0.3	6.0	0.3	7.0	0.4	8.0	0.4	9.0	0.5	10.0	0.5	11.0	0.6	87
4	1.0	0.1	2.0	0.1	3.0	0.2	4.0	0.3	5.0	0.3	6.0	0.4	7.0	0.5	8.0	0.6	9.0	0.6	10.0	0.7	11.0	0.8	86
5	1.0	0.1	2.0	0.2	3.0	0.3	4.0	0.3	5.0	0.4	6.0	0.5	7.0	0.6	8.0	0.7	9.0	0.8	10.0	0.9	11.0	1.0	85
6	1.0	0.1	2.0	0.2	3.0	0.3	4.0	0.4	5.0	0.5	6.0	0.6	7.0	0.7	8.0	0.8	9.0	0.9	9.9	1.0	10.9	1.1	84
7	1.0	0.1	2.0	0.2	3.0	0.4	4.0	0.5	5.0	0.6	6.0	0.7	6.9	0.9	7.9	1.0	8.9	1.1	9.9	1.2	10.9	1.3	83
8	1.0	0.1	2.0	0.3	3.0	0.4	4.0	0.6	5.0	0.7	5.9	0.8	6.9	1.0	7.9	1.1	8.9	1.3	9.9	1.4	10.9	1.5	82
9	1.0	0.2	2.0	0.3	3.0	0.5	4.0	0.6	4.9	0.8	5.9	0.9	6.9	1.1	7.9	1.3	8.9	1.4	9.9	1.6	10.9	1.7	81
10	1.0	0.2	2.0	0.3	3.0	0.5	3.9	0.7	4.9	0.9	5.9	1.0	6.9	1.2	7.9	1.4	8.9	1.6	9.8	1.7	10.8	1.9	80
11	1.0	0.2	2.0	0.4	2.9	0.6	3.9	0.8	4.9	1.0	5.9	1.1	6.9	1.3	7.9	1.5	8.8	1.7	9.8	1.9	10.8	2.1	79
12	1.0	0.2	2.0	0.4	2.9	0.6	3.9	0.8	4.9	1.0	5.9	1.2	6.8	1.5	7.8	1.7	8.8	1.9	9.8	2.1	10.8	2.3	78
13	1.0	0.2	1.9	0.4	2.9	0.7	3.9	0.9	4.9	1.1	5.8	1.3	6.8	1.6	7.8	1.8	8.8	2.0	9.7	2.2	10.7	2.5	77
14	1.0	0.2	1.9	0.5	2.9	0.7	3.9	1.0	4.9	1.2	5.8	1.5	6.8	1.7	7.8	1.9	8.7	2.2	9.7	2.4	10.7	2.7	76
15	1.0	0.3	1.9	0.5	2.9	0.8	3.9	1.0	4.8	1.3	5.8	1.6	6.8	1.8	7.7	2.1	8.7	2.3	9.7	2.6	10.6	2.8	75
16	1.0	0.3	1.9	0.6	2.9	0.8	3.8	1.1	4.8	1.4	5.8	1.7	6.7	1.9	7.7	2.2	8.7	2.5	9.6	2.8	10.6	3.0	74
17	1.0	0.3	1.9	0.6	2.9	0.9	3.8	1.2	4.8	1.5	5.7	1.8	6.7	2.0	7.7	2.3	8.6	2.6	9.6	2.9	10.5	3.2	73
18	1.0	0.3	1.9	0.6	2.9	0.9	3.8	1.2	4.8	1.5	5.7	1.9	6.7	2.2	7.6	2.5	8.6	2.8	9.5	3.1	10.5	3.4	72
19	0.9	0.3	1.9	0.7	2.8	1.0	3.8	1.3	4.7	1.6	5.7	2.0	6.6	2.3	7.6	2.6	8.5	2.9	9.5	3.3	10.4	3.6	71
20	0.9	0.3	1.9	0.7	2.8	1.0	3.8	1.4	4.7	1.7	5.6	2.1	6.6	2.4	7.5	2.7	8.5	3.1	9.4	3.4	10.3	3.8	70
21	0.9	0.4	1.9	0.7	2.8	1.1	3.7	1.4	4.7	1.8	5.6	2.2	6.5	2.5	7.5	2.9	8.4	3.2	9.3	3.6	10.3	3.9	69
22	0.9	0.4	1.9	0.7	2.8	1.1	3.7	1.5	4.6	1.9	5.6	2.2	6.5	2.6	7.4	3.0	8.3	3.4	9.3	3.7	10.2	4.1	68
23	0.9	0.4	1.8	0.8	2.8	1.2	3.7	1.6	4.6	2.0	5.5	2.3	6.4	2.7	7.4	3.1	8.3	3.5	9.2	3.9	10.1	4.3	67
24	0.9	0.4	1.8	0.8	2.7	1.2	3.7	1.6	4.6	2.0	5.5	2.4	6.4	2.8	7.3	3.3	8.2	3.7	9.1	4.1	10.0	4.5	66
25	0.9	0.4	1.8	0.8	2.7	1.3	3.6	1.7	4.5	2.1	5.4	2.5	6.3	3.0	7.3	3.4	8.2	3.8	9.1	4.2	10.0	4.6	65
26	0.9	0.4	1.8	0.9	2.7	1.3	3.6	1.8	4.5	2.2	5.4	2.6	6.3	3.1	7.2	3.5	8.1	3.9	9.0	4.4	9.9	4.8	64
27	0.9	0.5	1.8	0.9	2.7	1.4	3.6	1.8	4.5	2.3	5.3	2.7	6.2	3.2	7.1	3.6	8.0	4.1	8.9	4.5	9.8	5.0	63
28	0.9	0.5	1.8	0.9	2.6	1.4	3.5	1.9	4.4	2.3	5.3	2.8	6.2	3.3	7.1	3.8	7.9	4.2	8.8	4.7	9.7	5.2	62
29	0.9	0.5	1.7	1.0	2.6	1.5	3.5	1.9	4.4	2.4	5.2	2.9	6.1	3.4	7.0	3.9	7.9	4.4	8.7	4.8	9.6	5.3	61
30	0.9	0.5	1.7	1.0	2.6	1.5	3.5	2.0	4.3	2.5	5.2	3.0	6.1	3.5	6.9	4.0	7.8	4.5	8.7	5.0	9.5	5.5	60
31	0.9	0.5	1.7	1.0	2.6	1.5	3.4	2.1	4.3	2.6	5.1	3.1	6.0	3.6	6.9	4.1	7.7	4.6	8.6	5.2	9.4	5.7	59
32	0.8	0.5	1.7	1.1	2.5	1.6	3.4	2.1	4.2	2.6	5.1	3.2	5.9	3.7	6.8	4.2	7.6	4.8	8.5	5.3	9.3	5.8	58
33	0.8	0.5	1.7	1.1	2.5	1.6	3.4	2.2	4.2	2.7	5.0	3.3	5.9	3.8	6.7	4.4	7.5	4.9	8.4	5.4	9.2	6.0	57
34	0.8	0.6	1.7	1.1	2.5	1.7	3.3	2.2	4.1	2.8	5.0	3.4	5.8	3.9	6.6	4.5	7.5	5.0	8.3	5.6	9.1	6.2	56
35	0.8	0.6	1.6	1.1	2.5	1.7	3.3	2.3	4.1	2.9	4.9	3.4	5.7	4.0	6.6	4.6	7.4	5.2	8.2	5.7	9.0	6.3	55
36	0.8	0.6	1.6	1.2	2.4	1.8	3.2	2.4	4.0	2.9	4.9	3.5	5.7	4.1	6.5	4.7	7.3	5.3	8.1	5.9	8.9	6.5	54
37	0.8	0.6	1.6	1.2	2.4	1.8	3.2	2.4	4.0	3.0	4.8	3.6	5.6	4.2	6.4	4.8	7.2	5.4	8.0	6.0	8.8	6.6	53
38	0.8	0.6	1.6	1.2	2.4	1.8	3.2	2.5	3.9	3.1	4.7	3.7	5.5	4.3	6.3	4.9	7.1	5.5	7.9	6.2	8.7	6.8	52
39	0.8	0.6	1.6	1.3	2.3	1.9	3.1	2.5	3.9	3.1	4.7	3.8	5.4	4.4	6.2	5.0	7.0	5.7	7.8	6.3	8.5	6.9	51
40	0.8	0.6	1.5	1.3	2.3	1.9	3.1	2.6	3.8	3.2	4.6	3.9	5.4	4.5	6.1	5.1	6.9	5.8	7.7	6.4	8.4	7.1	50
41	0.8	0.7	1.5	1.3	2.3	2.0	3.0	2.6	3.8	3.3	4.5	3.9	5.3	4.6	6.0	5.2	6.8	5.9	7.5	6.6	8.3	7.2	49
42	0.7	0.7	1.5	1.3	2.2	2.0	3.0	2.7	3.7	3.3	4.5	4.0	5.2	4.7	5.9	5.4	6.7	6.0	7.4	6.7	8.2	7.4	48
43	0.7	0.7	1.5	1.4	2.2	2.0	2.9	2.7	3.7	3.4	4.4	4.1	5.1	4.8	5.9	5.5	6.6	6.1	7.3	6.8	8.0	7.5	47
44	0.7	0.7	1.4	1.4	2.2	2.1	2.9	2.8	3.6	3.5	4.3	4.2	5.0	4.9	5.8	5.6	6.5	6.3	7.2	6.9	7.9	7.6	46
45	0.7	0.7	1.4	1.4	2.1	2.1	2.8	2.8	3.5	3.5	4.2	4.2	4.9	4.9	5.7	5.7	6.4	6.4	7.1	7.1	7.8	7.8	45

	Dep	D.Lat	Dep	D.Lat	Dep	D.Lat	Dep	D.Lat	Dep	D.Lat	Dep	D.Lat	Dep	D.Lat	Dep	D.Lat	Dep	D.Lat	Dep	D.Lat	Dep	D.Lat	
	1′		2′		3′		4′		5′		6′		7′		8′		9′		10′		11′		

DISTANCE

Read the columns downwards for Courses 0° – 45° and upwards from 45° – 90°

TRAVERSE TABLES

COURSE	12' D.Lat	12' Dep.	13' D.Lat	13' Dep.	14' D.Lat	14' Dep.	15' D.Lat	15' Dep.	16' D.Lat	16' Dep.	17' D.Lat	17' Dep.	18' D.Lat	18' Dep.	19' D.Lat	19' Dep.	20' D.Lat	20' Dep.	COURSE
0	12.0	0.0	13.0	0.0	14.0	0.0	15.0	0.0	16.0	0.0	17.0	0.0	18.0	0.0	19.0	0.0	20.0	0.0	90
1	12.0	0.2	13.0	0.2	14.0	0.2	15.0	0.3	16.0	0.3	17.0	0.3	18.0	0.3	19.0	0.3	20.0	0.3	89
2	12.0	0.4	13.0	0.5	14.0	0.5	15.0	0.5	16.0	0.6	17.0	0.6	18.0	0.6	19.0	0.7	20.0	0.7	88
3	12.0	0.6	13.0	0.7	14.0	0.7	15.0	0.8	16.0	0.8	17.0	0.9	18.0	0.9	19.0	1.0	20.0	1.0	87
4	12.0	0.8	13.0	0.9	14.0	1.0	15.0	1.0	16.0	1.1	17.0	1.2	18.0	1.3	19.0	1.3	20.0	1.4	86
5	12.0	1.0	13.0	1.1	13.9	1.2	14.9	1.3	15.9	1.4	16.9	1.5	17.9	1.6	18.9	1.7	19.9	1.7	85
6	11.9	1.3	12.9	1.4	13.9	1.5	14.9	1.6	15.9	1.7	16.9	1.8	17.9	1.9	18.9	2.0	19.9	2.1	84
7	11.9	1.5	12.9	1.6	13.9	1.7	14.9	1.8	15.9	1.9	16.9	2.1	17.9	2.2	18.9	2.3	19.9	2.4	83
8	11.9	1.7	12.8	1.8	13.9	1.9	14.9	2.1	15.8	2.2	16.8	2.4	17.8	2.5	18.8	2.6	19.8	2.8	82
9	11.9	1.9	12.8	2.0	13.8	2.2	14.8	2.3	15.8	2.5	16.8	2.7	17.8	2.8	18.8	3.0	19.8	3.1	81
10	11.8	2.1	12.8	2.3	13.8	2.4	14.8	2.6	15.8	2.8	16.7	3.0	17.7	3.1	18.7	3.3	19.7	3.5	80
11	11.8	2.3	12.8	2.5	13.7	2.7	14.7	2.9	15.7	3.1	16.7	3.2	17.7	3.4	18.7	3.6	19.6	3.8	79
12	11.7	2.5	12.7	2.7	13.7	2.9	14.7	3.1	15.7	3.3	16.6	3.5	17.6	3.7	18.6	4.0	19.6	4.2	78
13	11.7	2.7	12.7	2.9	13.6	3.1	14.6	3.4	15.6	3.6	16.6	3.8	17.5	4.0	18.5	4.3	19.5	4.5	77
14	11.6	2.9	12.6	3.1	13.6	3.4	14.6	3.6	15.5	3.9	16.5	4.1	17.5	4.4	18.4	4.6	19.4	4.8	76
15	11.6	3.1	12.6	3.4	13.5	3.6	14.5	3.9	15.5	4.1	16.4	4.4	17.4	4.7	18.4	4.9	19.3	5.2	75
16	11.5	3.3	12.5	3.6	13.5	3.9	14.4	4.1	15.4	4.4	16.3	4.7	17.3	5.0	18.3	5.2	19.2	5.5	74
17	11.5	3.5	12.4	3.8	13.4	4.1	14.3	4.4	15.3	4.7	16.3	5.0	17.2	5.3	18.2	5.6	19.1	5.8	73
18	11.4	3.7	12.4	4.0	13.3	4.3	14.3	4.6	15.2	4.9	16.2	5.3	17.1	5.6	18.1	5.9	19.0	6.2	72
19	11.3	3.9	12.3	4.2	13.2	4.6	14.2	4.9	15.1	5.2	16.1	5.5	17.0	5.9	18.0	6.2	18.9	6.5	71
20	11.3	4.1	12.2	4.4	13.2	4.8	14.1	5.1	15.0	5.5	16.0	5.8	16.9	6.2	17.9	6.5	18.8	6.8	70
21	11.2	4.3	12.1	4.7	13.1	5.0	14.0	5.4	14.9	5.7	15.9	6.1	16.8	6.5	17.7	6.8	18.7	7.2	69
22	11.1	4.5	12.1	4.9	13.0	5.2	13.9	5.6	14.8	6.0	15.8	6.4	16.7	6.7	17.6	7.1	18.5	7.5	68
23	11.0	4.7	12.0	5.1	12.9	5.5	13.8	6.0	14.7	6.3	15.6	6.6	16.6	7.0	17.5	7.4	18.4	7.8	67
24	11.0	4.9	11.9	5.3	12.8	5.7	13.7	6.1	14.6	6.5	15.5	6.9	16.4	7.3	17.4	7.7	18.3	8.1	66
25	10.9	5.1	11.8	5.5	12.7	5.9	13.6	6.3	14.5	6.8	15.4	7.2	16.3	7.6	17.2	8.0	18.1	8.5	65
26	10.8	5.3	11.7	5.7	12.6	6.1	13.5	6.6	14.4	7.0	15.3	7.5	16.2	7.9	17.1	8.3	18.0	8.8	64
27	10.7	5.4	11.6	5.9	12.5	6.4	13.4	6.8	14.3	7.3	15.1	7.7	16.0	8.2	16.9	8.6	17.8	9.1	63
28	10.6	5.6	11.5	6.1	12.4	6.6	13.2	7.0	14.1	7.5	15.0	8.0	15.9	8.5	16.8	8.9	17.7	9.4	62
29	10.5	5.8	11.4	6.3	12.2	6.8	13.1	7.3	14.0	7.8	14.9	8.2	15.7	8.7	16.6	9.2	17.5	9.7	61
30	10.4	6.0	11.3	6.5	12.1	7.0	13.0	7.5	13.9	8.0	14.7	8.5	15.6	9.0	16.5	9.5	17.3	10.0	60
31	10.3	6.2	11.1	6.7	12.0	7.2	12.9	7.7	13.7	8.2	14.6	8.8	15.4	9.3	16.3	9.8	17.1	10.3	59
32	10.2	6.4	11.0	6.9	11.9	7.4	12.7	7.9	13.6	8.5	14.4	9.0	15.3	9.5	16.1	10.1	17.0	10.6	58
33	10.1	6.5	10.9	7.1	11.7	7.6	12.6	8.2	13.4	8.7	14.3	9.3	15.1	9.8	15.9	10.3	16.8	10.9	57
34	9.9	6.7	10.8	7.3	11.6	7.8	12.4	8.4	13.3	8.9	14.1	9.5	14.9	10.1	15.8	10.6	16.6	11.2	56
35	9.8	6.9	10.6	7.5	11.5	8.0	12.3	8.6	13.1	9.2	13.9	9.8	14.7	10.3	15.6	10.9	16.4	11.5	55
36	9.7	7.1	10.5	7.6	11.3	8.2	12.1	8.8	12.9	9.4	13.8	10.0	14.6	10.6	15.4	11.2	16.2	11.8	54
37	9.6	7.2	10.4	7.8	11.2	8.4	12.0	9.0	12.8	9.6	13.6	10.2	14.4	10.8	15.2	11.4	16.0	12.0	53
38	9.5	7.4	10.2	8.0	11.0	8.6	11.8	9.2	12.6	9.9	13.4	10.5	14.2	11.1	15.0	11.7	15.8	12.3	52
39	9.3	7.6	10.1	8.2	10.9	8.8	11.7	9.4	12.4	10.1	13.2	10.7	14.0	11.3	14.8	12.0	15.5	12.6	51
40	9.2	7.7	10.0	8.4	10.7	9.0	11.5	9.6	12.3	10.3	13.0	10.9	13.8	11.6	14.6	12.2	15.3	12.9	50
41	9.1	7.9	9.8	8.5	10.6	9.2	11.3	9.8	12.1	10.5	12.8	11.2	13.6	11.8	14.3	12.5	15.1	13.1	49
42	8.9	8.0	9.7	8.7	10.4	9.4	11.1	10.0	11.9	10.7	12.6	11.4	13.4	12.0	14.1	12.7	14.9	13.4	48
43	8.8	8.2	9.5	8.9	10.2	9.5	11.0	10.2	11.7	10.9	12.4	11.6	13.2	12.3	13.9	13.0	14.6	13.6	47
44	8.6	8.3	9.4	9.0	10.1	9.7	10.8	10.4	11.5	11.1	12.2	11.8	12.9	12.5	13.7	13.2	14.4	13.9	46
45	8.5	8.5	9.2	9.2	9.9	9.9	10.6	10.6	11.3	11.3	12.0	12.0	12.7	12.7	13.4	13.4	14.1	14.1	45
COURSE	Dep.	D.Lat	Dep.	D.Lat	Dep.	D.Lat	Dep.	D.Lat	Dep.	D.Lat	Dep.	D.Lat	Dep.	D.Lat	Dep.	D.Lat	Dep.	D.Lat	COURSE
	12'		13'		14'		15'		16'		17'		18'		19'		20'		

DISTANCE

Section 20

Read the columns downwards for Courses 0° – 45° and upwards from 45° – 90°

TRAVERSE TABLES

C O U R S E	DISTANCE																
	21′		22′		23′		24′		25′		26′		27′		28′		29′	
°	D. Lat.	Dep.	D. Lat.	Dep.	D. Lat.	Dep.	D. Lat.	Dep.	D. Lat.	Dep.	D. Lat.	Dep.	D. Lat.	Dep.	D. Lat.	Dep.	D. Lat.	Dep.	
0	21.0	0.0	22.0	0.0	23.0	0.0	24.0	0.0	25.0	0.0	26.0	0.0	27.0	0.0	28.0	0.0	29.0	0.0	90
1	21.0	0.4	22.0	0.4	23.0	0.4	24.0	0.4	25.0	0.4	26.0	0.5	27.0	0.5	28.0	0.5	29.0	0.5	89
2	21.0	0.7	22.0	0.8	23.0	0.8	24.0	0.8	25.0	0.9	26.0	0.9	27.0	0.9	28.0	1.0	29.0	1.0	88
3	21.0	1.1	22.0	1.2	23.0	1.2	24.0	1.3	25.0	1.3	26.0	1.4	27.0	1.4	28.0	1.5	29.0	1.5	87
4	20.9	1.5	21.9	1.5	22.9	1.6	23.9	1.7	24.9	1.7	25.9	1.8	26.9	1.9	27.9	2.0	28.9	2.0	86
5	20.9	1.8	21.9	1.9	22.9	2.0	23.9	2.1	24.9	2.2	25.9	2.3	26.9	2.4	27.9	2.4	28.9	2.5	85
6	20.9	2.2	21.9	2.3	22.9	2.4	23.9	2.5	24.9	2.6	25.9	2.7	26.9	2.8	27.8	2.9	28.8	3.0	84
7	20.8	2.6	21.8	2.7	22.8	2.8	23.8	2.9	24.8	3.0	25.8	3.2	26.8	3.3	27.8	3.4	28.8	3.5	83
8	20.8	2.9	21.8	3.1	22.8	3.2	23.8	3.3	24.8	3.5	25.7	3.6	26.7	3.8	27.7	3.9	28.7	4.0	82
9	20.7	3.3	21.7	3.4	22.7	3.6	23.7	3.8	24.7	3.9	25.7	4.1	26.7	4.2	27.7	4.4	28.6	4.5	81
10	20.7	3.6	21.7	3.8	22.7	4.0	23.6	4.2	24.6	4.3	25.6	4.5	26.6	4.7	27.6	4.9	28.6	5.0	80
11	20.6	4.0	21.6	4.2	22.6	4.4	23.6	4.6	24.5	4.8	25.5	5.0	26.5	5.2	27.5	5.3	28.5	5.5	79
12	20.5	4.4	21.5	4.6	22.5	4.8	23.5	5.0	24.5	5.2	25.4	5.4	26.4	5.6	27.4	5.8	28.4	6.0	78
13	20.5	4.7	21.4	4.9	22.4	5.2	23.4	5.4	24.4	5.6	25.3	5.8	26.3	6.1	27.3	6.3	28.3	6.5	77
14	20.4	5.1	21.3	5.3	22.3	5.6	23.3	5.8	24.3	6.0	25.2	6.3	26.2	6.5	27.2	6.8	28.1	7.0	76
15	20.3	5.4	21.3	5.7	22.2	6.0	23.2	6.2	24.1	6.5	25.1	6.7	26.1	7.0	27.0	7.2	28.0	7.5	75
16	20.2	5.8	21.1	6.1	22.1	6.3	23.1	6.6	24.0	6.9	25.0	7.2	26.0	7.4	26.9	7.7	27.9	8.0	74
17	20.1	6.1	21.0	6.4	22.0	6.7	23.0	7.0	23.9	7.3	24.9	7.6	25.8	7.9	26.8	8.2	27.7	8.5	73
18	20.0	6.5	20.9	6.8	21.9	7.1	22.8	7.4	23.8	7.7	24.7	8.0	25.7	8.3	26.6	8.7	27.6	9.0	72
19	19.9	6.8	20.8	7.2	21.7	7.5	22.7	7.8	23.6	8.1	24.6	8.5	25.5	8.8	26.5	9.1	27.4	9.4	71
20	19.7	7.2	20.7	7.5	21.6	7.9	22.6	8.2	23.5	8.6	24.4	8.9	25.4	9.2	26.3	9.6	27.3	9.9	70
21	19.6	7.5	20.5	7.9	21.5	8.2	22.4	8.6	23.3	9.0	24.3	9.3	25.2	9.7	26.1	10.0	27.1	10.4	69
22	19.5	7.9	20.4	8.2	21.3	8.6	22.3	9.0	23.2	9.4	24.1	9.7	25.0	10.1	26.0	10.5	26.9	10.9	68
23	19.3	8.2	20.3	8.6	21.2	9.0	22.1	9.4	23.0	9.8	23.9	10.2	24.9	10.5	25.8	10.9	26.7	11.3	67
24	19.2	8.5	20.1	8.9	21.0	9.4	21.9	9.8	22.8	10.2	23.8	10.6	24.7	11.0	25.6	11.4	26.5	11.8	66
25	19.0	8.9	19.9	9.3	20.8	9.7	21.8	10.1	22.7	10.6	23.6	11.0	24.5	11.4	25.4	11.8	26.3	12.3	65
26	18.9	9.2	19.8	9.6	20.7	10.1	21.6	10.5	22.5	11.0	23.4	11.4	24.3	11.8	25.2	12.3	26.1	12.7	64
27	18.7	9.5	19.6	10.0	20.5	10.4	21.4	10.9	22.3	11.3	23.2	11.8	24.1	12.3	24.9	12.7	25.8	13.2	63
28	18.5	9.9	19.4	10.3	20.3	10.8	21.2	11.3	22.1	11.7	23.0	12.2	23.8	12.7	24.7	13.1	25.6	13.6	62
29	18.4	10.2	19.2	10.7	20.1	11.2	21.0	11.6	21.9	12.1	22.7	12.6	23.6	13.1	24.5	13.6	25.4	14.1	61
30	18.2	10.5	19.1	11.0	19.9	11.5	20.8	12.0	21.7	12.5	22.5	13.0	23.4	13.5	24.2	14.0	25.1	14.5	60
31	18.0	10.8	18.9	11.3	19.7	11.8	20.6	12.4	21.4	12.9	22.3	13.4	23.1	13.9	24.0	14.4	24.9	14.9	59
32	17.8	11.1	18.7	11.7	19.5	12.2	20.4	12.7	21.2	13.2	22.0	13.8	22.9	14.3	23.7	14.8	24.6	15.4	58
33	17.6	11.4	18.5	12.0	19.3	12.5	20.1	13.1	21.0	13.6	21.8	14.2	22.6	14.7	23.5	15.2	24.3	15.8	57
34	17.4	11.7	18.2	12.3	19.1	12.9	19.9	13.4	20.7	14.0	21.6	14.5	22.4	15.1	23.2	15.7	24.0	16.2	56
35	17.2	12.0	18.0	12.6	18.8	13.2	19.7	13.8	20.5	14.3	21.3	14.9	22.1	15.5	22.9	16.1	23.8	16.6	55
36	17.0	12.3	17.8	12.9	18.6	13.5	19.4	14.1	20.2	14.7	21.0	15.3	21.8	15.9	22.7	16.5	23.5	17.0	54
37	16.8	12.6	17.6	13.2	18.4	13.8	19.2	14.4	20.0	15.0	20.8	15.6	21.6	16.2	22.4	16.9	23.2	17.5	53
38	16.5	12.9	17.3	13.5	18.1	14.2	18.9	14.8	19.7	15.4	20.5	16.0	21.3	16.6	22.1	17.2	22.8	17.9	52
39	16.3	13.2	17.1	13.8	17.9	14.5	18.7	15.1	19.4	15.7	20.2	16.4	21.0	17.0	21.8	17.6	22.5	18.3	51
40	16.1	13.5	16.9	14.1	17.6	14.8	18.4	15.4	19.2	16.1	19.9	16.7	20.7	17.4	21.4	18.0	22.2	18.6	50
41	15.8	13.8	16.6	14.4	17.4	15.1	18.1	15.7	18.9	16.4	19.6	17.1	20.4	17.7	21.1	18.4	21.9	19.0	49
42	15.6	14.1	16.3	14.7	17.1	15.4	17.8	16.1	18.6	16.7	19.3	17.4	20.1	18.1	20.8	18.7	21.6	19.4	48
43	15.4	14.3	16.1	15.0	16.8	15.7	17.6	16.4	18.3	17.0	19.0	17.7	19.7	18.4	20.5	19.1	21.2	19.8	47
44	15.1	14.6	15.8	15.3	16.5	16.0	17.3	16.7	18.0	17.4	18.7	18.1	19.4	18.8	20.1	19.5	20.9	20.1	46
45	14.8	14.8	15.6	15.6	16.3	16.3	17.0	17.0	17.7	17.7	18.4	18.4	19.1	19.1	19.8	19.8	20.5	20.5	45

	Dep.	D. Lat.	Dep.	D. Lat.	Dep.	D. Lat.	Dep.	D. Lat.	Dep.	D. Lat.	Dep.	D. Lat.	Dep.	D. Lat.	Dep.	D. Lat.	Dep.	D. Lat.	C O U R S E
	21′		22′		23′		24′		25′		26′		27′		28′		29′		
	DISTANCE																		

Read the columns downwards for Courses 0° – 45° and upwards from 45° – 90°

TRAVERSE TABLES

COURSE	30' D.Lat	30' Dep.	40' D.Lat	40' Dep.	50' D.Lat	50' Dep.	60' D.Lat	60' Dep.	70' D.Lat	70' Dep.	80' D.Lat	80' Dep.	90' D.Lat	90' Dep.	100' D.Lat	100' Dep.	200' D.Lat	200' Dep.	COURSE
0	30.0	0.0	40.0	0.0	50.0	0.0	60.0	0.0	70.0	0.0	80.0	0.0	90.0	0.0	100.0	0.0	200.0	0.0	90
1	30.0	0.5	40.0	0.7	50.0	0.9	60.0	1.0	70.0	1.2	80.0	1.4	90.0	1.6	100.0	1.7	200.0	3.5	89
2	30.0	1.0	40.0	1.4	50.0	1.7	60.0	2.1	70.0	2.4	80.0	2.8	89.9	3.1	99.9	3.5	199.9	7.0	88
3	30.0	1.6	39.9	2.1	49.9	2.6	59.9	3.1	69.9	3.7	79.9	4.2	89.9	4.7	99.9	5.2	199.7	10.5	87
4	29.9	2.1	39.9	2.8	49.9	3.5	59.9	4.2	69.8	4.9	79.8	5.6	89.8	6.3	99.8	7.0	199.5	14.0	86
5	29.9	2.6	39.8	3.5	49.8	4.4	59.8	5.2	69.7	6.1	79.7	7.0	89.7	7.8	99.6	8.7	199.2	17.4	85
6	29.8	3.1	39.8	4.2	49.7	5.2	59.7	6.3	69.6	7.3	79.6	8.4	89.5	9.4	99.5	10.5	198.9	20.9	84
7	29.8	3.7	39.7	4.9	49.6	6.1	59.6	7.3	69.5	8.5	79.4	9.7	89.3	11.0	99.3	12.2	198.5	24.4	83
8	29.7	4.2	39.6	5.6	49.5	7.0	59.4	8.4	69.3	9.7	79.2	11.1	89.1	12.5	99.0	13.9	198.1	27.8	82
9	29.6	4.7	39.5	6.3	49.4	7.8	59.3	9.4	69.1	11.0	79.0	12.5	89.0	14.1	98.8	15.6	197.5	31.3	81
10	29.5	5.2	39.4	6.9	49.2	8.7	59.1	10.4	68.9	12.2	78.8	13.9	88.6	15.6	98.5	17.4	197.0	34.7	80
11	29.4	5.7	39.3	7.6	49.1	9.5	58.9	11.4	68.7	13.4	78.5	15.3	88.3	17.2	98.2	19.1	196.3	38.2	79
12	29.3	6.2	39.1	8.3	48.9	10.4	58.7	12.5	68.5	14.6	78.3	16.6	88.0	18.7	97.8	20.8	195.6	41.6	78
13	29.2	6.7	39.0	9.0	48.7	11.2	58.5	13.5	68.2	15.7	77.9	18.0	87.7	20.2	97.4	22.5	194.9	45.0	77
14	29.1	7.3	38.8	9.7	48.5	12.1	58.2	14.5	67.9	16.9	77.6	19.4	87.3	21.8	97.0	24.2	194.1	48.4	76
15	29.0	7.8	38.6	10.4	48.3	12.9	58.0	15.5	67.6	18.1	77.3	20.7	86.9	23.3	96.6	25.9	193.2	51.8	75
16	28.8	8.3	38.5	11.0	48.1	13.8	57.7	16.5	67.3	19.3	76.9	22.1	86.5	24.8	96.1	27.6	192.3	55.1	74
17	28.7	8.8	38.3	11.7	47.8	14.6	57.4	17.5	66.9	20.5	76.5	23.4	86.1	26.3	95.6	29.2	191.3	58.5	73
18	28.5	9.3	38.0	12.4	47.6	15.5	57.1	18.5	66.6	21.6	76.1	24.7	85.6	27.8	95.1	30.9	190.2	61.8	72
19	28.4	9.8	37.8	13.0	47.3	16.3	56.7	19.5	66.2	22.8	75.6	26.0	85.1	29.3	94.6	32.6	189.1	65.1	71
20	28.2	10.3	37.6	13.7	47.0	17.1	56.4	20.5	65.8	23.9	75.2	27.4	84.6	30.8	94.0	34.2	187.9	68.4	70
21	28.0	10.8	37.3	14.3	46.7	17.9	56.0	21.5	65.4	25.1	74.7	28.7	84.0	32.3	93.4	35.8	186.7	71.7	69
22	27.8	11.2	37.1	15.0	46.4	18.7	55.6	22.5	64.9	26.2	74.2	30.0	83.4	33.7	92.7	37.5	185.4	74.9	68
23	27.6	11.7	36.8	15.6	46.0	19.5	55.2	23.4	64.4	27.4	73.6	31.3	82.8	35.2	92.1	39.1	184.1	78.1	67
24	27.4	12.2	36.5	16.3	45.7	20.3	54.8	24.4	63.9	28.5	73.1	32.5	82.2	36.6	91.4	40.7	182.7	81.3	66
25	27.2	12.7	36.3	16.9	45.3	21.1	54.4	25.4	63.4	29.6	72.5	33.8	81.6	38.0	90.6	42.3	181.3	84.5	65
26	27.0	13.2	36.0	17.5	44.9	21.9	53.9	26.3	62.9	30.7	71.9	35.1	80.9	39.5	89.9	43.8	179.8	87.7	64
27	26.7	13.6	35.6	18.2	44.6	22.7	53.5	27.2	62.4	31.8	71.3	36.3	80.2	40.9	89.1	45.4	178.2	90.8	63
28	26.5	14.1	35.3	18.8	44.1	23.5	53.0	28.2	61.8	32.9	70.6	37.6	79.5	42.3	88.3	46.9	176.6	93.9	62
29	26.2	14.5	35.0	19.4	43.7	24.2	52.5	29.1	61.2	33.9	70.0	38.8	78.7	43.6	87.5	48.5	174.9	97.0	61
30	26.0	15.0	34.6	20.0	43.3	25.0	52.0	30.0	60.6	35.0	69.3	40.0	77.9	45.0	86.6	50.0	173.2	100.0	60
31	25.7	15.5	34.3	20.6	42.9	25.8	51.4	30.9	60.0	36.1	68.6	41.2	77.1	46.4	85.7	51.5	171.4	103.0	59
32	25.4	15.9	33.9	21.2	42.4	26.5	50.9	31.8	59.4	37.1	67.8	42.4	76.3	47.7	84.8	53.0	169.6	106.0	58
33	25.2	16.3	33.5	21.8	41.9	27.2	50.3	32.7	58.7	38.1	67.1	43.6	75.5	49.0	83.9	54.5	167.7	108.9	57
34	24.9	16.8	33.2	22.4	41.5	28.0	49.7	33.6	58.0	39.1	66.3	44.7	74.6	50.3	82.9	55.9	165.8	111.8	56
35	24.6	17.2	32.8	22.9	41.0	28.7	49.1	34.4	57.3	40.2	65.5	45.9	73.7	51.6	81.9	57.4	163.8	114.7	55
36	24.3	17.6	32.4	23.5	40.5	29.4	48.5	35.3	56.6	41.1	64.7	47.0	72.8	52.9	80.9	58.8	161.8	117.6	54
37	24.0	18.1	31.9	24.1	39.9	30.1	47.9	36.1	55.9	42.1	63.9	48.1	71.9	54.2	79.9	60.2	159.7	120.4	53
38	23.6	18.5	31.5	24.6	39.4	30.8	47.3	36.9	55.2	43.1	63.0	49.3	70.9	55.4	78.8	61.6	157.6	123.1	52
39	23.3	18.9	31.1	25.2	38.9	31.5	46.6	37.8	54.4	44.1	62.2	50.3	69.9	56.6	77.7	62.9	155.4	125.9	51
40	23.0	19.3	30.6	25.7	38.3	32.1	46.0	38.6	53.6	45.0	61.3	51.4	68.9	57.9	76.5	64.3	153.2	128.6	50
41	22.6	19.7	30.2	26.2	37.7	32.8	45.3	39.4	52.8	45.9	60.4	52.5	67.9	59.0	75.5	65.6	150.9	131.2	49
42	22.3	20.1	29.7	26.8	37.2	33.5	44.6	40.1	52.0	46.8	59.5	53.5	66.9	60.2	74.3	66.9	148.6	133.8	48
43	21.9	20.5	29.3	27.3	36.6	34.1	43.9	40.9	51.2	47.7	58.5	54.6	65.8	61.4	73.1	68.2	146.3	136.4	47
44	21.6	20.8	28.8	27.8	36.0	34.7	43.2	41.7	50.4	48.6	57.5	55.6	64.7	62.5	71.9	69.5	143.9	138.9	46
45	21.2	21.2	28.3	28.3	35.4	35.4	42.4	42.4	49.5	49.5	56.6	56.6	63.6	63.6	70.7	70.7	141.4	141.4	45
	Dep.	D.Lat	Dep.	D.Lat	Dep.	D.Lat	Dep.	D.Lat	Dep.	D.Lat	Dep.	D.Lat	Dep.	D.Lat	Dep.	D.Lat	Dep.	D.Lat	COURSE
	30'		40'		50'		60'		70'		80'		90'		100'		200'		DISTANCE

Read the columns downwards for Courses 0° – 45° and upwards from 45° – 90°

TO FIND THE D.R. POSITION AND COURSE AND DISTANCE BY CALCULATOR

The same results as obtained by the Traverse Tables can be achieved very simply by the use of a scientific calculator.

The same examples as given on page 27 are repeated below. The working as shown may look somewhat lengthy but with practice the calculation can be done very quickly and accurately.

Example (A) To find vessel's D.R. Position
A vessel in Lat. 17°20'N., Long. 38°41'W. steers 320°(N.40°W.) for 54 miles. What position has she arrived at?

To find D. Lat. \qquad D. Lat. = Distance x cos Co.

Quantity		Entry	Reading
Course	→	40	40
		cos	0.76604
		STO 1	0.76604
Dist.	→	54	54
		x	54
		RCL 1	0.76604
D. Lat.	←	=	41.4

To find Dep. \qquad Dep. = Dist. x sin Co.

Quantity		Entry	Reading
Course	▸	40	40
		sin	0.64279
		STO 1	0.64279
Dist.	▸	54	54
		x	54
		RCL 1	0.64279
Dep.	←	=	34.7

To find D. Long. $$D. Long. = \frac{Dep.}{cos\ Mean\ Lat.}$$

Mean Lat. = Initial Lat. + ½ D. Lat. = 17°20'N. + 20'.5 = 17°40'.5N. (N.B. a mental approximation for Mean Lat. will do.)

Quantity		Entry	Reading
Mean Lat.	▸	17.68	17.68
		cos	0.95277
		STO 1	0.95277
Dep.	▸	34.7	34.7
		÷	34.7
		RCL 1	0.95277
D. Long.	←	=	36.4

Lat. from	17°20'N.	Long. from	38°41'W.
D. Lat.	41'.4N.	D. Long.	36'.4W.
D.R. Position	18°01'.4N.		39°17'.4W.

Example (B) To find the Course and Distance

What is the True Course and Distance to steer from Lat. 49°57'N., Long. 6°00'W. to Lat. 43°04'N., Long. 9°38'W.

Lat. from	49°57'N.		Long. from	6°00'W.
Lat. to	43°04'N.		Long. to	9°38'W.
D. Lat.	6°53'S. = 413'S		D. Long.	3°38'W.= 218'W.

Mean Lat. = 43°04' + 3°26'.5 = 46°30'.5N. (N.B. a mental approximation for Mean Lat. will do.)

To find Dep.   Departure = D. Long. x cos. mean Lat.

Quantity		Entry	Reading
Mean Lat.	→	46.5	46.5
		cos	0.68835
		STO 1	0.68835
D. Long.	→	218	218
		x	218
		RCL 1	0.68835
Dep	←	=	150

To find the Course.

$$\tan \text{Co.} = \frac{\text{Dep.}}{\text{D. Lat.}}$$

Quantity		Entry	Reading
Dep.	→	150	150
		÷	150
D. Lat.	→	413	413
		=	0.3632
		arc	0.3632
Course	←	tan	20

Therefore the Course is S.20°W.

To find the Distance.

$$\text{Distance} = \frac{\text{D. Lat.}}{\cos \text{Co.}}$$

Quantity		Entry	Reading
Course	→	20	20
		cos	0.93969
		STO 1	0.93969
D. Lat.	→	413	413
		÷	413
		RCL 1	0.93969
Distance	←	=	439.5

So the Course is S.20°W. and the Distance 439.5 miles.

Note: These formulae assume that the earth is flat which is why this routine is often referred to as Plane Sailing. This assumption is reasonable for distances up to 500 or 600 miles. Therefore do not use for distances greater than this.

Section 20

MIDDLE LATITUDE SAILING

For distances greater than 500-600 miles the same procedures can be followed except that a correction has to be applied to the mean latitude.

This corrected MEAN latitude is called the MIDDLE latitute.

Correction to apply to MEAN LAT. to obtain MIDDLE LAT.

Mean Lat.	2°	4°	6°	8°	10°	11°	12°	13°	14°	15°	16°	17°	18°	19°	20°	21°	Mean Lat.
11	-129	-125	-118	-110	-100	-93	-87	-80	-72	-64	-57	-48	-38	-29	-18	-8	11
12	-114	-111	-105	-98	-89	-83	-77	-71	-64	-57	-49	-42	-33	-23	-15	-5	12
13	-102	-100	-95	-88	-79	-75	-69	-63	-57	-51	-43	-36	-27	-20	-12	-3	13
14	-93	-90	-86	-80	-72	-67	-62	-57	-51	-45	-38	-31	-24	-16	-9	0	14
15	-85	-83	-79	-73	-65	-61	-56	-51	-46	-40	-34	-27	-21	-13	-6	+1	15
16	-79	-76	-72	-66	-60	-56	-51	-46	-41	-36	-30	-24	-17	-10	-4	+4	16
17	-72	-70	-66	-61	-55	-51	-47	-42	-37	-32	-27	-21	-15	-8	-2	+6	17
18	-67	-65	-61	-56	-50	-46	-43	-38	-34	-29	-24	-18	-12	-6	+1	+8	18
19	-62	-60	-57	-52	-46	-43	-39	-35	-30	-25	-21	-15	-9	-3	+3	+10	19
20	-58	-56	-53	-48	-42	-39	-35	-31	-27	-22	-18	-13	-7	-1	+5	+13	20
22	-50	-48	-45	-41	-36	-33	-29	-25	-22	-17	-13	-8	-3	+3	+9	+15	22
24	-44	-42	-40	-36	-31	-28	-24	-21	-17	-13	-8	-4	+1	+6	+12	+17	24
26	-39	-37	-35	-31	-26	-23	-20	-16	-13	-9	-5	0	+5	+10	+15	+21	26
28	-34	-32	-30	-26	-22	-19	-16	-12	-9	-5	-1	+3	+8	+13	+18	+23	28
30	-30	-29	-26	-22	-18	-15	-12	-9	-6	-2	+2	+6	+11	+16	+21	+26	30
35	-22	-21	-18	-15	-10	-7	-5	-1	+2	+6	+10	+14	+18	+23	+28	+33	35
40	-16	-14	-12	-8	-4	-1	+2	+5	+8	+12	+16	+20	+25	+29	+34	+40	40
45	-11	-10	-7	-3	+1	+4	+7	+11	+14	+18	+22	+27	+31	+36	+41	+47	45
50	-8	-6	-3	+1	+6	+9	+12	+16	+20	+24	+28	+33	+38	+44	+49	+55	50
55	-5	-3	0	+5	+10	+14	+17	+21	+25	+30	+35	+40	+46	+52	+58	+65	55
60	-3	-1	+3	+8	+14	+18	+22	+27	+32	+37	+43	+49	+55	+62	+69	+77	60

Examples:

To find course and distance from 42°03'N 70°04'W to 36°59'N 25°10'W.

Departure position	42°03'N	70°04'W
Destination position	36°59'N	25°10'W

D. Lat   5°04'S   D. Long 44°54'E
„ = 304   „ = 2694

Mean Lat. = 39°31'N
(from table) corr. = −   13'

Middle Lat. 39° 18'

To find Departure
Dep = d.long Cos middle Lat.

Quantity		Entry	Reading
Middle Lat.	→	39.3	39.3
		cos	0.77384
		STO 1	0.77384
D. Long.	→	2694	2694
		x	2694
		RCL 1	0.77384
Departure	←	=	2084.73

34

To find course $\qquad$ Tan course = $\dfrac{\text{Departure}}{\text{D. Lat.}}$

Quantity		Entry	Reading
Dep.	→	2084.73	2084.73
		÷	2084.73
D. Lat.	→	304	304
		=	6.85765
		avc Tan	81.7035

Course = S 81°42'.17E

To find distance $\qquad$ Dist. = $\dfrac{\text{D. Lat.}}{\text{cos course}}$

Quantity		Entry	Reading
Course	→	81.7035	81.7035
		cos	0.14430
		STO 1	0.14430
D. Lat.	→	304	304
		÷	304
		RCL 1	0.14430
Dist.	←	=	2106.77

Distance = 2106.8

Conversely suppose the vessel starts from a position 42°03'N 70°04'W and steers S81°42'E for a distance of 2106.8 miles. What would be her D.R.

To find D. Lat.   D. Lat. = distance x cos Co.

Quantity		Entry	Reading
Course	→	81.7	81.7
		cos	0.14436
		STO 1	0.14436
Distance	→	2106.8	2106.8
		x	
		RCL 1	0.14436
D. Lat.	←	=	304.13

Latitude departure	= 42°03'N		Mean Lat.	= 39°31'
D. Lat. (304)	= 5°04'S		Corr.	= – 13'
Arrival D.R. Lat.	= 36°59'N		Middle Lat.	= 39°18'

To find Departure   Dep. = Dist x Sin Co

Quantity		Entry	Reading
Course	→	81.7	81.7
		sin	0.98953
		STO 1	0.98953
Distance	→	2106.8	2106.8
		x	2106.8
		RCL 1	0.98953
Departure	←	=	2084.73

To find D. Long $\qquad$ D. Long. = $\dfrac{\text{Dep.}}{\text{cos mid. lat.}}$

Quantity		Entry	Reading
Mid. Lat.	→	39.3	39.3
		cos	0.77384
		STO 1	0.77384
Dep.	→	2084.5	2084.73
		÷	2084.73
		RCL 1	0.77384
D. Long.	←	=	2694

Longitude departure	= 70°04'W
D. Long. 2694	= 44°54'E
Arrival D.R. Long.	= 25°10'W

OCEAN PASSAGE PLANNING

It may be practicable, though hardly desirable, to embark upon a short coastal passage with a minimum of planning; but this is not true of an ocean passage. Thousands of small craft each year complete happy and successful ocean passages. These vessels are of many different types and sizes; one thing they have in common is that the skipper or the navigator has taken a great deal of care in planning the passage.

The planning of objectives are simple: to stay out of trouble, and to take maximum advantage of the elements. The planning itself is also relatively straightforward given all the data which is readily available.

Staying out of trouble means; firstly, avoiding the risk of encountering tropical revolving storms (hurricanes); secondly, making sure that passages are not unduly slowed by constant headwinds or unfavourable currents, or made dangerous by poor visibility.

The elements are harnessed by planning a route which takes advantage of favourable currents and also gives a good chance of being able to sail free and lay your objective.

TROPICAL REVOLVING STORMS

This is the technical name given to violent storms which have their beginnings in some equatorial ocean, and in which winds exceeding one hundred knots are not unknown. Normally, the TRS is known locally by another name. Broad indications about months where these may be expected are as shown in the Table at foot of page.

Tropical revolving storms do not occur in the South Atlantic, nor in the eastern South Pacific.

It is an important responsibility of the ocean passage planner to limit to a minimum the risk of encountering a TRS. Indeed, it is unlikely that insurance cover can be obtained unless this is done. Note that the data shown at foot of page are merely indications, and navigators should use the best possible recorded data.

ROUTEING CHARTS

The main planning tool is the routeing charts; these are published by the British Admiralty. For each of five ocean areas there are twelve routeing charts which show average expected conditions for each month of the year. The references are:

> Chart No.
> 5124 – North Atlantic Ocean (including Mediterranean)
>
> 5125 – South Atlantic Ocean
>
> 5126 – Indian Ocean
>
> 5127 – North Pacific Ocean
>
> 5128 – South Pacific Ocean

The charts are based on observations made over many years and show practically all the information you need in order to plan your route: winds, frequency of strong winds (force seven and above), currents, ice limits, fog and low visibility frequency, air temperatures, sea temperatures, tracks of tropical revolving storms or a note that none has been observed in that month, shipping routes.

Much of the data can be relied upon without serious reservation; but winds do not come into that category because they are dependant upon a, perhaps temporary, weather system. The method of depicting winds enables you to say, for example, "In that position, in January, there is an 80% chance of wind from North through East." One in five navigators will be disappointed and therefore may look disapprovingly at the routeing chart; but this does not negate its value!

Area	Months	Local Name
Western North Atlantic	June to November	Hurricane
Southern Indian Ocean	November to May	Cyclone
Australasia	December to April	Willy-willy
Western North Pacific	Any; but most likely June to November	Typhoon
Eastern North Pacific	June to November	Hurricane
Bay of Bengal and Arabian Sea	Mainly April to December	Cyclone

PLANNING THE ROUTE

The best route to choose depends mainly on the avoidance of ice, TRS and other adverse weather, and the harnessing of favourable winds and currents. The windward ability of the vessel and the requirement of the crew should also be considered.

A good example is the traditional route from Europe to the Caribbean. A direct route would lead the boat through unfavourable winds and probably unpleasant weather. The route which nearly all navigators choose takes in the Canary Islands, then leads further south, nearing the Cape Verde Islands, where the north-east trade winds and the north equatorial current can be picked up, culminating in a 'downhill' passage on the great circle to the south and west.

A great circle track may save scores or hundreds of miles compared with a rhumb line. Big ships plan the great circle course before the passage starts, and usually keep to it, making slight alterations a few times each day. This practice is not useful for sailing boats because it is rare to be able to follow with absolute precision a pre-planned track. A method used in small boats is to calculate a new great circle course daily, after a good position has been obtained.

CHARTS

Charts are expensive, and stowage space may be limited. A policy which many navigators have used with success is to hold what may be called "port approach" charts of areas which may be visited (scale about 1:150,000), and to rely on sailing directions (pilot books), for entry and anchorage details. You will also need small scale charts of ocean areas. Graph paper is useful for many jobs, including the plotting of sights.

SAILING DIRECTIONS

Published by the Admiralty, and covering the world, these volumes are often known as 'pilots'. They contain essential pilotage information for specific areas. Many other pilot books are also published commercially; and the navigator should give himself plenty of time to consider the options and make his choice.

OTHER PUBLICATIONS

You will, of course, need your almanac. Do not be tempted to go to sea with your ephemerides in a computer! Problems can arise when your passage takes you past the end of a calendar year. Reed's contains guidance for you to use last year's almanac for this year's sights; but it is better to remember to buy ahead. Reed's is published each September for the following year. A further volume for the serious passage maker is 'Reed's Ocean Navigator'; this goes into great detail for everything from astro navigation to traffic separation schemes.

The Admiralty publishes volumes entitled 'List of Lights and Fog Signals'. It also produces books entitled 'List of Radio Signals'; the latter cover communications, navigational aids and weather information. You will need the volumes which relate to your planned areas and activities.

Two books written by Jimmy Cornell and published by Adlard Coles have received favourable attention by ocean navigators. These are 'World Cruising Routes' — the title is self-explanatory — and 'World Cruising Handbook', which is a tourist guide cum pilot book.

Finally, there is the famous 'Ocean Passages For The World', published by the Admiralty. This has an excellent section on passage planning, supported by many charts and illustrations, as well as detailed advice on practically every conceivable ocean route.

Happy landfalls!

Section 20

INDEX

A

B

INDEX

C

F

G

H

I

K

L

M

INDEX

N

O

P

R

INDEX

INDEX

INDEX

W

Y

Z